ATLAS OF HISTOLOGY

ATLAS OF HISTOLOGY

SAM J. PILIERO, PH.D.
PROFESSOR OF ANATOMY, NEW YORK MEDICAL COLLEGE

MYRON S. JACOBS, PH.D.
ASSOCIATE PROFESSOR OF ANATOMY, NEW YORK MEDICAL COLLEGE

SAUL WISCHNITZER, PH.D.
ASSOCIATE PROFESSOR OF BIOLOGY, YESHIVA UNIVERSITY

J. B. LIPPINCOTT COMPANY

Philadelphia · Montreal

Distributed in Great Britain by Pitman Medical Publishing Co., Limited, London

Library of Congress Catalog Card Number 65-18854

PRINTED IN THE UNITED STATES OF AMERICA

THIS BOOK IS DEDICATED TO

Harry A. Charipper, Ph.D.

PROFESSOR AND EMERITUS DIRECTOR, DEPARTMENT OF BIOLOGY,
NEW YORK UNIVERSITY

DISTINGUISHED TEACHER AND A LONG-TIME RESPECTED FRIEND
WHO PROVIDED US WITH THE FOUNDATIONS OF MORPHOLOGY

Preface

The primary objective for the beginning student in courses of histology is to learn microscopic structure. The best way to do this is by repeatedly examining the intricate patterns that appear in histologic sections. Such patterns are usually tissue and organ specific and should form the basis for histologic diagnosis. The application of colored dyes to tissue sections serves primarily to increase the contrast between the structural elements rather than to define new elements.

Some beginners become overly dependent on color contrasts and base their judgment of slides on this feature rather than on morphology. This is unfortunate, because different combinations of stains can bring about color reversal effects that will confuse them. Despite the aesthetic appeal of color illustrations, this Atlas consists entirely of black and white photomicrographs because this is the most unprejudiced means of studying microscopic morphology.

In selecting the slides, human material has been utilized, and all the photomicrographs appearing in the Atlas, therefore, relate to the human form unless otherwise specified. The authors hope that the plates may typify student collections in medical college laboratories throughout the country. Some of the photomicrographs, as may be expected for certain human tissues, exhibit signs of postmortem degeneration. It was felt desirable to include them rather than to replace them with superior preparations of animal tissues.

While ideal sections are presented in most histology textbooks because of their instructive value, these are found in the student laboratory with less frequency. Because of this, areas were selected for photography that were regarded as representative of the tissue or the organ. In addition, certain finer histologic structures are indicated in the Atlas which are not ordinarily found by all students because of the limited amount of time available in the histology laboratory.

The standard microscope procedure used in the study of histology in the laboratory is to scan the specimen first at low power and then to increase the magnification gradually. The same plan has been adopted for the Atlas. The organization of the Atlas is such that each series of figures pertaining to a structure is usually presented first at low (25 to 50X), then at intermediate (100 to 150X) and finally at high (400 to 450X) power. Since student microscopes differ slightly in magnifying powers at each level of magnification, it was felt unnecessary to give the exact magnification of each photomicrograph. Oil immersion objective lenses are less frequently used in the histology laboratory and where photographs were taken with such a lens (e.g., connective tissue cells), they are labeled oil immersion and are magnified about 1,200X.

Each chapter represents a textual and photographic unit. Because of the brevity of the text, only at the beginning of each chapter has it been possible for the descriptive material to correspond exactly to the figures found on the facing page. Figures are numbered consecutively within each chapter. The student is reminded that this is primarily an atlas and that the textual material is brief and is not intended to substitute for the more comprehensive treatment found in standard textbooks.

A limited number of electron micrographs has been included in the Atlas to emphasize for the student the fact that microscopic structure goes far beyond the limits of resolution of the light microscope. These electron micrographs point to the dynamic state of development currently existing in histology.

SAM J. PILIERO
MYRON S. JACOBS
SAUL WISCHNITZER

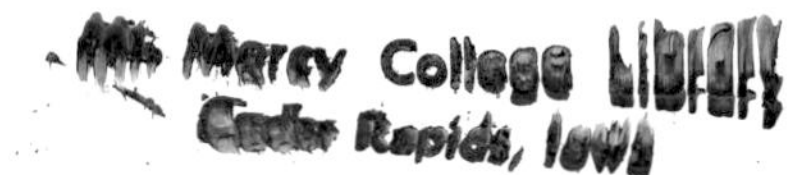

Acknowledgments

The authors thank Dr. Paul T. Medici, Professor of Biology, St. John's University; Dr. Leonard Grosso, Professor of Biology, Long Island University; and Mr. Victor Jelin, Research Associate, New York Medical College, for their critical reading of the text. We are indebted to them and to our many medical students for their helpful suggestions.

To Irene Markloff, Freda Slavin, Catherine Piliero and George Chinea, the authors are deeply indebted for their skill, patience and sincere dedication in assisting with the many technical phases of the book. In addition, the authors would like to acknowledge the many helpful suggestions made by Robert Tringali with regard to the technics of photography.

Grateful acknowledgment is made to the following scientists and their publishers for their permission to reproduce some of the electron micrographs included in the Atlas: Drs. E. C. Adams, A. T. Hertig, E. Horstmann, S. Ito, M. A. Jakus, H. Latta, K. R. Porter, D. Spiro and R. J. Stenger. Figures 1-4 and 2-17 are reproduced by permission of Dr. W. M. Copenhaver and The Williams & Wilkins Company, Baltimore. Figure 18-22 was reprinted by permission of The Rockefeller Institute Press from the *Journal of Cell Biology, 21*:397-428, June, 1964.

We wish to thank Dr. A. W. Pollister for supplying the special slide preparations used for Figures 1-3 and 1-5.

Contents

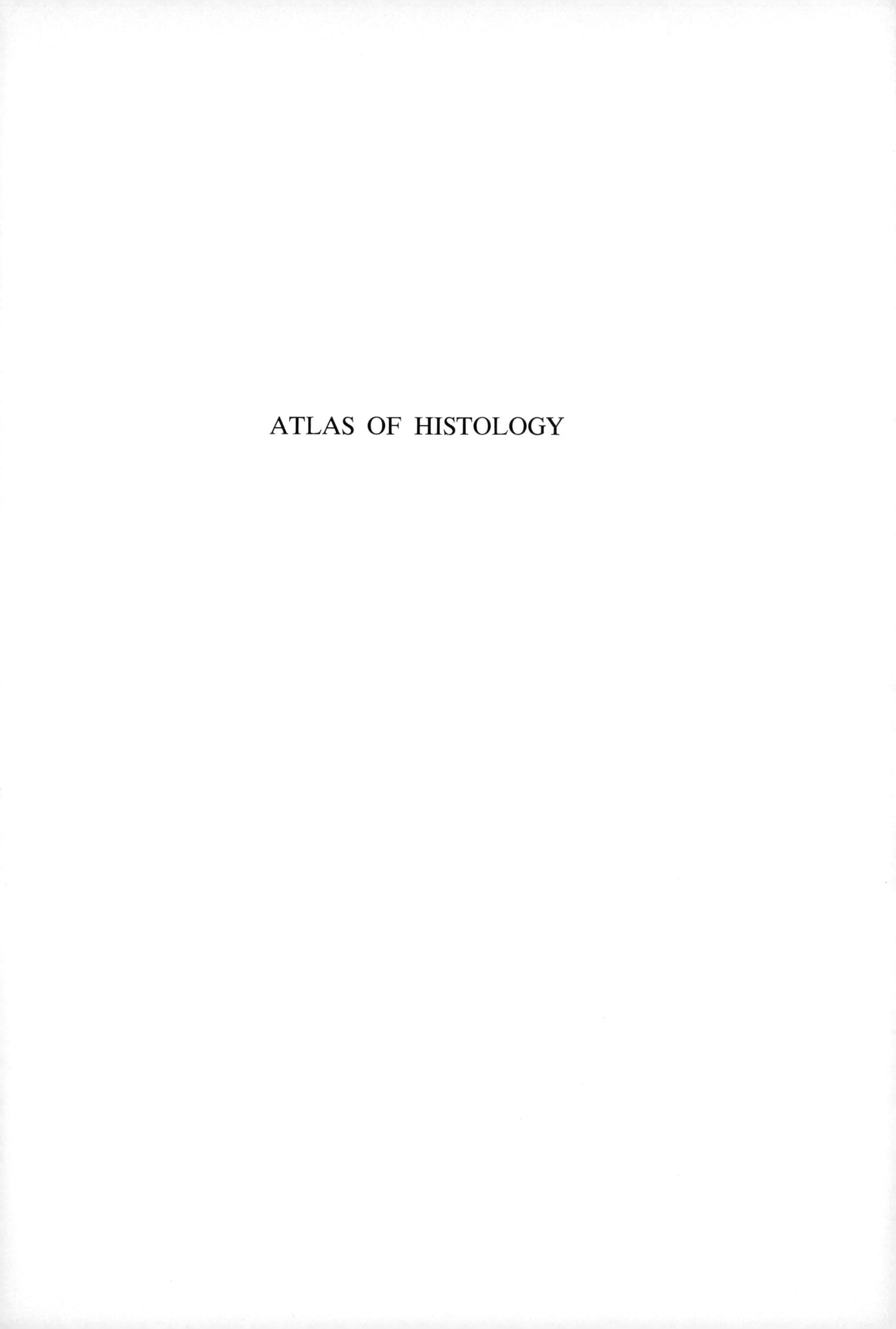

ATLAS OF HISTOLOGY

1 · Introduction—The Cell

A. Cytoplasm
B. Nucleus
C. Planes of Section

Histology is the study of the structure of tissues at the light and the electron microscope level. The tissues are preserved by fixation and processed so as to be suitable for thin or ultrathin sectioning. Tissue sections are stained in order to increase the contrast between the structural details.

Examination of tissues prepared by these means reveals that their structural (and functional) unit is the **cell** (Plate 1). This is a membrane-enclosed mass of protoplasm that almost always contains a **nucleus**.

While isolated cells (e.g., ova) are spherical, in tissues cellular shape is determined by its function and physical relationship with adjacent cells.

Size relationships on the microscopic and the submicroscopic levels are usually given in terms of μ (microns), mμ (millimicrons) or Å (Angstroms). The relationships of these units to the conventional metric unit, the millimeter, are:

$1\ \mu = 0.001$ mm. $= 10{,}000$ Å
$1\ \text{m}\mu = 0.001\ \mu = 10$ Å
1 Å $= 0.1\ \text{m}\mu = 0.0001\ \mu$

Although cell size varies greatly, the average diameter is usually between 10 and 25 μ. A guide which is often used to approximate the cellular dimensions as observed by the light microscope is the human red blood cell which averages 7.7 μ in dry preparations.

A. THE CYTOPLASM

In simple terms, the cytoplasm of the cell (Plate 2) can be considered to be all the non-nuclear material that is present. In most cells it consists of ground substance, organelles and inclusion bodies, all of which are enclosed within a plasma membrane.

PLATE 1—Cell

FIG. 1-1. Low-power survey electron micrograph of a liver cell. Note the central spherical nucleus (n), the numerous mitochondria (m) and a well-developed ergastoplasm (e). A portion of a bile canaliculus (bc) is evident where the microvilli project from the wall. × 6,500.

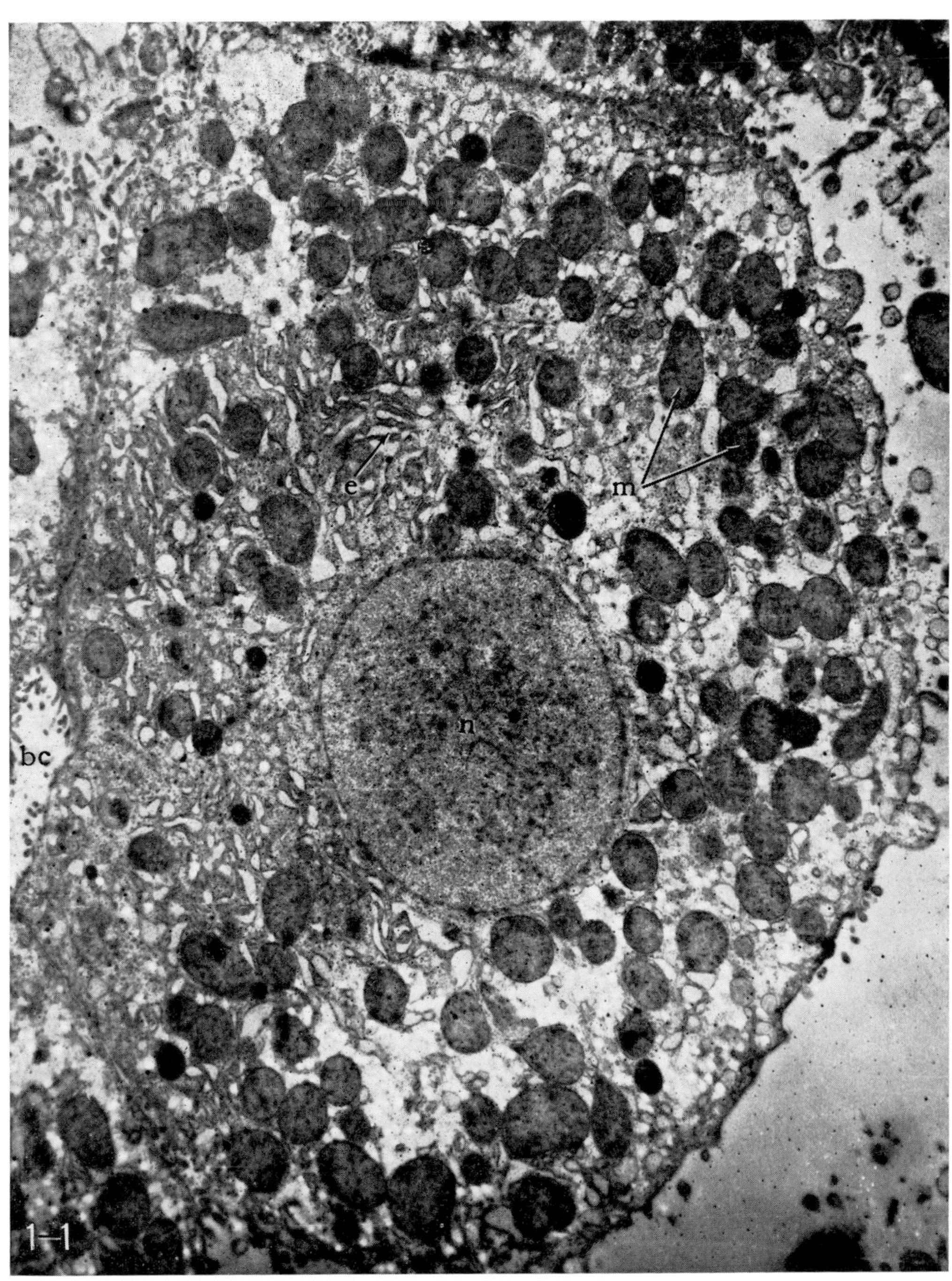
e
m
n
bc
1–1

1. Plasma Membrane

This complex lipoproteinaceous structure regulates the interchange of material between the cell and its environment. It is estimated that the membrane is approximately 75 Å in thickness. While it is seen only as a fine line with the light microscope, under the electron microscope it has been shown to be more complex. It consists of what has been termed a "unit membrane," 75 Å in thickness, which is composed of 3 zones: a clear zone, 35 Å thick, sandwiched between 2 zones, 20 Å thick, of greater density.

2. Ground Substance

This is the fundamental protoplasm of the non-nuclear portion of the cell. With the electron microscope the ground substance has been found to consist of a finely granular material that envelops the cellular organelles and inclusions. It consists of a fluid in a polyphasic colloidal state. The fact that it is mainly acidophilic in nature explains why the cytoplasm of most cells consistently takes up eosin in the H and E preparations commonly used in histology.

3. Organelles

Organelles are the specialized "living" elements found distributed throughout the ground substance of the cytoplasm.

4. Centrosome and Centrioles

The centrosome or cell center, located near the nucleus of a cell, is a highly gelled portion of the cytoplasm which is free of the usual organelles. Within the centrosome are 2 small bodies called centrioles which act as kinetic centers and are active in mitosis. In mitosis, the centrioles separate, giving rise to the astral rays. At the metaphase stage, the centrioles move to positions just outside the nucleus, and the rays appear to form the spindles.

5. Mitochondria

(Plates 1, 2 and 3, Figs. 1-3, 1-4 and 1-8)

These are rod-shaped, granular or filamentous bodies, 0.2 μ in width and 1 to 5 μ in length, found in all animal cells. They are visible in living cells (under darkfield or phase-contrast microscopes) and can be supravitally stained with Janus green B. Mitochondria were discovered in 1890 by Altman who recognized their significance as they pertain to cell life processes and therefore called them bioblasts. The use of differential centrifugation methods resulted in the demonstration that each serves as a site where a multienzyme system associated with oxidative phosphorylation is present. The activities of the enzymes are integrated and well coordinated. These findings implied that a considerable amount of structural organization is present beyond that revealed by the light microscope. To this end, electron micrographs by Palade in 1953 demonstrated the presence of outer and inner limiting membranes. The inner membrane reveals folds or **cristae** which extend, usually perpendicularly, in part or completely across the mitochondrial cavity which is filled with a homogenous matrix. It has been postulated that enzyme chains are localized on the internal surface of the inner membrane and the cristae. Consistent with this are the recent findings of mushroomlike subunits projecting from the cristae whose dimensions are at the level of enzyme molecules.

PLATE 2—Cytoplasm

FIG. 1-2. Electron micrograph of a portion of the cytoplasm of an amphibian oocyte, showing various organelles and inclusion bodies. These include mitochondria (m), Golgi complex (G), annulate lamella (a), vesicles (v), yolk platelets (y) and lipochondria (l). × 42,000.

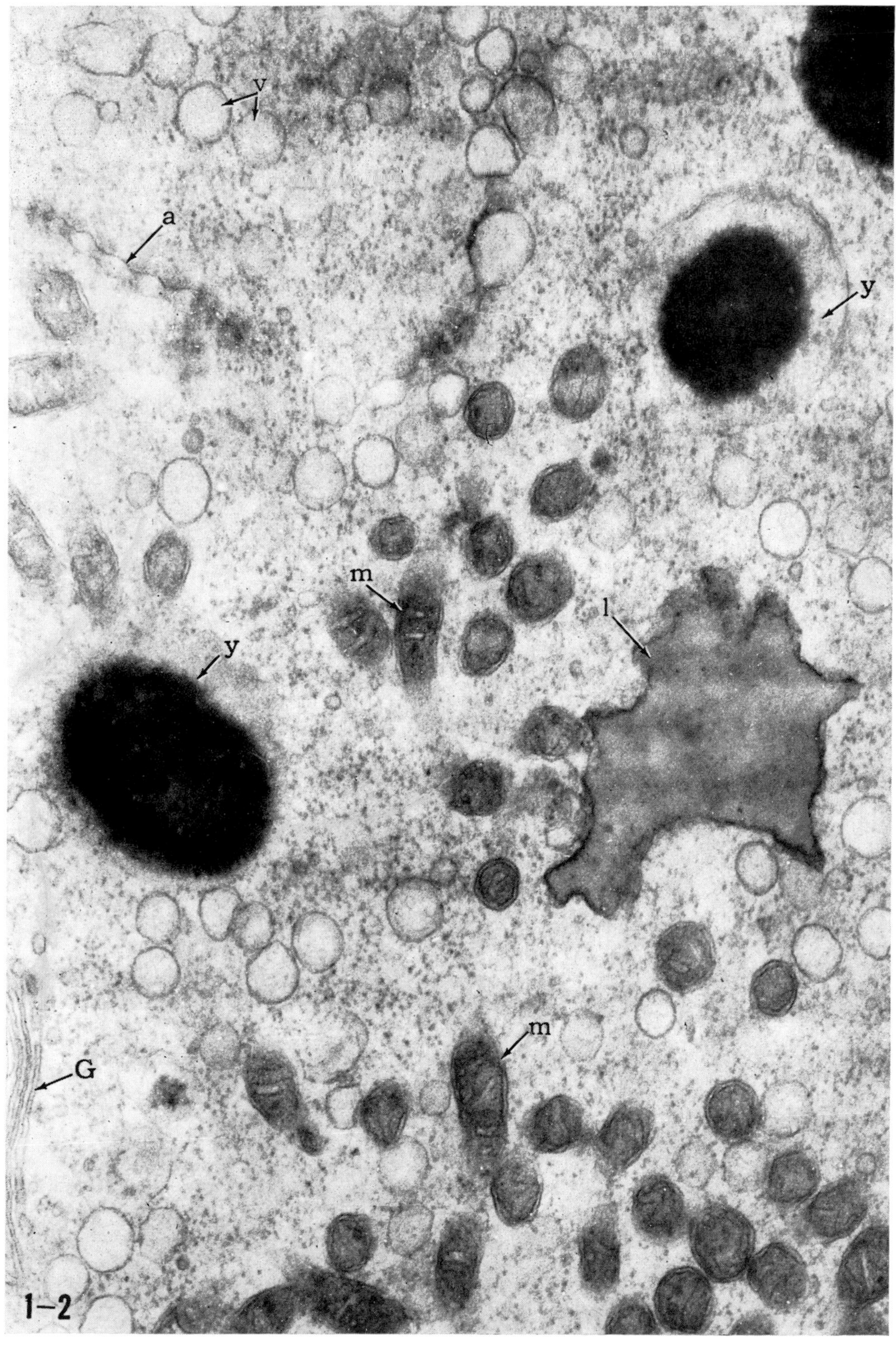
v
a
y
m
l
y
m
G
1–2

6. Golgi Complex
(Plates 2 and 3, Figs. 1-5 and 1-6)

During the early 19th century the idea gradually evolved that secretion is essentially an activity of the individual cell. However, it became clear in the late 19th century that the production of secretory material involved syntheses and segregation of new material in the form of morphologic structures and that discharge was a secondary phenomenon. By the early part of the 20th century, secretion began to be associated with the Golgi complex. The in-vivo existence of this organelle and its identity were long disputed and could not be resolved directly on the basis of light microscope evidence. With the advent of electron microscope studies it was shown that a basic ultrastructural organization characterizes the Golgi complex. This permits its identification in all cell types, even though the gross contours and the distribution may vary in different cells or under different physiologic conditions. The Golgi complex appears as a collection of vesicles of various sizes and shapes in the juxtanuclear zone; the vesicles fall into two types, small spherical ones and large broad flattened vesicles or **cisternae**. In addition, this membrane system is differentiated from the ergastoplasm by the absence of granules on its surface. The use of autoradiographic methods in conjunction with electron microscopy has demonstrated that the Golgi complex is a site for the segregation and the sequestration of secretory material formed in the endoplasmic reticulum.

7. Ergastoplasm
(Plates 1 to 4, Figs. 1-4 and 1-8)

This is the complex membranous system identifiable only by electron microscopy. It consists of a network of tubules, vesicles or cisternae associated with granular particles and is found to be especially well developed in basophilic areas of the cytoplasm (e.g., basal half of acinar cells). This basophilia has been shown to be due to the presence of numerous 250-Å particles, known as **microsomes** or **ribosomes**, which are organelles containing hydrolytic enzymes located on the outer surface of the membranous portion of the **ergastoplasm** or **endoplasmic reticulum**. The endoplasmic reticulum is a canalicular system of membrane-bounded cavities which ramify throughout the cytoplasm. Because of their probable high RNA content, they provide the affinity of cytoplasm for basic stains. This organelle is the probable site of protein synthesis, providing the protein material which may pass on to the Golgi complex.

PLATE 3—Mitochondria and Golgi Complex

FIG. 1-3. A low columnar cell from the salamander kidney showing numerous mitochondria (m) as fine filaments above and around the oval nucleus (n). The latter contains a nucleolus (nu). Note that the free surface of the cell has a ciliated border. Benda method. × 1,200. (From Dr. A. W. Pollister)

FIG. 1-4. An electron micrograph of a portion of a mitochondrion. The outer and inner limiting membrane (lm) enveloping the organelle as well as the numerous cristae (c) which subdivide the interior of the mitochondrion are clearly evident. The latter is filled with a homogenous material. Ergastoplasmic strands (e) are located on either side of the mitochondrion. Their ribosomal elements (r) are evident. × 60,000. (From Dr. K. Porter)

FIG. 1-5. Columnar cells from the duodenum of the guinea pig, showing the densely stained Golgi material. This organelle lies just above the oval nuclei. Osmic acid and Safranin O. × 1,200. (From Dr. A. W. Pollister)

FIG. 1-6. The membranes of the Golgi complex of an amphibian oocyte as seen with the electron microscope. At this stage, the cisternal elements (c) predominate. Numerous cytoplasmic vesicles are evident. × 47,000.

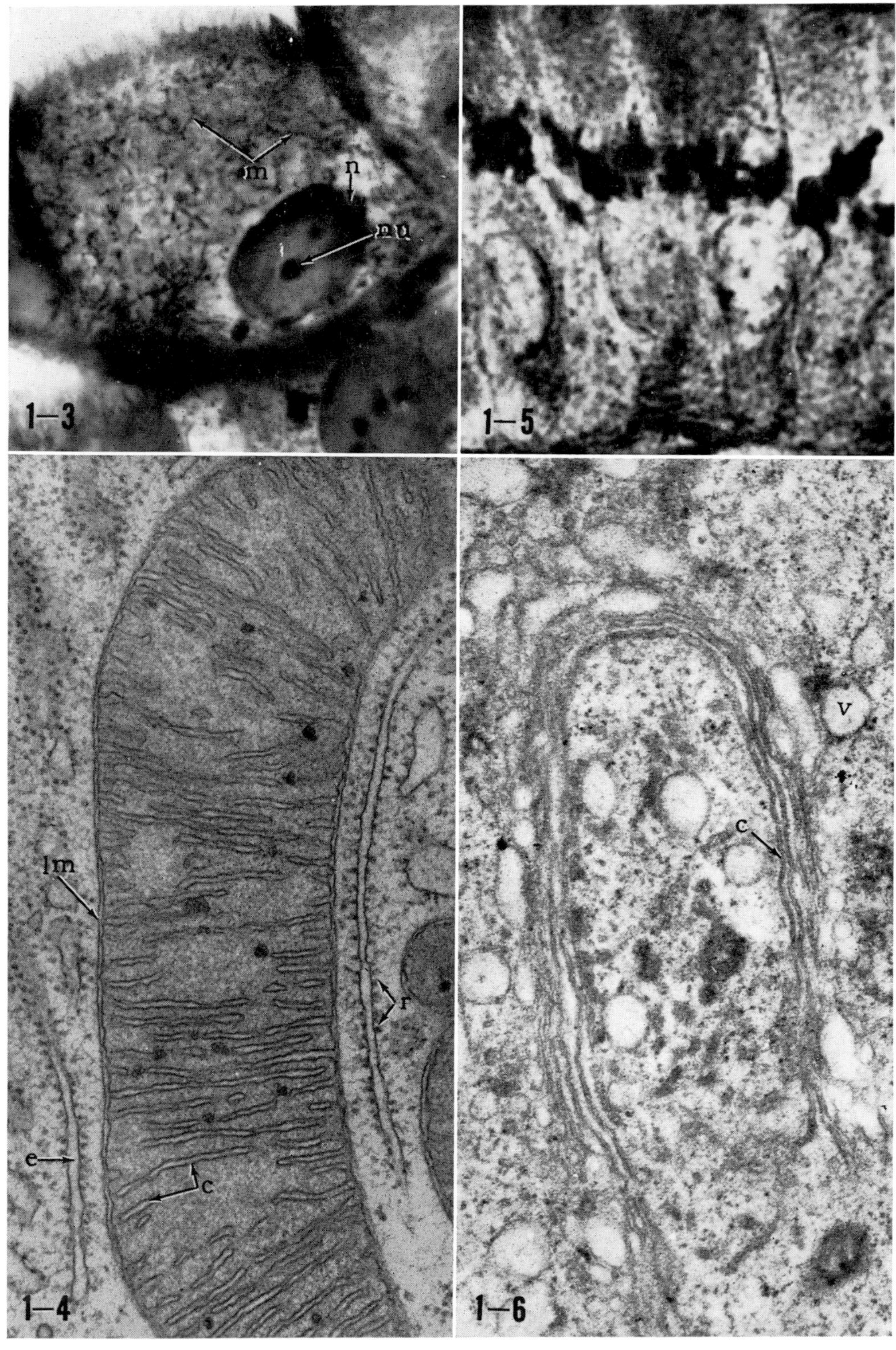
m
n
nu
1–3
1–5
lm
r
e
c
1–4
v
c
1–6

B. THE NUCLEUS
(Plates 1, 3 and 4, Fig. 1-3)

Each cell usually contains one nucleus, representing from 10 to 60 per cent of the cell mass, with a shape that usually varies between a sphere and an ovoid. The structural elements of the nucleus are the nuclear membrane, chromosomes, the nucleolus and nuclear sap (karyoplasm).

1. Nuclear Membrane

This is seen with the light microscope as a simple limiting membrane. However, with the electron microscope it has been shown to consist of a complex known as the **nuclear envelope**, composed of 2 lamellae separated by an intermembranous zone. The envelope is frequently interrupted where the 2 lamellae come together to form discontinuities which are known as **annuli** or **pores**. Associated with the annuli are dense tubular structures that form the **annular complex** which may be a site of nucleocytoplasmic interchange.

2. Chromosomes

The chromosomes, the carriers of heredity, can be considered as a repository of deoxyribonucleoproteins. Although the chromosomes are not evident in the interphase nucleus, they are demonstrable in the prophase and the metaphase. With the light microscope, the chromatin material characteristically appears as an irregular meshwork of threads, whereas when viewed under the electron microscope these fibers are seen to be made up of a mass of coarse granules.

3. Nucleolus

Unlike the situation described for the chromosomes, this nuclear organelle is evident only during interphase. The large type of nucleolus is a round structure and often may contain vacuoles. Utilizing the electron microscope, it has been shown to have no limiting membrane. Instead it consists of a dense mass of granules in which an irregular structural unit, the **nucleolonema**, may be present. The latter consists of particles of a different dimension from those of the nucleolar matrix. Nucleoli are characterized by the presence of ribonucleoproteins.

4. Nuclear Sap

Found between the chromatin granules and also filling the space between the granules and the nucleoli is the material which is known as the nuclear sap. Components of this material include proteins, enzymes, lipids, phosphorus compounds, various electrolytes and other substances.

C. PLANES OF SECTION

It is important for the student to familiarize himself with the plane of section through which a tissue or an organ is cut. This is critical because of the number of different appearances that a 3-dimensional structure will assume when sectioned variously.

PLATE 4—Nucleus

FIG. 1-7. Low-power survey electron micrograph of several granulosa cells from a mouse ovary follicle. The nuclei (n) make up a substantial portion of each cell. × 4,500.

FIG. 1-8. Enlargement of a section of a granulosa cell from an adjacent portion of Figure 1-7. The cytoplasm contains mitochondria (m), short ergastoplasmic strands (e), free clusters of ribosomal particles (r) and lipoid bodies (l). The bilamellar nuclear envelope (ne) is evident, on the inside of which, the chromatin (ch) is aggregated. The nucleolus (nu) is very prominent and is composed of two granular masses of different densities. × 16,000.

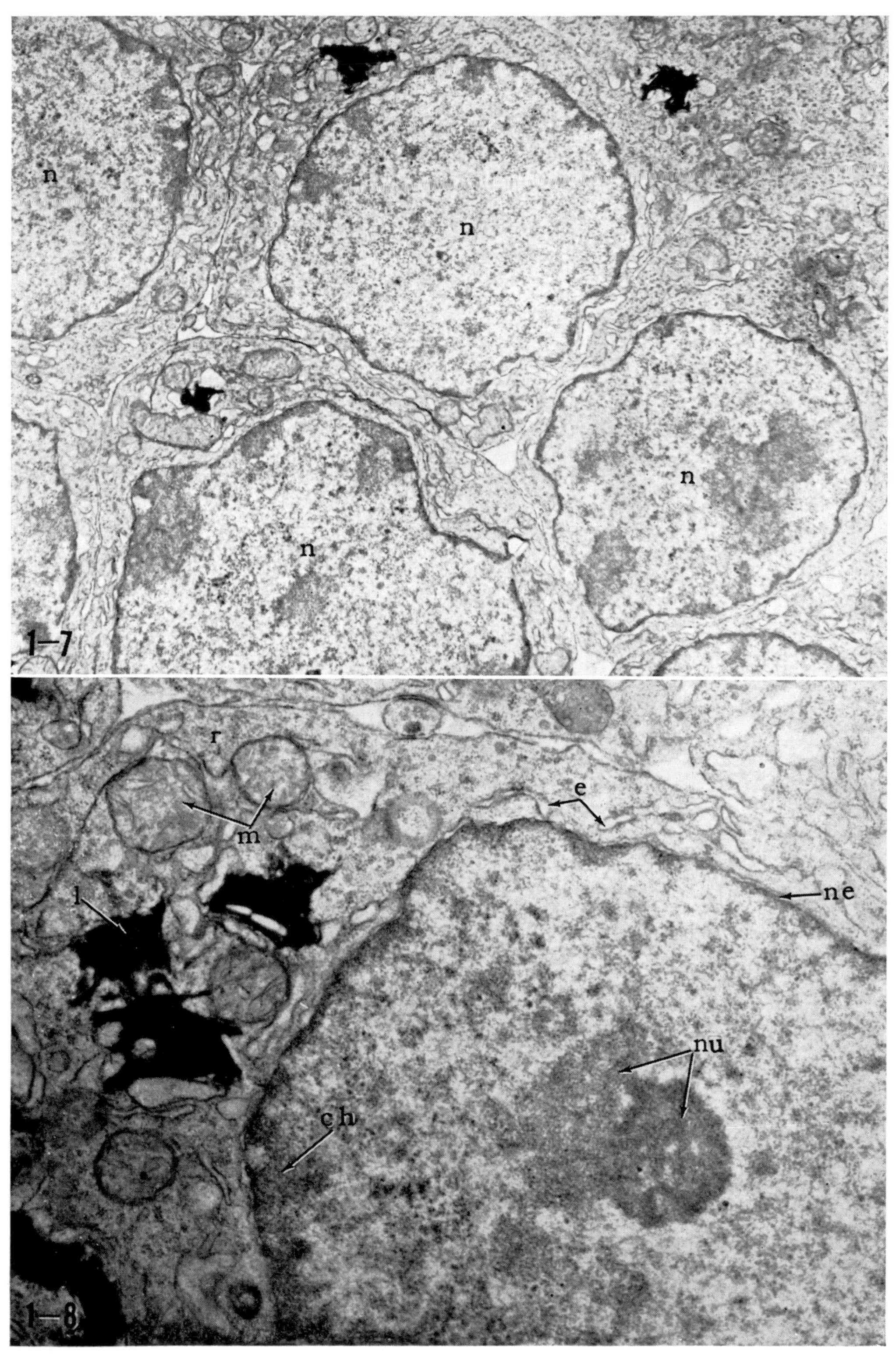
n
n
n
n
n
1–7
r
e
m
l
ne
nu
ch
1–8

For example, if a tubular structure such as a blood vessel, which basically has the shape of a cylinder, is cut **transverse to its long axis**, the resulting exposed surface has the shape of a **circle**.

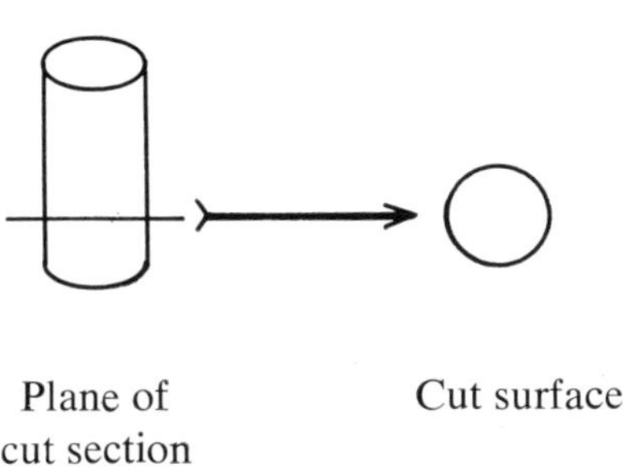

However, if this same tubular structure is sectioned **obliquely** (or **tangentially**), the surface that is exposed is quite different—thus:

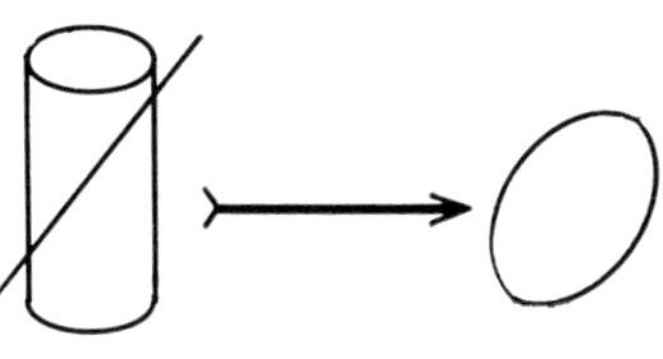

Plane of section Cut surface

Frequently, blood vessels take quite a tortuous course through an organ, and it would be technically impossible to section the tube through any one axis. The resulting picture can be quite puzzling for the beginning student—thus:

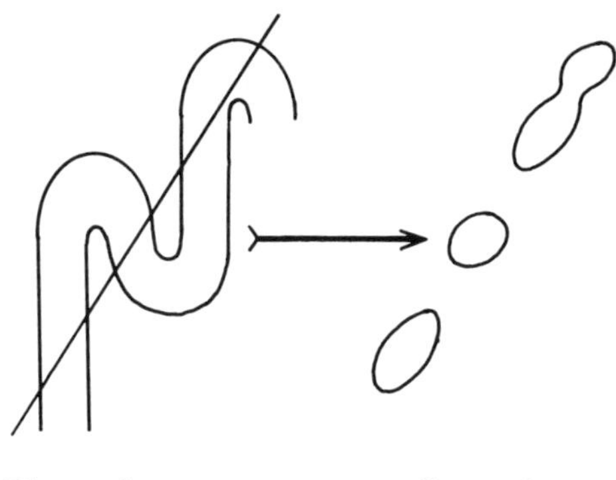

Plane of section Cut surface

Similar alterations of appearance take place for other structures which have basic 3-dimensional geometric shapes. The simplest shape to work with is a **sphere**. Examples of this structure in histology will be seen when the cell bodies of dorsal root (sensory) ganglia, malpighian corpuscles of the kidney and certain of the lymph glands are encountered. In the case of a sphere, no matter what the plane of section, the resulting structure will have a similar shape but different sizes, thus:

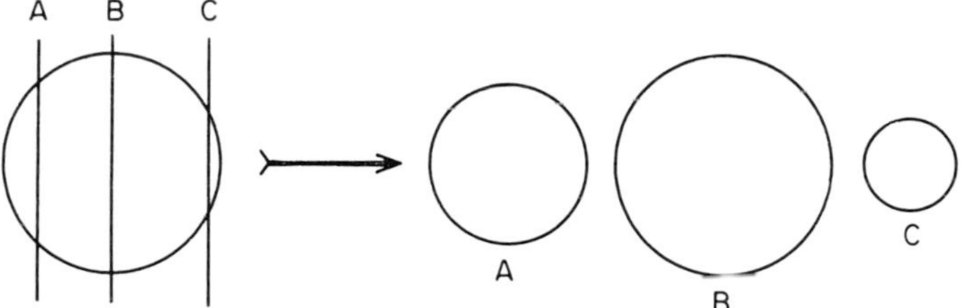

In the case of structures having roughly the shape of an **ellipsoid**, such as the kidney, the pars distalis of the pituitary, or cell bodies in autonomic ganglia, parathyroid glands, etc., the plane of section will alter radically the 2-dimensional cut surface, thus:

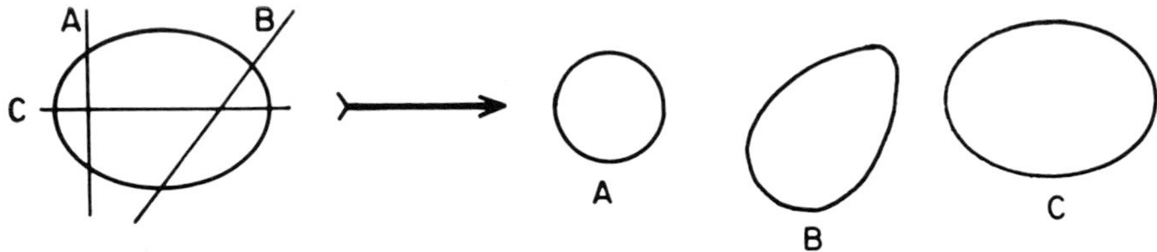

One of the most difficult mental reconstructions that must be made is in connection with one of the simplest topics in histology; viz, the epithelia. A simple example—a simple tall columnar epithelium—will familiarize the student with the problem:

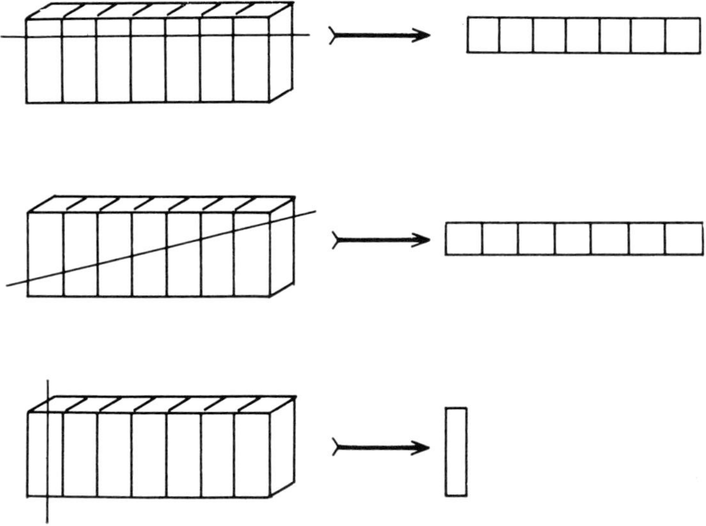

2 · Epithelial Tissues

A. INTRODUCTION

Epithelial tissues consist of cells which occur on free surfaces or as projections from a free surface and are bound together by junctional complexes (the zonular occludens, the zonular adhaerens and the desmosomes). In a transverse section of a hollow organ, therefore, the epithelial portion would be present on either the innermost or the outermost surface or on both surfaces.

An epithelium always appears as part of

PLATE 5—Epithelium

FIG. 2-1. Simple squamous epithelium constituting the endothelial lining (e) of a longitudinally sectioned arteriole from the developing skin of a finger. Note the spindle shape of these cells in profile view and that their centrally placed ovoid nuclei cause a slight bulging into the adjacent lumen. H & E stain. Oil immersion.

FIG. 2-2. Simple squamous epithelium of the mesothelium lining (m) of the small intestine. H & E stain. Oil immersion.

FIG. 2-3. Surface view of simple squamous epithelium of the peritoneum. Note the mosaic appearance and the serrated edges of these platelike cells. Their nuclei are centrally located. Silver nitrate stain. High power.

FIG. 2-4. Simple cuboidal epithelium of a longitudinal section of the thick ascending segment of Henle's loop (kidney). Note that the height of the cells is approximately equal to their width. The nuclei are round and centrally located. Mallory stain. High power.

FIG. 2-5. Simple columnar epithelium of the ductus choledochus in the wall of the duodenum. Note that these tall columnar cells have oval nuclei in the basal portion of the cells. A striated border (sb) is evident on the apical surface. H & E stain. High power.

FIG. 2-6. Simple columnar epithelium lining the intestinal tract in which the cells are not as tall as those seen in Figure 2-5. H & E stain. High power.

FIG. 2-7. Pseudostratified ciliated columnar epithelium from the respiratory region of the nasal cavity of a dog. Note that the nuclei lie at different levels. Mallory-Azan stain. High power. (c, cilia)

FIG. 2-8. Pseudostratified ciliated columnar epithelium from the trachea. Note the thick basement membrane (b) upon which the epithelium rests. Location of nuclei at different levels gives this epithelium a stratified appearance. Mallory-Azan stain. High power. (c, cilia)

FIG. 2-9. Transitional epithelium of the ureter. Note that the surface cells (sc) are characteristically larger and rounded or cuboid and that the cells of the lower portion appear to overlap each other. There is no distinguishable basement membrane bounding the lamina propria (lp). H & E stain. High power.

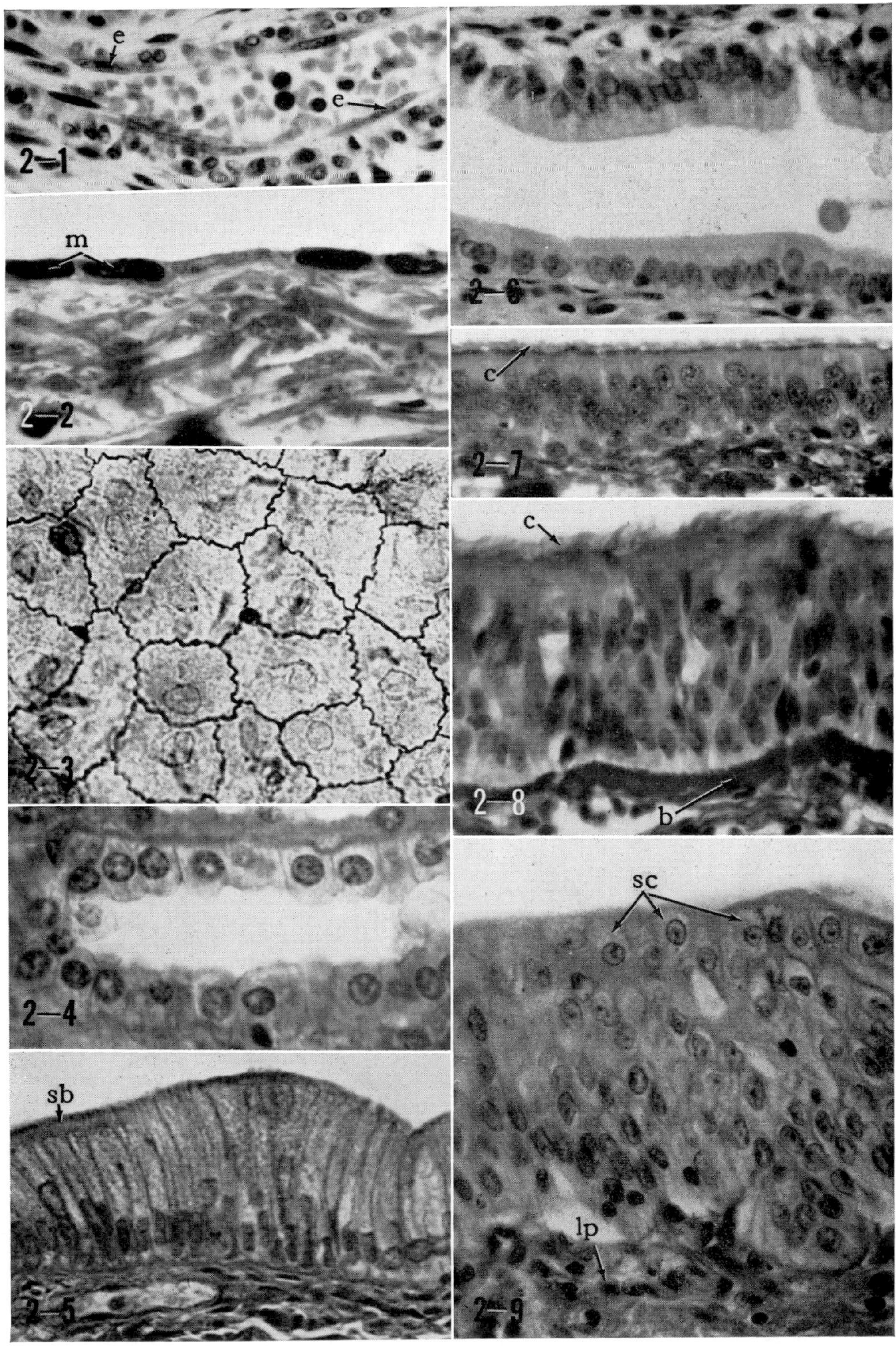
e
e
2—1
m
2—2
2—3
2—4
sb
2—5
2—6
c
2—7
c
b
2—8
sc
lp
2—9

an organ, and the epithelial structure assumes a specific shape depending on its function. Thus, for a protective function (e.g., integument) the epithelium consists of a covering sheet; for excretion (e.g., renal tubules) the epithelium consists of a tubular structure, etc.

Epithelium is classified as **simple** and **stratified**. A **simple epithelium** consists of a single layer thickness of cells; a **stratified epithelium** consists of more than one complete layer of cells. Depending on the shape of cells in a simple epithelia as viewed from the side, the epithelium is termed **simple squamous, simple cuboidal, simple columnar** or **pseudostratified**. Stratified epithelia are also classified according to cell shape. The student is cautioned that mechanical factors act differently on the various strata within a stratified epithelium and alter the normal tendency of cells to round up. To simplify classification among the stratified epithelia, the type of cell found on the free (or superficial) surface gives that epithelium its name. The following types of stratified epithelium are found: **stratified squamous, stratified columnar** and (infrequently) **stratified cuboidal** and **transitional** epithelium.

One of the most challenging tasks for the student in histology is to be able to recognize the various types of simple and stratified epithelia and to use them as diagnostic aids in recognizing the special tissues or organs they are associated with.

It is suggested that the student use the following schedule in studying the epithelia:

B. SIMPLE SQUAMOUS EPITHELIUM

(Plate 5, Figs. 2-1 to 2-3)

Squamous cells are flattened scalelike cells arranged as sheets to form linings on the inside (e.g., endothelium of blood vessels) or the outside (e.g., mesothelium of mesentery) of organs. This epithelial type also lines the body cavities and makes up the thin-walled portions of certain tubular structures where vital functions such as absorption of fluid (e.g., Henle's loop) or gaseous exchange (e.g., lung) take place. Typically, simple squamous cells are separated by narrow intercellular spaces. The cells contain centrally located spherical or ovoid nuclei, which results in a bulging of the cytoplasm when observed in profile view.

PLATE 6—Epithelium and Specializations

FIG. 2-10. Stratified columnar epithelium lining the lumen of the cavernous portion of the fetal urethra. Note that the surface cells are columnar, while the deeper cells are irregularly fusiform and polyhedral in shape. H & E stain. High power.

FIG. 2-11. Stratified squamous epithelium constituting the epidermis (ep) of thick skin. Nuclei in the deeper parts of this epithelium indicate that numerous cell layers are present. Note that the nuclei are difficult to see in the broad, lighter staining zone occupying the upper three fifths of the epithelium. H & E stain. Intermediate power.

FIG. 2-12. Stratified squamous epithelium covering thin skin. Note the darker staining cells of the basal layer and the progressive flattening of cells toward the surface. H & E stain. Intermediate power. (ep, epidermis)

FIG. 2-13. Specialized striated, cuticular border (sb) covering the apical surface of simple columnar epithelial cells of the small intestine. Masson stain. High power. (g, goblet cell; l, lymphocytes)

FIG. 2-14. Specialized brush border (bb) of simple cuboidal cells lining the proximal convoluted tubules of the kidney. The brush border can be seen adjacent to the lumen as the somewhat denser staining zone of cytoplasm. H & E stain. High power.

FIG. 2-15. Specialized nonmotile stereocilia (sc) on the free surface of the pseudostratified columnar cells of the ductus epididymis. H & E stain. High power.

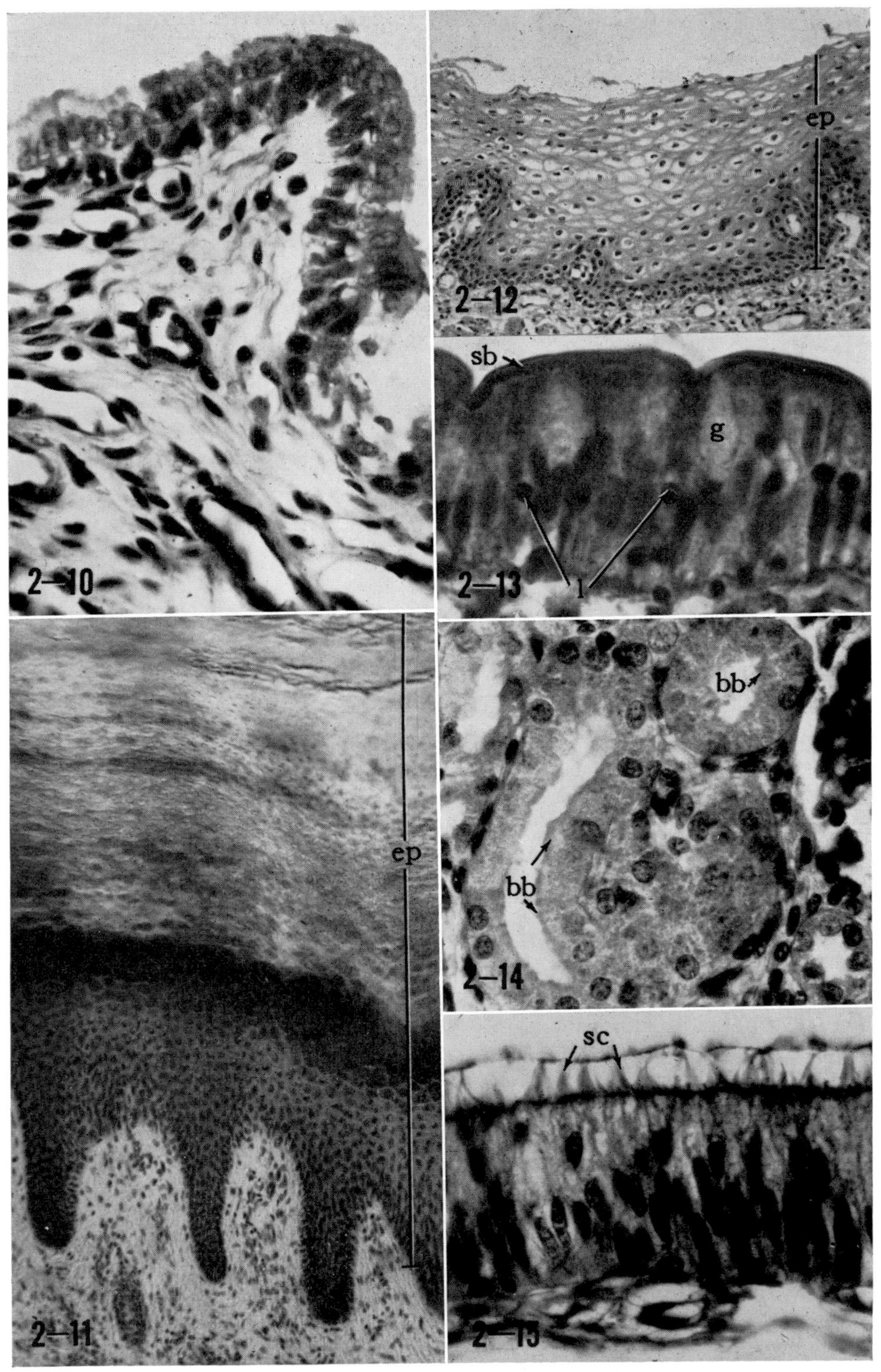
2–10
ep
2–12
sb
g
l
2–13
ep
bb
bb
2–14
sc
2–11
2–15

C. SIMPLE CUBOIDAL EPITHELIUM (Plate 5, Fig. 2-4)

Cuboidal cells primarily make up the walls of tubular structures (e.g., distal portions of renal tubules in kidney), excretory ducts of salivary and other glands, and cord-like structures in hepatic lobules. They are also found as lining cells of thyroid follicles and as the germinal epithelial covering and granulosa cells of immature follicles in the ovary. Because of the "wrap-around" effect when arranged about a small lumen or tube, cuboidal cells are modified or molded into pyramidal or truncated prismatic-shaped elements. Typically, cuboidal cells have a round, centrally placed nucleus.

D. SIMPLE COLUMNAR EPITHELIUM (Plate 5, Figs. 2-5 and 2-6)

These are tall prismatic cells which are associated chiefly with secretory and absorptive functions. Typically, they possess an oval nucleus oriented at right angles to the major cell axis. The nucleus is usually located away from the free surface near the basal end of the cell. The cytoplasm is frequently granular, but these formed elements vary in amount depending on the cell's special function and its state of activity. This kind of epithelium is prominently associated with the luminal surface of the gastrointestinal tract. A common variation of columnar cells at many internal locations is the **goblet cell**, a unicellular mucus-secreting gland.

E. PSEUDOSTRATIFIED COLUMNAR EPITHELIUM (Plate 5, Figs. 2-7 and 2-8)

These cells are irregularly columnar or cuboidal, with their nuclei located at different levels. This kind of epithelium gives the appearance of a stratified type as a result of (1) cellular crowding, (2) stratification of nuclei, (3) lack of uniformity of the cell and (4) the loss of connection with the free surface on the part of some cells. This type of epithelium is found in the large excretory ducts (e.g., parotid) and in the male urethra. On the mucous membrane of the respiratory passages (e.g., trachea and bronchi), the free surface of the cells is ciliated.

F. TRANSITIONAL EPITHELIUM (Plate 5, Fig. 2-9)

Transitional epithelium is well adapted to mechanical changes due to contraction and distension as the fluid pressure within a hollow organ changes. Thus, in the **contracted condition**, the epithelium consists of many cell layers covering a smaller area with a cell organization as follows: (1) cells on the free surface are larger than elsewhere in the epithelium and bulge into the adjacent lumen; (2) basal cells are cuboidal to columnar; and (3) intermediate layers consist of irregular polyhedral cells. On the other hand, in the **distended (stretched) condition**, the epithelium consists of only a few layers

PLATE 7—Microvilli and Desmosomes

FIG. 2-16. Electron micrograph of the microvilli forming the striated border of the intestinal epithelium of a hamster. × 40,000. (From Dr. S. Ito)

FIG. 2-17. Electron micrograph showing epithelial attachments (desmosomes, d) in stratified epithelium of esophagus of bat. Fine tonofibrils can be seen in the cytoplasm adjacent to the desmosomes and in other regions of the cytoplasm. × 60,000. (n, nucleus) (From Dr. K. Porter)

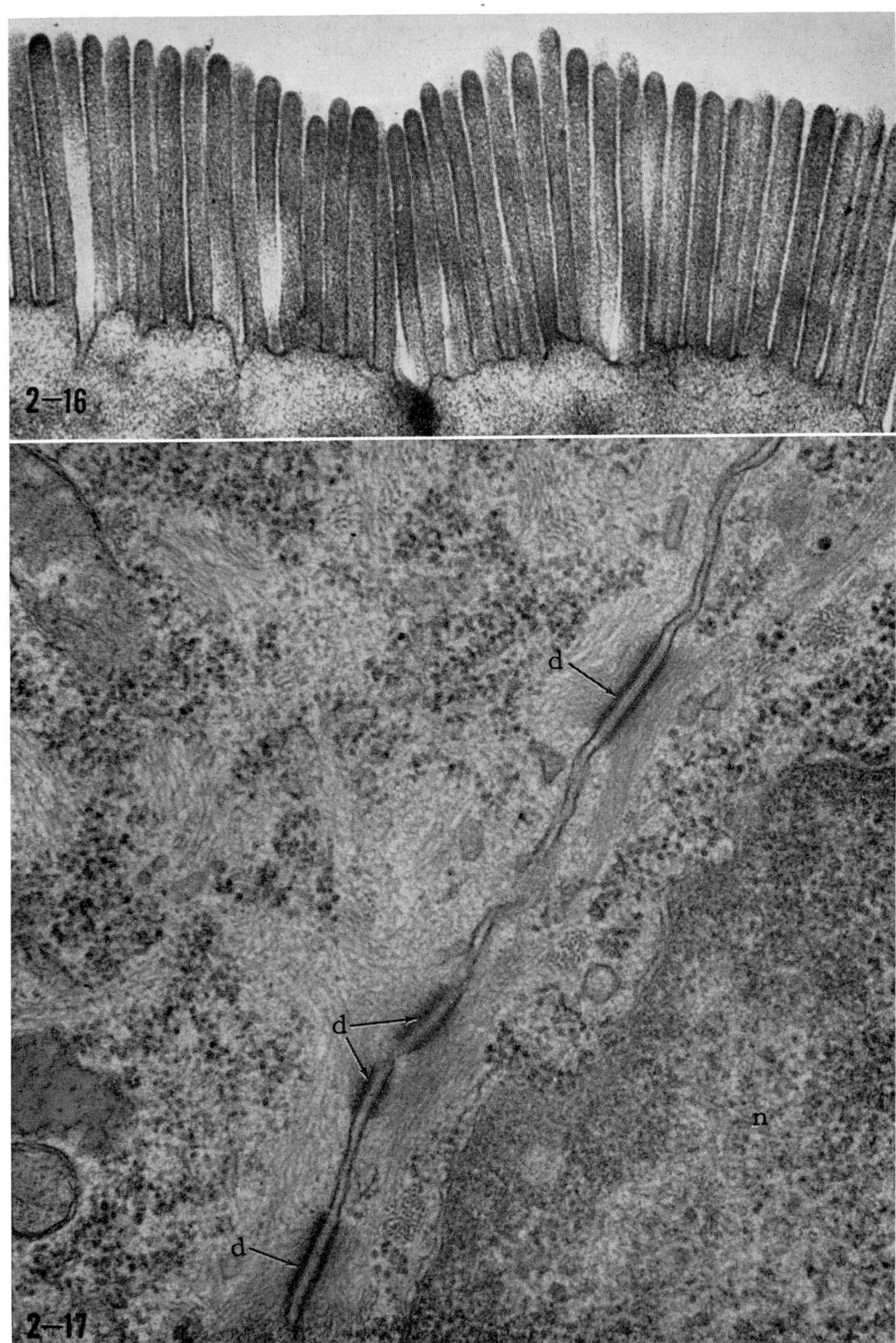
2–16
d
d
d
n
2–17

covering a greater area with a cell organization usually as follows: (1) a layer of surface cells of large squamous elements and (2) a basal layer of irregular cuboidal cells. This epithelial type is found in association with the mucous membrane of most of the excretory passages of the urinary system.

G. STRATIFIED COLUMNAR EPITHELIUM

(Plate 6, Fig. 2-10)

The cells of this type vary as follows: (1) surface elements are tall and prismatic and not connected with the basement membrane underlying the epithelium; (2) basal cells are small, ovoid or polyhedral elements which do not reach the free surface. This epithelial type is rare and is found in areas of the nasopharynx, the larynx and the cavernous part of the male urethra.

H. STRATIFIED SQUAMOUS EPITHELIUM

(Plate 6, Figs. 2-11 and 2-12)

This is the main protective epithelium of the body and consists of many cell layers. The deepest layer (basal) which rests on a basement membrane consists of small, uniformly placed cuboidal to columnar or prismatic cells which appear as a distinct row in most sections. Above the basal layer, many layers of cells begin to appear which are more irregular in shape, being polygonal and larger than the cells of the basal layer. Here, **desmosomes** (intercellular bridges of cytoplasm) which bind the cells together are prominent and give the cells a prickly appearance. As the free surface is approached, the cells are more flattened, and at the surface they are squamous. Areas of dry epithelia show the **process of cornification**, whereas, with some exceptions, this does not occur in the moist epithelial areas. This variety of epithelium is found over the entire outer surface of the body and the orifices of cavities opening upon it. It lines the mucous membranes of the mouth, the pharynx, the esophagus, the lower anal canal below the anal valves, portions of the larynx, the external auditory canal, the conjunctiva, the vagina, the vestibule and the labia majora and minora, the meatus portion of the male urethra and an area near the outlet of the female urethra.

I. SPECIAL MODIFICATIONS

Special modifications include the following:

1. **Striated cuticular border** (e.g., simple columnar epithelium in the small intestine) is an example of **microvilli**, which are minute nonmotile protoplasmic projections from epithelial cells adapted for absorption (Figs. 2-13 and 2-16).
2. **Brush border** (e.g., simple columnar epithelium of proximal convoluted tubules of the kidney) is a more prominent area of microvilli (Fig. 2-14).
3. **Cilia** (ciliated pseudostratified epithelium of the trachea) are motile, minute, protoplasmic projections which appear as hairlike structures (Fig. 2-8).
4. **Stereocilia** (pseudostratified or stratified columnar epithelium with stereocilia of the epididymis) are fibrillated nonmotile brushlike ends of the cells (Fig. 2-15).
5. **Desmosomes (intercellular bridges)** are seen best in deeper cell layers of stratified squamous epithelium of thick skin. These are considered to be primarily thickenings of the cell membranes at the points where cells adhere. Electron micrographs reveal that the tonofibrils, fine fibrils within the cytoplasm, terminate in the desmosomes rather than passing from cell to cell (Fig. 2-17).
6. **Terminal bars** (e.g., columnar cells) are found at the distal junctions of adjacent columnar cells serving to maintain firmer attachment of the cells to one another. They have been shown by electron microscopic studies to consist of a dark double membrane with an intervening pale cleft, thereby being similar to desmosomes (Fig. 2-17).
7. **Basement membrane** (e.g., trachea) is an extracellular layer which serves to attach certain epithelial tissues to the underlying connective tissues (Fig. 2-8).

3 · Exocrine Glands

A. Introduction
B. Schema for Classification of Glands
C. Serous vs. Mucous Secretions

A. INTRODUCTION

The glands of the body fall generally into 2 major functional categories, the **exocrine** and the **endocrine glands**. Although both are derived almost entirely from a surface epithelium and represent merely specializations of epithelial cells, they differ markedly in the manner of secretion and also in the nature of the material secreted. The endocrine glands consist of cells which border on vascular channels and pour their products directly into the bloodstream; these, the **glands of internal secretion**, are (with the exception of the islets of Langerhans) treated separately as the endocrine system. The other, far larger, group is the exocrine glands which consist of cell aggregates that pour their secretions into a **duct** or a **system of ducts** which in turn for the most part passively conveys the material onto the epithelial surface of an organ that is external to the gland.

PLATE 8—Glands

FIG. 3-1. Part of a simple tubular gland and adjacent stroma (s) from the endometrium of the uterus. The gland opens onto the luminal surface (l). H & E stain. High power.

FIG. 3-2. Longitudinal section through simple tubular glands of the small intestine. These glands, the crypts of Lieberkühn, are lined by a simple columnar epithelium. H & E stain. High power. (l, lumen of gland)

FIG. 3-3. Sebaceous glands from the scalp, demonstrating the simple alveolar type of gland. Note the duct (d) opening into the hair follicle lumen (hf). H & E stain. High power.

FIG. 3-4. Section of the upper portion of the duodenum showing simple tubular glands (c, the crypts of Lieberkühn), and compound tubular glands (Bg, Brunner's glands). Note that the terminal portion of the tubules of Brunner's glands appear as tubules (t) and alveoli (a). H & E stain. Intermediate power. (sm, submucosal connective tissue)

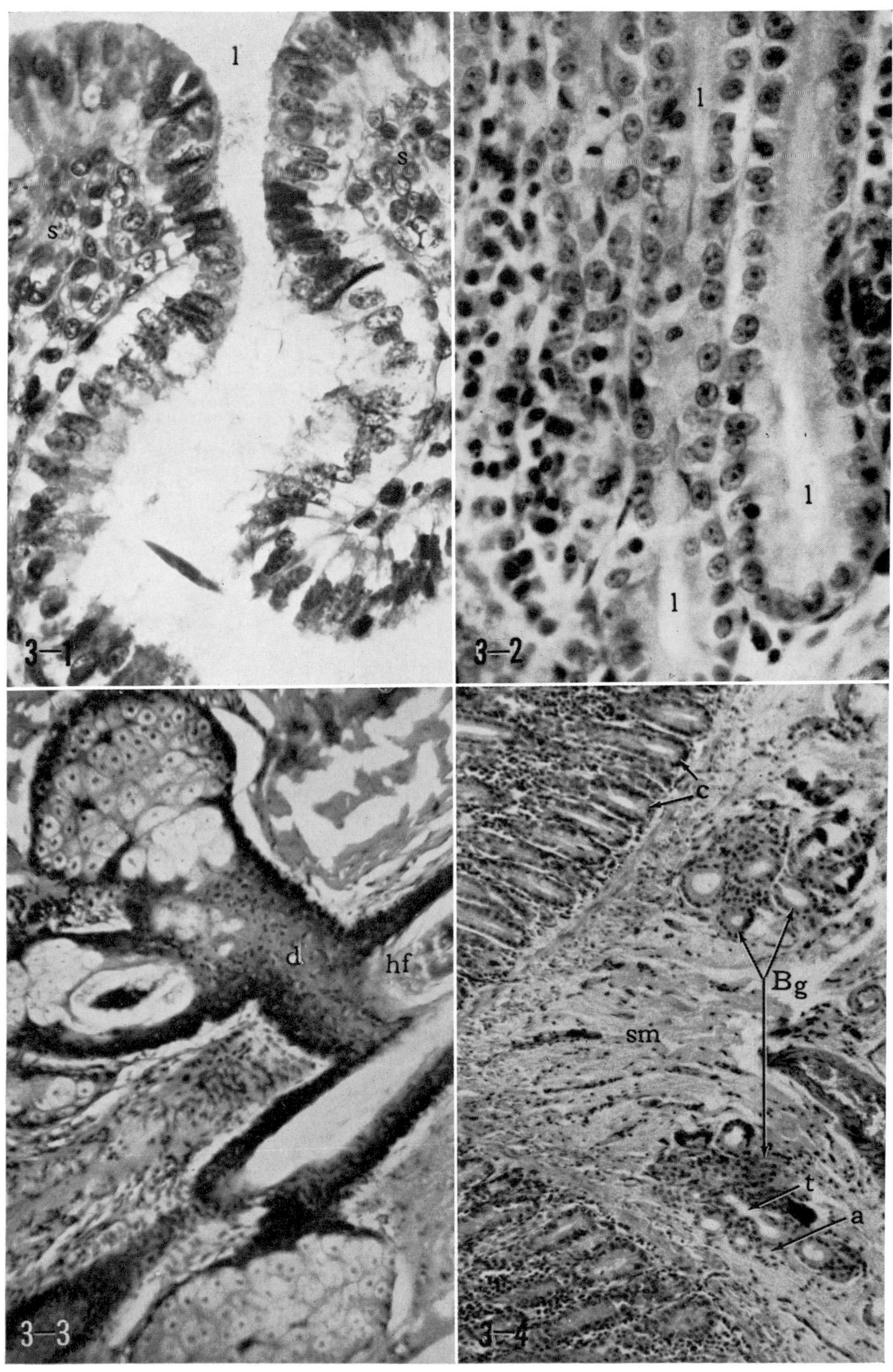
l
s
s
3–1
l
l
l
3–2
d
hf
3–3
c
Bg
sm
t
a
3–4

Regardless of whether one deals with an endocrine or an exocrine gland, the contained functional (parenchymal) cells can be regarded as a special modification of epithelium. Gland cells are usually aggregated around a lumen or a blood space. In these locations they may have a typical simple squamous, simple cuboidal or simple columnar appearance. On the other hand, glandular cells may be modified into a pyramidal shape (if molded around a lumen) or into cords of cuboidal, ovoid or polygonal cells (if to conform to blood spaces).

B. SCHEMA FOR CLASSIFICATION OF GLANDS

It should be understood that because of great variability of glandular specialization in the body, no system of classification can be all-inclusive. Most commonly, however, multicellular exocrine glands are classified according to their structure and not according to the nature of the material secreted. Glands usually consist of functional, secreting portions, the **secretory end pieces**, and one or more nonfunctional (but occasionally functional) conducting portion(s), the **excretory duct**. If the conducting system or duct is unbranched, the gland is described as **simple**. If the duct exhibits even the simplest type of branching, the gland should be referred to as **compound**.

Secretory end pieces have various shapes, but usually they appear in tubelike or grapelike clusters referred to as **tubular** or **alveolar** (sometimes used interchangeably with **acinar**) groupings of secretory cells.

Based on the above considerations, the following morphologic classifications of glands might be anticipated. (Remember that the first part of the gland's designation refers to the duct system and the second part to the secretory end pieces). Examples are given:

1. **Simple tubular glands**—glands found in the fundic and the pyloric portions of the stomach, intestinal glands (crypts of Lieberkühn), sweat glands, most of Brunner's glands, uterine glands, ceruminous glands (in the external ear) (Figs. 3-1, 3-2)
2. **Simple alveolar glands**—sebaceous glands of all types (free, attached, Meibomian glands of the eyelid, penile glands of Tyson, glands of Zeis in the eyelid) (Fig. 3-3)
3. **Simple tubulo-alveolar glands**—perhaps a few elements in the following glands are of this type: Brunner's glands, esophageal glands, minor salivary glands, respiratory glands (Fig. 3-4)
4. **Compound tubular glands**—bulbourethral glands, glands of the cardiac portion of the stomach, some of Brunner's glands and some glands of the esophagus. Although not thought of in the same light as other glands, the kidney, the testis and the liver also fall into this category (Figs. 3-5, 3-6).
5. **Compound alveolar glands**—mammary gland (Fig. 3-7)

PLATE 9—Glands

FIG. 3-5. Kidney cortex to show the multiple duct systems of this compound tubular gland. H & E stain. Low power.

FIG. 3-6. Seminiferous tubules of the testis, revealing their compound tubular nature. Mallory stain. Low power.

FIG. 3-7. Budding alveoli of the mammary gland, a compound alveolar gland. H & E stain. Intermediate power.

FIG. 3-8. Compound tubulo-alveolar gland. Survey of the parotid gland reveals the tubular and alveolar appearance of its secretory end-pieces as well as the complex branching of its ducts. H & E stain. Low power.

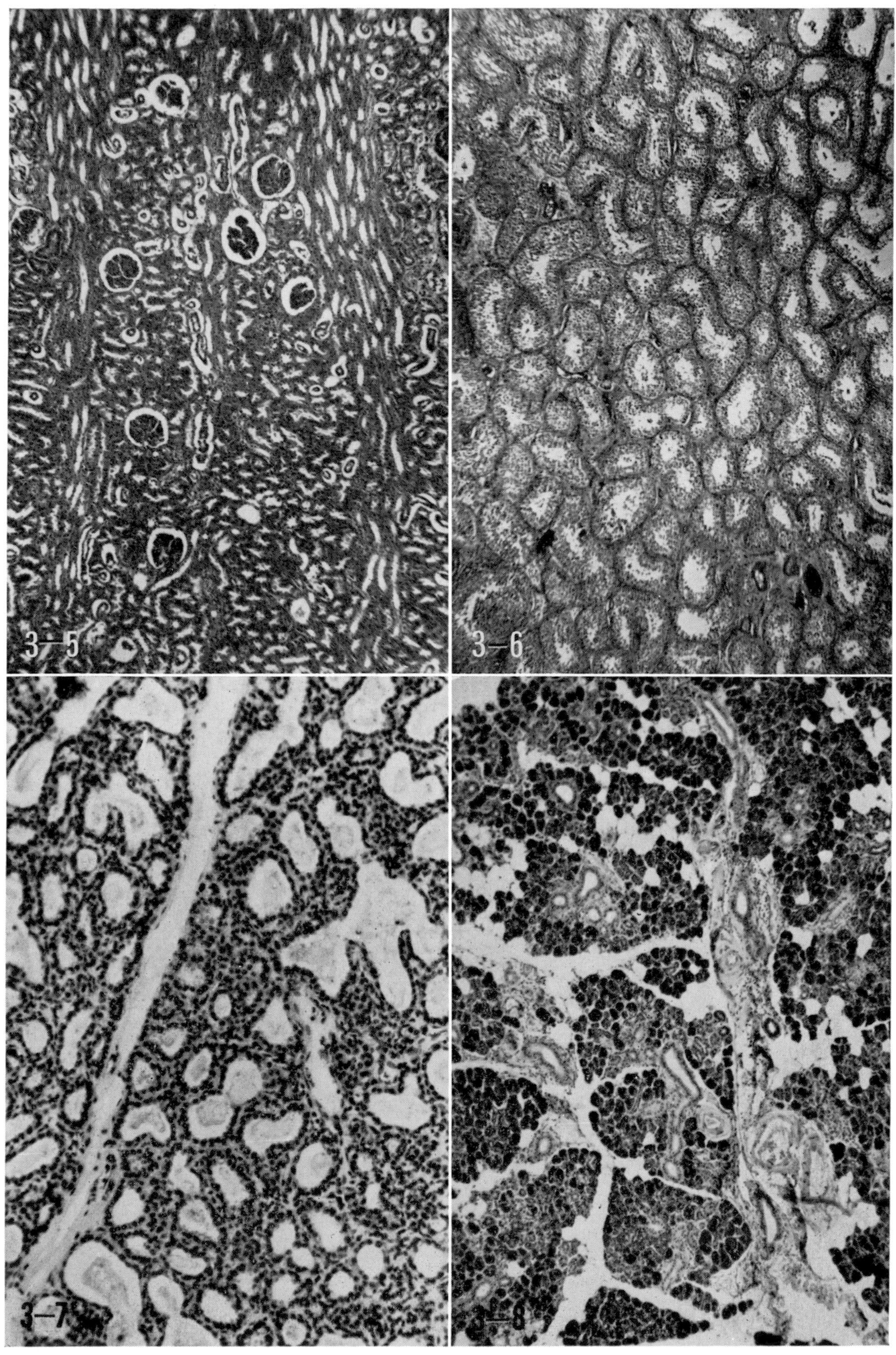
3–5
3–6
3–7
3–8

6. **Compound tubulo-alveolar glands**—parotid gland, submaxillary gland, sublingual gland, exocrine portion of the pancreas, respiratory glands, esophageal glands, lacrimal gland, glands of Wolfring in the eyelid, prostatic glands, some of the bulbo-urethral glands (Fig. 3-8).

In addition to the structural classification, it is desirable that the student be informed briefly about the system of gland classification based on the mode of secretion. This system refers to the appearance of gland cells at the time of secretion. Three types are included under this classification:

1. **Merocrine (eccrine) glands**—secreted material passes through plasma membrane with little or no change in over-all appearance of the cells.
2. **Apocrine glands**—secreted material breaks off the apex of the secreting cell, and both are discharged into an adjacent lumen.
3. **Holocrine glands**—as secretion is formed intracellularly, the entire gland cell degenerates and is discharged, with its contents, into an adjacent lumen.

C. SEROUS VS. MUCOUS SECRETIONS

Regardless of its morphologic classification, a gland generally will elaborate either a watery, albuminous secretion having high biochemical activity, or a thick, viscous material that may have low chemical activity. The former type of secretion is referred to as serous, the latter as mucous.

Serous secretions are commonly associated with glands that produce enzymes. In this connection, the enzyme precursors accumulate in the cytoplasm of gland cells as **zymogen granules**. These granules are semifluid in life, but after fixation they take on a coarse granular appearance and demonstrate an affinity for basic dyes.

Mucous secretions are associated especially with the moist epithelial surfaces of the gastrointestinal, the respiratory and the genitourinary systems. Mucus provides a necessary lubricant that reduces the frictional forces acting on the epithelial surface. At the same time, by being mixed with the luminal contents, as in the case of the gastrointestinal tract, mucus can render a mass into a form more easily acted on by digestive enzymes.

4 · Connective Tissue

A. INTRODUCTION

The connective tissues are characterized, in contrast with the epithelia, by a paucity of cells and an abundance of intercellular material of varying nature. They can be classified under two major headings, **connective tissue proper** and **supporting tissue** (cartilage and bone).

Connective tissue proper always contains fibers in its intercellular substance; it (1) cushions organs; (2) connects, invests, encapsulates and suspends organs, and (3) forms the framework or stroma in organs, thus supporting the functional or parenchymal elements. Depending on whether the intercellular fibers are loosely or densely arranged, one speaks of **loose connective tissue** or **dense connective tissue**. Similarly, if the fibers are regularly arranged between cells, one speaks of **regular** (i.e., regularly arranged) **connective tissue** while connective tissue with irregular networks of fibers are referred to as being irregularly arranged.

The **supporting tissues** are similar to connective tissue proper in that there are rela-

PLATE 10—Areolar Connective Tissue Fibers and Cells

FIG. 4-1. Areolar connective tissue section through the subcutaneous loose connective tissue from the leg. H & E stain. Low power. (c, collagen fibers; e, elastic fibers)

FIG. 4-2. Intermediate-power from a portion of section in Figure 4-1. (c, collagen fibers; e, elastic fibers)

FIG. 4-3. Collagen fibers (c) from the submucosa of the small intestine. H & E stain. Oil immersion. (te, tissue eosinophil)

FIG. 4-4. Connective tissue cells from the lamina propria of the small intestine. H & E stain. Oil immersion. (f, fibroblasts; l, lymphocytes)

FIG. 4-5. Connective tissue cells from a region similar to that in Figure 4-4. H & E stain. Oil immersion. (f, fibroblasts; 1, lymphocytes; 1c, epithelial lining cells of mucosa)

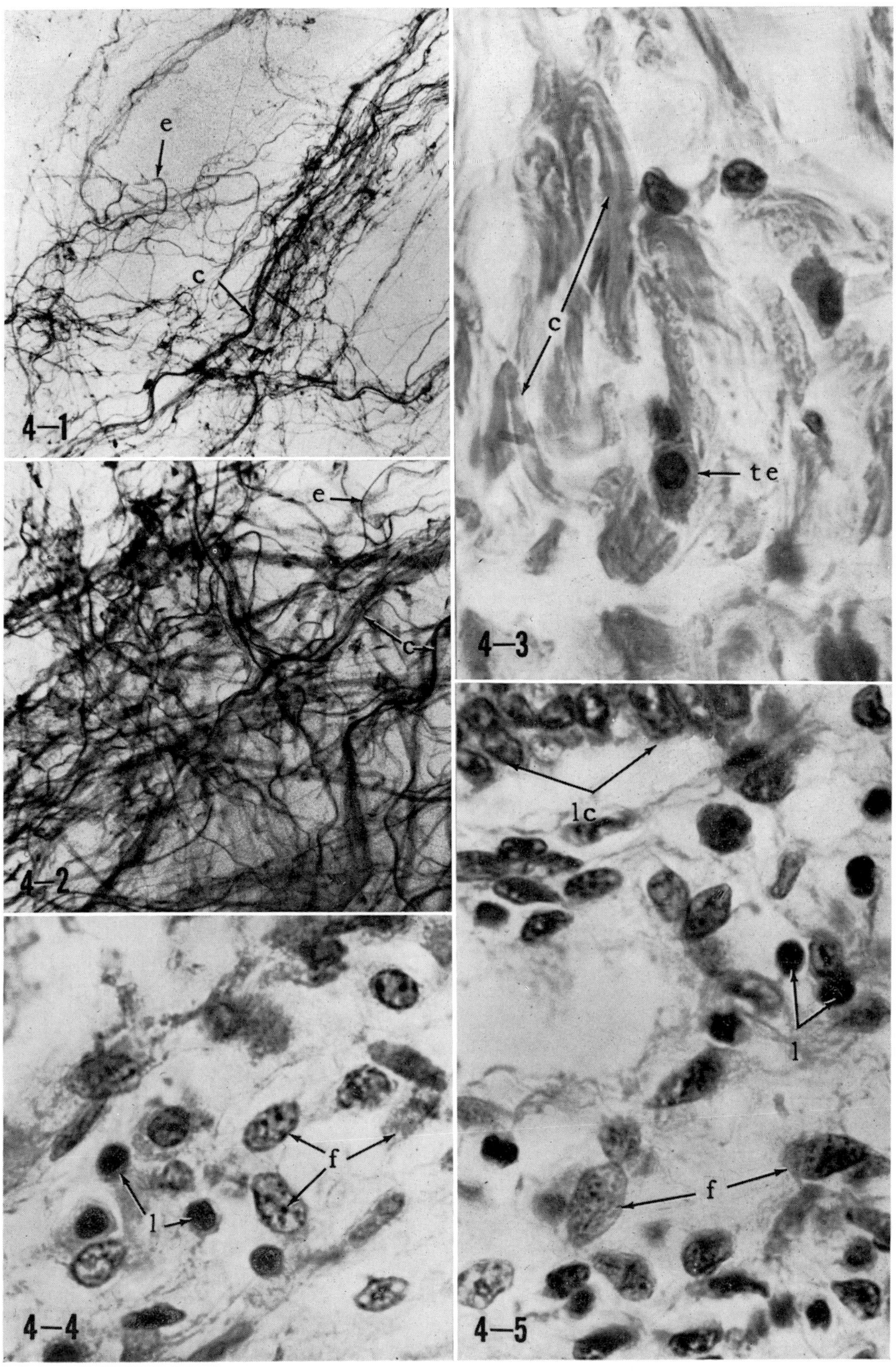
e
c
4–1
e
c
4–2
c
te
4–3
lc
l
f
l
4–4
f
4–5

tively few cells associated with much intercellular material. However, further specialization of this cell-fiber organization brings about the creation of a solid or semisolid state that is capable of supporting considerable weight.

B. CONNECTIVE TISSUE PROPER

1. Loose Connective Tissue (Areolar C. T.) (Figs. 4-1 and 4-2)

The main mass is intercellular substance which contains:

a. *Collagenous or White Fibers.* Fibers are long, usually wavy threads forming bundles and running in all directions (Fig. 4-3).

b. *Elastic or Yellow Fibers.* Fibers are long, thin, branching threads which anastomose freely. They appear straight in the naturally fixed state and wavy in teased preparations (Figs. 4-1, 4-2).

c. *Reticular Fibers.* These are characteristically thin, highly branched fibers, usually forming delicate networks. They are best observed by silver impregnation technics. Fibers may be immature collagenous (precollagenous) fibers.

d. *Amorphous Ground Substance.* This consists of proteinaceous, homogenous material in which collagenous, elastic and reticular fibers are embedded. The ground substance is believed to be derived from connective tissue cells (Fig. 4-16).

Regarding the origin of fibers, this question is still in dispute. Either they may arise within connective tissue cells, being given off, or they may arise between the cells through a condensation or crystallization of an intercellular substance secreted by the cell.

The cellular elements may include:

1. **Fibroblasts.** Mature cells (fibrocytes) are long and flat with ovoid, pale-staining nuclei and clear cytoplasm, usually found adjacent to the surface of collagen bundles (Figs. 4-4, 4-5). Young cells may closely resemble mesenchymal cells.

2. **Mesenchymal (Undifferentiated) Cells.** These cells are irregularly stellate in shape, similar to immature fibroblasts, usually smaller than mature fibroblasts, and constitute the major cell type in undifferentiated connective tissue of the embryo and the adult (Plate 11, Figs. 4-6, 4-7).

3. **Macrophages** (histiocytes, clasmatocytes, etc.). In the loose connective tissue their shape depends on the state of activity. They are smaller than adult fibroblasts, appearing to have a small, distinct round nucleus and an irregular but distinct cell membrane. The cytoplasm contains varying numbers of coarse granules and vacuoles depending on the cell's state of activity. Fixed macrophages vary from ovoid to irregularly elongate elements with membranous processes. In the free macrophage type (active condition), the cell migrates toward an inflammatory site, tends to round up and puts forth bleblike pseudopodia (Fig. 4-8).

4. **Mast Cells** (Tissue Basophiles). These are irregularly ovoid cells with short pseudo-

PLATE 11—Connective Tissue Cells and Mesenchymal Tissue

FIG. 4-6. Developing subepidermal connective tissue from the back of an embryo. H & E stain. Intermediate power. (m, mesenchyme; ea, early areolar tissue; v, developing vessel; ep, developing epidermis)

FIG. 4-7. High power, from section in Figure 4-6. (i, intercellular substance; mc, mesenchymal cells with processes)

FIG. 4-8. Lamina propria of small intestine showing various connective tissue cells. H & E stain. Oil immersion. (te, tissue eosinophils; p, plasma cell; f, fibroblasts; ma, macrophages)

FIG. 4-9. Mast cell (mc) in a perivascular location from the lamina propria of the small intestine. H & E stain. Oil immersion. (en, endothelial nuclei of small vessels)

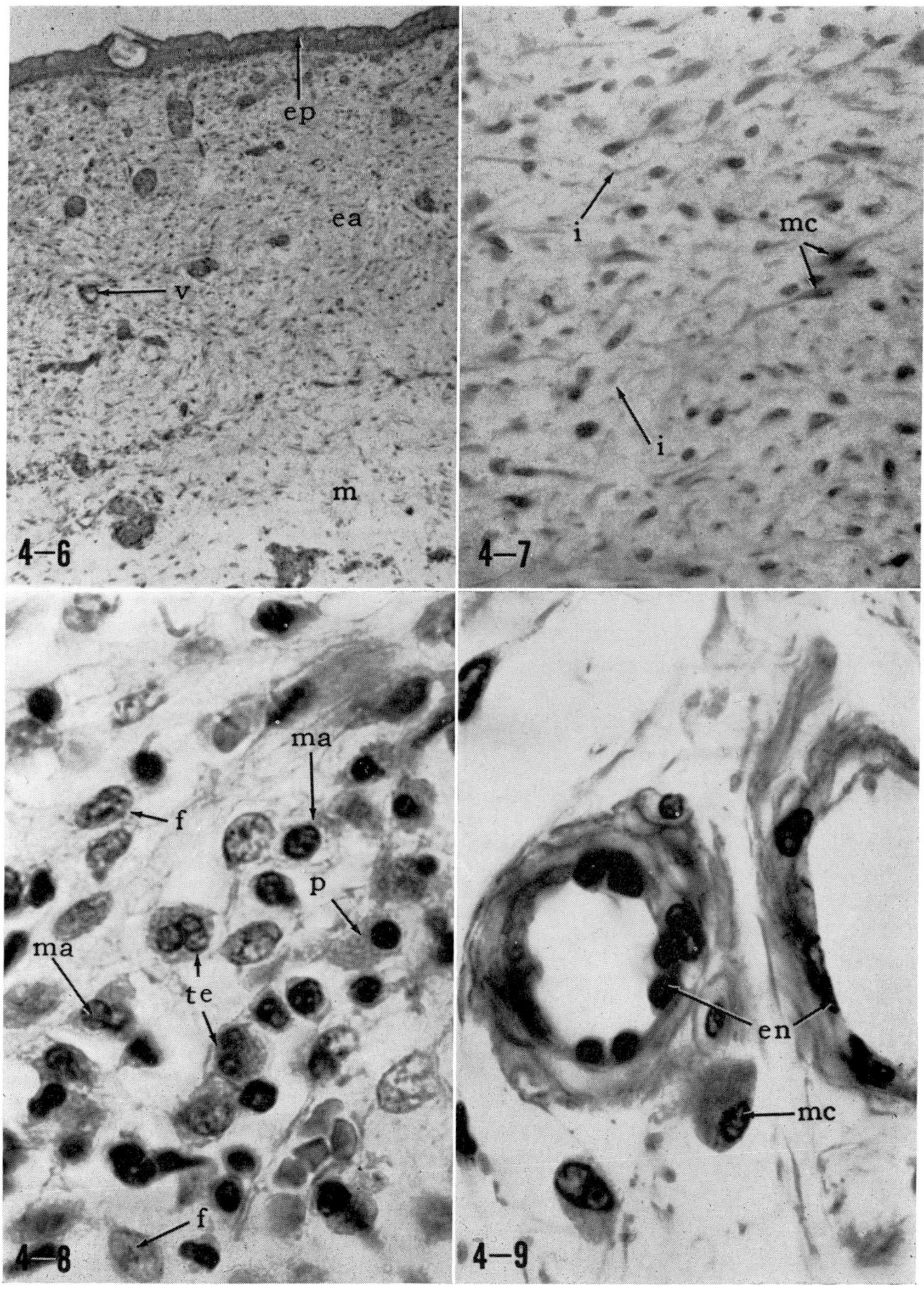
ep
ea
v
m
4–6
i
mc
i
4–7
ma
f
p
ma
te
f
4–8
en
mc
4–9

podia and large, coarse basophilic-staining granules that mask a pale-staining nucleus. They tend to lie along blood vessels. Mast cells are believed to elaborate heparin and also possibly histamine and serotonin (Fig. 4-9).

5. **Tissue Eosinophils.** They appear as polymorphonuclear, round to ovoid cells with large pink granules. Increases are associated with parasitism and allergic conditions. These cells can usually be found in the lamina propria of the gastrointestinal tract. (See Figs. 4-3, 4-8.)

6. **Plasma Cells.** This type of cell is usually irregularly ovoid with a distinct outline and characteristically has an eccentric round to oval nucleus consisting of coarse chromatin granules that sometimes are distributed in rosette or cartwheel arrangement. It is a lymphocytic type of cell, associated with antibody production and rarely found in most connective tissues under normal conditions. However, connective tissue of the lamina propria in the digestive tract should be examined (Plate 12, Figs. 4-10, 4-11).

7. **Pigment Cells** (Chromatophores, Melanocytes, Etc.). These elongated cells with short, irregular outgrowths contain yellow, brown or black granules. They are primarily in the dermis of the skin and in the choroid and the iris of the eye (See Figs. 21-4, 21-5 and 21-13).

8. **Reticular Cells.** This type has a stellate appearance and is very similar to the mesenchymal cell, with the important exception that the processes adhere to those of neighboring elements, forming a 3-dimensional network (rete). Reticular cells contain flat, oval nuclei and a nongranular cytoplasm. (See Plate 15, Figs. 4-23, 4-24.)

9. **Fat Cells.** These are large, ovoid cells with nuclei flattened against the periphery in signet ring fashion. Fat cells have nutritive, mechanical and conservation functions (Figs. 4-12, 4-13).

2. Fetal and Young Connective Tissue

a. *Mesenchymal Connective Tissue* (Mesenchyme). This is derived from the middle germinal layer of mesoderm and, before any definitive organs have differentiated, constitutes the sole tissue between ectoderm and entoderm. As time progresses, the cells of mesenchymal connective tissue are acted upon by genetically directed chemical organizers to differentiate along divergent lines in specific locations to form various organs and vascular tissue. The predominant features of mesenchymal connective tissue are its characteristic cells (see above) and a homogeneous intercellular material (matrix) that contains no fibers. (See Figs. 4-6, 4-7.)

b. *Mucous Connective Tissue.* This represents an early differentiation of mesenchyme. Cells tend to be more elongated than mesenchymal cells and in some cases are quite spindle-shaped. In contrast with mesenchyme, delicate fibers are now present in the intercellular spaces, and the semifluid ground substance, homogeneous in the living state, may have a faintly granular appearance due to postmortem precipitation of proteinaceous material in the jellylike matrix. There is a tendency of the fibers to line up in parallel

PLATE 12—Connective Tissue Cells and Adipose Tissue

FIG. 4-10. Plasma cells (p), fibroblasts (f), macrophage (m) and lymphocyte (1) from the lamina propria of the small intestine. H & E stain. Oil immersion.

FIG. 4-11. Same section of Figure 4-10 showing a different cell population of the lamina propria. (1, lymphocytes; f, fibroblast; p, plasma cells)

FIG. 4-12. Adipose tissue (a) in adventitia of the lower third of the esophagus. H & E stain. Intermediate power. (c, collagen fibers)

FIG. 4-13. Adipose tissue overlying the capsule of the adrenal gland. Also observe numerous blood vessels. H & E stain. Intermediate power.

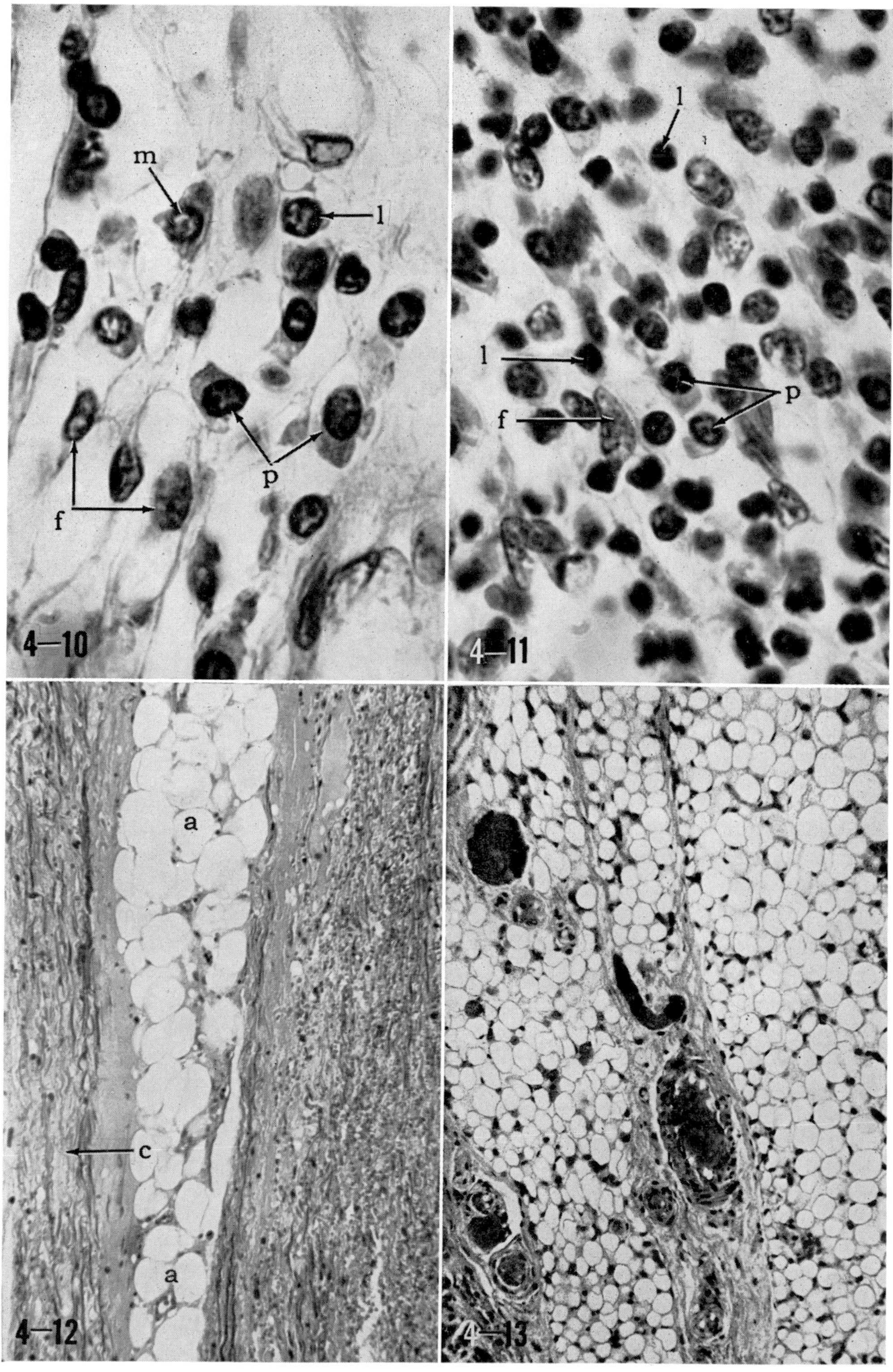
m
l
p
f
4—10
l
l
p
f
4—11
a
c
a
4—12
4—13

fashion. Mucous connective tissue constitutes the Wharton's jelly of the umbilical cord and is also frequently seen under the skin of embryos (Plate 13, Figs. 4-14 to 4-16).

3. Dense Connective Tissue With Irregularly Arranged Fibers

Elements are the same as in loose connective tissue, but its fibers are always more numerous and thicker. In addition to the dense arrangement of fibers into irregular networks, cells are present in varying numbers. This type of dense connective tissue is associated mainly with the dermis of skin, the submucosa of the intestinal tract and parts of the urinary tract (Plate 14, Figs. 4-17, 4-18).

4. Dense Connective Tissue With Regularly Arranged Fibers

This tissue makes up the tendons, the ligaments and the aponeuroses of the body. The predominant feature consists of thick fiber bundles arranged in parallel fashion. The chief cell type is the fibroblast, but normally these are few in number. Ground substance is minimal. Reticular fibers, difficult to see in the ordinary H & E preparation, attach the constituent fibers of each fiber bundle to each other.

a. *Tendons and Most Ligaments*. This is connective tissue in which the constituent fibers are collagenous. Here, fibroblasts, called tendon cells, are observed. These cells are squeezed between fibers into elongated elements and frequently are found as cell nests lined up in linear fashion in the interfibrillar spaces (Plate 14, Figs. 4-19, 4-20).

b. *Elastic (Yellow) Connective Tissue*. This tissue is similar in most respects to tendon except that all or the majority of the constituent fibers are elastic in nature. Coarse elastic fibers branch in one plane of space, and more delicate collagenous fibers may be found in the spaces between elastic fibers. Elastic connective tissue is limited in distribution to the ligament flava of vertebrae, the true vocal cords, the ligamentum stylohyoideum and a few other sites (Plate 15, Figs. 4-21, 4-22).

c. *Aponeurosis*. This is similar to tendon except that it is constructed of many superimposed layers, the parallel fibers of each layer often running in a different direction from those of the next layer.

C. SPECIAL FORMS OF CONNECTIVE TISSUE

1. Reticular Tissue

This tissue consists of reticular fibers and primitive reticular cells. The reticular fibers form the 3-dimensional stromal network of lymphoid organs in which lymph cells are enmeshed. Reticular fibers sometimes are termed **argyrophilic fibers**, since they have an affinity for silver stains (Figs. 4-23, 4-24).

PLATE 13—Mucous Connective Tissue

FIG. 4-14. Survey section of Wharton's jelly of the umbilical cord of a fetus. Note the nature of this embryonic connective tissue which is of the mucous variety. H & E stain. Low power. (v, umbilical vessels)

FIG. 4-15. Intermediate-power view of a portion of Figure 4-14, revealing the loose connective tissue network of collagen fibers and fibroblastic cells characteristic of mucous connective tissue. Note portions of the two umbilical arteries (a) and the umbilical vein (v).

FIG. 4-16. High-power view of a portion of Figure 4-14, showing the large fibroblastic cells (f) with some of their collagenic fibrillar processes (c) anastomosing with each other and embedded in a homogeneous, gelatinous ground substance (g) containing thin collagenous fibers (cf).

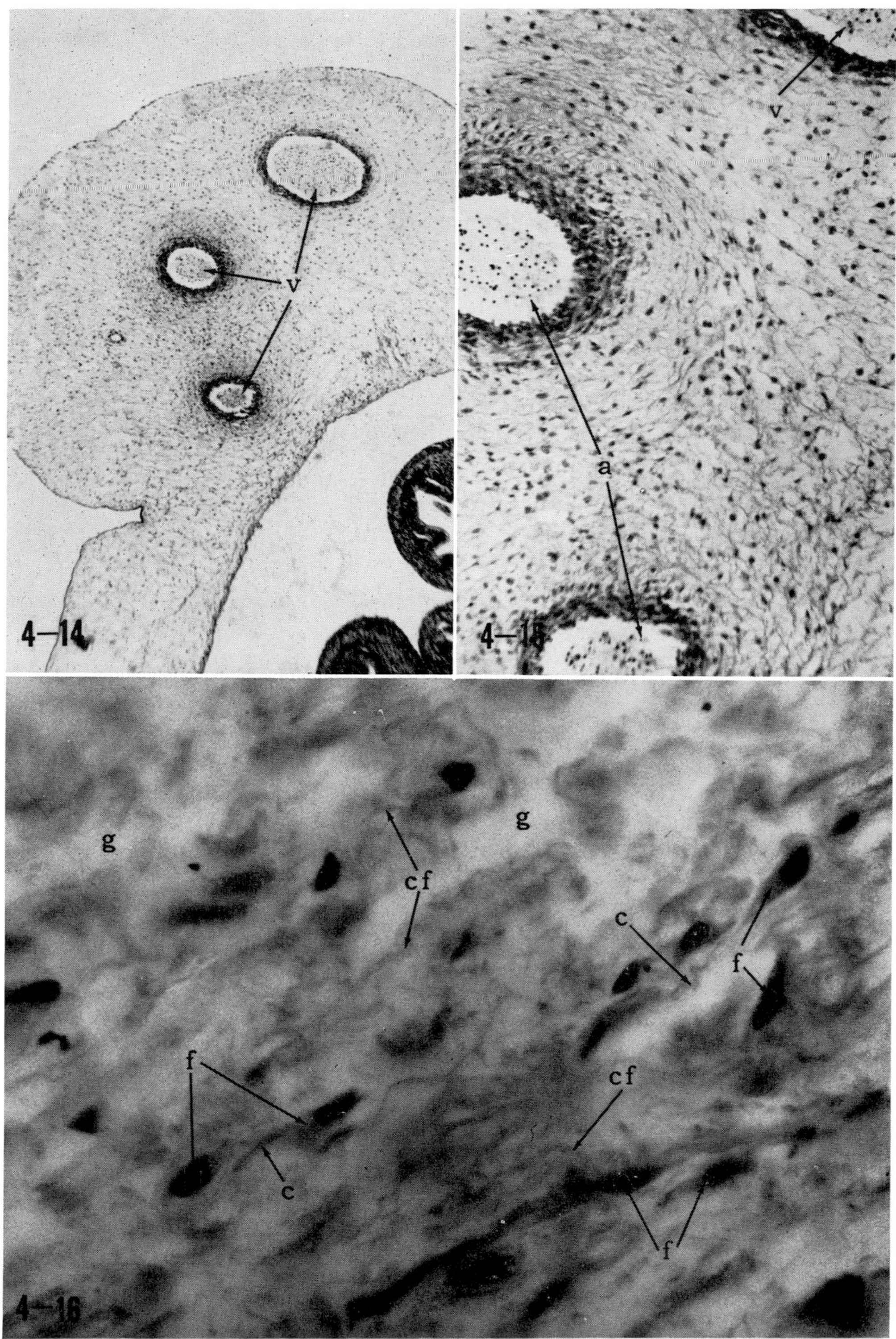
v
4—14
v
a
4—15
g
g
cf
c
f
f
f
c
cf
f
4—16

2. Adipose Connective Tissue

This tissue consists of concentrations of closely packed fat cells found in various parts of the body, e.g., panniculus adiposus. (See Figs. 4-12, 4-13.)

D. SUPPORTING TISSUES

1. Cartilage

This represents a supporting type of connective tissue in which the intercellular matrix has a stiff but flexible consistency. It is derived from mesenchyme, and growth occurs either from a surface membrane, the perichondrium (**appositional type**), or by division of cells within an existing mass of cartilage (**interstitial type**). Mature cartilage cells (**chondrocytes**) are located in ovoid spaces (**lacunae**) surrounded by matrix. Connective tissue fibers are always present in the matrix. Cartilage is an avascular tissue, and nutriment is supplied to its viable elements by diffusion from vessels in the surrounding connective tissue proper.

a. *Hyaline Cartilage* (Plates 16, 17 [Figs. 4-29 and 4-30], and 26). The name of this type of cartilage derives from the fact that the matrix has a glassy, homogeneous appearance in life. The matrix contains collagen fibers and an amorphous ground substance. The fibers cannot be seen microscopically because they have the same refractive index as the rest of the matrix. This is the most frequently occurring form of cartilage in the adult, and is commonly found at articular surfaces of bones and at various levels of the respiratory system. In the fetus, hyaline cartilage has a much wider distribution, being present as the model, in miniature, of much of the future axial bony skeleton.

b. *Fibrocartilage* (Fibrous Cartilage) (Plates 17 [Figs. 4-31 and 4-32] and 18). This type owes its name to the fact that its intercellular matrix contains heavy concentrations of coarse collagen fiber bundles. These bundles can be seen weaving back and forth, forming a rough latticework about the chondrocytes, with lacunae and their enclosed cells frequently arranged in rows. Fibrocartilage is limited in distribution, usually being found where an additional strengthening support or attachment is needed. It is generally associated with intervertebral disks, tendon, bone and hyaline cartilage and, in the adult, need not be directly related to a perichondrium.

c. *Elastic Cartilage* (Plate 19). The name relates to the presence of a system of branching elastic fibers in the matrix. The presence of elastic fibers, in addition to collagenous fibers, makes this type more flexible than the other types of cartilage. Its distribution is quite restricted; it is found only in the external ear, the epiglottis and the larynx.

2. Bone (Plates 20 and 21)

This is a supporting form of connective tissue in which the intercellular system of collagen fibers and matrix has become ossified by the deposition of mineral salts. It is similar to cartilage in being ultimately derived from mesenchyme. It differs from cartilage in the important respect that growth

PLATE 14—Dense Connective Tissue

FIG. 4-17. Dense irregularly arranged connective tissue (ct) in the base of the plica circularis from a longitudinal section of dog jejunum. Masson stain. Intermediate power.

FIG. 4-18. High-power view of dense connective tissue with irregularly arranged fibers from the reticular layer of the dermis (monkey). H & E stain.

FIG. 4-19. Longitudinal section of tendon (rabbit) to demonstrate dense connective tissue with regularly arranged fibers. H & E stain. Intermediate power.

FIG. 4-20. High-power view of an adjacent portion of Figure 4-19. Note the closely packed parallel collagen bundles and the fibroblasts arranged between the bundles. H & E stain.

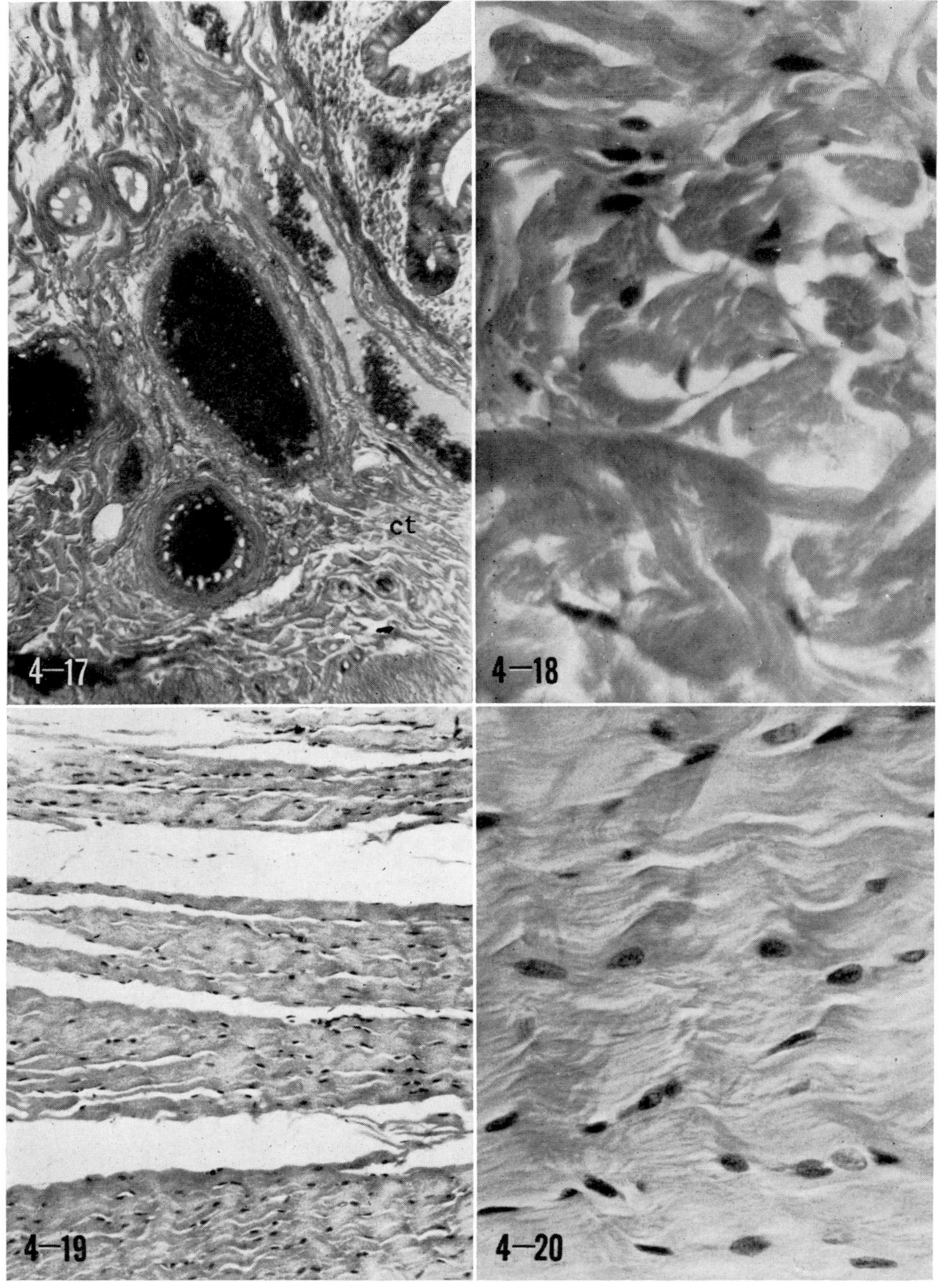
ct
4–17
4–18
4–19
4–20

always takes place by deposition on a surface (**appositional** or **lamellar type**) and never by interstitial growth.

All mature bony structures are covered by a membrane (**periosteum**) as is the case with most cartilage. In addition, mature bone cells (**osteocytes**) reside within lacunae, just as chondrocytes do in cartilage. In this feature, however, lacunae in bone contrast sharply with those in cartilage in that their outlines are more irregular and they communicate with each other by means of delicate channels (**canaliculi**).

An obstacle that all too frequently slows down learning on the part of the student is a simple matter of the semantics related to bone. Students should not confuse the terms **compact** and **spongy (cancellous) bone** with the terms **cartilage replacement (endochondral)** and **intramembranous bone**. The first pair of terms refers strictly to bone architecture, the second pair to the vital processes by which bone grows (**osteogenesis**). In a long bone created by both types of growth, one can find both the cancellous and the compact types of bone.

1. The two morphologic types of bone will now be considered.

a. *Spongy (Cancellous) Bone*. This type consists of tiny, irregular pieces (**spicules, trabeculae**) of bone and exists in both immature and adult bony structures. It is laid down in fetal mesenchyme and in adult connective tissue. For an osteocyte to survive, it must be no further than 0.2 mm. from a blood capillary. This means that pieces of spongy bone can be no more than 0.4 mm. thick. Thus, cancellous bone consists of interconnected spicules, each of which measures less than half a millimeter in thickness. Spongy bone always is found at various stages of development in all the named bones of the body.

Each spicule consists of a matrix of calcified material that surrounds both the osteocytes in their lacunae and the canaliculi. Canaliculi, in addition to connecting adjacent lacunae, open onto the surface of the spicule. Modified mesenchymal cells which give rise to bone (**osteoblasts**) are found in varying numbers on the surface of each spicule (Fig. 4-41).

b. *Compact (Dense) Bone*. This type of bone is present as **plates (lamellae)** in most of the long, the flat and the irregularly shaped bones of the adult. It develops secondarily from spongy bone. Thus, in the fetal and the early postpartal condition, most sites of future compact bony structures can be found as small areas of cancellous bone.

Compact bone results from the appositional deposition of osseous material in lamellae. Since osteocytes cannot survive farther than 0.2 mm. from a feeding blood vessel, these lamellae develop close to their blood supply. In long bones, these plates, depending on their location, are referred to as **circumferential (periosteal), haversian, interstitial** or **endosteal lamellae**. The osteocytes of plates furthest removed from their nutrient vessel receive blood via the lacunae and the canalicular channels of bone cells closer to the vessel. Compact bone can be formed at the surface of a long bone by the

PLATE 15—Connective Tissue Fibers

FIG. 4-21. Distinct elastic fibers (e), collagen fibers (c) and fat cells (f) in a longitudinal section of the adventitia of the lower third of the esophagus. H & E stain. High power.

FIG. 4-22. Note the presence of numerous elastic fibers (e) in the tunica intima of the common carotid artery. Mallory stain. High power. (l, lumen of vessel)

FIG. 4-23. Argyrophilic (reticular) fibers (r) between the tubules of the kidney. Rio-Hortega stain. Intermediate power. (g, glomerulus)

FIG. 4-24. Reticular fibers (r) around epididymal tubules. Silver nitrate stain. High power.

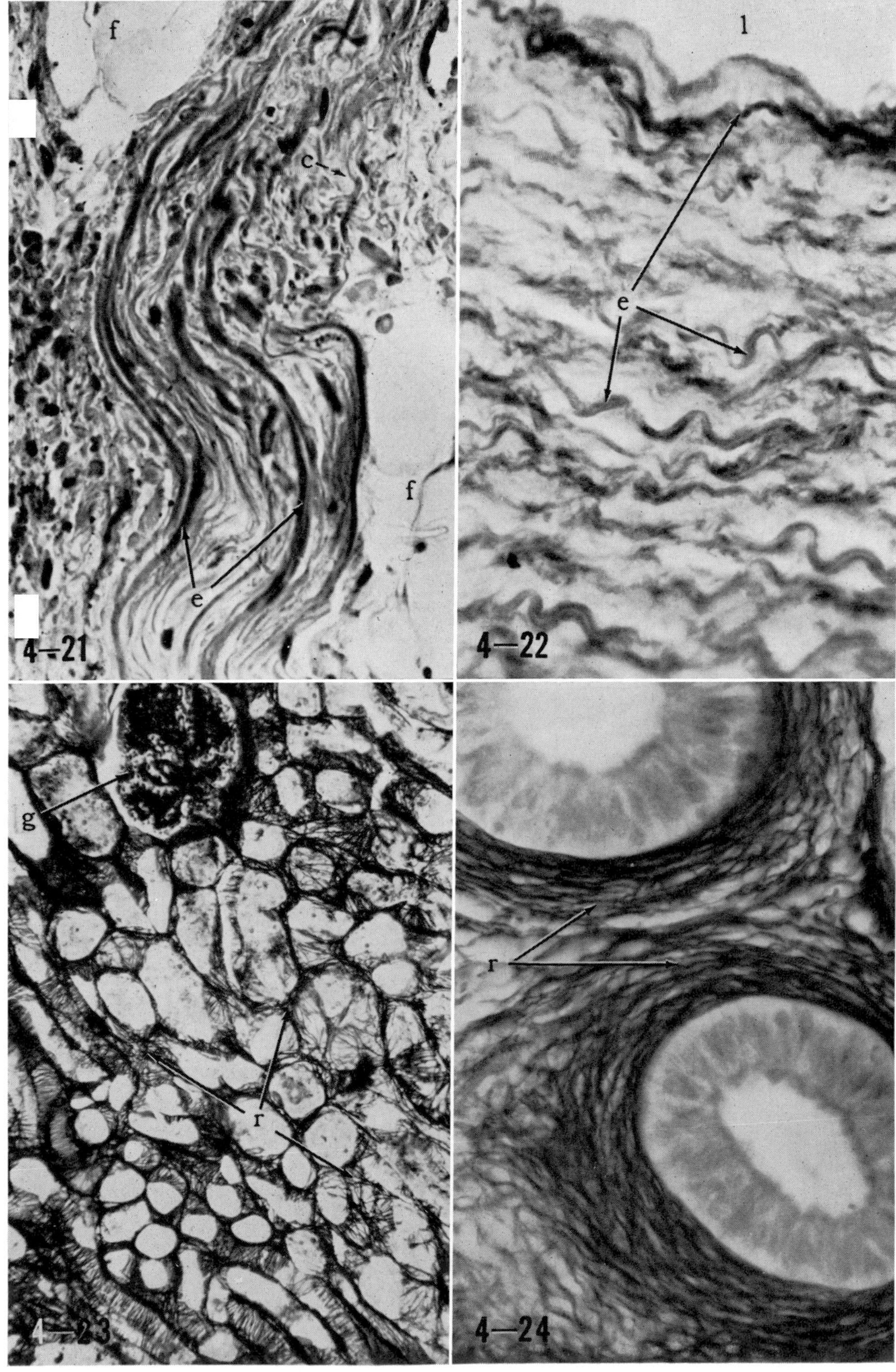
f
c
f
e
4–21
l
e
4–22
g
r
4–23
r
4–24

periosteum and internally by endosteum or epiphysial disks. In flat bones, the lamellae collectively are known as tables (Figs. 4-42 to 4-48).

2. Although bone is formed by two different physiologic processes, which will be considered next, both processes depend on 3 factors: (1) a rich vascularity to supply the energy requirements and to bring to the area, in ionic form, the minerals necessary for ossification; (2) osteoblasts depositing around themselves a soft, **pre-bone matrix** (**osteoid tissue**) which contains collagen fibers and ground substance; (3) secretion by osteoblasts of alkaline phosphatase into the surrounding osteoid tissue for the precipitation of mineral salts; and (4) remodeling of bone by the selective resorption of old bone and the addition of new bone. Resorption is associated with the presence of osteoclasts (multinucleated phagocytic giant cells). These cells are rarely seen in normal mature bone.

a. *Cartilage Replacement by Bone (Endochondral Osteogenesis)* (Plates 22 to 25). Large portions of most adult bones do not develop directly from mesenchyme. Instead, mesenchyme first lays down a miniature model of the future bone (or part of a bone) in cartilage, and this cartilage is subsequently broken down and replaced by bone.

The development of bone by cartilage replacement is followed most easily in long bones and involves most, but not all, of the **diaphysis** (shaft), the **metaphysis** (bridge connecting shaft and end) and the **epiphysis** (end). Sequentially, the steps involved in endochondral ossification include:

(1) Creation of a cartilage model, completely ensheathed by a perichondrium

(2) Alteration of cartilage (maturation and calcification) in the center of the model simultaneously with penetration from the surface of vascular buds (**periosteal buds**) carrying modified mesenchymal cells and osteoblasts toward the central area of calcifying cartilage

(3) Deposition of bone on the surface of the spicules of calcified cartilage. This central area (**diaphysial center**) constitutes a **primary center of ossification.**

(4) Further excavation of the diaphysial center occurs, and increase in size of the primary center of ossification takes place at the expense of the cartilage proximal and distal to it. This cartilage frequently exhibits a characteristic linear zonation from the ends of the model toward the center. These include zones of resting (reserve) cartilage, actively dividing cartilage, hypertrophic maturing cartilage with phosphatase activity, calcifying cartilage matrix around dying chondrocytes, and calcified cartilage spicules with an encrustment of bone.

(5) Creation of secondary centers of ossification at the ends of the cartilage model occurs, duplicating the steps that have just been enumerated.

A change in the nature of the fibrous investment around the skeletal model from a perichondrium to a periosteum immediately precedes replacement of the cartilage by

PLATE 16—Hyaline Cartilage

FIG. 4-25. Survey of the trachea depicting hyaline cartilage (hc). H & E stain. Low power. (ps, pseudostratified columnar epithelium; tg, tracheal glands)

FIG. 4-26. High-power view of a portion of section in Figure 4-25. (ps, pseudostratified columnar epithelium; tg, tracheal glands; hc, hyaline cartilage)

FIG. 4-27. Hyaline cartilage primordium of phalangeal joint from a section of developing finger. H & E stain. Intermediate power.

FIG. 4-28. Nests of cells in hyaline cartilage (hc) with adjacent perichondrium (p). Note the presence of collagen fibers (c) in the matrix of cartilage and seromucous nature of tracheal glands (tg). H & E stain. Intermediate power.

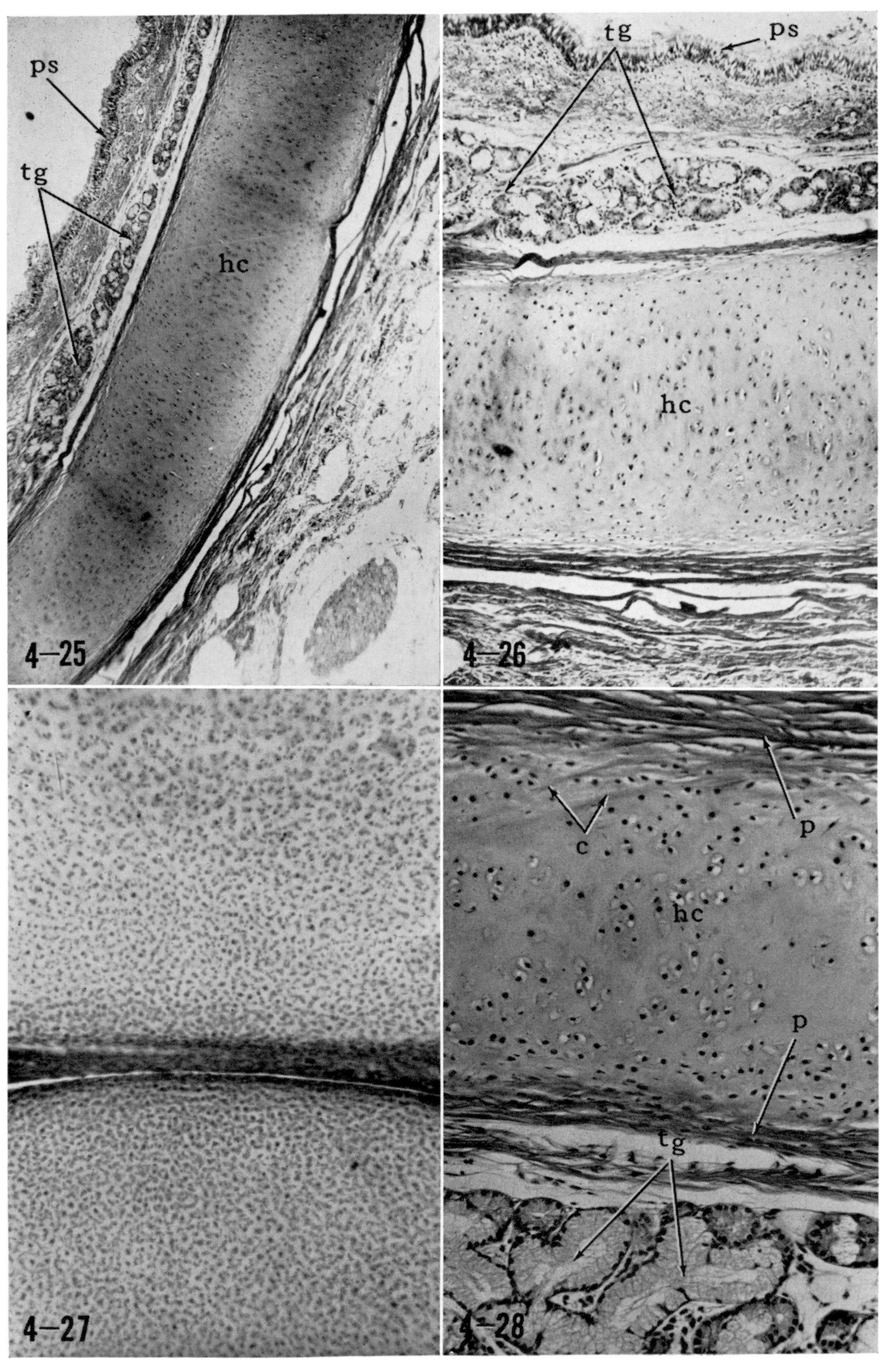
ps
tg
hc
4–25
tg
ps
hc
4–26
4–27
c
p
hc
p
tg
4–28

bone. As bone gradually replaces cartilage, this altered membrane (now called a periosteum) lays down a cylindrical bony collar around the axial structure to strengthen it where central cavitation is occurring. This collar is cancellous at first; it is converted by additional osteogenic activity into compact bone. The penetration of vascular buds into the diaphysial center, in addition to providing the necessary elements for endochondral osteogenesis, brings in hemopoietic elements. The spaces found in the central cavity of the diaphysis are transformed into a continuous system of channels containing marrow.

Growth in length (of long bones) or in size (in irregular shaped bones) depends on an adequate reserve of cartilage. Growth ceases when this reserve has been used up, i.e., replaced by bone. Depending on the particular bone, this may occur in childhood or may extend into adulthood.

b. *Membrane Bone Formation (Intramembranous Osteogenesis)* (Plate 25). This method of bone formation is associated primarily with the development of the flat and the irregularly shaped bones of the head. In fetal life, the mesenchyme in a general area where such a bone will develop becomes extremely vascular, and certain mesenchymal cells become transformed into osteoblasts. Osteoid matrix is laid down and ossified in the form of tiny **trabeculae**.

Osteogenic activity is restricted mainly to one plane of space and is designed to expand the osseous growth rapidly along this plane. Such a feature frequently can be appreciated by observing that osteoblasts tend to be more concentrated at certain points along the surfaces of existing trabeculae. Bone of this type, as it develops, therefore takes the form of thin sheets of cancellous bone made up of delicate, interconnected trabeculae.

The mesenchyme that surrounds each trabecula serves the same function as a typical periosteum. However, a true periosteum is created on the peripheral, flat surface of the developing mass. As time passes, the cancellous nature of the bone is changed by the osteogenic activity of the periosteum. Gradually, by periosteal deposition of layers (**lamellae**) of new bone on top of the old, and also by fusion of trabeculae, the structure is transformed into a plate of compact bone. As seen in the adult, most flat bones contain very little cancellous osseous material. Usually, such structures consist of two flat plates of compact bone separated by a marrow space (the diploë). Any residuum of spongy bone will be found in the diploë.

PLATE 17—Hyaline and Fibrocartilage

FIG. 4-29. Interstitial growth of hyaline cartilage in developing phalangeal bone of fetus. Note that this field contains numerous nests of chondrocytes (n) within lacunae, each nest of cells being the result of mitotic divisions of a single parent cell. Observe the homogeneous appearance of the cartilage matrix (m). H & E stain. Intermediate power.

FIG. 4-30. Hyaline cartilage from the trachea. Numerous cell nests indicate the interstitial type of growth in this region. Observe the chondrocytes within lacunae (ch), the territorial matrix (t), the interterritorial matrix (i) and the capsules (ca). H & E stain. Intermediate power.

FIG. 4-31. Low-power view of atypical fibrocartilage (rabbit), emphasizing the dense regular collagen fibers. H & E stain.

FIG. 4-32. Large numbers of chondrocytes in lacunae of fibrocartilage with collagen fibers producing a masking effect at this magnification. Refer to Figure 4-34 to observe the appearance of the chondrocytes in this section. H & E stain. Low power.

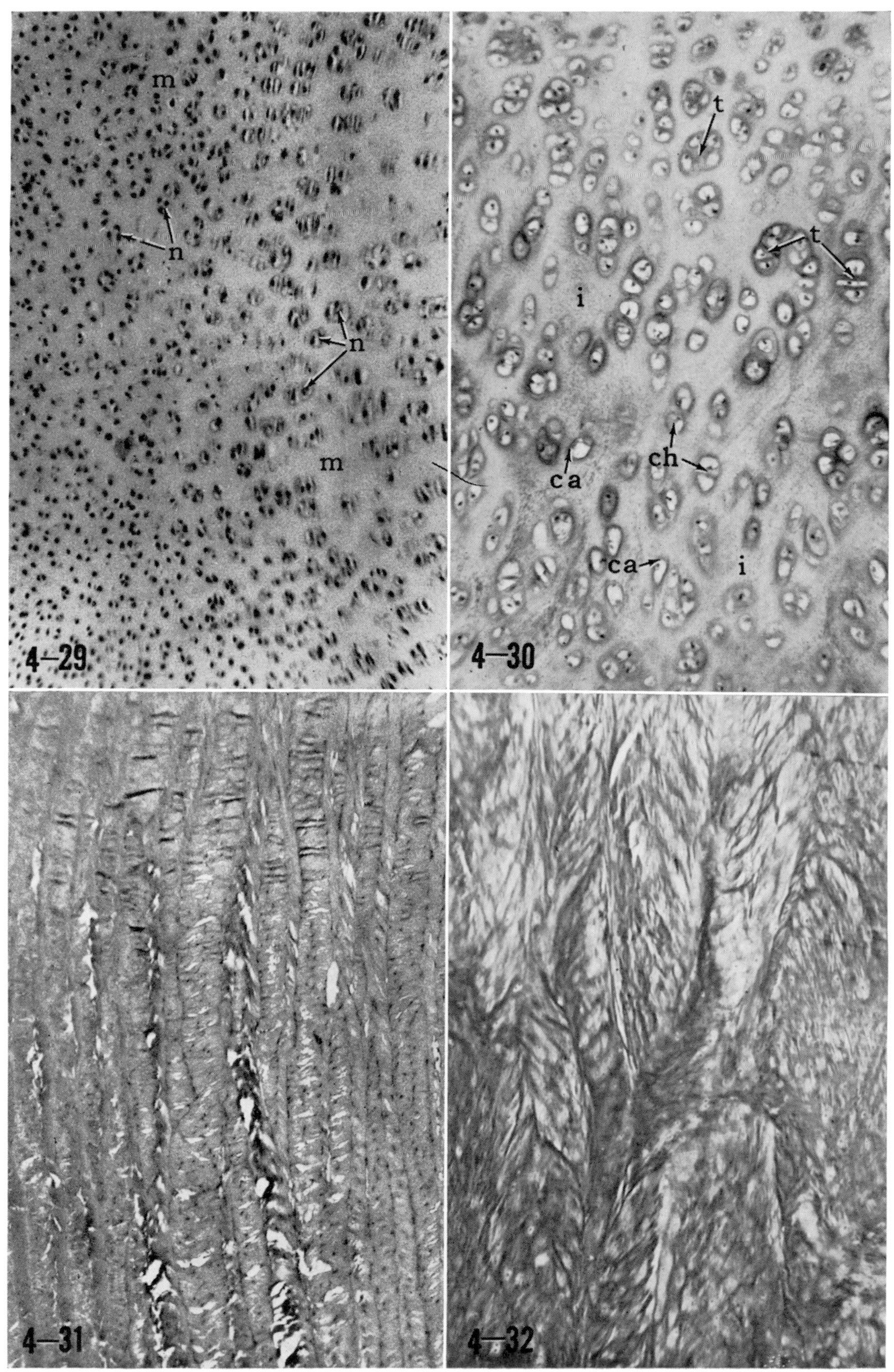
m
n
n
m
4–29
t
t
i
ca
ch
ca
i
4–30
4–31
4–32

PLATE 18—Fibrocartilage

FIG. 4-33. Intermediate-power view of Figure 4-31, showing the presence of chondrocytes (c) and fibroblasts (f) in a section of fibrocartilage.

FIG. 4-34. Intermediate-power view of a portion of Figure 4-32, revealing numerous chondrocytes (c) of fibrocartilage. H & E stain.

FIG. 4-35. High-power view of an adjacent portion of Figure 4-33, showing both chondrocytes (c) and fibroblasts (f).

FIG. 4-36. High-power view of an adjacent portion of Figure 4-34. Note that 3 chondrocytes in lacunae are present.

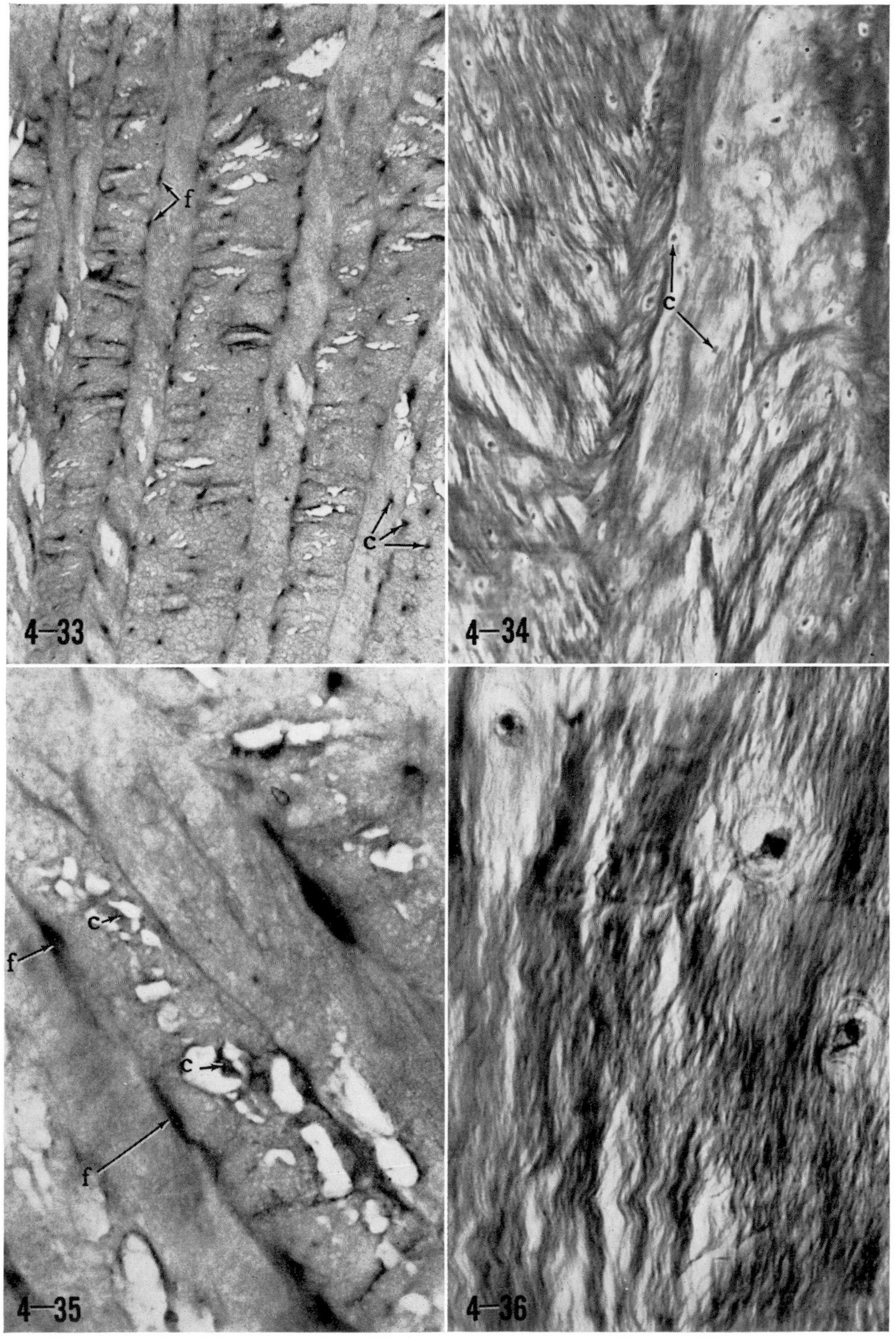
f
c
c
4–33
4–34
c
f
c
f
4–35
4–36

PLATE 19—Elastic Cartilage

FIG. 4-37. Survey section of elastic cartilage from the external ear. Cartilage cells within lacunae appear as light perforations in the darker matrix. The dark appearance of the matrix is due to the presence of elastic fibers (refer to Fig. 4-38). Note the perichondrium (p) and vessel (v) outside the cartilage. Elastin stain. Low power.

FIG. 4-38. Intermediate-power view of a portion of Figure 4-37, demonstrating the large number of anastomosing and interlacing elastic fibers in the matrix. Note the cartilage cells (cc) in the lacunae.

FIG. 4-39. Elastic cartilage near the perichondrial surface (p) from a section of the epiglottis. H & E stain. High power. (cc, cartilage cells in lacunae; c, capsules; e, elastic fibers)

FIG. 4-40. High-power view of a portion of Figure 4-38, demonstrating the branching nature of elastic fibers (bf) in elastic cartilage. Outlines of lacunae (l) are easily seen, but the contained chondrocytes (ch) are not brought out by the stain.

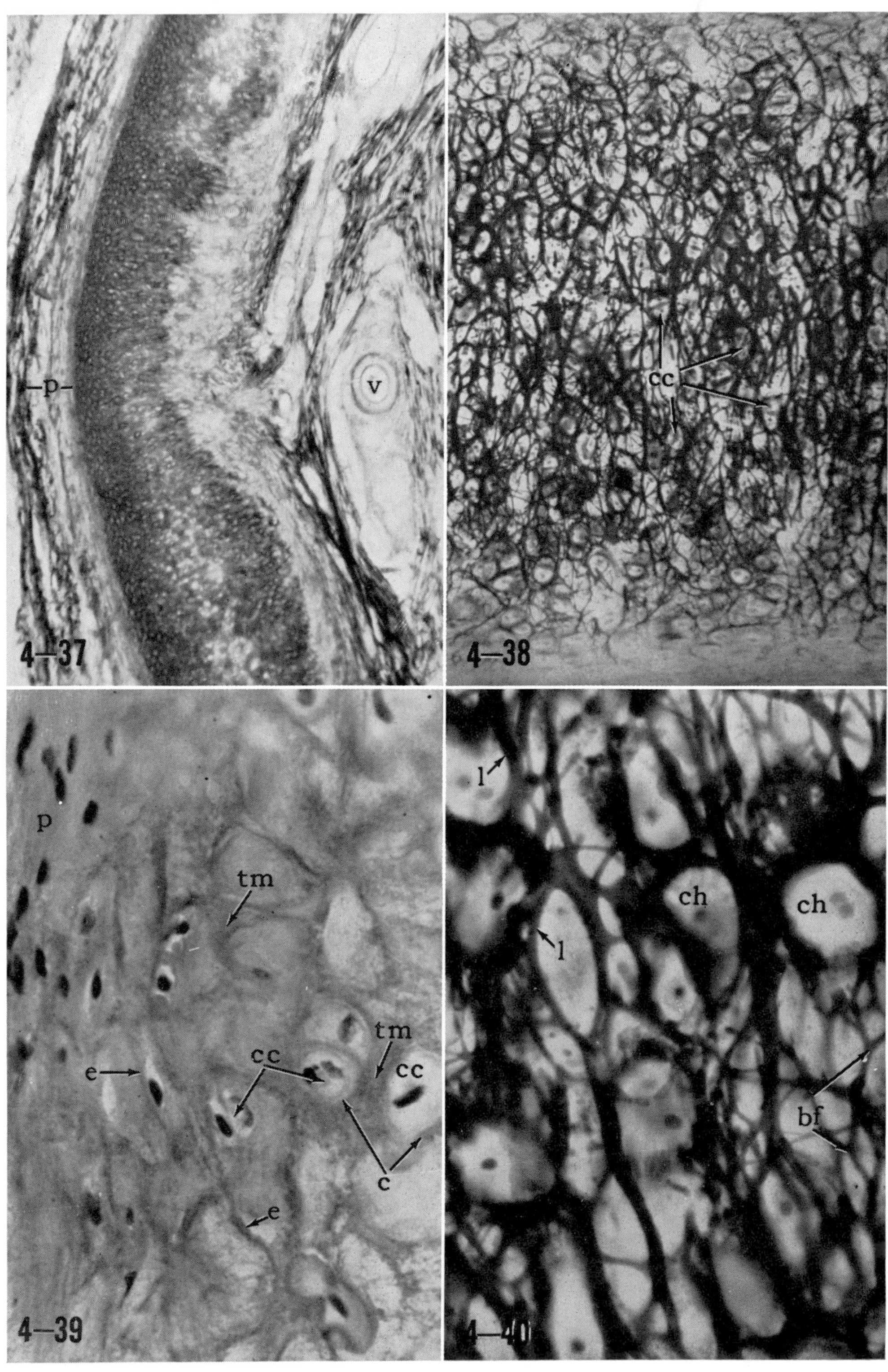
p
v
4–37
cc
4–38
p
tm
tm
cc
cc
e
e
c
4–39
l
l
ch
ch
bf
4–40

PLATE 20—Bone

FIG. 4-41. Cancellous bone of the upper end of the femur. Note infiltration of fat among myeloid cells. Giant cell (megakaryocyte) is evident in lower left corner. H & E stain. Low power. (s, spicules of bone enclosing marrow [m]).

FIG. 4-42. Longitudinal section of decalcified compact bone. Note numerous osteocytes which appear as black dots at this magnification. H & E stain. Low power. (H, haversian canals; V, Volkmann's canals)

FIG. 4-43. Intermediate-power view of section of Figure 4-42. In addition to haversian (H) and Volkmann (V) canals, note lacunae (1) containing osteocytes.

FIG. 4-44. Longitudinal section of decalcified compact bone. Note faint striations, indicative of various lamellae, showing lacunae containing osteocytes. H & E stain. High power. (H, haversian canal).

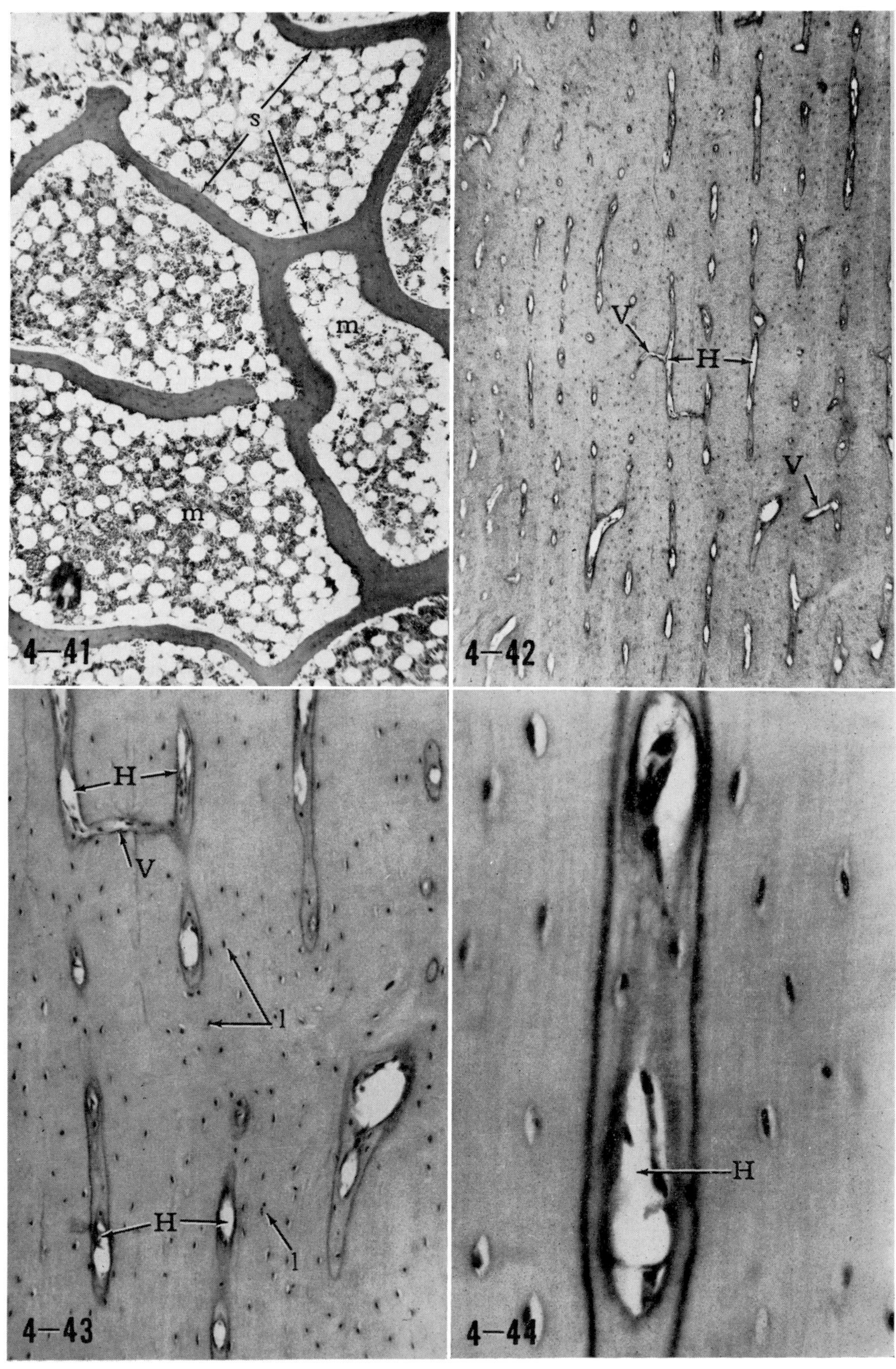
s
m
m
4–41
V
H
V
4–42
H
V
l
l
H
l
4–43
H
4–44

PLATE 21—Bone

FIG. 4-45. Cross section of compact bone. Undecalcified ground unstained section. Low power. (Hs, haversian systems; H, haversian canals; V, Volkmann's canal; il, interstitial lamellae)

FIG. 4-46. Intermediate-power view of section of Figure 4-45. Note concentric lamellae (cl) in haversian systems as well as interstitial lamellae (il). Lacunae are especially prominent in this section.

FIG. 4-47. Appearance of mature haversian system of section of Figure 4-45 under high power. Especially note the radiating canaliculi (c) communicating between adjacent lacunae.

FIG. 4-48. High-power view of an adjacent section of Figure 4-45. Large haversian canal indicates incomplete formation of this haversian system.

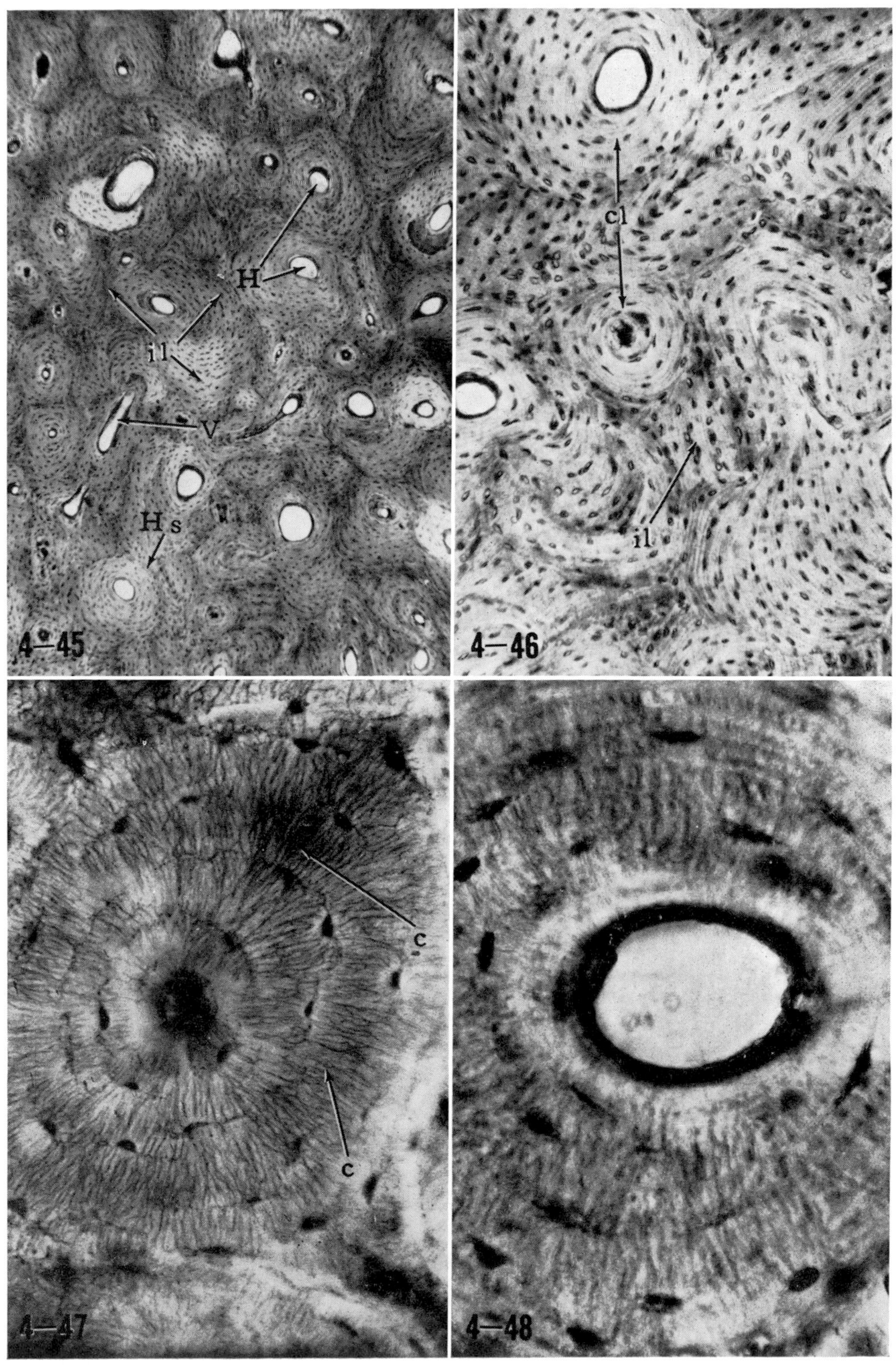

H
il
V
Hs
4–45
cl
il
4–46
c
c
4–47
4–48

PLATE 22—Endochondral Bone Formation

FIG. 4-49. Endochondral ossification of vertebra (fetal). H & E stain. Low power. (rc, resting cartilage; mc, maturing cartilage; cc, calcified cartilage spicules with bony covering; pc, perichondrium; po, periosteum; o, layer of osteoblasts; pb, plate of bone)

FIG. 4-50. Endochondral ossification of phalangeal bone of finger. H & E stain. Low power. (dc, dividing cartilage cells; mc, maturing cartilage; cc, calcified cartilage with bony overgrowth; bc, bone collar; po, periosteum; m, primitive marrow cavity)

FIG. 4-51. Intermediate-power view of section of Figure 4-50, showing the transitional zone where bone is being deposited on calcified cartilage spicules (cc). Note lacunae (1) containing debris of dying chondrocytes.

FIG. 4-52. Endochondral bone formation taken from a section of the back of an embryo. Note deposition of bone on the spicules of calcified cartilage (cc). H & E stain. Intermediate power.

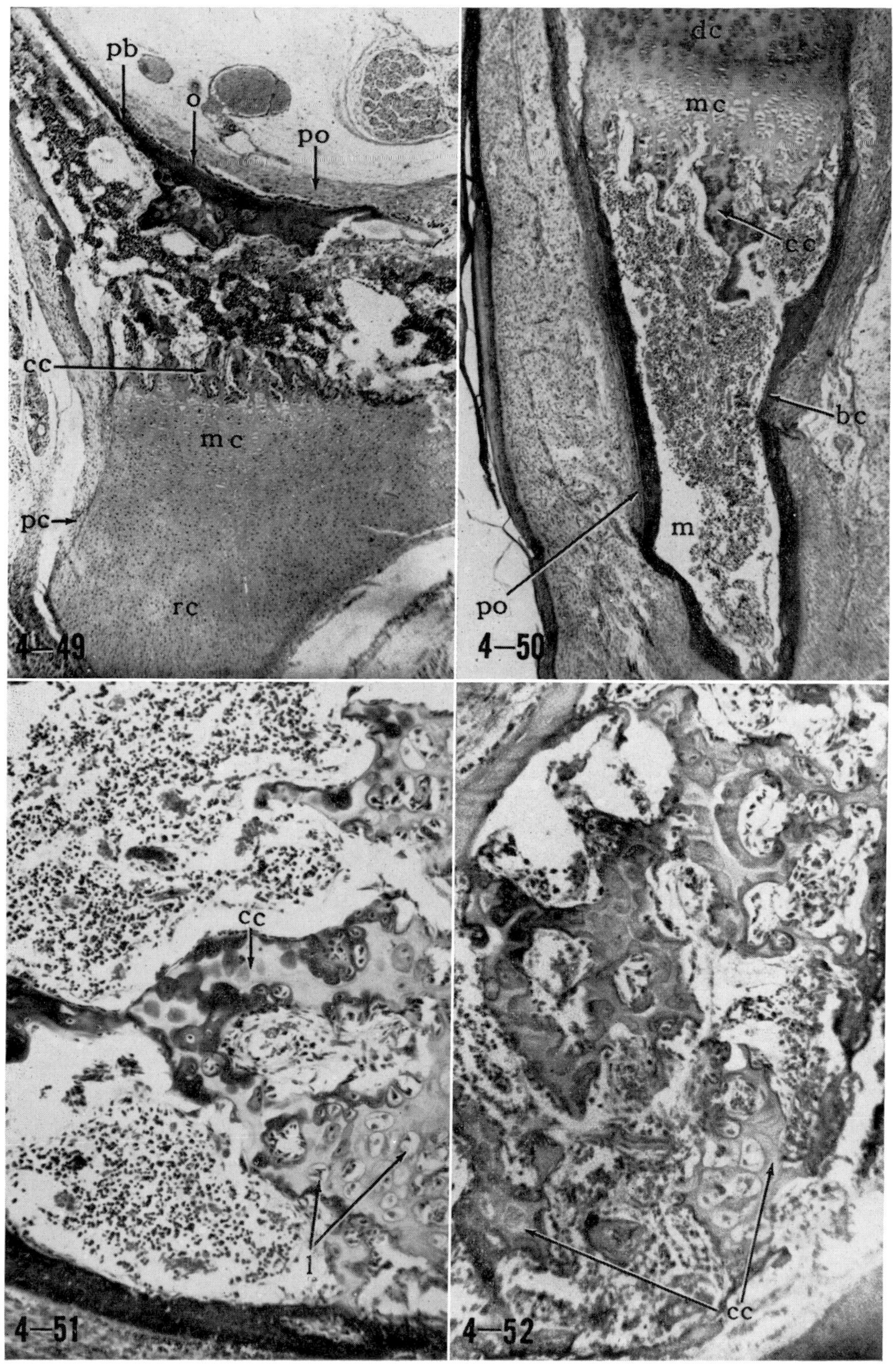
pb
o
po
cc
mc
pc
rc
4–49
dc
mc
cc
bc
m
po
4–50
cc
l
4–51
cc
4–52

PLATE 23—Endochondral Bone Formation

FIG. 4-53. Endochondral ossification of phalangeal bone of the finger. H & E stain. Intermediate power. (cc, calcified cartilage with bony overgrowth; bc, bone collar; op, osteogenic layer of periosteum; fp, fibrous layer of periosteum; m, primitive marrow cavity; bs, bony spicules; o, layer of osteoblasts; vt, vascularized osteogenic tissue within the bone collar)

FIG. 4-54. Intermediate-power view of endochondral ossification of phalangeal bone of the finger. Note the transitional zone where bone is being deposited on calcified cartilage spicules (cc) and regions of maturing cartilage (mc) and dividing cartilage cells (dc). H & E stain. (m, primitive marrow cavity)

FIG. 4-55. Endochondral ossification of vertebra (fetal). Note the numerous bony spicules (bs) and related osteoblasts (o). H & E stain. Intermediate power. (m, primitive marrow cavity)

FIG. 4-56. Adjacent portion of Figure 4-55, showing the transitional zone where bone is deposited on calcified cartilage spicules (cc) and the zone of maturing cartilage (mc). H & E stain. Intermediate power. (m, primitive marrow cavity)

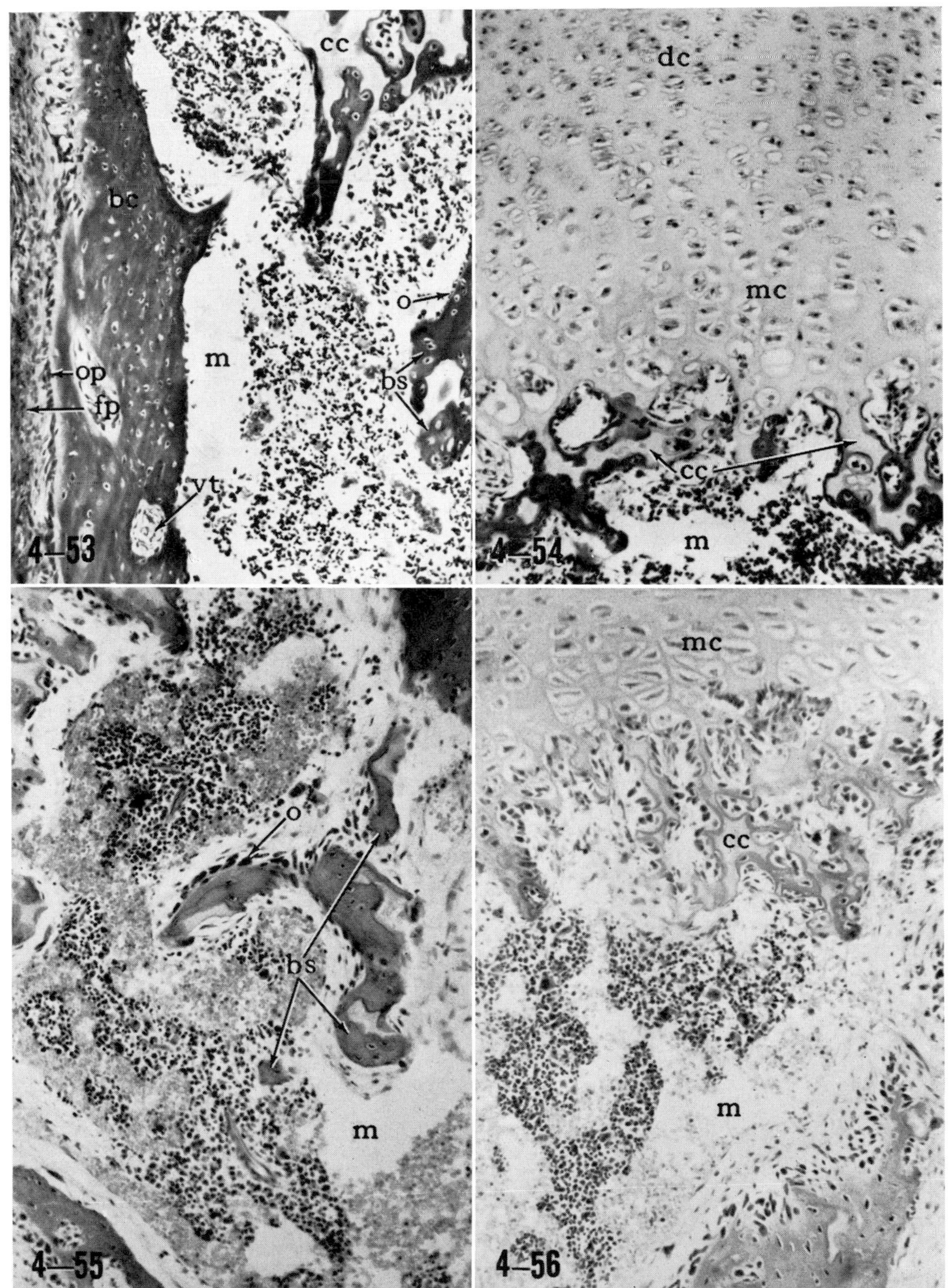
cc
bc
o
m
op
fp
bs
vt
4—53
dc
mc
cc
m
4—54
o
bs
m
4—55
mc
cc
m
4—56

PLATE 24—Endochondral Bone Formation

FIG. 4-57. Endochondral ossification in phalangeal bone of finger, showing the nature of the bone collar (bc) and the periosteum (po). H & E stain. High power. (o, osteoblasts; os, osteocytes)

FIG. 4-58. Endochondral ossification in a fetal vertebra. Note the long spicule of calcified cartilage (cc) projecting downward into the primitive marrow space (m) and covered by a thin layer of bone. An osteoclast (oc), present in a Howship's lacuna (Hl), can be observed. Numerous osteoblasts (o) can also be seen. H & E stain. High power.

FIG. 4-59. Endochondral ossification in a fetal vertebra, showing the deposition of bone on calcified cartilage spicules (cc) by osteoblasts (o). H & E stain. High power. (v, vessel with blood cells in the primitive marrow cavity)

FIG. 4-60. Endochondral ossification in a fetal vertebra, showing two spicules of bone and related osteoblasts (o) and osteocytes within lacunae (os). H & E stain. High power. (v, vessel with blood cells in the marrow cavity)

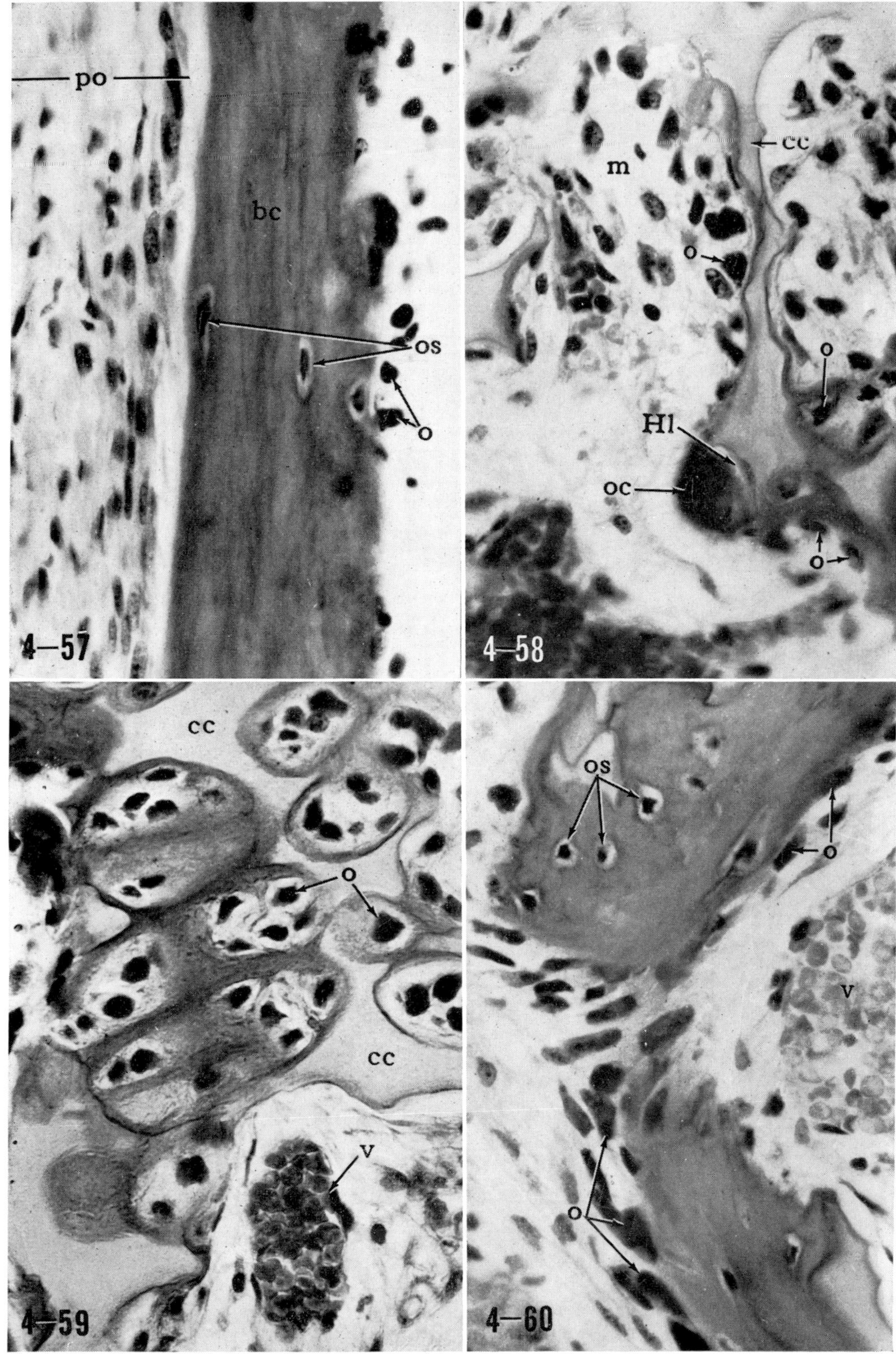
po
bc
os
o
4–57
cc
m
o
o
Hl
oc
o
o
4–58
cc
o
cc
v
4–59
os
o
v
o
4–60

PLATE 25—Endochondral and Intramembranous Bone Formation

FIG. 4-61. Longitudinal thick section through the proximal end of a fetal long bone, demonstrating endochondral bone formation. H & E stain. Low power. (ep, epiphysial ossification center; rc, reserve cartilage; dc, dividing cartilage; mc, maturing cartilage; epl, epiphysial plate; di, diaphysial bone)

FIG. 4-62. Epiphysial plate in a fetal long bone. Note that little reserve cartilage (rc) remains and that a broad zone of actively dividing cartilage cells (dc) is present. H & E stain. Intermediate power. (ep, epiphysial ossification center; mc, maturing cartilage; cc, calcified cartilage spicules on which diaphysial bone is being deposited)

FIG. 4-63. Longitudinal section through compact flat bone of skull, formed by the intramembranous method. H & E stain. Low power. (d, diploë containing marrow and fat cells; p, periosteum)

FIG. 4-64. A longitudinal section of membrane bone adjacent to that shown in Figure 4-63. Note the presence of numerous osteocytes within the lacunae. H & E stain. Intermediate power.

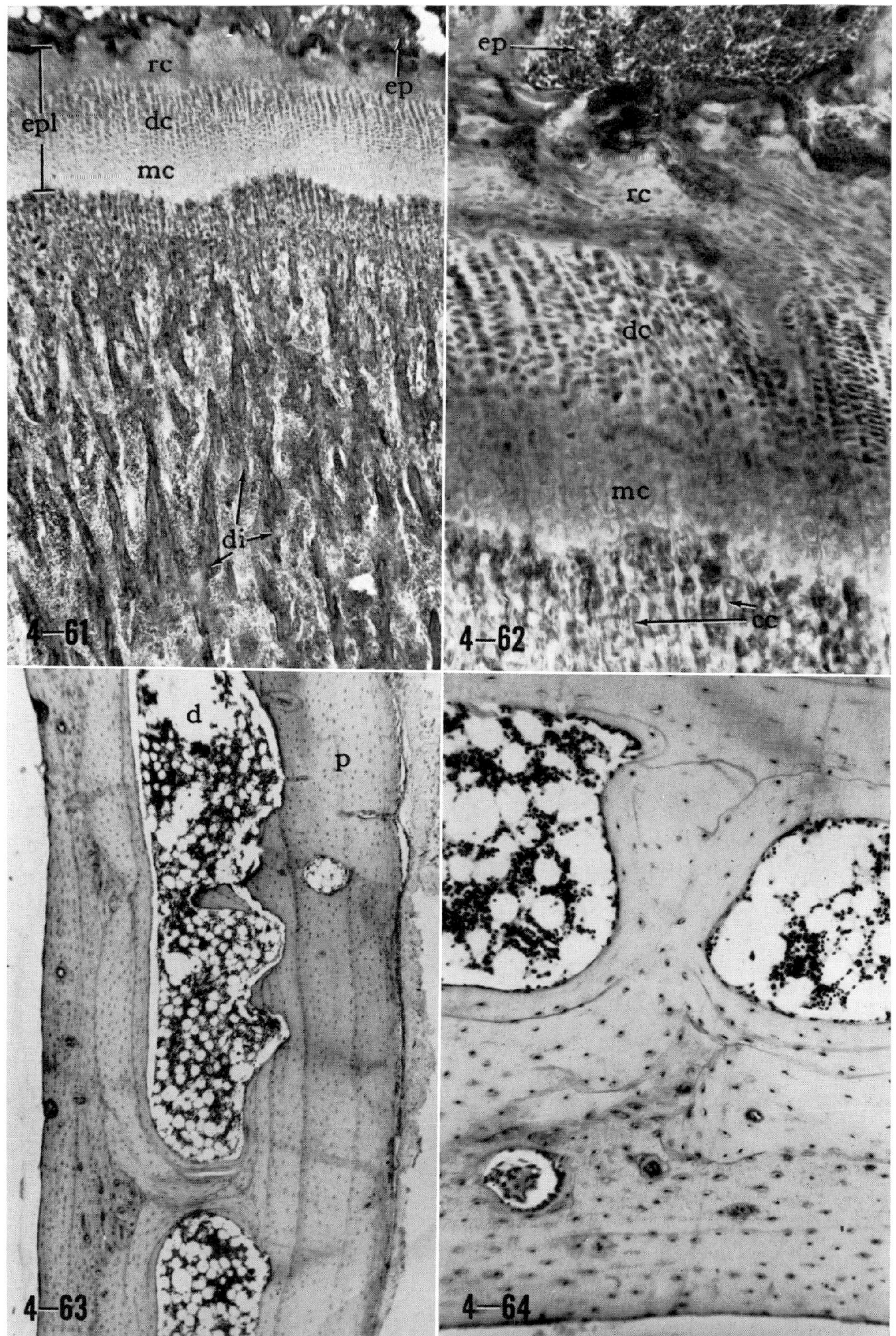

rc
ep
epl
dc
mc
di
4—61
ep
rc
dc
mc
cc
4—62
d
p
4—63
4—64

PLATE 26—Articular Cartilage

FIG. 4-65. Developing synovial interphalangeal articulation in fetal finger. Note that the articular surfaces (as) of hyaline cartilage lack a perichondrium. H & E stain. Low power. (sf, synovial fold; jc, joint capsule)

FIG. 4-66. Intermediate power of a portion of Figure 4-65, demonstrating the fibrous nature of the synovial fold (sf) in this joint and its relationship to the articular cartilages (ac). (sc, synovial cavity; jc, joint capsule)

FIG. 4-67. Articular cartilages. The joint cavity appears as a narrow white line arching across the middle of the figure. Note that these cartilages are of the hyaline variety and that at their surfaces they each lack a perichondrium. H & E stain. Intermediate power.

FIG. 4-68. High-power representation of a portion of the articular cartilage shown at the right in Figure 4-66. Note that the chondrocytes are somewhat flattened near the articular surface (as).

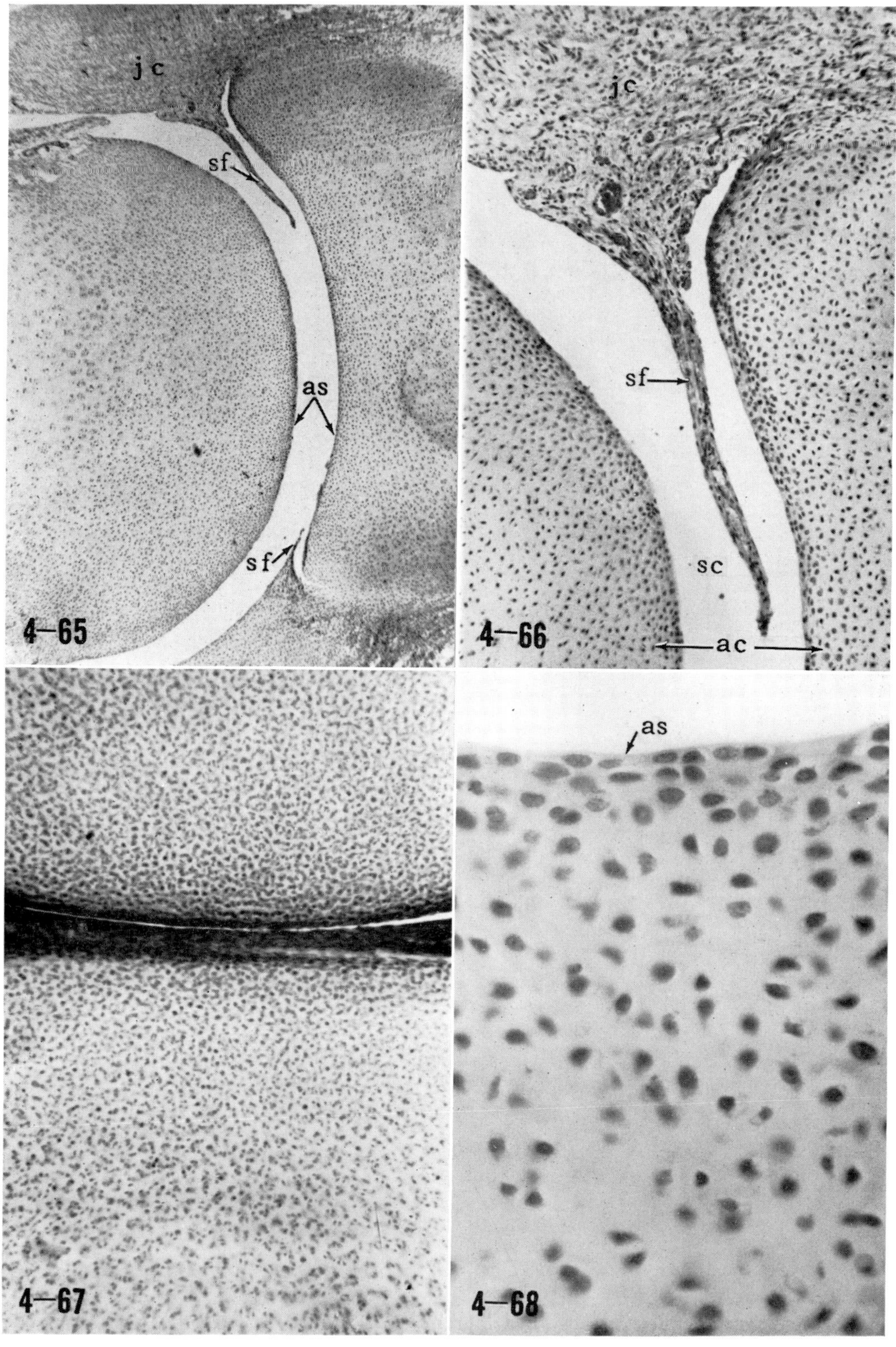
jc
sf
as
sf
4—65
jc
sf
sc
ac
4—66
4—67
as
4—68

5 · Blood and Bone Marrow

A. Blood Components
B. Blood Smear Technic
C. Bone Marrow

A. BLOOD COMPONENTS

Blood is a fluid tissue of variable constitution consisting of a ground substance, the plasma, in which are suspended the cellular elements.

1. Plasma

Plasma constitutes approximately 55 per cent of whole blood and consists of water (90%), protein (7%), carbohydrate (0.1%), electrolytes (0.9%), lipid, mineral salts, hormones, antibodies, enzymes and dissolved gases.

2. Cell Types

The following types and numbers of cellular elements are normally present:

a. *Erythrocytes* (Red Blood Cells) (Figs. 5-1 to 5-3). The normal red blood cell count in an adult man ranges from 5.0 to 5.5 million per cu. mm. of blood and from 4.5 to 5.0 million per cu. mm. in an adult woman. Erythrocytes are nonmotile, elastic, acidophilic-staining, biconcave disks which have lost their nuclei during maturation. The cells measure approximately 7.7 μ in diameter and 1.9 μ in thickness in dry prepara-

PLATE 27—Blood Cells

Fig. 5-1. Erythrocytes from a peripheral blood smear from a normal subject. Wright's stain. Oil immersion. (p, platelets)

Fig. 5-2. Erythrocytes from a peripheral blood smear from a patient with thalassemia minor. Note the presence of anisocytosis and poikilocytosis. Wright's stain. Oil immersion. (t, target cells; po, tear drop poikilocytes; bs, erythrocyte showing basophilic stippling; h, hypochromic erythrocytes; hy, hyperchromic erythrocytes; p, platelets; mi, microcytes; ma, macrocyte)

Fig. 5-3. A few reticulocytes from a peripheral blood smear from an erythropoietin-stimulated rat. New methylene blue stain. Oil immersion. (o, mature form; y, young form)

Fig. 5-4. Granular leukocytes from a peripheral blood smear from a normal subject. Wright's stain. Oil immersion. (A, stab [band] neutrophil; B, segmented neutrophil; C, bilobed eosinophil; D, mature basophil)

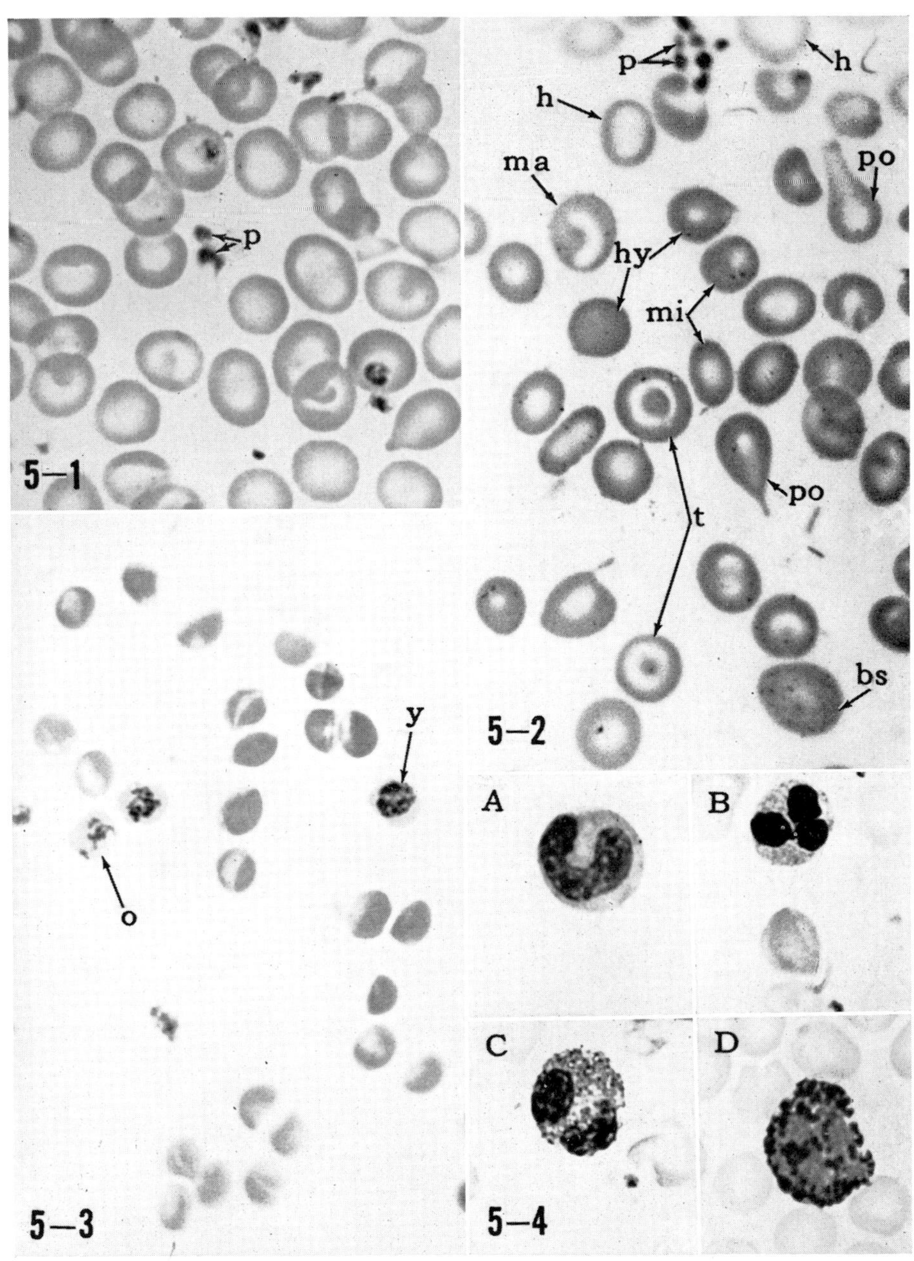
p
5—1
p
h
h
ma
po
hy
mi
po
t
bs
5—2
y
o
5—3
A
B
C
D
5—4

tions. The color of blood (yellow-green in unstained preparations) is due to the presence of **hemoglobin**, an iron-bearing protein complex, in the erythrocyte. Hemoglobin has the capacity to form a loose combination with oxygen in the lungs and exchanges oxygen for carbon dioxide in the tissues of the body. Hemoglobin then transports the carbon dioxide to the lungs. The life span of normal erythrocytes is approximately 110 to 130 days.

b. *Leukocytes* (White Blood Cells). The normal white blood cell count ranges from 5,000 to 10,000 per cu. mm. of blood in adults, regardless of sex. However, the number of leukocytes in the circulating blood varies at different times of the day (**diurnal variation**) and under a variety of conditions. In general, the life span, depending on the type of leukocyte, varies from hours to 5 days; in fact, the life span of some cells may possibly extend to 30 days or more. Leukocytes are generally divided into **granular types** (neutrophils, eosinophils and basophils) and **agranular types** (lymphocytes and monocytes).

1. Granular Types

a. *Neutrophils* (Heterophilic Leukocytes) (Fig. 5-4). This cell type, which is the most numerous of the leukocytes, numbers from 3,000 to 6,500 per cu. mm. of blood (55%-65%). The neutrophil possesses a polymorphic (usually 3 to 5 lobes depending on the age of maturation), dense nucleus, with the cytoplasm containing fine, homogenous, neutral-staining granules. In dry preparations, the cells measure approximately 10 to 12 μ in diameter. A nuclear appendage is joined to a lobe of the nucleus by a fine strand of chromatin. This configuration appears as a "drumstick" and is characteristically visible in approximately 3 per cent of the cells in blood smears from women. This "drumstick" is said to be the sex chromosome. The neutrophil is active primarily outside the vascular system, especially in inflammatory conditions; it migrates into the tissues, setting up a barrier and phagocytosing foreign debris.

b. *Eosinophils* (Acidophilic Leukocytes) (Fig. 5-4). This cell type normally numbers from 50 to 300 per cu. mm. of blood (1-3%). Although it is generally similar in morphology to the neutrophil, it differs markedly from the latter in possessing in its cytoplasm characteristic coarse, uniform, spherical granules which have a strong affinity for acid stains. The polymorphic nucleus usually has 2 lobes. The eosinophil apparently is associated with allergic reactions, having to do with the decomposition of protein and the release of histamine.

c. *Basophils* (Basophilic Leukocytes) (Fig. 5-4). Normally, only 25 to 50 basophils per cu. mm. of blood (0-0.75%) are present. This cell usually has an indented, elongated or S-shaped, pale, loosely arranged chromatic nucleus and unevenly distributed basophilic or metachromatic-staining gran-

PLATE 28—Blood Cells

FIGS. 5-5 to 5-12. Agranular leukocytes from peripheral blood smears taken from a normal subject and from a patient with infectious mononucleosis. Wright's stain. Oil immersion.

FIG. 5-5. Small lymphocyte.

FIG. 5-6. Large lymphocyte with azurophilic granules in the cytoplasm.

FIG. 5-7. Large lymphocytes.

FIG. 5-8. Monocyte with two segmented neutrophils (n).

FIG. 5-9. Monocyte with a few azurophilic granules in the cytoplasm.

FIG. 5-10. Monocyte with the nucleus resembling brain convolution and a segmented neutrophil (n).

FIG. 5-11. Monocyte and a large lymphocyte (1) with azurophilic granules in the cytoplasm.

FIG. 5-12. Smudge cell (s) and a lymphocyte (1).

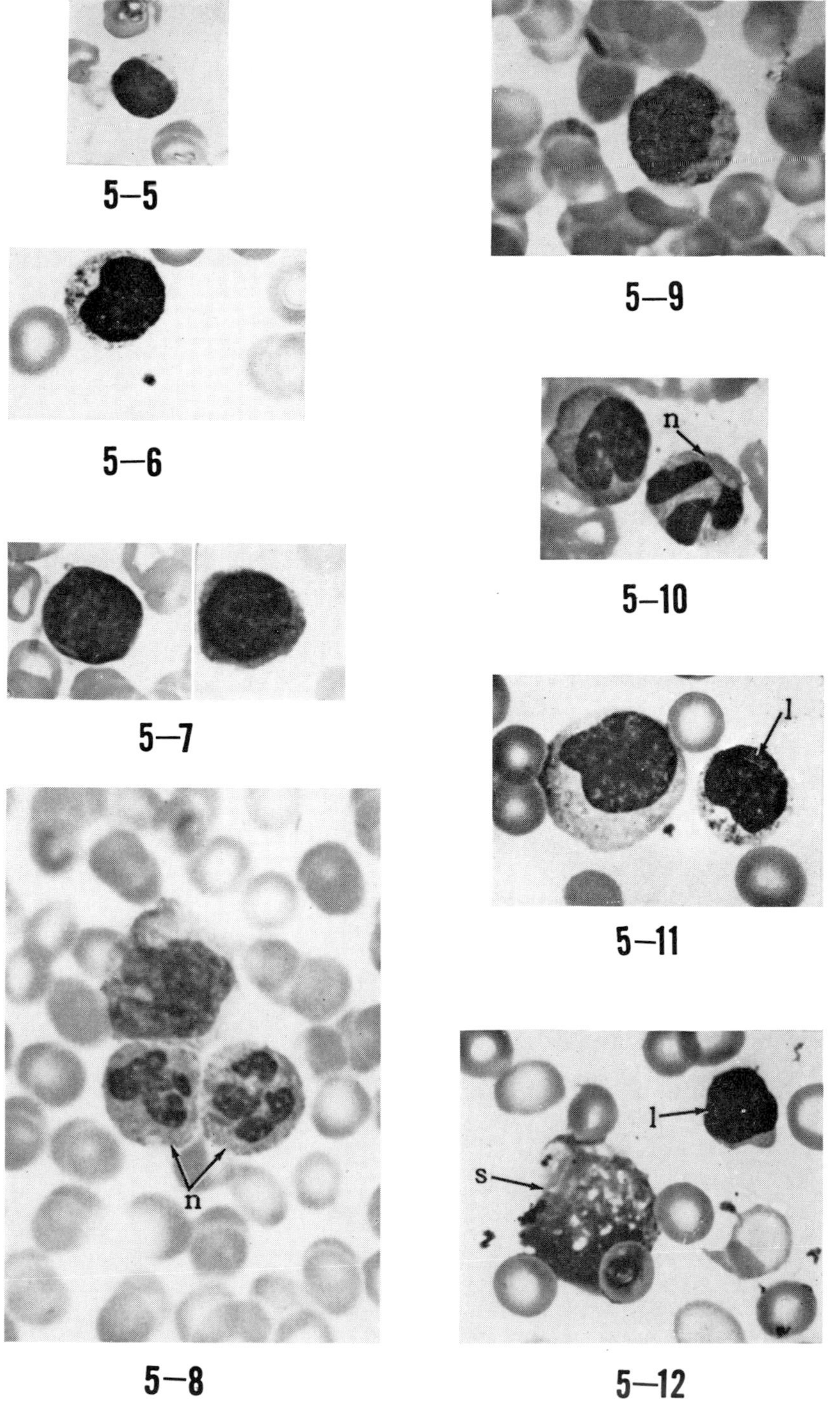
5–5
5–9
5–6
n
5–10
5–7
l
5–11
n
l
s
5–8
5–12

ules. These granules often appear to mask or overlie the nucleus. In size, the cell is similar to the neutrophil. The basophil is mainly associated with the production of the anticoagulant, heparin.

2. Agranular Types (Plate 28)

a. *Lymphocytes* (Small to Large Mononuclear Cells) (Figs. 5-5 to 5-7). These cells vary in size, the majority being of the small type which measure 6 to 9 μ in diameter. Large lymphocytes usually measure 20 to 30 μ, and the medium-sized lymphocytes have diameters falling in a range between 9 and 20 μ. The following is a cytologic description which pertains predominantly to the small lymphocytes which number approximately 1,500 to 3,000 cells per cu. mm. of blood (25-33%). Characteristically, this cell has a round or slightly indented nucleus. The interior structure of the nucleus typically has several areas of deep-staining chromatin clumps. In addition, there is usually condensation of chromatin at the membrane which stains intensely so that reflected light tends to give a perinuclear silver lining or halo effect. The cytoplasm usually consists of a narrow rim of basophilic, unevenly stained material which contains tiny globular structures. These globules become especially evident in infectious mononucleosis. Although lymphocytes are often classified as agranular leukocytes, in approximately one third of the cells a few azurophilic granules (spherical reddish- or purple-staining granules) are present. Another feature that should be kept in mind, especially in making preparations, is that lymphocytes are fragile cells and easily squashed, giving them bizarre appearances. The function of the lymphocyte is still controversial (Fig. 5-12).

b. *Monocytes* (Large Mononuclears) (Figs. 5-8 to 5-11). Normally, 300 to 500 monocytes per cu. mm. of blood (3-7%) are present. The typical monocyte measures 15 to 25 μ in diameter; however, in dry preparations they may become stretched so that their diameter may be increased to 30 μ. Generally, the chromatin granules of the nucleus are less densely and more linearly arranged than those of the lymphocyte. In addition, the nucleus is generally eccentric, oval or kidney shaped and possesses a thin membrane. Old monocytes characteristically have a nucleus with superimposed lobes (nuclear folds) appearing as "brainlike convolutions." Typically, the cytoplasm is more abundant in relation to the nucleus and has a pale gray-blue color in stained preparations. Like the lymphocyte, these cells are often classified as agranular leukocytes but generally do contain a variable number of fine, evenly distributed, lightly basophilic staining granules. A few unevenly distributed, prominent azurophilic granules may be present. Frequently vacuoles are seen in the cytoplasm. The main function of the mono-

PLATE 29—Bone Marrow

FIG. 5-13. Section of bone marrow from the epiphysis of a femur. Note the nests of darker staining elements which mainly represent erythroid cells (e) among the mass of granular leukocytic elements (lighter staining). The vacuolization represents fatty infiltration of the myeloid tissue. H & E stain. Intermediate power.

FIG. 5-14. Adjacent bone marrow section of Figure 5-13 at a slightly higher magnification. H & E stain. Intermediate power. (e, erythroid nests; 1, leukocytic elements; f, fat cells; bs, bony spicule)

FIG. 5-15. High-power view of a section of marrow of a vertebra (fetal). H & E stain. (e, erythroid cells scattered among leukocytic elements; m, megakaryocyte; vs, venous sinuses)

FIG. 5-16. High-power view of a section of a portion of Figure 5-14, showing an area with a greater concentration of darker staining erythroid cells among the leukocytic elements and fatty infiltration (f) of the marrow.

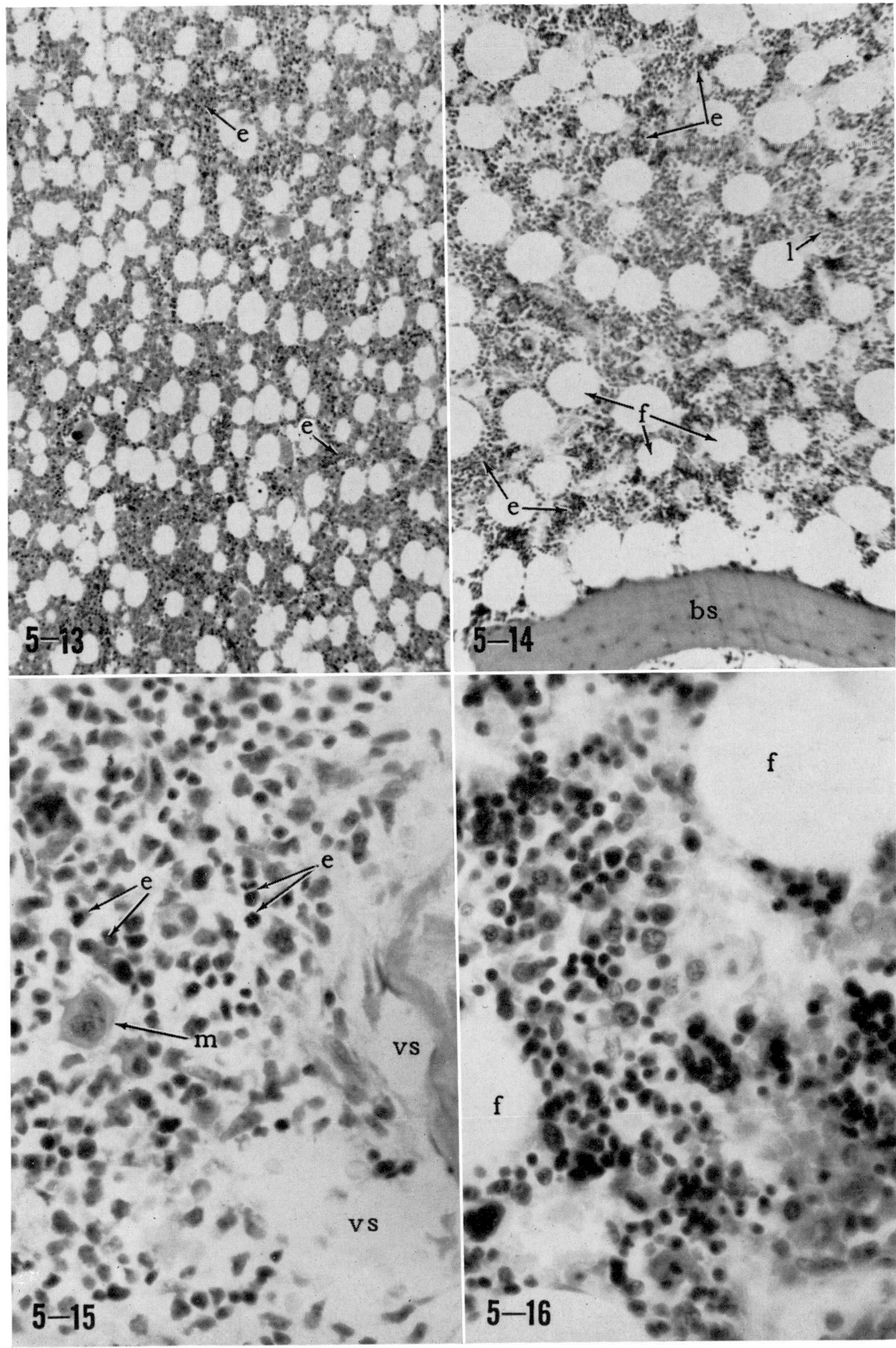
e
e
5-13
e
l
f
e
bs
5-14
e
e
m
vs
vs
5-15
f
f
5-16

cyte is phagocytosis and digestion of foreign debris.

c. *Thrombocytes* (Platelets) (Fig. 5-22). The normal platelet count ranges from 200 to 400 thousand per cu. mm. of blood. Thrombocytes are fragments of megakaryocytic cytoplasm appearing as round or oval biconcave disks averaging 3 microns in diameter. In dry preparations, the platelet consists of a refractile inner part (the chromomere), which contains purple granules, and a pale homogeneous outer part (the hyalomere) which stains a pale blue. The primary function of platelets is in the process of hemostasis. Specifically, platelets (1) mechanically plug small rents in vessels, (2) liberate vasoconstrictor substances, (3) contribute specific activity to the coagulation mechanism by producing thromboplastin, and (4) promote clot retraction.

B. BLOOD SMEAR TECHNIC

1. Clean the tip of your finger with alcohol, dry and secure some blood from your finger by piercing the tip with a sterile blood lancet. Discard the first drop of blood. Proceed to cover a clean glass slide as follows:

a. Touch the blood to the surface of the slide near one end.

b. Touch the blood with a second slide held so that its edge makes an acute angle of approximately 30° with the first slide. This will permit the blood to run along the line of contact between the slides.

c. Rapidly draw the angled slide with even pressure to the other end of the first slide.

d. Rapidly air-dry the slide by shaking it with a waving motion.

2. Prepare several slides in the same manner; then stain as follows:

a. Add Wright's blood stain (enough to cover the prepared smear) and allow to stand 1 to 2 minutes

b. Without removing the staining fluid, add a similar amount of phosphate buffer (or distilled water) and allow to stand 2 to 4 minutes. Gently agitate the staining mixture by blowing on the slide.

c. Wash in running water and dry.

3. Examine the blood smears in the following way:

a. Examine with the low-power objective, followed by high-power, and finally by oil-immersion, noting whether the red blood cells are normal in size, shape and hemoglobin content.

b. Study the morphology of the various types of leukocytes present.

c. A differential count of 300 cells is to be completed with the oil-immersion lens. Do *not* count the same field twice. Record your count in tabular form.

PLATE 30—Leukocytic Series

FIG. 5-17. Cells of the granulocytic series taken from bone marrow smears of normal subjects and patients with myelogenous leukemia. Wright's stain. Oil immersion. (A, hemocytoblast; B, two myeloblasts; C, early promyelocyte [note the beginning of granulation in the cytoplasm]; D, neutrophilic myelocyte; E, neutrophilic metamyelocyte; F, band [b] and segmented neutrophils; G, eosinophilic myelocyte; H, eosinophilic metamyelocyte; I, bilobed eosinophil; and J, two mature basophils)

FIG. 5-18. Cells of the agranulocytic series. The lymphocytic series were taken from bone marrow smears from a patient with acute lymphatic leukemia. Those of the monocytic series were taken from bone marrow smears from a patient with acute monocytic leukemia. Wright's stain. Oil immersion. (A, two lymphoblasts; B, early prolymphocyte; C, 5 lymphocytes of varying sizes and characteristics; D, late monoblast to early promonocyte; E, promonocyte [atypical type with highly granular cytoplasm]; and F, monocyte)

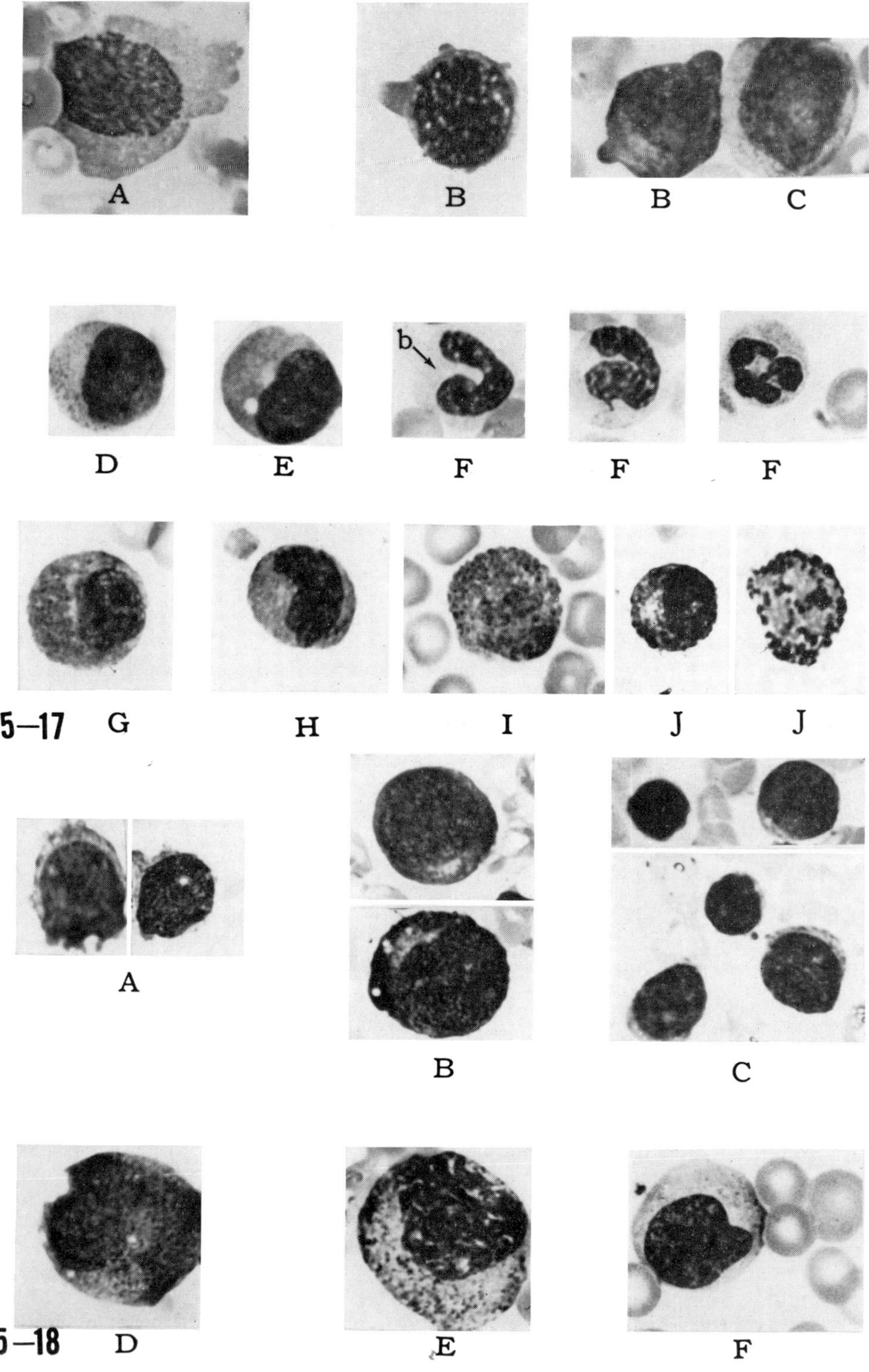
A
B
B C
D
E
b
F
F
F
5–17 G
H
I
J
J
A
B
C
5–18 D
E
F

C. BONE MARROW

In healthy individuals, the constant maintenance of blood cells is the result of a continuous precise balance between cell formation (hemopoiesis) and destruction. This precise balance is even more remarkable if we consider the life spans of the various cellular elements and the replacement that is continually required. Deviation from the normal levels reflects an imbalance between blood formation and destruction.

1. Prenatal Hematopoiesis

The formed elements of the blood originate from embryonal connective tissue, the mesenchyme, through proliferation of the primitive blood cells in the blood islands of the yolk sac. Blood formation ceases in the yolk sac by the 9th week and then is taken over by the liver. In the liver, hematopoiesis actually commences at about the 6th week and is extravascular. Finally, the marrow or myeloid period of hematopoiesis comes into being between the 2nd and the 5th month, depending on the type of bone, and becomes the permanent site of granulopoiesis and erythropoiesis. Strands of vascularized mesenchyme grow into the developing bone and cause a resorption of their centers. The resultant spaces become the site of active proliferation of the mesenchymal cell which differentiates into the different types of myeloid cells (granulocytes and erythrocytes). With the maturation of organs and tissues, the fixed mesenchymal cells fall into relative obscurity, remaining as stem cells which lie in intimate relation with the reticular cells and more flattened forms which line blood and lymph sinuses (specialized endothelial cells). These are the **reticuloendothelial cells** which are the adult counterpart of embryonal mesenchymal cells and are widely distributed throughout the body. In lymphatic tissues (spleen, lymph nodes and thymus) lymphopoiesis and monopoiesis actively takes place.

2. Postnatal Hematopoiesis

Still one of the most disputed issues in hematology today is the interrelationship of blood cells. However, this does not affect factual descriptions covering the structural features of the developmental stages of blood cells. Before elaborating on the structural characteristics, a summary of the theories of cell origin is in order.

The major issues concern the following:

a. The identification of mother cells of the various lines

b. The concept that all blood cells belong to a single family group *vs.* the existence of separate, distinct families of cells (unitarian *vs.* dualist and trialist theories)

c. The development of all blood cells outside the vascular channels *vs.* the development of leukocytes outside such channels and erythrocytes inside them.

In essence, all agree that the myeloid elements of the bone marrow develop through the differentiation of a free stem cell, the **hemocytoblast**. In lymphatic tissue, lymphocytes develop from younger forms which have the same structure as the hemocytoblast of the marrow.

Proponents of the **unitarian theory** agree that all elements are derived from a common mother cell and that both hemocyto-

PLATE 31—Thrombocytic Series

FIGS. 5-19 to 5-22. Thrombocytic series taken from bone marrow and blood smears from a normal subject. Wright's stain. Oil immersion.

FIG. 5-19. Megakaryoblast (mb).

FIG. 5-20. Promegakaryocyte with granular cytoplasm (pm).

FIG. 5-21. Granular megakaryocyte (m) with an ingested segmented neutrophil (n) and a lymphocyte (1).

FIG. 5-22. Platelets in clusters (pc) and individually arranged (pi) among erythrocytes.

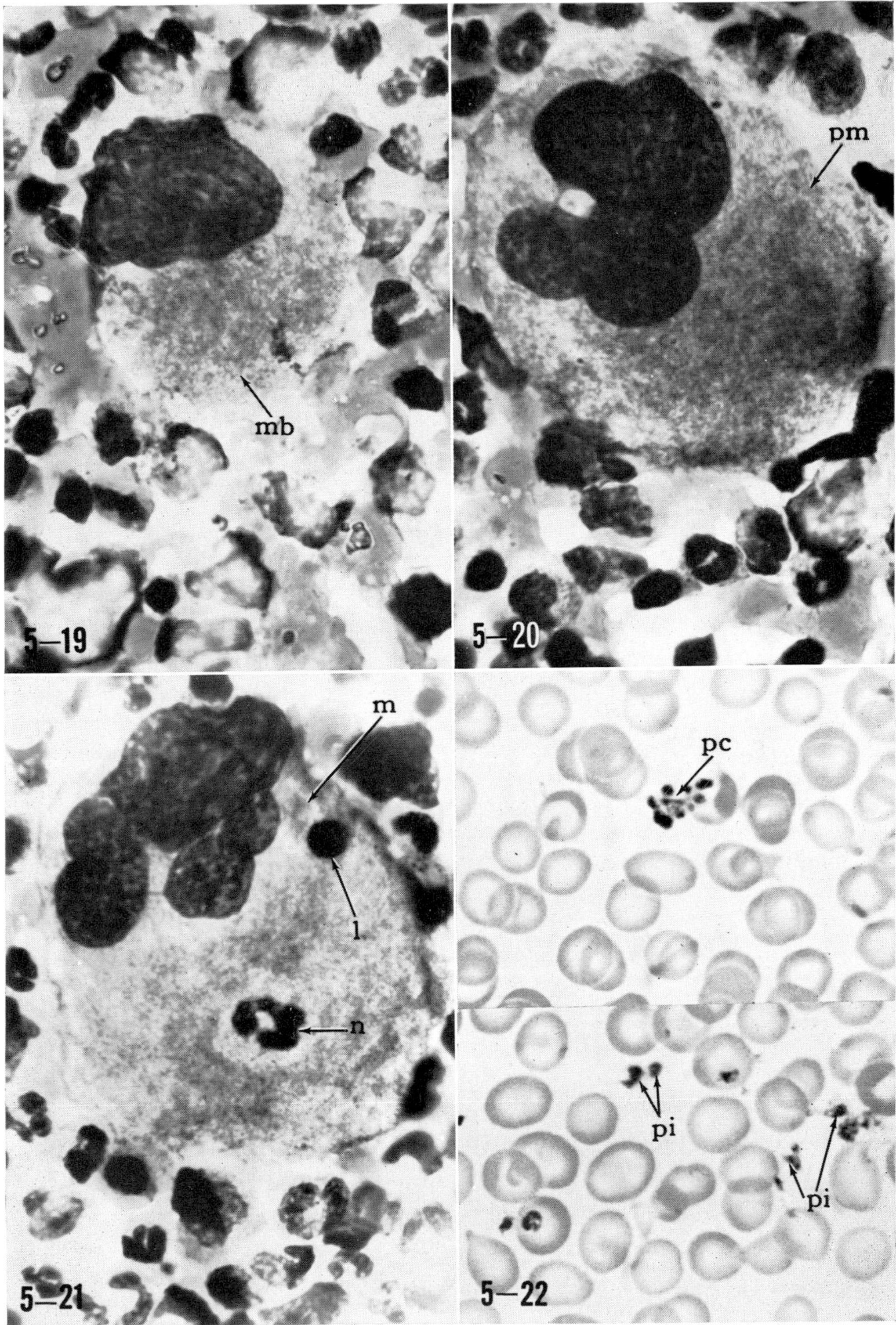
mb
5–19
pm
5–20
m
l
n
5–21
pc
pi
pi
5–22

blasts and lymphocytes have identical developmental potentialities. **Dualists** contend that the agranular leukocytes are derived from one stem cell, whereas the granular leukocytes and the erythrocytes come from a different stem cell. Finally, elaborating on the dualists' belief, the **trialists** introduce separate stem cells for the lymphocytes and the monocytes.

3. Structure of the Bone Marrow (Plate 29)

a. Bone marrow consists of a variety of myeloid cells (in red marrow) as well as fat cells, blood vessels and a fine reticular frame work for the support of the vessels and the cells present. In general, the deposition of fat follows the growth of the marrow spaces. In adults, the primary hemopoietic center resides in the **red marrow** and is limited to vertebrae, sternum, ribs, clavicles, scapulae and bones of the skull and the pelvis, with some foci in the epiphyses of long bones.

b. Bone marrow aspiration is a widely used hematologic procedure. The most satisfactory aspiration sites are the upper portion of the sternum, the area immediately distal to the iliac crest and the spinous processes of the 3rd and the 4th lumbar vertebrae. The student is referred to *Wintrobe's Clinical Hematology* for an account of the technics for obtaining and preparing marrow. A differential count of a marrow preparation is to be performed in the laboratory and is to be completed in similar fashion to the differential count of blood, except that it will be necessary to count from 1,000 to 1,500 nucleated cells for accurate results. However, before attempting a differential count, the student must be trained in the morphologic identification of each type found in marrow preparations.

c. In order to simplify your learning of the various nucleated blood cells in the marrow, the following outline is presented. It reveals that primitive cells have certain similar morphologic features and that these cells undergo changes as they mature.

1. The size of early cells is large; they become increasingly smaller with maturity.

2. Nuclear size also decreases with maturity.

3. The cytoplasm stains characteristically basophilic in immature cells but, in most cells, becomes acidophilic as development proceeds.

4. The nucleus of early cells has a fine lacelike arrangement of chromatin, is nonlobulated, contains nucleoli, and stains reddish-blue. With maturity, the nuclear chromatin becomes coarse and clumped, and the nucleus tends to lobulate, becomes nonnucleolated, and is decidedly basophilic.

5. Granular leukocytes contain no cytoplasmic granules in their earliest developmental forms (**blasts**). In the myelocytic forms, however, nonspecific, metachromatic granules are sparsely distributed throughout the cytoplasm. As maturation proceeds, these

PLATE 32—Erythroid Series

FIGS. 5-23 to 5-26. Maturation sequence of the erythroid series taken from bone marrow smears of normal subjects and patients with hemolytic anemias. Wright's stain. Oil immersion.

FIG. 5-23. Rubriblast with cytoplasmic tags.

FIG. 5-24. Four prorubricytes in varying stages.

FIG. 5-25. Four rubricytes in varying stages.

FIG. 5-26. Five metarubricytes in varying stages.

FIG. 5-27a. Diffusely basophilic erythrocytes from a peripheral blood smear from a patient with thalassemia minor. Wright's stain. Oil immersion.

FIG. 5-27b. Reticulocytes from a blood smear of an erythropoietin-stimulated rat. New methylene blue stain. Oil immersion.

FIG. 5-28. Mature erythrocytes from blood smears. Wright's stain. Oil immersion.

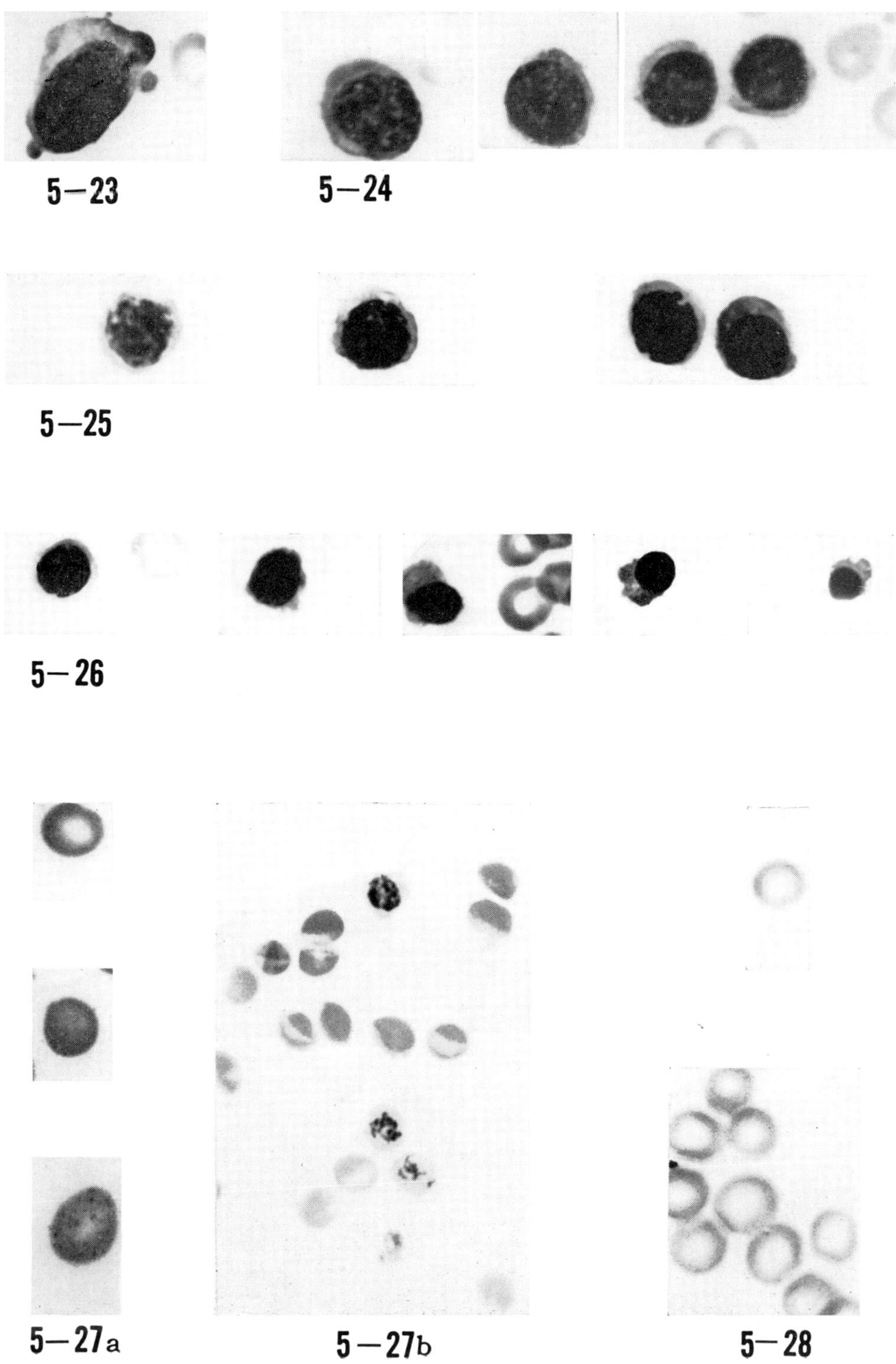
5–23
5–24
5–25
5–26
5–27a
5–27b
5–28

cells finally contain more specific, adult-type granules in large numbers.

With the above in mind, a brief consideration of the sequential morphology of the various cell series is in order.

4. Granulocytic Series (Fig. 5-17)

a. *Myeloblast*. The diameter of this cell ranges from 11 to 18 μ. The nucleus is round and contains delicate lacelike chromatin strands. However, condensation of chromatin can be found; apparently this is restricted to the areas around the several basophilic-staining nucleoli.

b. *Progranulocyte* (Promyelocyte). The nucleus becomes coarser, and nucleoli may or may not be present. Nonspecific granules appear in varying numbers and sizes.

c. *Myelocyte*. Specific cytoplasmic granulation of neutrophilic, eosinophilic or basophilic types occurs. Cell size is smaller, and the nuclear-cytoplasmic ratio is changed so that it presents a relatively larger amount of cytoplasm, which is still predominantly basophilic. Nuclear chromatin is further thickened.

d. *Metamyelocyte* (Juvenile). The nucleus becomes indented, smaller and coarser as to chromatin material. Specific granulation persists, and the cytoplasm usually stains much as it does in the fully developed cells.

e. *Band* (Stab). The nuclear indentation is marked, revealing the appearance of a horseshoe-shaped nucleus.

f. *Segmented* (Polymorphonuclear). The description of this cell was given in the section on Blood.

5. The Lymphocytic Series (Fig. 5-18)

a. *Lymphoblast*. This cell has characteristics which are similar to those of the myeloblast, and its identity is usually assumed from the recognition of differentiated mature cell stages that accompany it, especially in pathologic states such as leukemia.

b. *Prolymphocyte*. The nuclear chromatin structure is coarser than that of the blast form and finer than that of the mature large lymphocyte. Nucleoli may be present.

c. *Lymphocyte*. The description was given in the section on Blood.

6. The Monocytic Series (Fig. 5-18)

a. *Monoblast*. These cells are identified as such only in patients with monocytic leukemia. Characteristically they are similar to the myeloblast.

b. *Promonocyte*. The nuclear chromatin structure is finer than that of the mature monocyte. Nucleoli are usually present.

c. *Monocyte*. The description was given in the section on Blood.

7. The Plasmacytic Series

a. *Plasmablast* (Myeloma Cell). These cells are seen only in patients with plasmacytic leukemia or multiple myeloma. The cells contain a relatively large nucleus, which is usually eccentrically located with characteristic blastic type chromatin and the presence of one or more nucleoli. The basophilic cytoplasm tends to be more opaque than that of other blast cell types.

b. *Proplasmacyte*. The nuclear chromatin structure is coarser than that of the blast form and finer than that of the mature form. A nucleolus is usually present.

c. *Plasmacyte* (Plasma Cell). The diameter of this cell ranges from 10 to 20 μ. Characteristically the nucleus is round and eccentric in location, with the chromatin consisting of coarse deeply staining blocks. In fixed tissue preparations, the chromatin blocks often appear to be arranged in spoke-wheel fashion. There is an abundance of basophilic cytoplasm, usually characterized by a perinuclear light-staining area. Small globules and vacuoles are often demonstrable.

8. The Thrombocytic Series (Plate 31)

a. *Megakaryoblast.* Typically, megakaryoblasts have characteristics which are similar to other blast cells except for their larger size.

b. *Promegakaryocyte.* This cell is larger than the megakaryoblast, ranging from 25 to 50 μ. The nucleus contains nucleoli, may or may not be lobulated, and has a coarse linear chromatin arrangement. A number of fine bluish to purplish-red granules appear in the cytoplasm.

c. *Megakaryocyte.* These cells are quite large, ranging from 50 to 100 μ in diameter. The nucleus usually has multiple lobulations and contains no visible nucleoli. The cytoplasmic granules are more numerous, often aggregate, and stain purplish-red.

d. *Metamegakaryocyte.* This cell is similar to the megakaryocyte with the exception that the granular thrombocytes begin to differentiate at the periphery of the cytoplasm.

e. *Thrombocyte* (Platelet). The cell is as previously described in the section on Blood.

9. The Erythrocytic Series (Plate 32)

a. *Rubriblast* (Proerythroblast, Pronormoblast). The youngest precursor of the erythrocyte is similar to other blast cells. Only rarely can one detect slight differences from other blast cells. These differences include a nuclear chromatin that is somewhat coarser and a cytoplasm that demonstrates a more opaque royal-blue staining reaction.

b. *Prorubricyte* (Basophilic Erythroblast or Normoblast). The cell is smaller than the rubriblast, the chromatin is coarser, nucleoli are usually absent or indistinct, and the cytoplasm is basophilic.

c. *Rubricyte* (Polychromatic Erythroblast or Normoblast). The cell and its nucleus are still smaller, and the chromatin is even more condensed. The development of hemoglobin is apparent in the cytoplasm of many of these cells as demonstrated by their bluish-red to reddish staining properties.

d. *Metarubricyte* (Orthochromatic Erythroblast or Normoblast). The nucleus is even smaller and the nuclear chromatin is even more condensed; apart from this, the cytoplasm appears to be completely hemoglobinized.

e-1. *Reticulocytes.* These cells are non-nucleated and recognized only with supravital stains such as brilliant cresyl blue or new methylene blue. These cells appear to have a fibrillar chromatin network, densely arranged in young reticulocytes; this becomes very sparsely arranged as the cells increase in age. Other cells containing nuclear fragments such as Howell-Jolly bodies are often mistaken for reticulocytes.

e-2. *Diffusely Basophilic Erythrocyte* (Polychromatic Erythrocyte). This is a non-nucleated cell with a slightly basophilic cytoplasm; it is slightly larger than the mature erythrocyte.

f. *Erythrocyte* (Red Blood Cell). This cell is as previously described in the section on Blood.

6 · Muscle Tissue

A. Introduction *B. Muscle Types*

A. INTRODUCTION

Muscle, the third of the basic tissues to be considered, differs sharply from epithelia and connective tissues in that it consists of aggregates of elongate cells designed for a single function, that of contraction. Its cellular elements, usually called **muscle fibers**, are bound together by connective tissue. The prefix **sarco-** is used to designate many of the structural features of muscle fibers. Thus, **sarcoplasm** refers to muscle cytoplasm, **sarcolemma** refers to the cell membrane, and **sarcosomes** refers to cytoplasmic inclusion bodies. Additional specific terms will be mentioned later.

Factors that are essential for efficient muscle contraction include a suitable histologic and ultrastructural morphology, an adequate blood supply to satisfy the high metabolic requirements, and means for evoking the contractile response. It is understandable therefore that: (1) light and electron microscopes reveal the muscle fiber to be an elongate prismatic or spindle-shaped structure and to contain myofibrils which in turn are made up of myofilaments, such a complex of structures being capable of shortening; (2) a rich blood supply exists to provide the necessary metabolic precursors for the high energy requirements of muscle contraction; and (3) specialized structures related

PLATE 33—Smooth Muscle

FIG. 6-1. Survey appearance of bundles of smooth muscle fibers from the muscularis externa of the lower third of the esophagus. The smooth muscle has been cut transversely (t) and longitudinally (l). H & E stain. Low power.

FIG. 6-2. Transversely cut smooth muscle fibers (t) of the muscularis mucosa of the middle third of the esophagus. H & E stain. Intermediate power.

FIG. 6-3. Transversely sectioned muscularis externa of the small intestine to show smooth muscle fibers and the central position of their nuclei (n). H & E stain. High power.

FIG. 6-4. Longitudinal section of smooth muscle fibers in various stages of contraction from the muscularis externa of the small intestine. Note the pleated nuclei (n) characteristic of the contracting state. H & E stain. High power.

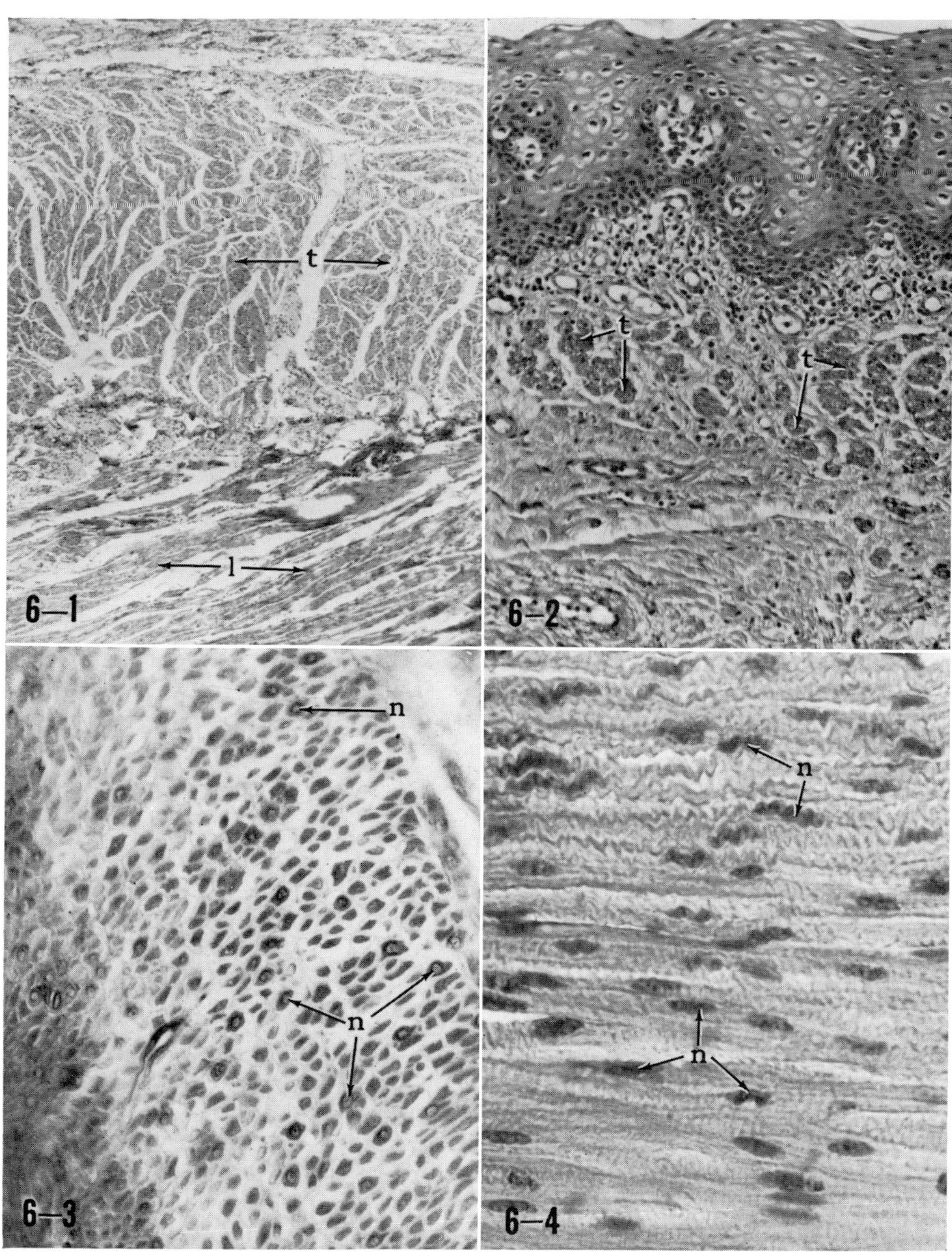
t
t
t
l
6—1
6—2
n
n
6—3
n
n
6—4

to the nervous system exist which, by means of bioelectric stimuli, trigger the contractile process.

B. MUSCLE TYPES

Muscle histology varies according to the type of contraction that it has to undergo. On this basis, 3 major muscle types are distinguished: **smooth, skeletal** and **cardiac**.

1. Smooth Muscle (Figs. 6-1 to 6-6)

Smooth muscle is so named because it frequently appears as smooth-surfaced layers or bands in the walls of hollow organs and undergoes a smooth, slow and rhythmic, tonic type of contraction. Among the 3 forms of muscle this type has by far the widest distribution throughout the body.

In addition to its wide distribution along the walls of the gastrointestinal, the respiratory and the genitourinary tracts, it is found in varying amounts in most blood vessels, in connection with the intrinsic musculature of the eyes (ciliary and pupillary muscles), the skin (arrectores pilorum muscle) and in certain lymphoid organs.

The mature smooth muscle fiber has a spindle shape that varies in length from 20 to 500 μ. Short isolated fibers are frequently found in small arterioles, intestinal villi and the fibroelastic partitions (septa) of the spleen, whereas the longest smooth muscle fibers are found in the gravid uterus. Such a variety of sizes of smooth muscle fibers is associated with the special contractile needs in organs subserving a variety of functions. This size differential can be appreciated better if one equates fiber length with the diameter of a red blood cell. In this analogy, smooth muscle fibers vary in length from 3 to 70 red blood cell diameters. It is of interest that although the fiber length demonstrates such variability, fiber diameter, at its thickest point, almost never exceeds the diameter of a single erythrocyte.

An elongated nucleus is always present near the center of each smooth muscle cell. When such a fiber is not undergoing shortening, the nucleus has a cigar-shaped appearance. During contraction, however, the nucleus becomes distorted and acquires a characteristic sinusoidal shape, making histologic identification of the tissue very simple.

The sarcolemma is exceedingly thin and is difficult to see with the light microscope. Similarly, extremely thin myofibrils distributed in a scanty sarcoplasm give to the muscle fiber a vaguely longitudinally striated appearance.

When smooth muscle forms a sheath around the wall of a viscus organ, all fibers tend to be parallel with each other and are held together by a reticulum made up of reticular and delicate collagen fibers. Contraction of such a mass of muscle is not an all-or-none phenomenon. Rather, groups of fibers shorten slowly and spread this activity to adjacent fiber groups. This type of gradual contraction frequently can be seen with the light microscope in the form of dark, irregu-

PLATE 34—Smooth and Skeletal Muscle

FIG. 6-5. Longitudinal section through a villus of the small intestine to demonstrate isolated smooth muscle cells (s) in its core of lamina propria (lp). H & E stain. High power. (sb, striated border of epithelium)

FIG. 6-6. Smooth muscle contraction bands (b) in the muscularis externa portion of the duodenum. H & E stain. High power. (n, nuclei of smooth muscle cells)

FIG. 6-7. Survey section of skeletal muscle bundles cut longitudinally. Note that this form of muscle may appear striated, depending on the type of preparation employed. Mallory-Azan stain. Low power. (en, endomysium)

FIG. 6-8. Survey section of skeletal muscle cut transversely, revealing the subdivisions into large and small bundles (b). Iron hematoxylin stain. Low power.

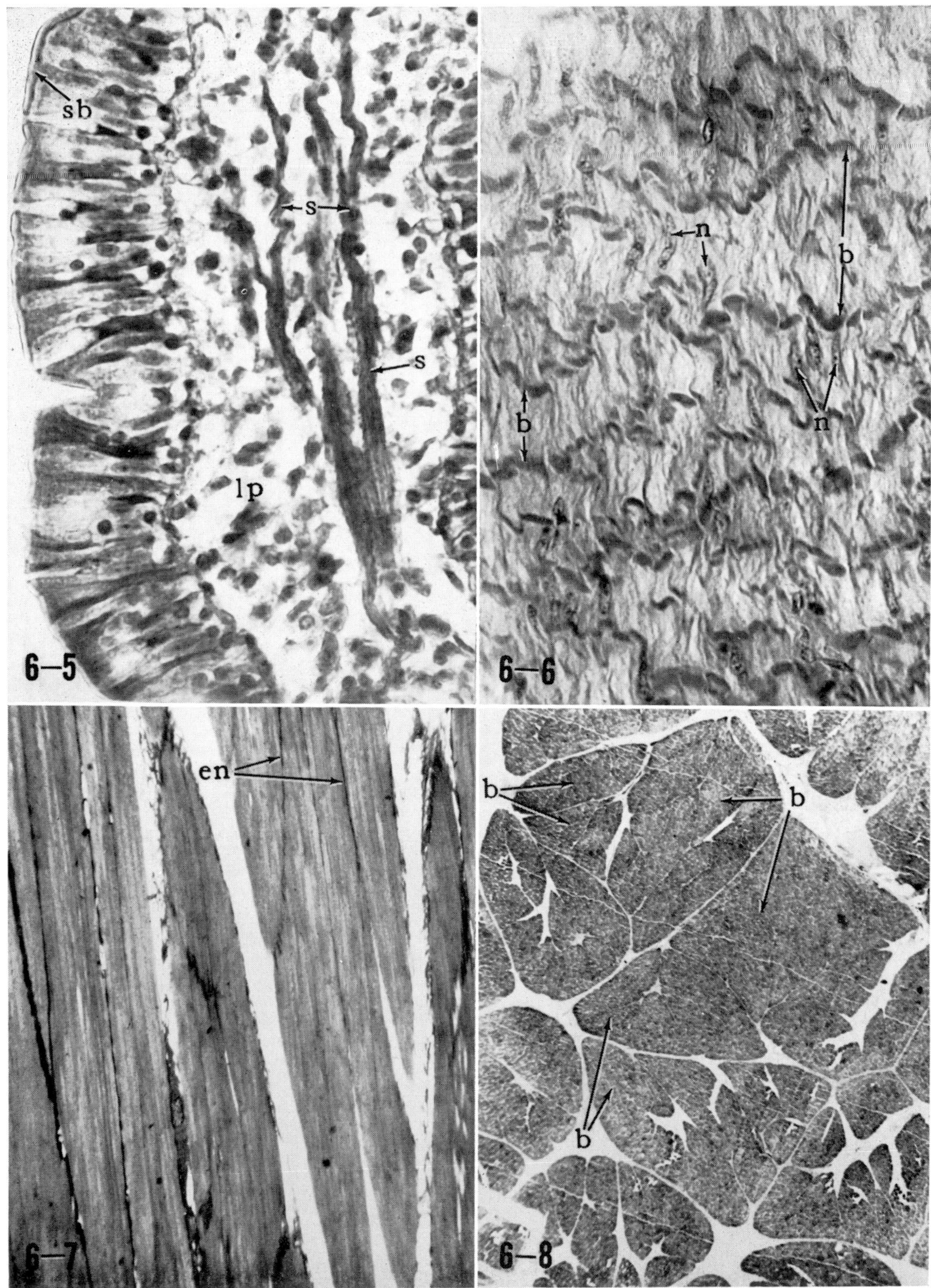
sb
s
s
lp
6–5
n
b
b
n
6–6
en
6–7
b
b
b
6–8

lar lines known as **contraction bands**, spreading across a few to many adjacent fibers. These represent local areas of contraction that, because of the associated protoplasmic condensation, take more stain than uncontracted portions of the fibers.

The term **involuntary muscle** is frequently used interchangeably with smooth muscle. The term refers to the fact that contraction occurs without voluntary control. Since involuntary contraction is also associated with certain of the skeletal muscles, and cardiac muscle as well, the term is not entirely appropriate.

Smooth muscle contraction is both involuntary, and hence reflex, and tonic in nature. **Muscle tonus** refers to the state of muscle activity in which the fibers are readied for contraction. Although the term tonic activity is applied to both smooth and skeletal muscle, the visible expression of contraction associated with or superimposed on the muscle tonus differs in the two types of muscle. In smooth muscle, the tonic type of contraction is slow and gradual, whereas in skeletal muscle it is brisk and immediate.

The nervous regulation of smooth muscle activity is via networks of autonomic nerve fibers which ramify over and terminate on individual muscle elements. Such nerve fibers require special stains in order to be seen easily with the light microscope.

The energy requirements for smooth muscle contraction are much lower than for the other types of muscle. This is reflected in a much sparser vascular supply. Capillary loops ramify on and among the smooth muscle fibers.

2. Skeletal Muscle (Figs. 6-7 to 6-16)

Skeletal muscle represents the greatest bulk of the body's musculature. Since most of these muscles run across movable joints, contraction results in movement of a part of the body. Contraction in the vast majority of skeletal muscles is under the controlling influence of the cerebral cortex. Consequently, this type is sometimes called **voluntary muscle**. In addition, since the individual muscle fibers seem to contain transverse striations, the term **striated** or **striped muscle** is often used. However, the latter term refers to cardiac muscle as well.

The mature skeletal muscle fiber is a multinucleated cell and has a cylindrical shape which varies from 1 to 40 mm. in length and from 10 to 100 μ in diameter. In the human and most other mammalian forms the nuclei lie peripherally, immediately subjacent to a thick distinct sarcolemma.

Individual muscle fibers are surrounded by a thin connective tissue covering of fine collagen fibers termed the **endomysium**. Several or many skeletal muscle fibers are collected into a **muscle fascicle** or **bundle** which, in turn, is covered by a somewhat heavier layer of loose connective tissue, the **perimysium**. Finally, several or many fascicles are combined into one of the named muscles, which is also covered by a sheath of connective tissue, the **epimysium**.

Each skeletal muscle fiber can be considered to be contained within a cylindrical bag or limiting membrane, the **sarcolemma**, that is filled with sarcoplasm and elongate contractile elements, the **myofibrils (fibrils,**

PLATE 35—Skeletal Muscle

FIG. 6-9. Demonstration of the profuse pattern of small blood vessels about skeletal muscle fibers from a carmine-injected preparation. Low power.

FIG. 6-10. Intermediate-power view of a portion of Figure 6-8. Note the perimysium (p) surrounding the fasciculi, and the endomysium (en) surrounding each of the muscle fibers.

FIG. 6-11. Intermediate-power view of a portion of Figure 6-9.

FIG. 6-12. High-power view of skeletal muscle fibers cut longitudinally to demonstrate clearly the darker isotropic bands and lighter anisotropic bands. Mallory-Azan stain.

6–9
en
en
p
6–10
6–11
6–12

myofibrillae). These myofibrils are capable of contraction because they are made up of **myofilaments** which contain long, organic molecular chains that shorten. The myofilaments are parallel structures, alternately thin and thick, and contain regions of greater and lesser denseness. Collectively, these features of myofilaments give to the myofibrils and also the muscle fiber as a whole the appearance of distinct transversely striated structures.

The system of cross striations of the myofibril can be analogized to white and black checkers alternately stacked one upon the other. The **light disk**, bands or striations as seen with the ordinary microscope appear as clear elements because they transmit incident light. Such a property is known as **isotropism**. The **dark disks** owe their dark appearance to the fact that they bend light waves away from the optical axis of the microscope. This deflection of light waves is caused by **anisotropism**, a property of the protein component of myofilaments that bends (**refracts**) the light twice (**birefringence, double refractiveness**) in its passage through the tissue.

Along the myofibrils in noncontracted or resting muscle, **A** (for anisotropic) or **Q** (for the German noun Querscheibe or cross disk) **disks (bands**) regularly alternate with **I** (for isotropic) or **J disks (bands**).

Each dark A (Q) band, in turn, contains a clear, less dense zone, the **H band** (after its discoverer Hensen or for the German adjective helle or bright) that extends across the myofibril like a pale wafer. The H band is also bisected by a thinner, dark line or zone of greater density, the **M band**.

Adjacent to each complex of disks that constitutes a single anisotropic segment of the myofibril, i.e., the A (Q), the H and the M bands, is found the lighter staining isotropic disk. This, the I or J disk, also has internal markings. Running across its center is a distinct dark zone, the **Z disk or band** (for the German noun Zwischenscheibe or middle disk; also known as Krause's membrane or Dobie's line). The Z disks, as well as the M disks, differ from the other characteristic bands in that they are not confined solely to myofibrils. Actually, they appear to be transverse membranous structures that pass without interruption across a muscle fiber to become attached to the sarcolemma. They probably function to hold the myofibrils together. Sometimes an additional pair of much finer disks, the **N bands**, can be found flanking both surfaces of the Z disks.

With the light microscope, A, I, Z and H bands can be found without too much difficulty. The M and the N disks require the use of the electron microscope to be seen readily, unless insect muscle is being examined. The bands may readily be made out with electron microscopy in cardiac muscle as well as in skeletal muscle (see Figs. 6-25, 6-27, 6-28 and 6-29).

PLATE 36—Skeletal Muscle

FIG. 6-13. Cross section of bundles of skeletal muscle fibers (rabbit). H & E stain. High power. (n, peripherally located nuclei)

FIG. 6-14. Cross section of isolated skeletal muscle fibers, showing the distribution of fibrils in Cohnheim's fields (Cf). H & E stain. High power. (en, endomysium; p, perimysium; v, blood vessels; n, nuclei of muscle fibers)

FIG. 6-15. High-power view of a portion of Figure 6-9, showing the vascular pattern of small blood vessels coursing parallel with the skeletal muscle fibers and also revealing transverse branches. Note the faint striations of muscle fibers.

FIG. 6-16. Cross section of myotendinous junction (mt). H & E stain. Low power. (t, compact bundles of collagenous fibers; m, skeletal muscle bundles)

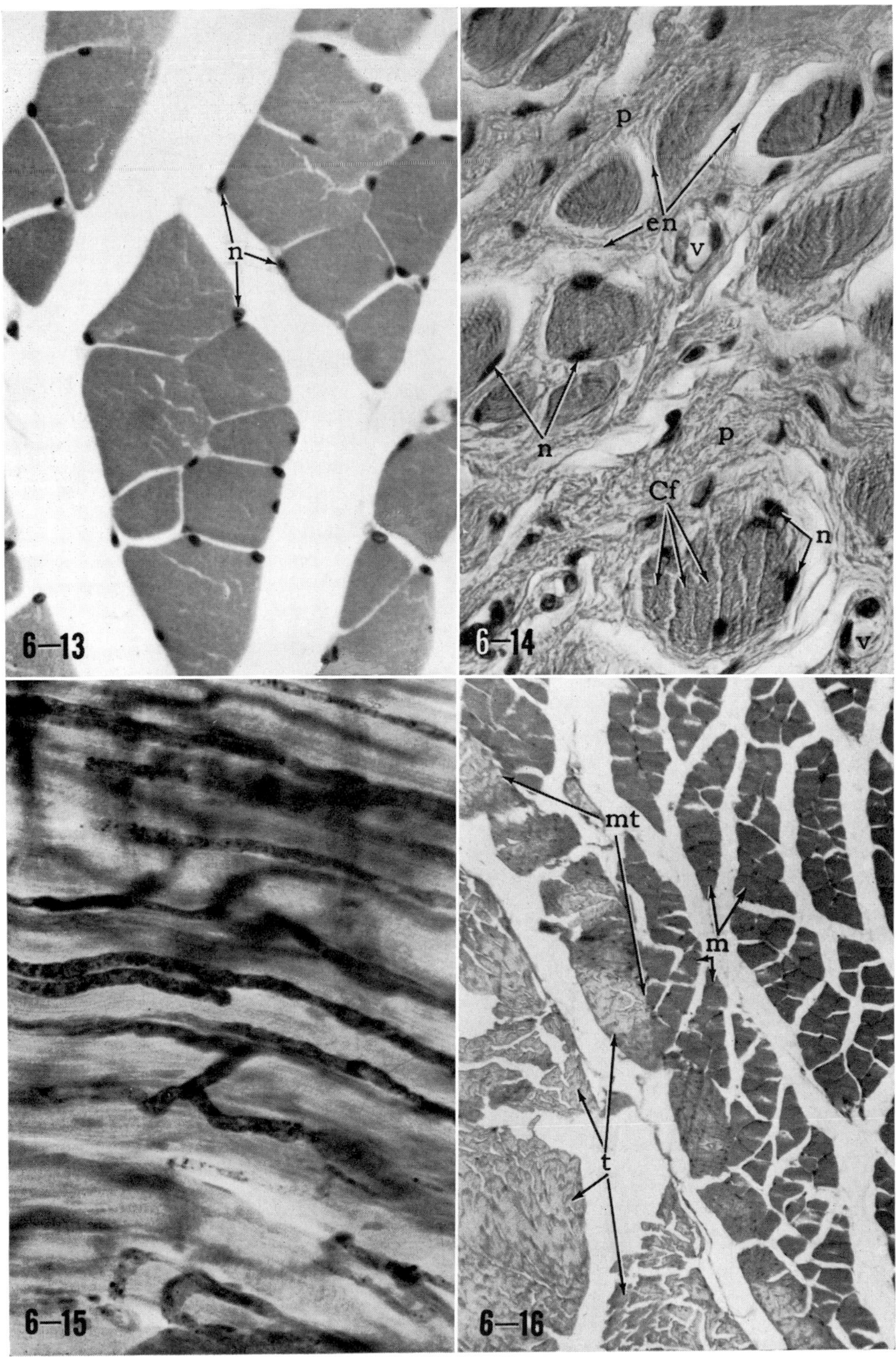
n
6–13
p
en
v
n
p
Cf
n
v
6–14
6–15
mt
m
t
6–16

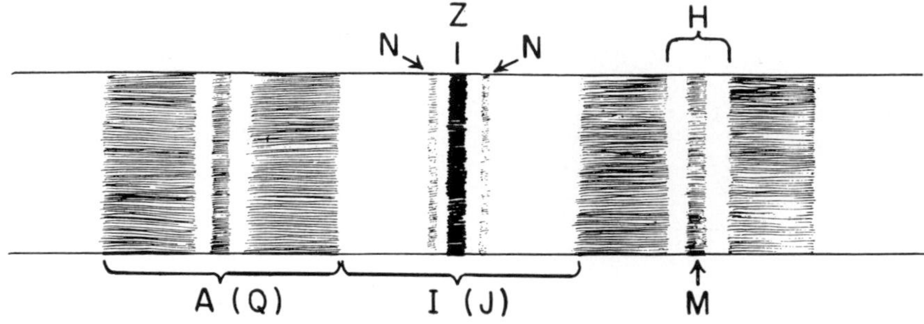

The diagram that appears above illustrates the arrangement of bands that exists in a myofibril of resting muscle. Based on a regular periodicity of the disks just enumerated along the axis of the myofibril, a structural and functional unit of muscle has been established. This unit, the **sarcomere**, consists of an A disk and halves of two adjacent I disks. Sarcomeres, therefore, represent successive segments of the myofibril between adjacent Z disks.

Contraction of a muscle, due to movement of the filaments in myofibrils, is associated with a thickening and shortening of the fibers of from 1/10 to 1/2 of their original length. Simultaneously, the transverse striations are more difficult to visualize in contracted muscle, because they are closer together than in the resting condition. Contraction affects the appearance of the alternating dark and light bands as seen with the light microscope. The length of the A (Q) band is not changed, but the I (J) band is considerably shortened. Although the length of the A band is not changed, the lighter H disk which is contained within it is almost obliterated by movement into this zone of acting filaments. However, a marked shortening of the I band occurs, as the thicker myosin filaments move toward the Z disk.

Metabolism in skeletal muscle requires a mechanism for supplying the fibers with large amounts of oxygen and nutriments and for eliminating waste products associated with the formation of lactic acid. These requirements are met by a rich blood supply, loosely termed muscular branches, coming from named arteries. By the time blood has reached an individual muscle fiber, it is flowing through a rich capillary network that utilizes the endomysial connective tissue to course along and around the fiber.

In addition to a rich vascularity, muscle metabolism is associated with the presence of formed elements, mitochondria (sarcosomes), in the sarcoplasm. The mitochondria as well as droplets of glycogen and lipid material tend to be concentrated near certain of the cross bands of the fiber.

The sarcoplasm also contains a reddish-brown pigment, **myoglobin**, that is mainly responsible for the characteristic color of

PLATE 37—Cardiac Muscle

FIG. 6-17. Survey section of cardiac muscle, showing the pattern of muscle fibers. H & E stain. Low power.

FIG. 6-18. Longitudinal section of cardiac muscle, revealing the branching and anastomosing nature of the muscle fibers with centrally placed nuclei. H & E stain. Intermediate power.

FIG. 6-19. Longitudinal section of cardiac muscle especially to show the intercalated disks (i) and the vascular pattern (v) between muscle fibers. Resorcin-fuchsin stain. Intermediate power.

FIG. 6-20. Cross section of cardiac muscle, showing the arrangement of the muscle fibers within the bundles. H & E stain. Intermediate power.

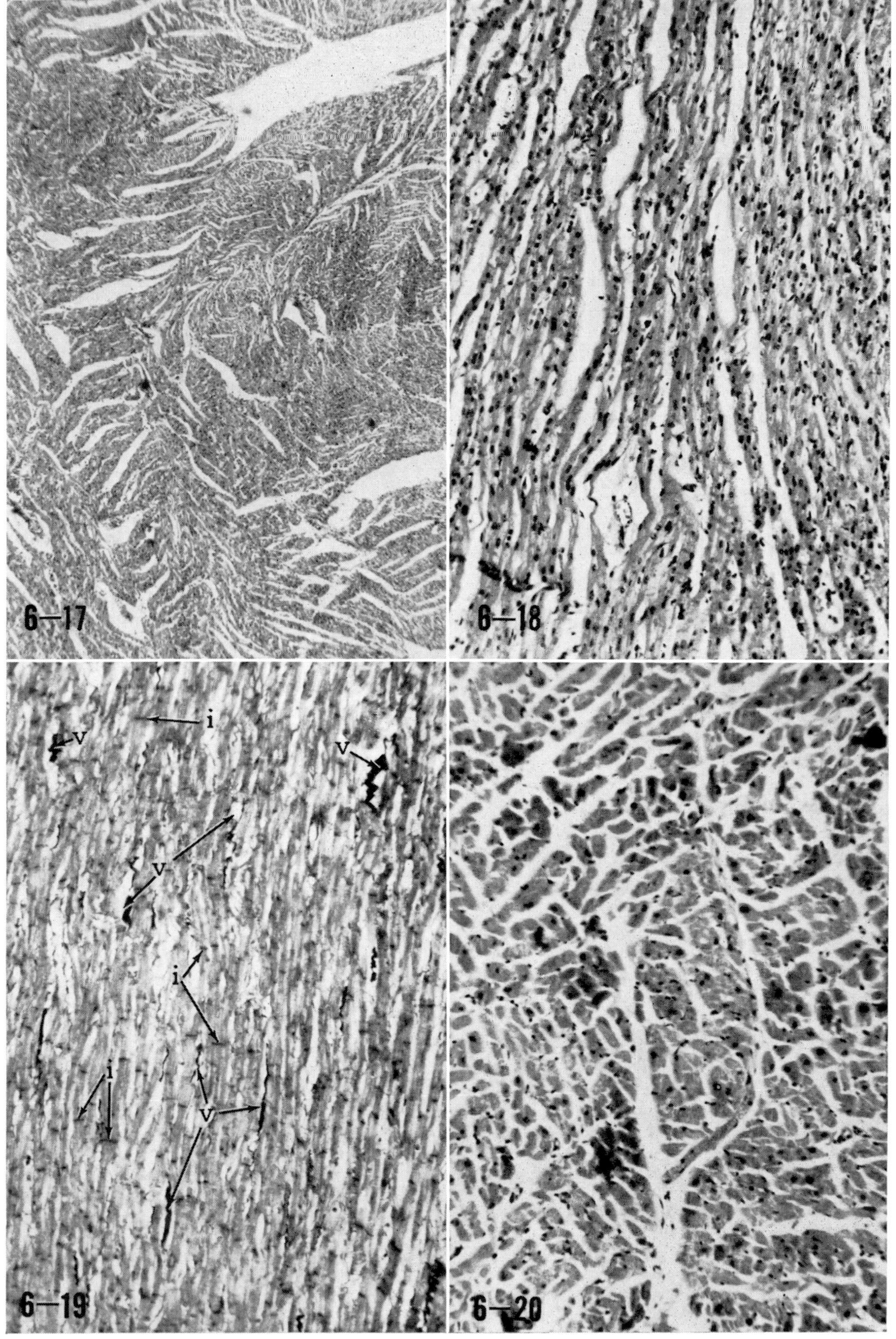
6–17
6–18
6–19
i
v
v
v
i
i
v
6–20

muscle. On the basis of the sarcoplasmic content of myoglobin, muscle may appear dark (**red fibers**) or pale (**white fibers**) in color. Red muscle fibers contain a more abundant and granular sarcoplasm, fewer and coarser myofibrils showing less regular transverse banding, more nuclei and greater vascularity than white muscle. These distinguishing features explain why red muscle fibers generally do not contract as quickly, are less easily fatigued and, therefore, can maintain contraction for longer periods of time than white fibers. In man, most of the named muscles contain a mixture of red and white fibers. However, there is a strong tendency for the muscles which act against gravity to maintain normal posture to contain more red fibers. Conversely, muscles that are suddenly shortened (**phasic contraction**) in the performance of a voluntary movement tend to contain more white than red muscle fibers.

Normal function of skeletal muscle depends not only on the special histology of this tissue but also on the intimate relationship existing between muscle and nerve. Special nerve endings with motor and sensory functions are found on muscle fibers. These will be discussed in the section on nervous tissue under the headings **motor end plates** and **muscle spindles**.

3. Cardiac Muscle (Figs. 6-17 to 6-29)

As the name implies, cardiac muscle is restricted to the myocardium of the heart. Cardiac muscle is similar in some respects to both of the other muscle types. It most closely resembles skeletal muscle in that it has a similar, though less obvious, system of transverse striations on longitudinal myofibrils and also in that it contracts briskly. On the other hand, it is also similar to smooth muscle in that it contains centrally placed nuclei and contracts involuntarily.

Cardiac muscle also exhibits certain unique histologic features that are correlated with the specialized function of the heart. In the first place, it is composed of many individual fibers, as in the other types of muscle, but in a continuum of branching, anastomosing "fibers" which form a **syncytium**. The "fibers" in continuity are arranged in spiral fashion around the atria and the ventricles of the heart and provide the structural basis for contraction in that organ.

An additional specialization of cardiac muscle is found in connection with the so-called conducting system of the heart. In a few restricted locations at the junction of the endocardium, the innermost heart layer, with the myocardium, certain of the muscle "fibers" become modified. These, the **Purkinje fibers**, are paler, contain more sarcoplasm and fewer myofibrils, and are thicker than ordinary cardiac muscle elements. The Purkinje fibers are believed to activate the various myocardial regions of the heart to produce its characteristic pattern of contractile activity.

PLATE 38—Cardiac Muscle

FIG. 6-21. Longitudinal section of cardiac muscle, showing its branching and cross-striated nature. Intercalated disks (id) and muscle nuclei (mn) are evident as well as fibroblasts (f) between muscle fibers. Mallory stain. High power.

FIG. 6-22. Cross-sectional appearance of cardiac muscle under the endocardium (e). Note the pattern of branching fibers (bf) and centrally placed nuclei (cn). H & E stain. High power.

FIG. 6-23. Longitudinal section of cardiac muscle, especially demonstrating the branching nature of its fibers (bf). Also seen are intercalated disks (id), centrally placed nuclei (cn) and a blood vessel (v). H & E stain. High power.

FIG. 6-24. Cross section of cardiac muscle fibers to demonstrate myofibrils (stippled appearance of the sarcoplasm). Also note the centrally placed muscle nuclei (cn). H & E stain. High power.

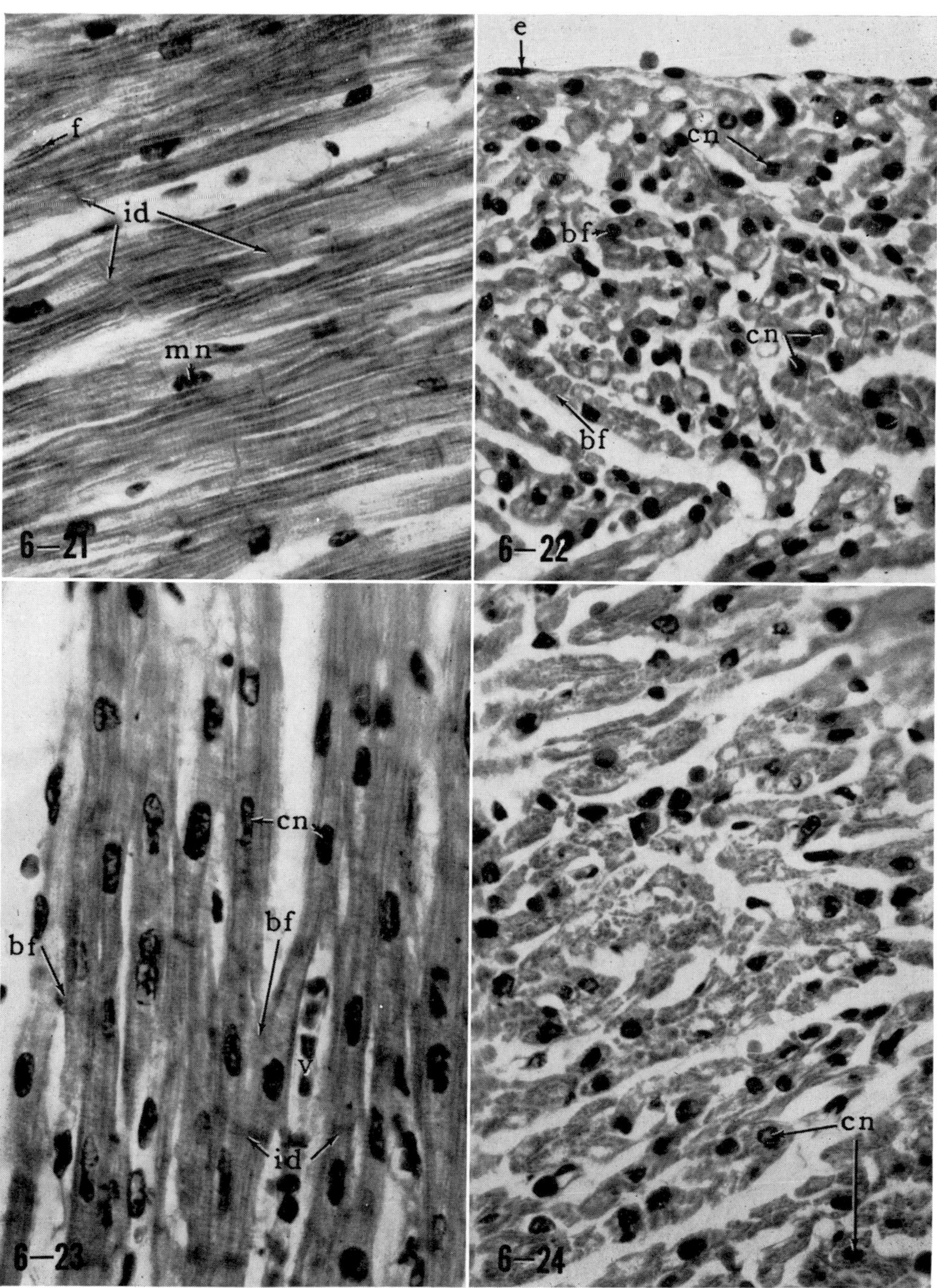
f
id
mn
6–21
e
cn
bf
cn
bf
6–22
cn
bf
bf
v
id
6–23
cn
6–24

Another unusual feature of cardiac muscle is the common presence of thick, transverse lines crossing the regions of the Z disks. Such stripes, known as **intercalated disks**, are quite variable in appearance and may appear as a solid transverse band or as a complete or incomplete set of steplike markings across the "fiber." They are present in varying numbers and have been shown by electron microscope studies to be fused plasma membranes of adjacent cells.

Because of the constant pumping action of the heart, cardiac muscle must be more richly supplied with blood than any other type of muscle. It is nourished by its own special system of vessels, the coronary arteries. In addition, cardiac muscle is innervated by sympathetic and parasympathetic fibers of the **visceral motor (autonomic) nervous system.** In contradistinction to skeletal muscle, denervation of the heart does not bring about a cessation of heart action. This is because cardiac muscle contains its own built-in conducting system. Such denervation serves solely to alter the rate of contraction of heart muscle.

PLATE 39—Cardiac Muscle

FIG. 6-25. Electron micrograph delineating the general cytologic features of cardiac muscle (rat). Near the left side, contiguous myocardial cells are limited by the sarcolemma, which shows numerous pinocytotic vesicles on its inner aspect and an investing basement membrane on its outer aspect. Large mitochondria with numerous cristae and without specific relationship to individual sarcomeres are noted. Tubular and vesicular segments of the sarcoplasmic reticulum are interspersed between the myofibrils. An intermediary vesicle is seen near the center of the micrograph. Cytoplasmic granules are evident, particularly in the right portion of the picture. The myofibrils, in longitudinal section, demonstrate the Z line and the I and the A bands. × 28,000.

FIG. 6-26. Field showing relationship of sarcoplasmic reticulum to perinuclear membranes (rat). The nucleus occupies the left portion of the micrograph. A pore in the perinuclear membranes is indicated by an arrow. Tubular and vesicular segments of the sarcoplasmic reticulum closely approximate the perinuclear membranes at several points. In the right portion of the picture an intermediary vesicle (i) and canalicular segments of the sarcoplasmic reticulum are shown in close apposition to mitochondria (m). × 42,000.

FIG. 6-27. Electron micrograph showing a longitudinal section of the myofibrils (dog). A 1:1 ratio of thick to thin A band myofilaments is particularly evident in the left lower portion of the sarcomere illustrated. The Z line, the I band, the A band, the H disk and the M line are recognized. Cross bridges between filaments are noted. × 95,000.

(Figs. 6-25 to 6-27 from Stenger, R. J., and Spiro, D.: J. Biophys. Biochem. Cytol. *9*:325)

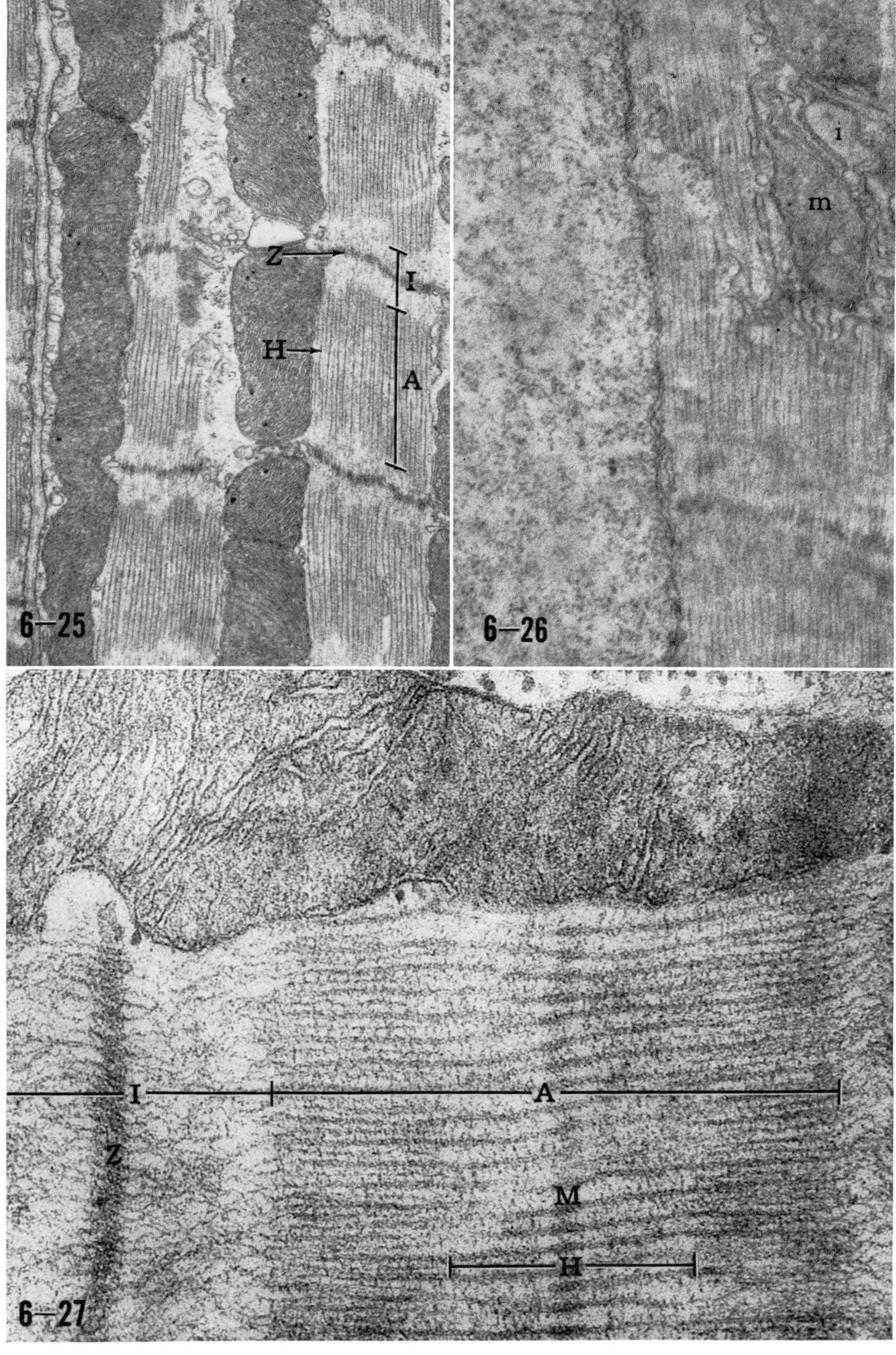
Z
I
H
A
6–25
i
m
6–26
I
A
Z
M
H
6–27

PLATE 40—Cardiac Muscle

FIG. 6-28. Electron micrograph showing a longitudinal section of a myofibril (rat). The Z line, the A and the I bands and the H disk are identified. In general, 2 thin myofilaments are found between 2 thick myofilaments in the A bands. This 1:2 ratio of thick to thin filaments is seen at the arrows. × 72,000.

FIG. 6-29. Electron micrograph showing an oblique section of the myofibrils (rat). The Z line, the I band, the A band and the H disk are shown. Both thick and thin filaments are present in the A band proper. × 68,000.

(Figs. 6-28 and 6-29 from Stenger, R. J., and Spiro, D.: J. Biophys. Biochem. Cytol. *9*:325)

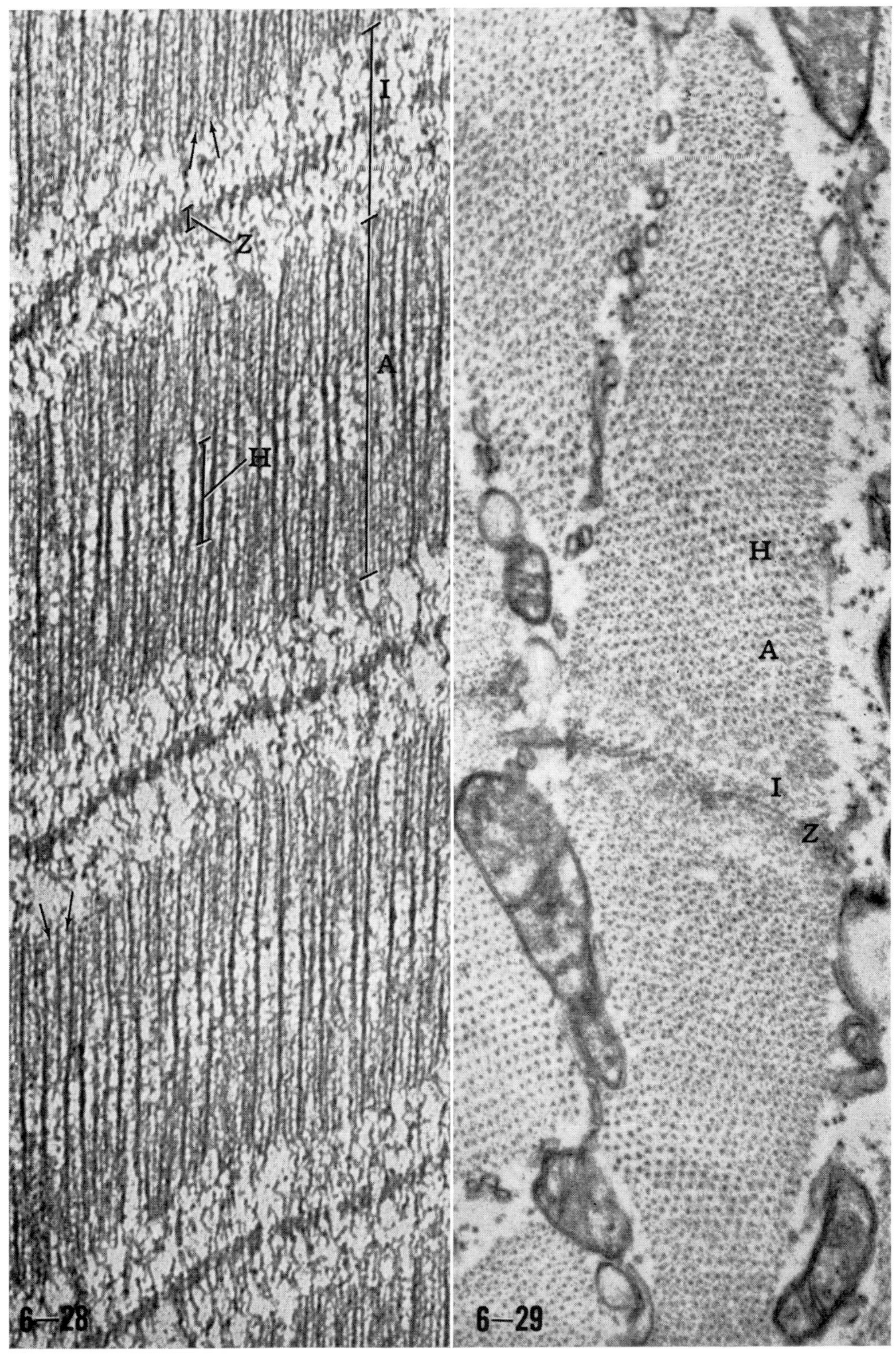
I
Z
A
H
6—28
H
A
I
Z
6—29

7 · Nervous Tissue

A. INTRODUCTION

Useful function in organs and tissues for the maintenance of life would not be possible without a means of signalling these structures to alter their rates of activity. The nervous system serves this role by conveying bioelectric messages to specific organs, causing them to accelerate or slow down the stereotyped functions with which they are associated. In addition to this vital influence on visceral function, the nervous system serves

PLATE 41—Spinal Ganglion

FIG. 7-1. Survey of spinal ganglion (dog). Note that the nerve cell bodies (nc) are characteristically round, that numerous nerve fibers (nf) are present and that the ganglion is encapsulated in connective tissue (ct). Mallory-Azan stain. Low power.

FIG. 7-2. Intermediate-power representation of a portion of Figure 7-1. (nc, nerve cell bodies; nf, nerve fibers; sc, satellite cells)

FIG. 7-3. Spinal ganglion, showing the characteristic occurrence of nerve cell bodies (nc) in groups separated by nerve fibers (nf). Note that postmortem shrinkage may give the false impression that the nerve cells are multipolar neurons. The presence of a single cell process (sp) found on only one or two neurons in this field indicates that the ganglion is sensory in nature. Acid fuchsin stain. Intermediate power.

FIG. 7-4. Two nerve cell bodies of spinal ganglion (dog) demonstrating their round appearance in section and their large centrally placed nuclei. Mallory-Azan stain. High power.

FIG. 7-5. A group of nerve cell bodies from the spinal ganglion (dog). Mallory-Azan stain. High power. (sc, satellite cell nuclei; nf, nerve fibers)

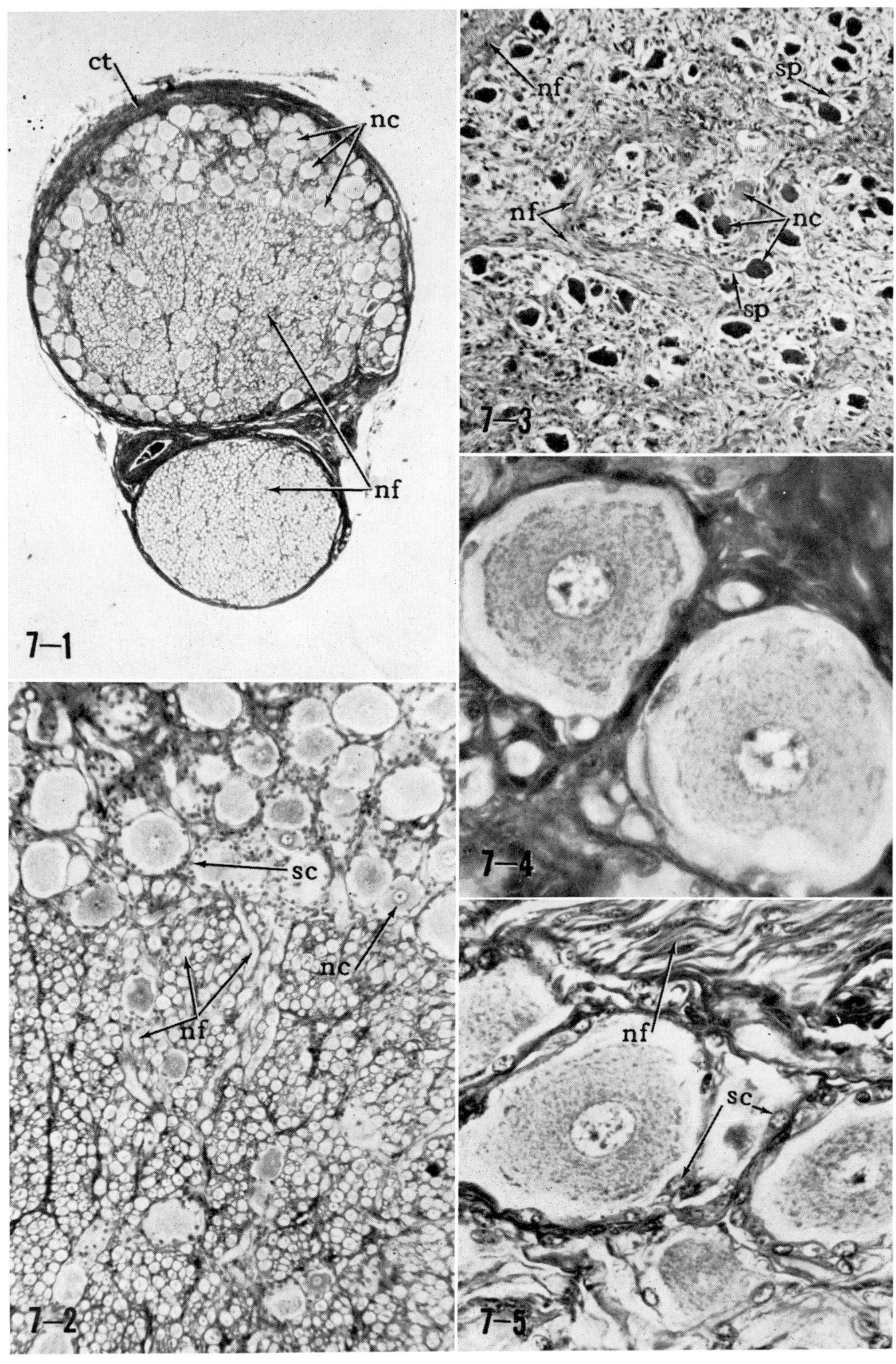
ct
nc
nf
7–1
sc
nc
nf
7–2
nf
sp
nf
nc
sp
7–3
7–4
nf
sc
7–5

as a central control board for receiving and sending instructions to skeletal muscle, thus integrating the fine adjustments of contraction and relaxation in agonist and antagonist muscle groups so that resulting movement is purposeful. All of these activities of the nervous system are accomplished in incredibly short periods of time.

It is commonly considered that nervous tissue consists solely of cells that are capable (1) of being excited (**irritability**) by stimuli arising in the external or the internal environment and (2) of conveying this excitation (**conduction**) by means of rapid, sequential changes of bioelectric charge from point to point along the cell. Since, however, the embryonic neural tube and neural crest, which produce all nerve cells, also produce the cellular elements that support the soft nervous tissue (**neuroglia**) and the cells that line the cavities of the central nervous system (**ependyma**), these latter must also be considered in this section.

B. THE NERVE CELL (NEURON)—GENERAL CONSIDERATIONS

A neuron consists of a nerve cell body and all its processes. Since the nerve cell body (**perikaryon**) contains the nucleus and cytoplasmic organelles for maintaining normal metabolism, it follows that the cell body is regarded as the **trophic center**. Understandably, therefore, pathologic processes that destroy the cell body irrevocably terminate normal function. A classic example of lost function from the destruction of nerve cell bodies is seen in poliomyelitis.

More variability exists in the size and the shape of nerve cell bodies than is found in any other basic tissue. Perikaryons range in size from 5 to 125 μ in diameter, but variations of shape seem much more startling. Some nerve cell bodies are spherical, ovoid, pear- or spindle-shaped structures; others are more angular and are rhomboidal, stellate or pyramidal elements. Such differences in cytoarchitecture have been associated with a multiplicity of function among different populations of neurons. Fortunately, a general consideration of the neuron does not necessitate learning all these permutations of perikaryon shape. It is adequate to know that, based on the embryology of the nervous system, 3 major types of cell bodies—and therefore neurons—exist.

1. Unipolar Neurons (Pseudounipolar, T-Cells or Monipolar) (Plate 41)

This type has an almost spherical shape with a large, round, usually centrally placed nucleus. Its name is derived from the fact that only one cell process exists, originating

PLATE 42—Motor Ganglion

FIG. 7-6. Appearance of the celiac ganglion, a motor ganglion of the autonomic nervous system. Note the numerous groups of nerve cell bodies. Silver stain. Low power.

FIG. 7-7. Intermediate-power representation of a portion of Figure 7-6. Most of the nuclei seen in nerve cells are in characteristic eccentric position. The fact that in this flat section many nerve cells can be seen giving rise to a single process and some to more than one process indicates that the cells are multipolar and that this must be a motor ganglion.

FIG. 7-8. A group of 3 multipolar nerve cell bodies from the celiac ganglion. Note the large, eccentrically placed nuclei and multiple processes that are characteristic of motor ganglion. Silver stain. High power.

FIG. 7-9. Nerve cells in myenteric (Auerbach's) plexus of the muscularis externa of the fundic portion of the stomach. The large and small nerve cells seen represent an intramural ganglion present within the meshwork of a plexus of autonomic nerve fibers. Note the eccentric position of the nuclei. Mallory stain. High power. (nc, nerve cells; m, smooth muscle; v, blood vessel)

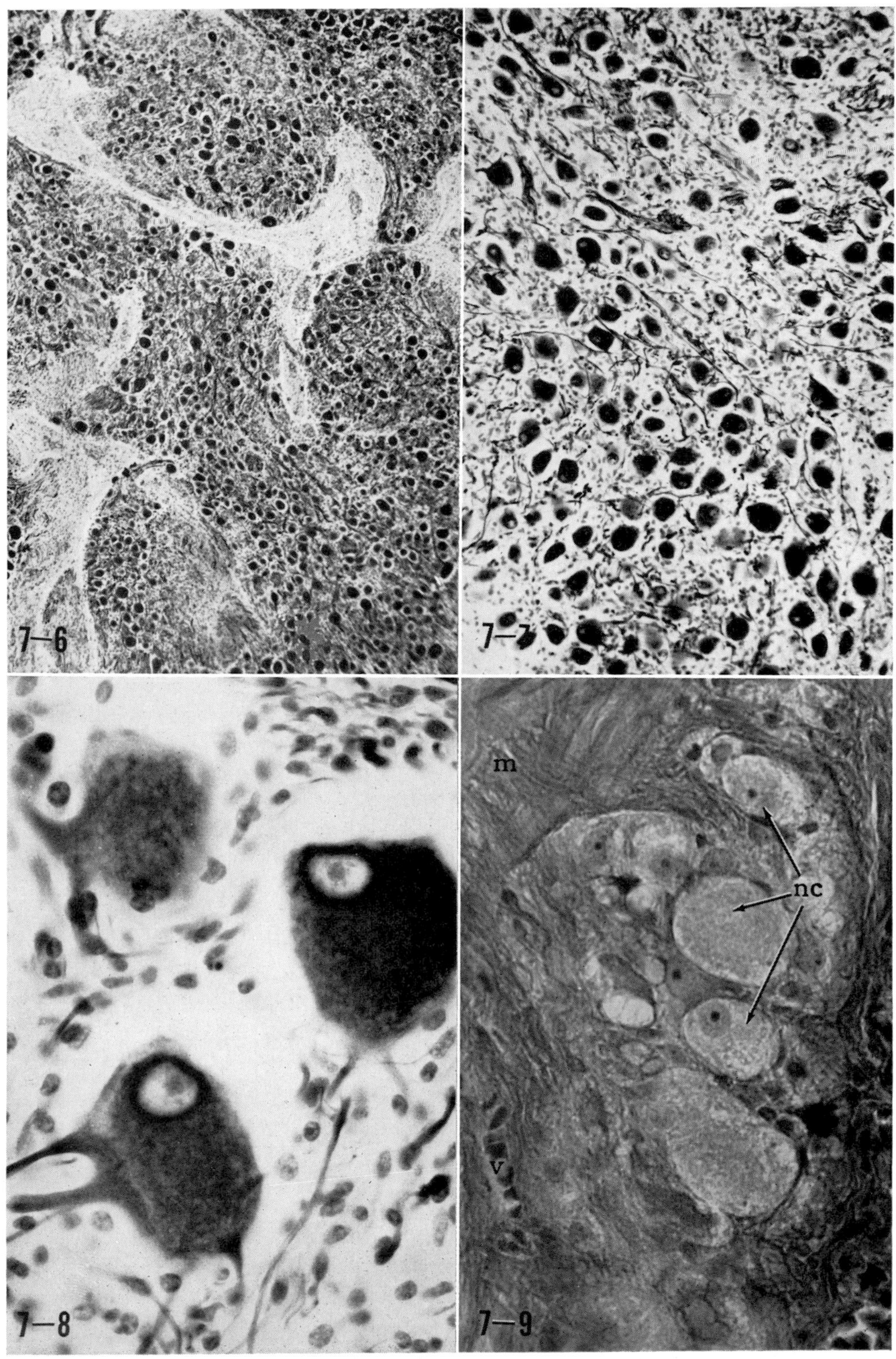
7–6
7–7
7–8
7–9
m
nc
v

from the nerve cell body. The unipolar neuron is almost exclusively sensory in function. That is, impulses utilizing neurons of this type travel from sensory nerve endings toward the central nervous system. (**C.N.S. is equivalent to the brain and the spinal cord.**) Since sensory nerve endings are located in all organs of the body as well as on its surface, it should be apparent that immense numbers of neurons in the peripheral nervous system (i.e., the total nervous system less the brain and the spinal cord) are strictly sensory in nature. With very few exceptions, such sensory neurons have their unipolar cell bodies located in sensory ganglia. (A ganglion is an aggregation of nerve cell bodies outside the C.N.S.). Sensory ganglia are found close to the spinal cord (**spinal, dorsal root or sensory ganglia**) and the brain (**trigeminal or semilunar ganglion of the trigeminal nerve, the geniculate ganglion of the facial nerve, the petrosal and the superior ganglia of the glossopharyngeal nerve and the nodose and the jugular ganglia of the vagus nerve**).

2. Bipolar Neurons

This type of neuron has an oval or fusiform-shaped cell body with a single process coming off each of the two ends or poles. Its nucleus is oval and may be slightly eccentric in position. Of functional significance is the limited distribution of bipolar neurons in the nervous system. They are found primarily in association with certain of the special senses of the body. Bipolar cell bodies are insinuated between epithelial cells in the schneiderian membrane of the nose as part of the pathway carrying impulses related to olfaction. Bipolar neurons constitute the major elements of the inner nuclear layer of the retina and thus form an important link in conveying to the brain the impulses related to vision. Furthermore, both divisions of the stato-acoustic nerve contain bipolar neurons. Bipolar cell bodies of the vestibular division of this nerve collectively form the **vestibular ganglion** located in the inner ear. Similarly, the bipolar cell bodies of the auditory portion of the stato-acoustic nerve collectively constitute the **spiral or cochlear ganglion**.

3. Multipolar Neurons
(Plate 42)

As the name implies, this neuron has an angular cell body with many poles and a process coming from each pole. This is the commonest neuron type and exists in many sizes and shapes. It generally has a large, centrally placed, spherical nucleus that contains a single prominent nucleolus.

Multipolar nerve cell bodies are found as aggregates within and outside the C.N.S. The vast majority of these neurons have their cell bodies located within the C.N.S. in regions that are known as nuclei. In connection with nervous tissue, **a nucleus** is an aggregation of nerve cell bodies inside the central nervous system; it is therefore the central counterpart of a ganglion. The remaining multipolar cell bodies are present outside the C.N.S. and are located in **sympathetic ganglia (chain or motor and**

PLATE 43—Nerve Fibers

Fig. 7-10. Myelinated nerve fibers teased from a nerve fixed with osmic acid. Low power.

Fig. 7-11. Intermediate-power view of a portion of Figure 7-10. Some fibers reveal nodes of Ranvier (R).

Fig. 7-12. High-power view of a portion of Figure 7-10. Note the central unstained axon (a) covered by myelin (m). (R, nodes of Ranvier)

Fig. 7-13. Section from the radial nerve, revealing the nature of the nerve fibers. Most of the nerve fibers are shown cut longitudinally, but a small fascicle in the upper right shows transversely cut fibers. H & E stain. Intermediate power. (m, myelin spaces [clear areas] surrounding axons; p, perineurium)

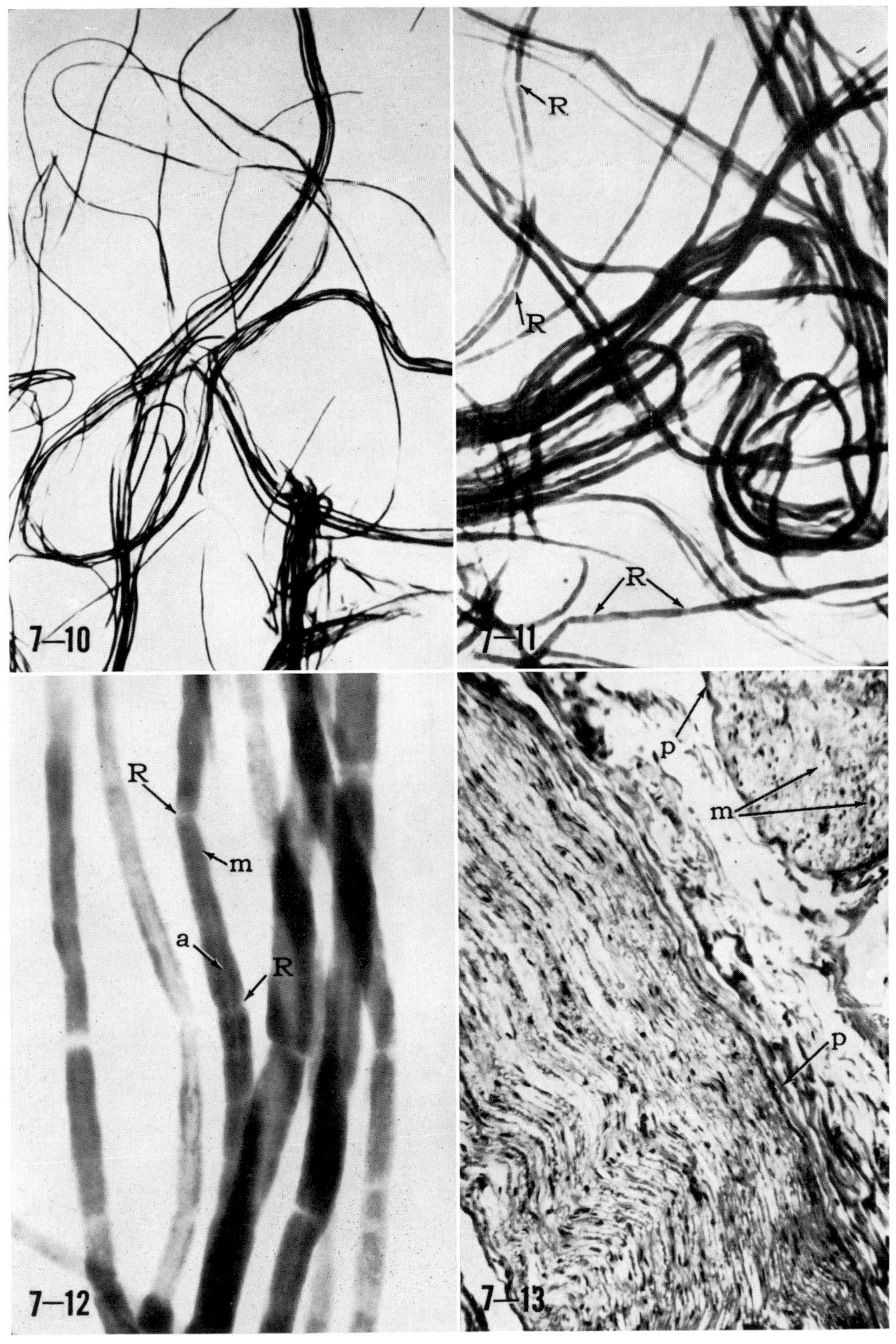
7–10
R
R
R
7–11
R
m
a
R
7–12
p
m
p
7–13

prevertebral or collateral ganglia) and parasympathetic ganglia (ciliary, otic, sphenopalatine and submandibular ganglia as well as ganglion cells located within the walls of hollow viscera such as **Auerbach's or myenteric and Meissner's or submucosal plexuses**).

With regard to function, the central nervous system can be considered to contain 2 types of nuclei and, therefore, 2 types of multipolar cells. The first type is known as an association nucleus; its contained multipolar neurons receive incoming impulses of a sensory nature and transmit these impulses or associate them with the next neuron in the nervous pathway. The second type of nucleus containing multipolar cell bodies is known as a **motor nucleus**. Activated multipolar neurons therein transmit impulses directly or indirectly (via another multipolar neuron) to a motor structure outside the C.N.S., such as a muscle or a gland.

C. THE NEURON—FINER STRUCTURE AND HISTOLOGY

According to the theory of one-way conductivity, impulses travel along certain processes of a neuron toward its cell body and, after arriving either in the cell body (in the case of bipolar and multipolar neurons) or in the vicinity of the cell body (in the case of monipolar neurons), travel along a single, usually thinner, process away from the perikaryon. The cell process which conveys impulses toward the cell body is known as the **dendron** or **dendrite**. The process which carries impulses away from the perikaryon is known as the **axon**.

In a multi-neuronal nervous pathway the terminations of an axon of one neuron come into a close physical relationship either with the dendrons or the cell body of the next neuron in the pathway. The region where these two neurons are in functional contact is known as the synapse; this has been the subject of many investigations. Until recent years, two major interpretations of the synapse existed. One was that the synapse represented a physical contact point and that impulses were directly transferred from neuron to adjacent neuron. The other view held that the synapse was not a contact point but rather an interneuronal space of dimensions beyond the resolving power of the light microscope and across which the impulse has to pass. On the basis of electron microscopic and neurophysiologic studies it is now established that the synapse is a narrow (0.02 μ) region bordered by the cell membrane of two adjacent neurons. This gap represents a barrier or obstacle which fleetingly slows down (synaptic delay) the passage of impulses along a nervous pathway. The barrier and adjacent membranes represent a region where bioelectric, biochemical and neurosecretory phases are

PLATE 44—Nerve Fibers

FIG. 7-14. High-power view of a portion of Figure 7-13. H & E stain. (S, nuclei of Schwann; a, axons; f, fibroblasts; n, neurilemma sheath)

FIG. 7-15. Longitudinal section of a nerve. Myelin has been dissolved out in this preparation, leaving the neurokeratin networks (nk) visible between the axon (a) and the neurilemma sheath (n). Acid fuchsin stain. High power. (R, node of Ranvier; S, nuclei of Schwann; f, fibroblast; e, endoneurium)

FIG. 7-16. Cross section of a nerve, showing component nerve bundles (rabbit). H & E stain. Intermediate power. (p, perineurium; ep, epineurium; v, blood vessel)

FIG. 7-17. Cross section of a nerve, showing component nerve bundles in the wall of the prostate (rabbit). Note the axons (a) with myelin spaces (m) containing neurokeratin and the neurilemma (n). Realize how a casual inspection of a section can result in confusing red blood cells for nerve fibers. H & E stain. High power. (p, perineurium; v, blood vessels; sm, smooth muscle cells)

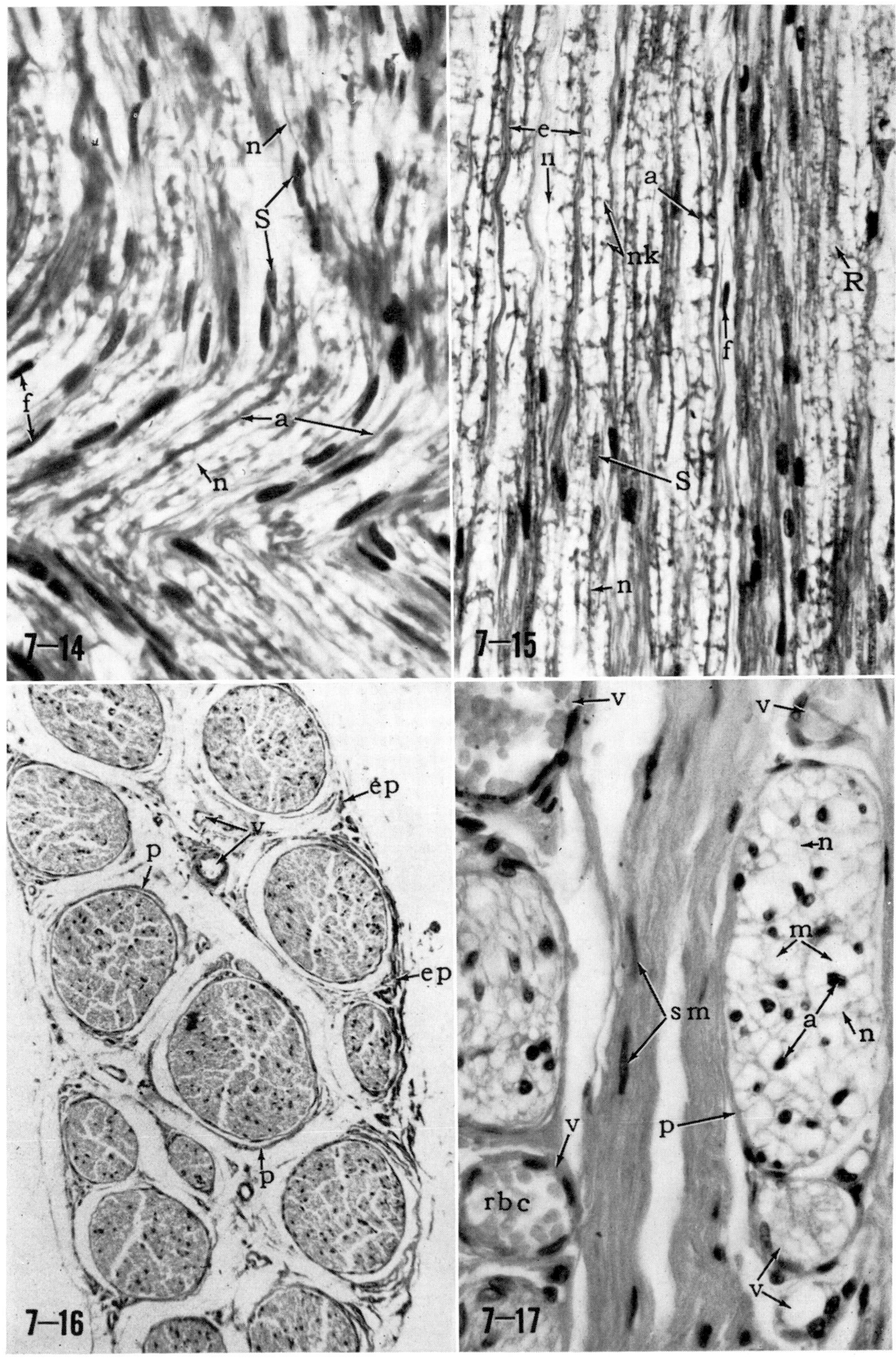
n
S
S
f
a
n
7–14
e
n
a
nk
R
f
S
n
7–15
ep
v
p
ep
p
7–16
v
v
n
m
sm
a
n
p
v
rbc
v
7–17

energized to permit electric polarization of the two membranes bordering the synaptic gap and enzymic degradation of material secreted by the axon terminal. The result is that the adjacent neuron becomes excited and an impulse is propagated.

Although, experimentally, impulses can be shown to be capable of coursing in both directions along an individual neuron, the polarization existing at the synapse permits transmission only from the axon to an adjacent dendron or cell body. It is this vital property of the synapse that provides the basis for the one-way conductivity of impulses in the normal function of nervous tissue.

1. The Nerve Cell Body

In many respects the nerve cell body resembles isolated cells found in other basic tissues.

a. It contains a **nucleus**, which is large and spherical in many multipolar and unipolar neurons, and possesses a distinct round, dark-staining **nucleolus**. A thick nuclear membrane, in conjunction with the distinct nucleolus located near the center of an abundant karyoplasm, gives to the nucleus a characteristic "fried egg" appearance. Because of the large size and the bold appearance of the nucleus in microscopic preparations, the beginning student frequently confuses the nucleus for the entire nerve cell body.

b. Surrounding the nucleus is a homogenous basophilic cytoplasm (**perikaryon**) in which many formed elements are suspended. In addition to mitochondria and Golgi vesicles, the neuroplasm contains a chromophilic substance, neurofibrils, and fat and pigment granules. The chromophilic substance in life tends to be dustlike, but after death it clumps together into large discrete granules known as **Nissl's substance** or **tigroid bodies**. Nissl's substance, a strongly basophilic material, is regularly present in cell bodies as well as in dendrons, but it is usually not found in axons. In pathologic processes involving nervous tissue, it is common for the Nissl's substance to become greatly reduced in quantity. This dissolution of Nissl's substance constitutes one of the 3 cardinal signs of **chromatolysis**, a cytologic syndrome of diseased neurons. The other two signs are **perikaryon swelling** (**hypertrophy**) and **displacement of the nucleus** to a peripheral position.

c. **Neurofibrils** are delicate filamentous strands coursing through the neuroplasm of the nerve cell body and its processes. These fibrils intertwine and form delicate networks that seem to be related, in a still undefined manner, to impulse transmission. Neurofibrils cannot be seen in ordinary stained preparations but require special methods, such as silver impregnation, for their demonstration.

d. **Pigment granules** also occur in the neuroplasm of nerve cell bodies. If pigment-containing neurons are present in large

PLATE 45—Motor and Sensory Nerve Endings

FIG. 7-18. Distribution of motor nerve endings in teased skeletal muscle preparation. Note the black nerve fibers (nf) superimposed on longitudinally oriented skeletal muscle fibers (sm). Silver impregnation. Low power.

FIG. 7-19. Intermediate-power magnification of a portion of Figure 7-18. Successive branching of nerve fibers is indicated by the arrows. Single nerve fibers from terminal branches lead to motor end plates (mp) on skeletal muscle fibers.

FIG. 7-20. High-power magnification of a portion of Figure 7-18, showing terminal branchings of a single nerve fiber and motor end plates (mp). Faint transverse striations in the muscle fibers can just be made out.

FIG. 7-21. Free sensory nerve endings in fetal skin of kitten. Note the nerve fibers in the deeper part of the dermis (d) giving off collaterals that pass toward the epidermis (ep). Silver impregnation. High power.

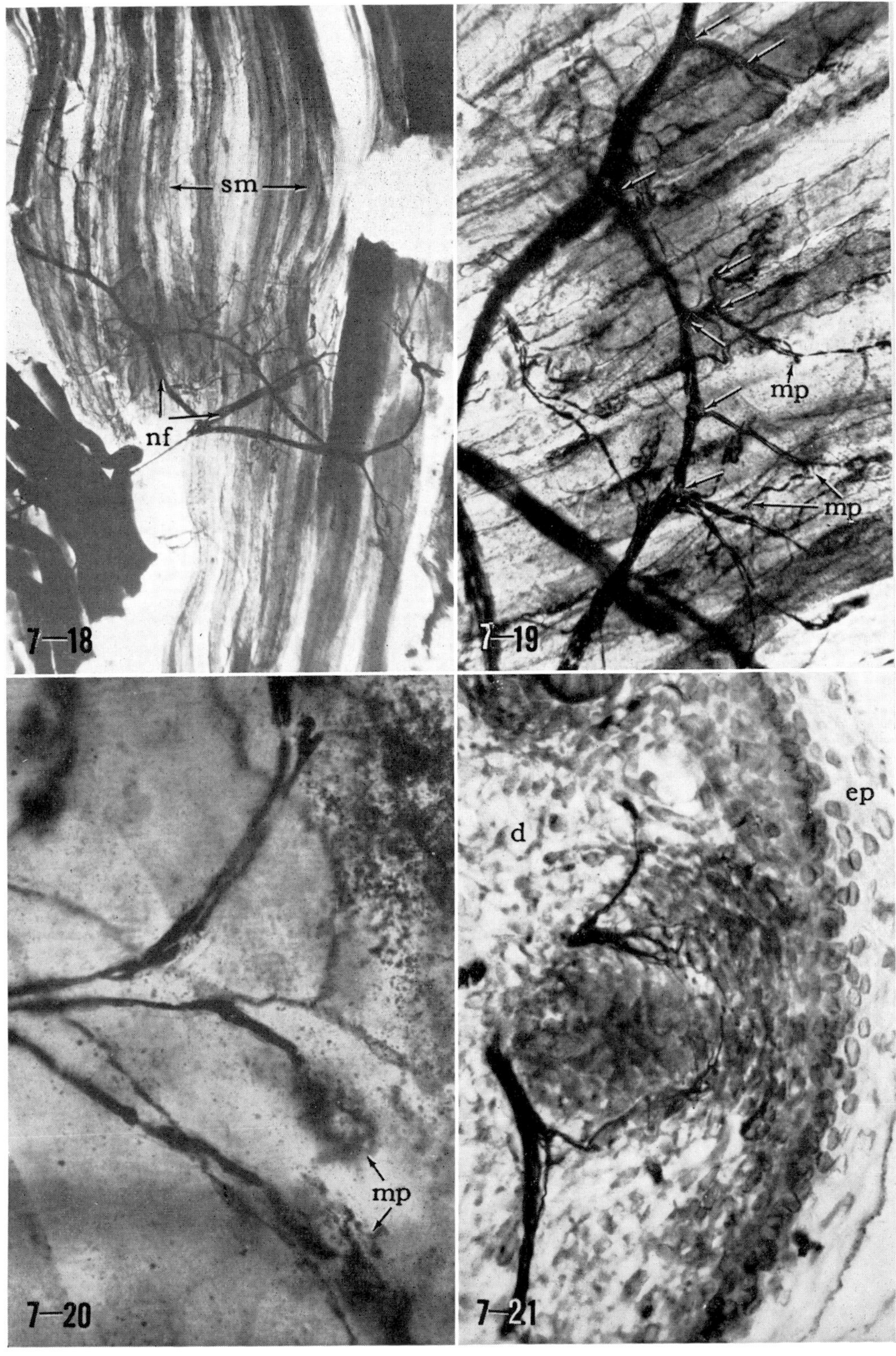
sm
nf
7—18
mp
mp
7—19
mp
7—20
d
ep
7—21

enough numbers, they can impart a characteristic color to that region. The two pigments that appear in greatest abundance in the nervous system are lipochrome and melanin. Lipochrome granules, yellow to brown in color, have a wide distribution and tend to be more common in larger monipolar and multipolar cell bodies. Lipochrome is apparently associated with the aging process, since it becomes more abundant with increasing age. Melanin, appearing as coarse, black granules in the neuroplasm, is much more restricted in its distribution than lipochrome.

2. Nerve Cell Processes (Fibers) (Plates 43 and 44)

The processes of nerve cell bodies, also known as **nerve fibers**, exist both within and outside the central nervous system. Although a minor histologic difference does exist between these central and peripheral fibers, basically they are similar in structure. The major distinction lies not in their histology but rather in the anatomic restriction of one type of process to the C.N.S. and the other to the peripheral nervous system.

Nerve fibers are characterized (1) by variations in thickness, (2) by the presence of tubular sheaths that begin very close to the nerve cell body, (3) by the appearance of periodic constrictions or **nodes of Ranvier** along their course, (4) by the fact that dendrites usually branch and arborize richly only near their termination and (5) by the presence at points of synapse of thorns (**spikes** or **gemmules**) on dendrites and of terminal swellings (**terminal buttons**) on axons.

Generally speaking, the thicker the fiber, the more rapidly can an impulse be transmitted along it. In the human, nerve cell processes range in thickness from 1 to 22 μ. Much of the fiber thickness, as will be discussed shortly, can be attributed to its myelin content.

Organs and dermatomes in the adult represent the final stage of development of blocks of embryonic material (**primary germinal rudiments and somites**). In the embryo these tiny primordia are locally innervated from the C.N.S. With the progressive growth of these structures, the basic pattern of innervation is retained. This sequence of events is the underlying explanation for the segmental arrangement of the adult peripheral nervous system. Each of the paired segmental structures is known as a nerve. **A nerve, therefore, consists of an accumulation of nerve cell fibers outside the central nervous system that serves a common area or structure**. Because all of the spinal nerves and most of the cranial nerves contain fibers which convey impulses related to both sensory and motor activities, it follows that these peripheral nerves are mixed and that the millions of fibers that they contain represent both functional dendrites and axons.

In contradistinction to what has just been described, accumulations of nerve cell fibers within the C.N.S. are called **tracts** rather than nerves. Tracts run up and down the spinal cord, the brain stem and the cerebrum

PLATE 46—Carotid Body

FIG. 7-22. Survey section of the carotid body. Groups of epithelioid cells can be seen as large black dots in a vascularized connective tissue stroma. H & E stain. Low power.

FIG. 7-23. Intermediate-power view of a section of the carotid body revealing its highly vascular nature (v). H & E stain. (e, polygonal epithelioid cells; ct, connective tissue stroma)

FIG. 7-24. High-power view of a section of the carotid body, demonstrating the granular nature of the cytoplasm of the polygonal epithelioid cells (e) and their relation to the surrounding sinusoids (s) and the connective tissue stroma (ct). H & E stain.

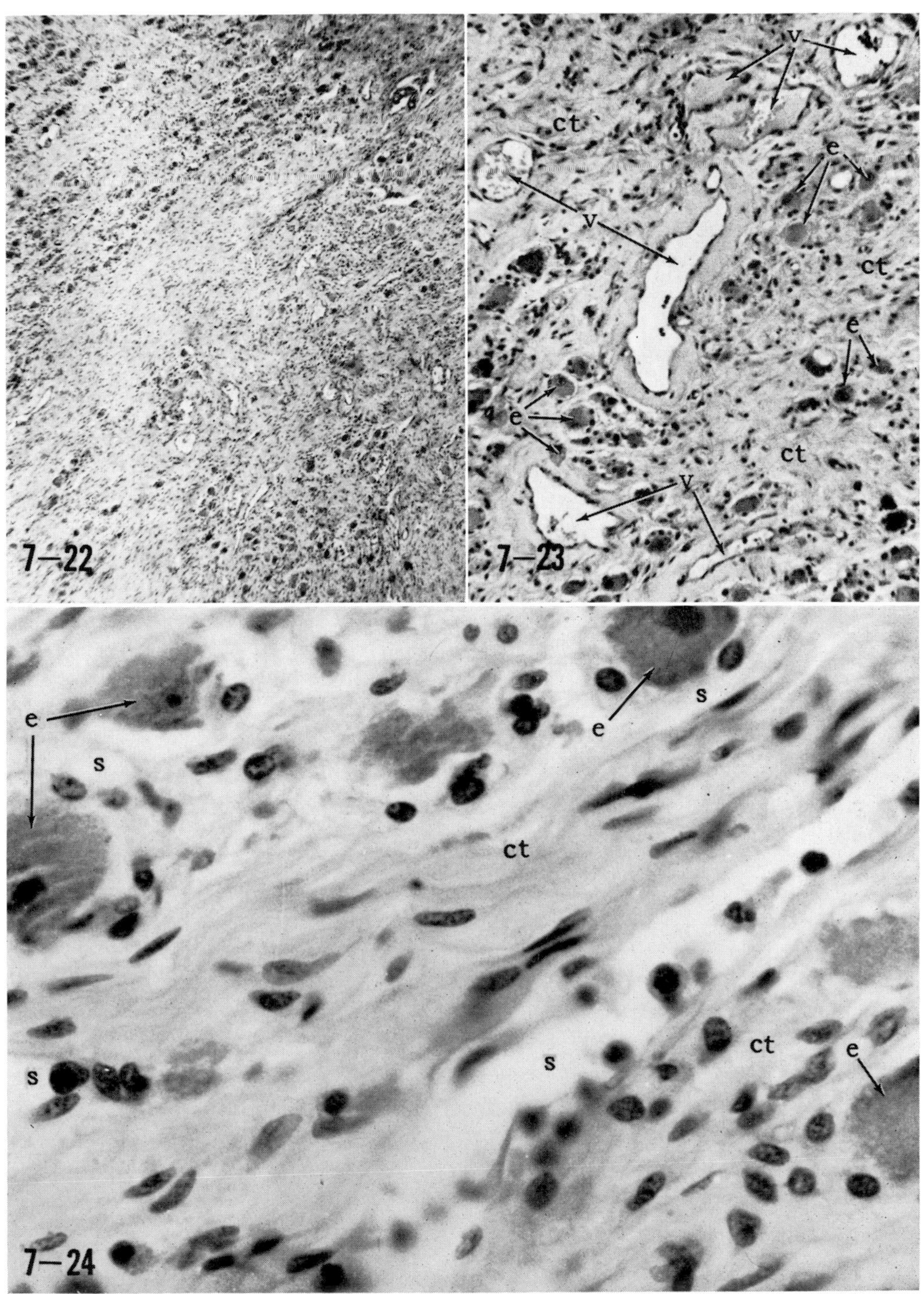

7–22
7–23
v
ct
e
v
ct
e
e
ct
v
7–24
e
s
e
s
ct
s
s
ct
e

and are composed almost entirely of axons.

Although the pattern, i.e., length, thickness and richness of branching, of each nerve cell process is quite variable, depending on neuron type and location, a few basic characteristics hold true for all. This consideration primarily concerns multipolar neuron processes because there are more of them. However, with slight modification it applies to the processes of monipolar and bipolar neurons as well.

In connection with multipolar neurons, all processes arising from the cell body except one are **dendrites**. The remaining fiber, the **axon**, arises from a slight conical elevation of the cell body. The elevation, or **axon hillock**, is probably created by the presence of large numbers of neurofibrils channeling into the axon from all parts of the perikaryon. The hillock is recognized microscopically by the fact that its neuroplasm is relatively clear, Nissl's substance being absent in this region. All processes rising from the nerve cell body are called **axis cylinders**.

Beginning very close to the nerve cell body, the neuroplasm of cell processes becomes invested with either one or two tubular sheaths. At least this is the traditional interpretation arrived at through light microscopy. The innermost sheath that surrounds most, if not all, nerve fibers, both in the peripheral and the central nervous systems, is known as the **myelin sheath**. Myelin is a lipoprotein material that is still thought of as an insulator. Differences in thickness of the myelin sheath and also of the axis cylinder account in great part for the variability of fiber size. The thickness of these elements is of basic importance to the rate of conduction of impulses. Nerve cell processes that possess a myelin sheath are referred to as **medullated** or **myelinated fibers** whereas those that lack any visible myelin are referred to as **nonmedullated, unmyelinated** and, sometimes, as **Remak's fibers**.

All nerve fibers in peripheral nerves, but none in central tracts, have a thin sheath, the **neurolemma** or **sheath of Schwann** that invests the myelin layer, if that is present. In the absence of a myelin layer, the neurolemma is in immediate contact with the axis cylinder. The neurolemma consists of a cellular sheath, the individual cells of which are called **Schwann cells**. The latter have a thin, tenuous cytoplasm that contains mitochondria and Golgi material, and their nuclei are flat and oval.

Based on electron micrographs of nerve cell processes, a new concept of the fiber has been superimposed on the traditional light microscope interpretation. It is widely believed now that Schwann cells are responsible for the formation of myelin and that

PLATE 47—Sensory Nerve Endings

FIG. 7-25. Pacinian corpuscle cut tangential to its longitudinal axis and present in the subcutaneous connective tissue. This is an example of the lamellated type of sensory ending and consists of a core (c) and a multilayered fibrous capsule (fc). H & E stain. Low power.

FIG. 7-26. Intermediate-power magnification of part of the pacinian corpuscle pictured in Figure 7-25. The central core (c) contains a nerve fiber, devoid of myelin, which terminates in a knoblike swelling (s). Note the granular appearance of the central core.

FIG. 7-27. High-power magnification of part of Figure 7-26. The fibrous capsule consists of numerous, thin connective tissue lamellae (fl) separated by clear lymphatic spaces (ls). Note the complex organization of the knoblike termination (s) of the nerve fiber.

FIG. 7-28. Cross-sectional appearance of a pacinian corpuscle located within the connective tissue of the pancreas. H & E stain. Intermediate power. (c, core; fc, fibrous capsule; at, acinar tissue of the pancreas)

FIG. 7-29. A portion of the pacinian corpuscle of Figure 7-28 shown at high-power magnification.

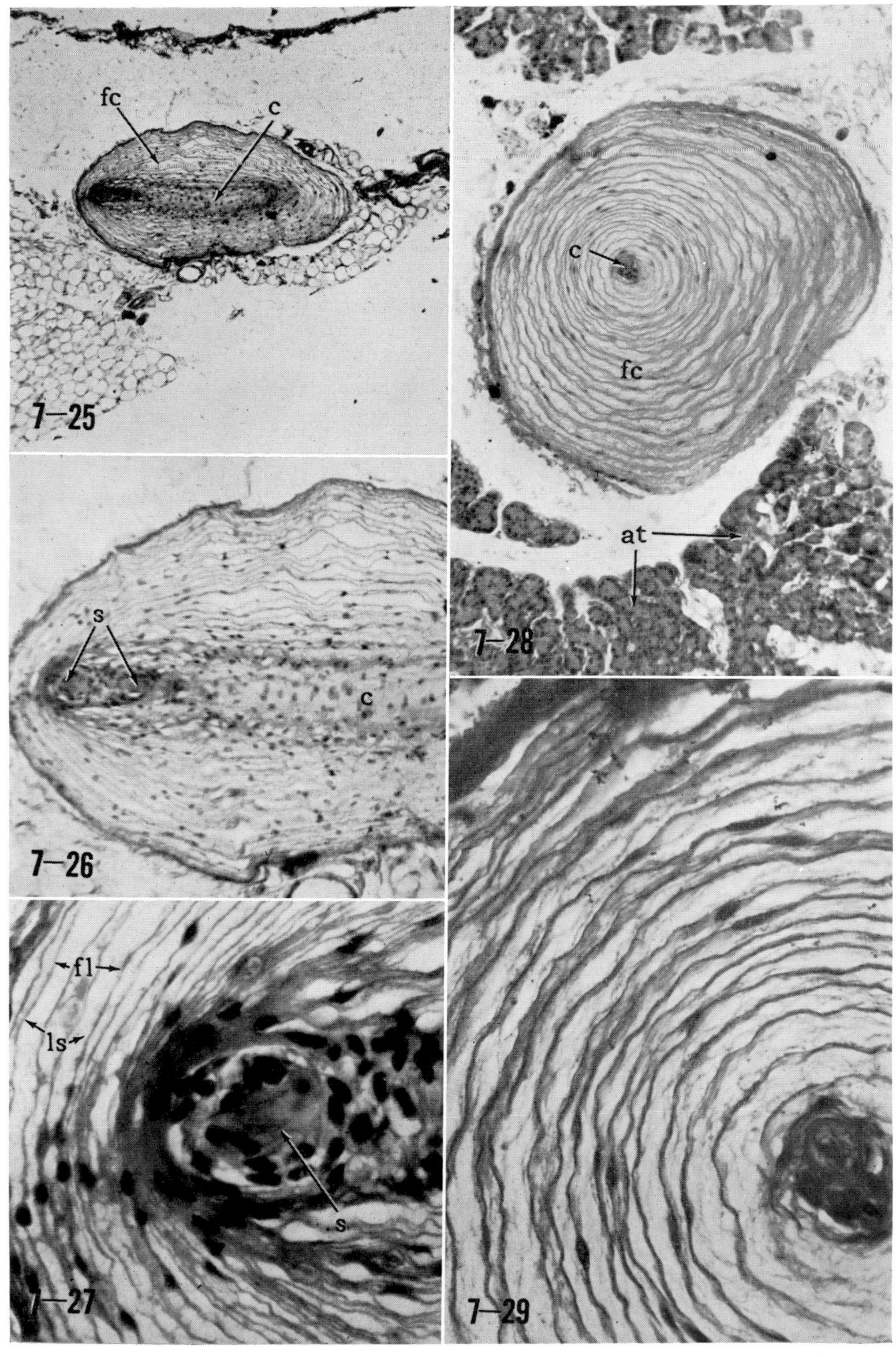
fc
c
7-25
c
fc
at
7-28
s
c
7-26
fl
ls
s
7-27
7-29

the myelin sheath is merely an elaboration of the cytoplasm of neurolemmal cells. This elaboration is in the form of a continuous spiral membrane around the fiber's neuroplasmic core. If this view is fully substantiated, it would be difficult for the beginner to conceive of the myelin sheath as being formed by Schwann cells orbiting around the neuroplasmic core of a fiber unless an analogy were given. If the student can see the similarity between this concept and its electrical counterpart, the problem is resolved at once. A noninsulated conducting wire should be visualized passing through the center of a coil of tightly wound wire. If, now, an electric current is suddenly passed through the single core wire, an electric field will be induced around the coil, and a flow of electrons will move in it in a counterclockwise direction. In terms of the developing nervous system, impulses commence to be transmitted along the neuroplasmic cores of most fibers before a myelin sheath has been laid down. It is possible that at certain critical stages of fetal and postpartal development of the nervous system, impulses traveling along these neuroplasmic cores induce transient bioelectric fields to form around them. These fields might, in a sense, polarize the Schwann cells so that elaboration of myelin would occur in a spiral fashion, just as a current was induced to flow in the wire coil. If the origin of myelin in peripheral nerve cell processes is so intimately associated with the neurolemma, it is also conceivable that on the submicroscopic level there is no such thing as a completely unmyelinated fiber.

Myelin is often present around the axis cylinders of fibers found in the central nervous system. However, in this location, Schwann cells and their associated neurolemmal sheaths are absent. Just how myelin is formed here is not fully understood. It is believed that one of the supporting elements (neuroglia; see later), possibly the oligodendroglial cell, may serve in this role.

Myelin and neurolemmal sheaths around peripheral nerve cell processes begin close to the spinal cord or the brain and are present almost to the end of the fibers. Usually the myelin sheath terminates abruptly, close to the motor or the sensory ending of a particular cell process. From this point on, the neuroplasm, usually covered by neurolemma, extends to its specialized nerve ending.

The myelin sheath is not a continuous tube around the neuroplasm as is the sheath

PLATE 48—Sensory Nerve Endings and Neuroglia

FIG. 7-30. Section of the integument to demonstrate the presence of two tactile (Meissner's) corpuscles (M). Note that these encapsulated endings somewhat resemble the shape of elongated turbans and that they are present within the dermal papillae (dp). H & E stain. Intermediate power.

FIG. 7-31. High-power view of Meissner's corpuscle shown in the left half of Figure 7-30.

FIG. 7-32. Neuroglia from white matter of the cerebrum. This preparation demonstrates only the nuclei. The group of three cells includes an oligodendrocyte (o) and two astrocytes (fa), probably of the fibrous variety. H & E stain. Oil immersion.

FIG. 7-33. Two groups of neuroglial cells present as satellite cells in the cerebral cortex. The 2 cells in relation to the neuron (nc) in the upper left corner are probably small protoplasmic astrocytes (pa) whereas the group of 4 glial cells around the other neuron are all oligodendrocytes (o). H & E stain. Oil immersion.

FIG. 7-34. A large nerve cell (nc) of the cerebral cortex showing 2 related oligodendrocytes (o). H & E stain. Oil immersion.

FIG. 7-35. Perivascular neuroglia in the cerebral cortex. The 2 neuroglial cells related to the capillary are an oligodendrocyte (o) and a microglial cell (m). Also note the protoplasmic astrocyte (pa) in the lower part of the field. H & E stain. Oil immersion. (en, endothelial cell nucleus)

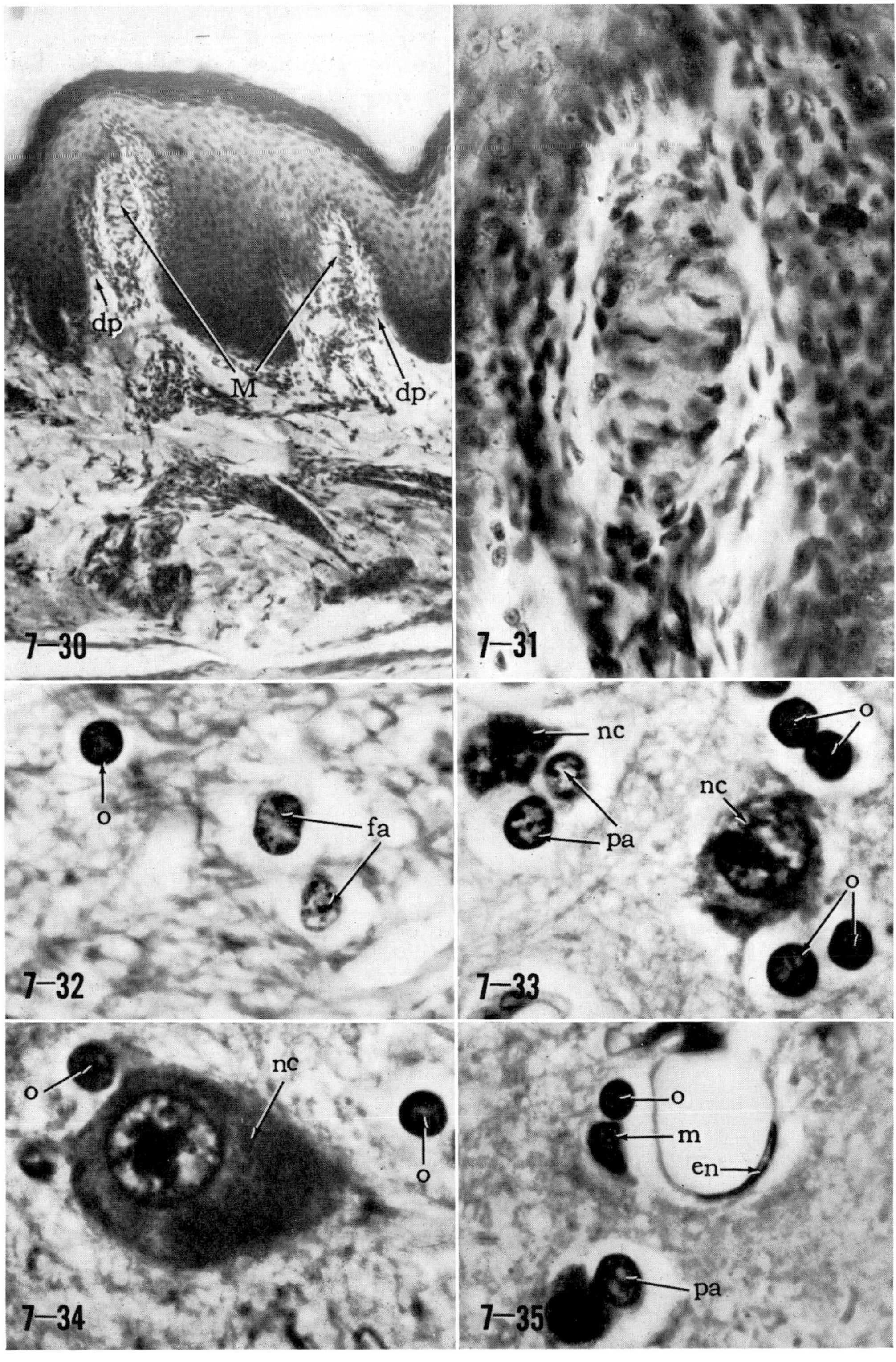
dp
M
dp
7–30
7–31
o
fa
7–32
nc
o
pa
nc
pa
o
7–33
nc
o
o
7–34
o
m
en
pa
7–35

of Schwann. For, beginning close to its origin, the myelin becomes periodically squeezed off against the neuroplasmic core. These constrictions or **nodes of Ranvier** represent circular regions of discontinuity or interruption in the myelin, so that the myelin sheath can be more realistically likened to a string of elongated beads rather than to a tube. In addition, the myelin is interrupted by clefts known as the incisures of Schmidt-Lantermann. The nodes are more closely spaced toward the peripheral termination of a nerve fiber and are further apart near the perikaryon. The region or segment of the nerve fiber between any two successive nodes of Ranvier is referred to as an internode. Internodes are from 0.05 to 1 mm. in length, the shorter ones being further away from the nerve cell body. Each internode is associated with a single Schwann cell. Despite the absence of a neurolemma around nerve fibers within the central nervous system, nodes of Ranvier and internodes are present.

Nodes of Ranvier must be of great importance for normal neuronal function. At these points of interruption in the myelin sheath the neurolemma dips down into a space that elsewhere is occupied by myelin and thus contacts the neuroplasmic core. Special features that demonstrate the basic importance of nodes of Ranvier are: (1) collateral branches of myelinated nerve cell processes arise only at nodes, and (2) in cases where regeneration of a damaged nerve fiber can take place, the dissolution of myelin that invariably occurs following the injury is stopped along the fiber at a node of Ranvier.

Spinal nerves and most cranial nerves are surrounded by a substantial covering of connective tissue made up primarily of collagen fibers. Since the connective tissue lies on the external surface of the nerve, it is referred to as the **epineurium**. Each nerve is composed in turn of smaller groups of neuron processes which are known as **nerve fascicles** or **bundles**. Extensions of epineurial connective tissue pass inwardly to surround each of the fascicles with a distinctly thinner fibrous layer known as the **perineurium**. Finally, from the perineurium, strands of delicate collagen fibers pass into each fascicle and come into relationship with most of the individual fibers, lying immediately adjacent to the neurolemma. This partial connective tissue covering of the discrete axons or dendrites is referred to as the **endoneurium**.

D. ENDINGS OF NERVE CELL PROCESSES

This section applies only to the peripheral nervous system whose component axons and

PLATE 49—Spinal Cord

FIG. 7-36. Half of central gray substance and surrounding white matter of the spinal cord. Note that the central gray contains nerve cell bodies (n). The pale appearance of the white matter is due to the dissolving of the myelin sheaths by the histologic reagents used. H & E stain. Low power. (dg, dorsal horn of central gray; vg, ventral horn of central gray; pw, peripheral white matter)

FIG. 7-37. A portion of the ventral horn of central gray of the spinal cord. Notice the varying appearances of the nerve cells (n). H & E stain. Intermediate power.

FIG. 7-38. Appearance of central gray (g) and bordering white matter (pw) of a section of spinal cord stained for myelin sheaths. Two nerve cells (n) containing poorly defined Nissl material can be made out. Observe the myelinated nerve fibers (f) in the longitudinal strip at the right side of the figure. Weil stain. High power.

FIG. 7-39. Appearance of two motor neurons in the central gray matter of the ventral horn of the spinal cord. Note that the Nissl material (N) in these cells is coarse and that the cell on top exhibits a characteristic large nucleus. Observe that the nucleus contains a nucleolus. Luxol fast stain. High power.

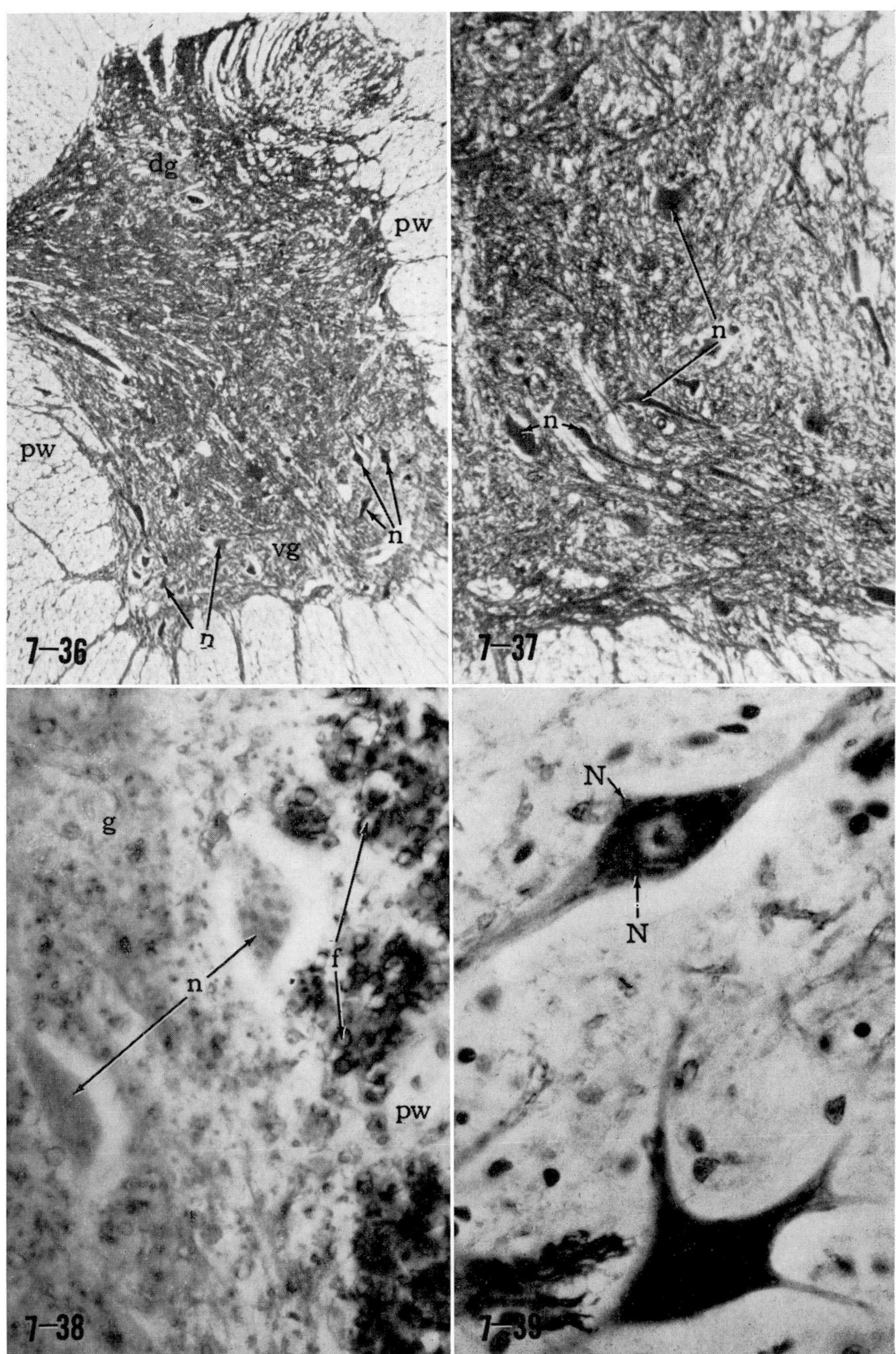
dg
pw
pw
n
n
vg
n
7–36
n
n
n
7–37
g
f
n
pw
7–38
N
N
7–39

dendrites either bring about a change in or, conversely, are excited by a change in the state of activity of a non-nervous structure. The peripheral structures primarily involved are skin, connective tissue, skeletal muscle and viscera. Nerve endings in these structures will be emphasized, since they are present in greater numbers and have a very wide distribution. However, it should be kept in mind that other nerve endings, more specialized in nature, exist in restricted locations and play an important role in relating man to his environment. Among this group are included the rods and the cones related to vision, taste buds sensitive to gustatory stimuli, the specialized hair cells in the organ of Corti that respond to sound, hair cells in the semicircular canals, saccule and utricle that react to movement and static position of the head, special endings in the aortic body, the carotid body and the carotid sinus that respond to alterations in blood pressure, and terminals in the heart that alter the rate of contraction of cardiac muscle.

A **nerve ending** is the specialized termination of a neuron cell process where the latter comes into structural and functional relationship with a peripheral, non-nervous structure. It represents the homologue of a synapse that links any two successive neurons in a nervous pathway. Depending on structural complexity, nerve endings are designated as **free** or **encapsulated**. The **free nerve ending** consists merely of a neuroplasmic core covered usually by its neurolemma. An **encapsulated nerve ending**, on the other hand, combines the fiber terminal with connective tissue elements into a complex, 3-dimensional structure that gives it special properties.

Near the termination of a nerve fiber, the fiber ordinarily loses its myelin sheath, if such is present, and undergoes a multiple branching. A single neuron process may have several or many nerve endings. The various types of endings will now be considered.

1. Motor Nerve Endings (Effector Endings) (Figs. 7-18 to 7-20)

Motor nerves primarily activate smooth muscle, glandular epithelium and skeletal muscle. These endings of the axonic nerve cell processes all are of the "free" variety. In the case of smooth muscle and glands, the terminals are believed to be of two types, **terminal nets** and **end swellings**. In the **terminal net type**, more commonly associated with smooth muscle, neuroplasmic cores of axons (**axoplasm**), covered by neurolemma, ramify on the external surface of the motor structures. In the terminal swelling type of ending, associated both with gland and

PLATE 50—Cerebral Cortex

FIG. 7-40. Survey section of cerebral cortex, showing how the cortical material follows the contours of a sulcus (s). The presence of large numbers of nerve cell bodies gives the section a black stippled appearance. Note the distribution of blood vessels (v). H & E stain. Low power. (m, molecular layer; eg, external ganglionic layer)

FIG. 7-41. Survey section of a deeper portion of the cerebral cortex (c) overlying the adjacent medulla (m). Note the high degree of vascularity (v). Nissl stain. Low power.

FIG. 7-42. Survey section of the cerebral cortex, showing isolated nerve cells (nc) and fibers (f) along with blood vessels (v). The Golgi method of staining used in this preparation results in black deposits of reduced silver salts in and around some of the nerve cells, their processes and neuroglia. The broad black band across the upper border of the figure is normal and due to the precipitation which occurs on the surface of the block, blood vessels and connective tissue fibers. Low power.

FIG. 7-43. Cerebral cortex showing nerve cells (nc). The very small, less dense cells distributed throughout the section are neuroglial elements. Nissl stain. Intermediate power.

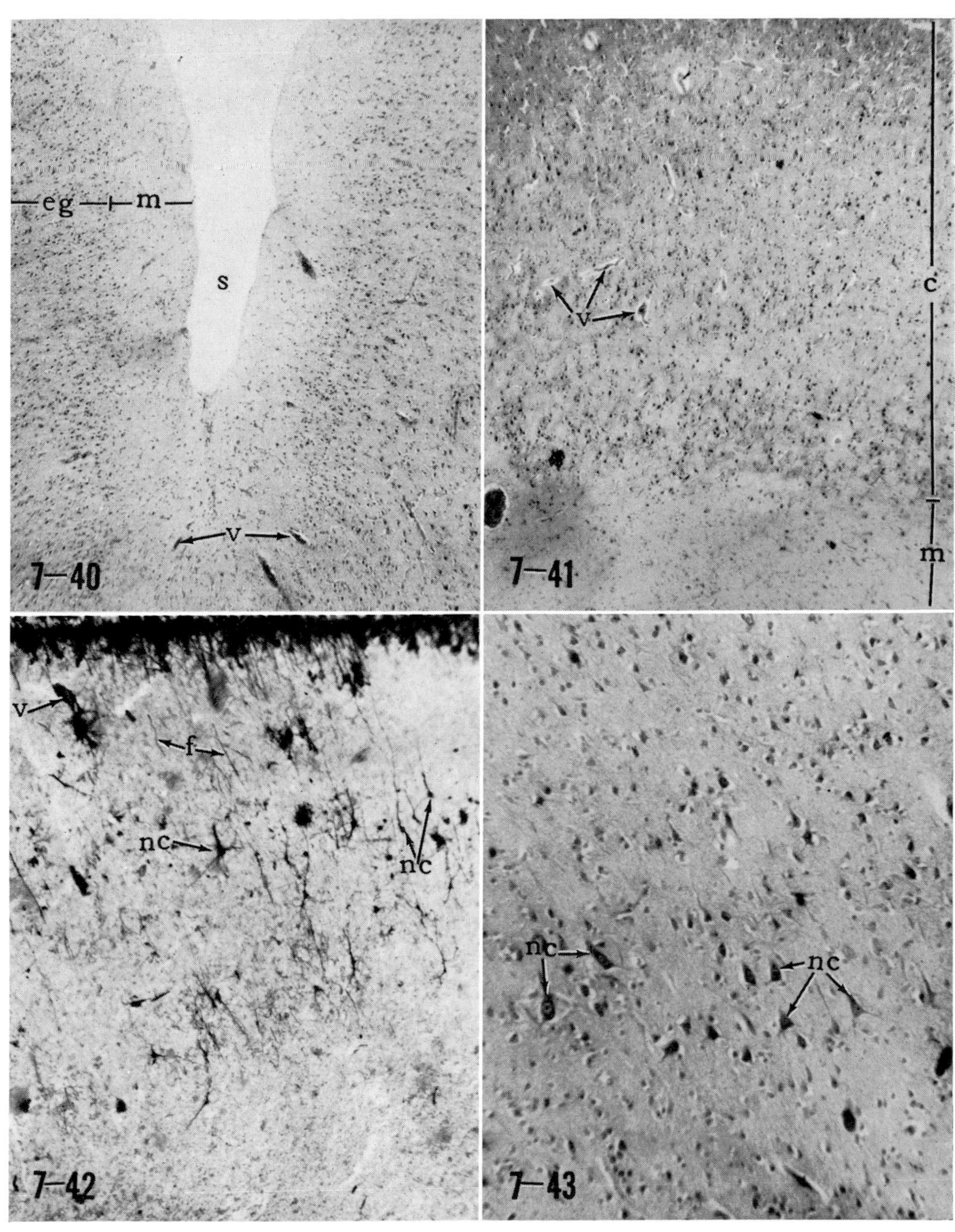
eg
m
s
v
7–40
c
v
m
7–41
v
f
nc
nc
7–42
nc
nc
7–43

smooth muscle cells, nerve endings from a single fiber demonstrate knoblike terminals. The **end knobs** or **swellings** rest on the surface of gland cells or smooth muscle fibers and bring about changes in the activity of the effector structures.

Nerve endings on skeletal muscle have been the subject of intensive investigations for many years, but their ultimate structure is still not completely known. Currently it is believed that these endings, known as **motor end plates**, which have a shape like that of "crows feet," consist of naked bars of axoplasmic material which fit, dovetail fashion, into grooves existing on the external surface of the sarcolemma of a muscle fiber. Relative to the sarcolemma, motor end plates are epilemmal in position.

The axons of motor neuron processes that innervate skeletal muscle are all myelinated. Near the end of the axon sequential branches are given off at the nodes of Ranvier. Each of these branches loses its myelin covering and passes to a different muscle fiber. The terminal branch arrives at the surface of the muscle fiber at a region that lacks transverse striations and displays here a moundlike elevation of special sarcoplasm, the **sole plate**. In this region of the sarcoplasm, nuclei and mitochondria are more abundant than elsewhere. Similarly, mitochondria in the nerve end plate axoplasm are more numerous than anywhere else along the nerve cell process. As with the synapse, a narrow gap exists here between neuroplasm and sarcoplasm, and it is this "barrier" which must be passed before the muscle fiber can contract.

2. Sensory Nerve Endings (Receptor Endings) (Figs. 7-21 to 7-24)

These endings are associated with the peripheral, functional origins of dendritic processes of sensory neurons. In contrast with motor endings, which are entirely of the free variety, sensory endings exhibit a wide range of complexity, and both free and encapsulated end organs can be identified.

a. The simplest sensory endings consist of isolated processes, devoid of myelin, which insinuate themselves between and around epithelial cells and connective tissue fibers. Such a free type of ending has, embryologically, a very rudimentary organization. It is perhaps not surprising, therefore, that sensory endings having the simplest structure, yet widest distribution, should be associated with two of the less sophisticated sensory modalities. These modalities, the subjective expressions (**sensations**) of which are **pain** and **light touch**, very early became indispensable elements in rapid, reflex responses that could mean the difference between life and death. In lower forms of life existing today, as well as in phylogenetically earlier forms of life, a cerebral cortex capable of interpreting environmental changes is absent. Such organisms cannot think or voluntarily initiate any activity. All they can do is respond reflexly in a characteristic fashion to any single stimulus. It is as if the stimulus acts like the trigger on a revolver. Once the trigger has been pulled, a series of events, in proper sequence, takes place and results in a motor activity that usually has a protective quality.

PLATE 51—Cerebral Cortex and Medulla

FIG. 7-44. Intermediate-power view, showing some of the cells of the cerebral cortex from a portion of Figure 7-42. (a, network of terminal branches of afferent fibers; p, large and small pyramidal cells; as, astrocyte; nc, nerve cell)

FIG. 7-45. Nerve cells (nc) and neuroglia (ng) of the cerebral cortex. H & E stain. High power.

FIG. 7-46. Two large pyramidal cells of the cerebral cortex. Golgi stain. High power.

FIG. 7-47. White matter of the cerebrum, demonstrating the abundance of myelinated fibers. H & E stain. Intermediate power.

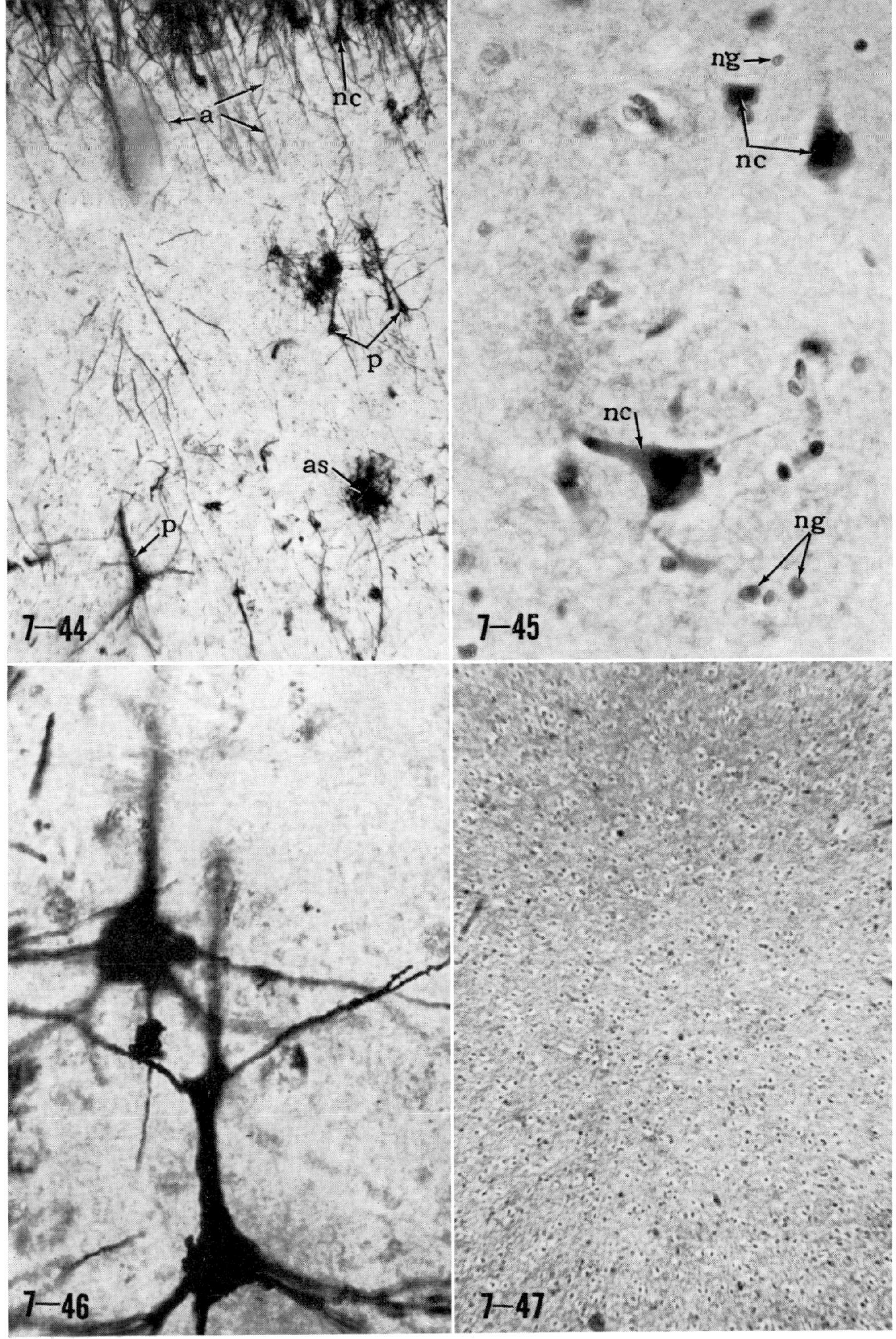
nc
a
p
as
p
7–44
ng
nc
nc
ng
7–45
7–46
7–47

Free sensory endings that respond to painful stimuli are mainly concentrated near the external surface of the body. They are especially numerous in the connective tissue and the epithelial layers of the skin. Pain endings are associated with unmyelinated or poorly myelinated dendritic processes.

b. Connective tissue elements are combined with the terminations of sensory nerve fibers into special endings that exhibit unusual shapes. These sensory apparatus are located in the dermis and the subcutaneous tissues, deep to mucous membranes, within the walls of certain viscera, within mesenteries and in the cornea and the conjunctiva of the eye. Included in this group of endings are the coiled **Meissner's corpuscles** that are activated by tactile stimuli, the **lamellated pacinian, genital** and **Golgi-Mazzoni corpuscles** which all respond to pressure, the tangled **end bulbs of Krause** that are stimulated by cold and the **neuromuscular spindles** and **neurotendinal organs of Golgi** which both respond to changes in tension. (See Figs. 7-25 to 7-31.)

E. NEUROGLIA (GLIA) (Figs. 7-32 to 7-35)

Scattered throughout the nervous system are found tiny cellular elements, non-neuronal in nature, which traditionally are regarded as functioning to support and bind together the nervous tissue. Collectively these cells constitute the **neuroglia** (Gr., nerve glue). More recent findings suggest functions for neuroglia that are quite dynamic. Thus, limited evidence indicates that neuroglia elaborate amino-oxidase, an enzyme that is active in neuroglial metabolism and also may be related to myelin formation. In addition, it is possible that certain neuroglial cells may enter into a type of synapse with neurons.

Three major types of neuroglial cells exist. Two of these (**astrocytes** and **oligodendrocytes**) are often considered together as the **macroglia** and have the same embryologic origin in ectoderm that neurons have. The third type, smaller than the others, is termed **microglia** and has its origin in mesoderm. The macroglia often line up around nerve cell bodies or fibers, in which locations they are referred to as **satellite cells** or **capsular cells** (amphicytes).

Neuroglial cells are difficult to demonstrate adequately by routine histologic methods. In ordinary preparations, only the nuclei stain in these small cells. Special stains employing metal impregnation (Golgi methods) demonstrate that a cytoplasm is present, that it varies in amount according to the neurog-

PLATE 52—Cerebellum

FIG. 7-48. Section through folia of cerebellum, showing the core of white matter (wm) and the outer cortex of gray matter (c). Note that the cortex consists of an outer molecular layer (m), an intermediate layer consisting of a single row of Purkinje cells (P) and an inner granular layer (g). H & E stain. Low power. (s, interfolia sulci)

FIG. 7-49. Intermediate-power view of a portion of Figure 7-48. The white matter (wm) consists mainly of myelinated fibers. The outer molecular layer (m) contains few scattered cells and the dendrites (d) of the cells of Purkinje (P), whereas the granular layer (g) is composed primarily of densely packed small cells. H & E stain.

FIG. 7-50. High-power view of a portion of Figure 7-48 especially to show the flask-shaped nature of the Purkinje cells (P). Note the dendrites (d) entering the molecular layer. The densely packed nuclei of nerve cells in the granular layer (g) are evident.

FIG. 7-51. Contrasting fiber-stained section of a region of the cerebellar cortex similar to that shown in Figure 7-50. Note that the molecular layer (m) contains parallel strata of nerve fibers running at right angles to the dendrites (d) of the Purkinje cells (P). Gross-Bielschowsky stain. High power. (g, granular layer; v, vessel)

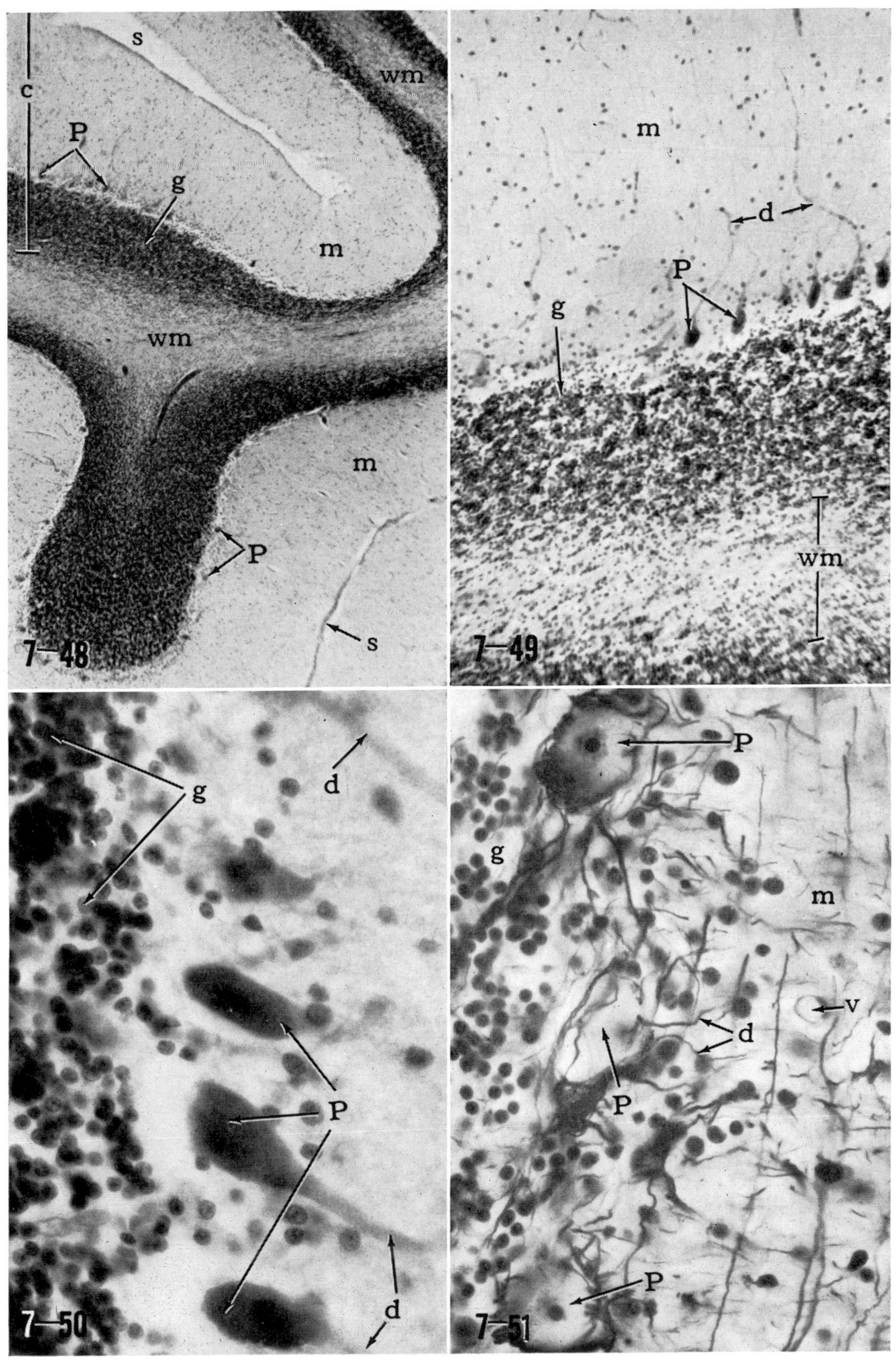
s
wm
c
P
g
m
wm
m
P
s
7—48
m
d
P
g
wm
7—49
g
d
P
d
7—50
P
g
m
v
d
P
P
7—51

lial type and that from it originate a varying number of short or long protoplasmic streamers or processes.

1. Astrocytes (Astroglia, Spider Cells)

These have a large number of cytoplasmic streamers which may be delicate and contain fibers (**fibrous astrocyte**) or may be thick and contain no fibers (**protoplasmic astrocyte**). The astrocytic nucleus is the largest in the glial series, is oval to spherical in shape, takes a very weak basophilic stain and contains rather little chromatin material. Both types of astrocytes contain a granular cytoplasm. In addition, fibrous and protoplasmic astrocytes both contain at least one perivascular foot (**pedicle**), a special cytoplasmic process that attaches the cell to an adjacent blood vessel.

Although these cells are found in both gray and white matter, the protoplasmic type is restricted almost entirely to central gray, whereas the fibrous variety is most abundant in white matter. Suggested astrocyte functions include (1) a system of cells that by means of processes and perivascular feet holds nervous tissue together; (2) a possible relationship with the elaboration of myelin and (3) a cell system that by means of its perivascular fat acts as a barrier (part of the blood-brain barrier) between blood and nervous tissue of the brain and the spinal cord.

2. Oligodendrocytes (Oligodendroglia)

These cells, when specifically stained for, appear to be slightly smaller, to contain less cytoplasm and to have fewer, shorter and more delicate cytoplasmic streamers than astrocytes. Their nuclei are perhaps the most characteristic feature in ordinary slide preparations, since they are rounder, smaller, richer in chromatin and, hence, more basophilic in staining than astrocyte nuclei.

Oligodendrocytes are often located closer to nerve cell bodies in gray matter and to fibers in white matter than are astrocytes. In the former location they are referred to as satellites because groups of them may form a loose investment around perikarya. In the latter location, they are referred to as the interfascicular type, since they tend to line up in rows along the surfaces of adjacent nerve fibers. It is widely believed that within the central nervous system oligodendrocytes may perform the same role in the formation of myelin that Schwann cells perform in the peripheral nerves.

3. Microglia

Microglia, the smallest of the neuroglia, are derived from mesoderm, probably by migration from septa of pia mater that penetrate the central nervous system. Less cytoplasm and fewer processes are present than in other neuroglial cell types. The most obvious feature of microglia in routine his-

PLATE 53—Meninges and Choroid Plexus

FIG. 7-52. Survey section of the dorsomedial sulcus region of the lumbar spinal cord demonstrating the pia-arachnoid coverings. Luxol fast blue & eosin stain. Low power. (p, pia mater; ss, subarachnoid space; a, arachnoid mater)

FIG. 7-53. Survey section of the choroid plexus of the 4th ventricle. Note the highly folded and vascular nature of this embryonic-appearing tissue, the tela choroidea. H & E stain. Low power.

FIG. 7-54. Portion of the choroid plexus of the 4th ventricle, showing the folds of the tela choroidea (tc) invaginating into the ventricle. Also note the highly vascular nature (v) of this tissue. H & E stain. Intermediate power.

FIG. 7-55. High-power view of a portion of the choroid plexus of the 4th ventricle, revealing the non-neural ependymal lining (e) of a few folds of the tela choroidea. H & E stain. (v, blood vessels; ct, connective tissue)

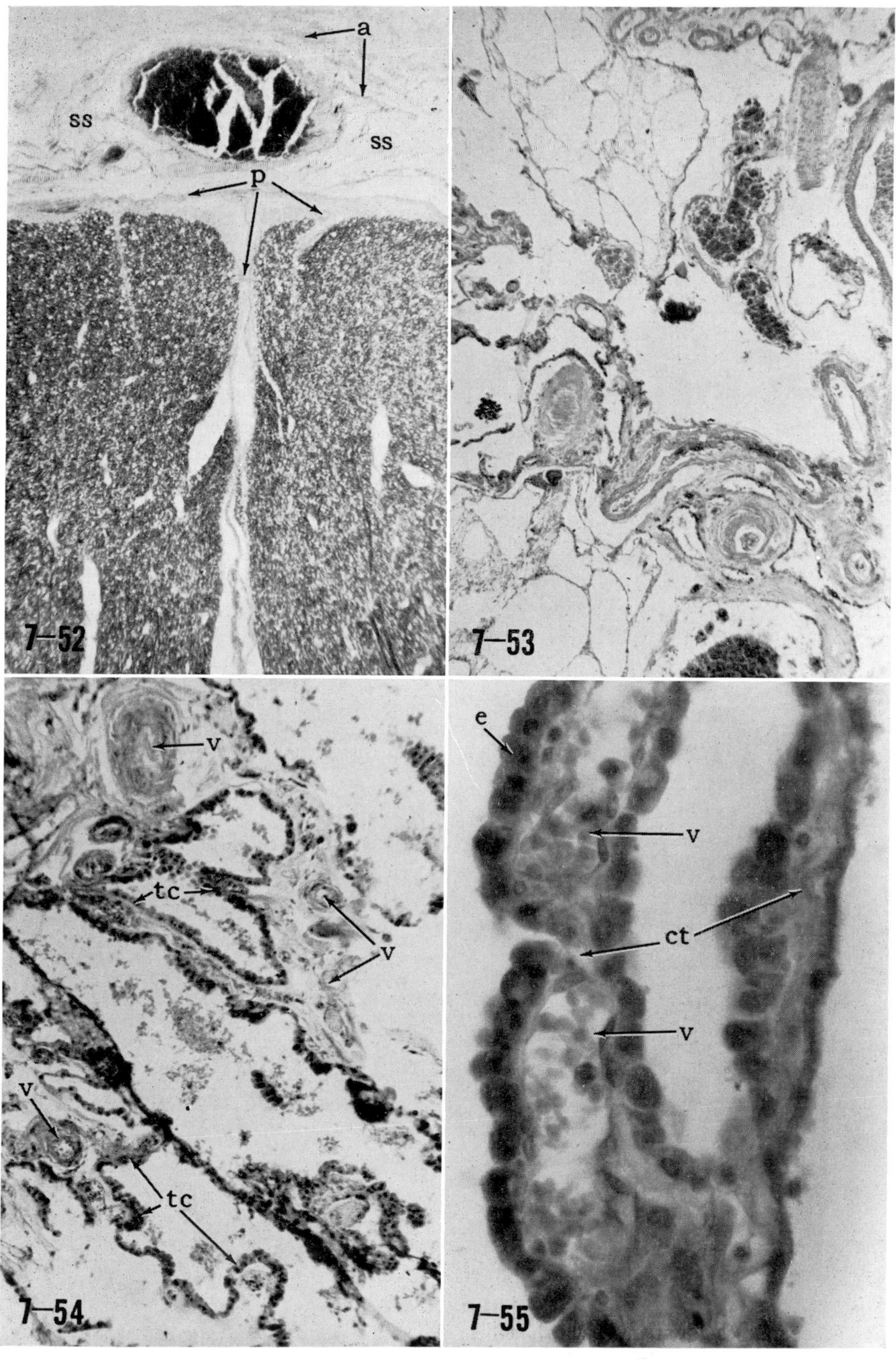
a
ss
ss
p
7–52
7–53
v
tc
v
v
tc
7–54
e
v
ct
v
7–55

tologic preparations is a densely staining, elongated nucleus.

Functionally, microglia represent the scavenger cells of the central nervous system. Under certain conditions they can be demonstrated to round up and ingest foreign material.

F. MICROSCOPIC STRUCTURE OF SOME PARTS OF THE NERVOUS SYSTEM

1. Spinal Cord (Plate 49)

The spinal cord is a cylindrical nervous structure lying loosely in the vertebral canal. Cross sections reveal a centrally placed zone, the **gray matter**, surrounded by a mantle of **white matter**.

The gray matter has roughly the form of the letter H and consists of dense groupings of nerve cell bodies, numerous unmyelinated nerve fibers, dendrites and a rich capillary blood supply. Very few myelinated fibers are present. The main support of these nervous elements is provided by neuroglial tissue. The upper halves of the vertical bars of the H configuration of the gray matter constitute the **posterior (dorsal) columns (horns)**, while the lower halves are known as the **anterior (ventral) columns**. In each half, a middle zone constitutes the **intermediate columns** with the connecting transverse bar across the midline being designated as the **gray commissure**. This commissure is divided into anterior and posterior gray commissures by the **central canal** which lies in the axis of the spinal cord. The central canal represents the cavity of the neural tube and is lined by ependymal cells (columnar cells) surrounded by a light granular area of neuroglia. The concavity on each lateral surface of the central gray matter is filled with a network of fine bundles of longitudinally running gray fibers. This, the **reticular formation**, is especially evident at cervical levels. At various levels of the spinal cord (cervical, thoracic, lumbar or sacral), the gray columns vary in shape and constitution.

The white matter of the cord covers the central gray columns. It is composed mainly of longitudinally running, myelinated nerve fibers held together by a feltwork of neuroglial fibers. Blood vessels are distributed throughout the white matter. The long-running myelinated fibers of the white matter are grouped into 3 major pairs of bundles or **funiculi**, the **anterior**, the **lateral** and the **posterior**. Each funiculus, in turn, contains smaller bundles of nerve fibers called **fasciculi**. At 32 levels of the cord, nerve fibers enter and leave via the spinal nerves.

2. Cerebral Cortex (Plates 50 and 51)

The cerebral cortex is a thin mantle of gray substance, averaging 2.5 mm. in thickness in man. It covers most of the brain. Due to an exuberant growth rate in organogenesis, the cortex becomes thrown into many elevations, the **gyri**, that are separated by depressions, the **sulci** and the **fissures**. Such foldings increase the free surface of the cortex to about 2,200 sq. cm. in man. Besides containing over 10 billion nerve cell bodies, the cerebral cortex includes an uncountable number of nerve fibers as well as neuroglia and blood vessels.

The cells of the cerebral cortex are of the multipolar type and exhibit wide variation in shape and size. They have been described according to neuron shape (e.g., **fusiform, pyramidal, spider** and **stellate cells**) and spatial organization (e.g., **horizontal cells**). Eponyms are also employed to identify them (e.g., **Betz, Cajal, Golgi** and **Martinotti cells**). Some of the better understood cells will be discussed briefly at this point to enable a clearer understanding of the histologic organization of the cerebral cortex.

a. *Pyramidal Cell.* These neurons possess cell bodies having the shape of a truncated pyramid and are present in many sizes—small, medium and large—ranging from 10

× 5 μ to 100 × 50 μ. The very largest of these cells is the **giant pyramid** or **Betz cell**.

Characteristically, pyramidal cells contain large, vesicular nuclei and Nissl bodies, which vary from fine to coarse, depending on cell size. From the apex of each cell body a single, long dendrite takes origin; other dendrites, usually shorter than the apical one, arise from the base of the cell. Both the cell body apex and the apical dendrite are directed toward the free surface of the cerebral cortex. The solitary axon of each pyramid arises from the basal cell surface and descends through the cortex to end in a deeper region or to continue into the underlying white matter. Pyramidal axons in the white matter are either association fibers, linking different regions of the cortex, or projection fibers that pass without synaptic interruption to levels of the central nervous system below the cerebral hemispheres.

b. *Stellate (Granule) Cells.* These are small cells, averaging 10 μ in diameter. Their rounded cell bodies have given rise to their designation as **granule cells**. Short dendrites with numerous branches and a short axon come off at regular intervals from the cell body. Stellate cells and their processes are confined to the cortex and are therefore concerned with intracortical connections.

c. *Fusiform (Spindle) Cells.* These are oval cells, roughly twice as long as they are wide, often regarded as **modified pyramidal cells**. In size, they approximate small and large pyramids. They possess a long terminal dendrite (similar to the apical dendrite) that is directed to the surface of the cortex. Basal dendrites are limited in number, and usually a single dendritic process extends downward from the fusiform cell. The axon also descends through the cortex from the cell to enter the white matter as a projection or association fiber.

A special type of fusiform cell is found restricted to the most superficial portion of the cerebral cortex. This, the **horizontal cell of Cajal**, possesses an axon and dendrites that run horizontally along the cortex for relatively great distances. It exhibits rich dendritic branchings. The horizontal cell is a cortical association neuron.

Another cortical association neuron of this general cell type is the **Martinotti cell**. This neuron has the configuration of an inverted pyramid in that the major apical process is the cell's axon, and the basal processes are all dendrites. This neuron also possesses a triangular cell body.

The cerebral cortex exhibits a laminar organization. Six reasonably defined layers, differing in thickness and density from one part of the brain to another, are present. These layers run parallel with the free surface and follow the irregular contours of the gyri and the sulci. Variations in the lamination are both obvious and subtle, and although only 52 major areas are generally recognized, thousands of subareas have been mapped.

a. *Plexiform (Molecular) Layer (Layer I).* This is the first or outermost layer of the cerebral cortex. It owes its name to the fact that fibers, arranged in a plexiform manner, predominate. Few cells are present, and these are mainly horizontal cells of Cajal. This layer receives the apical dendrites of pyramidal and fusiform cells and also axonic terminations of the Martinotti cells.

b. *Outer Granular Layer (Layer II).* This layer, immediately below layer I, contains very small pyramidal cells whose apical dendrites pass into the plexiform layer and whose axons descend to end mainly in the 5th and the 6th cortical layers.

c. *Outer Pyramidal Layer (Layer III).* This contains medium-sized pyramids in its superficial portion and larger pyramids in its deeper part. The apical dendrites of these cells terminate in layer I, while the basal dendrites and also the axons descend to the 5th and the 6th layers of the cortex. Many of the axons pass into the white matter.

d. *Inner Granular Layer (Layer IV).* This layer constitutes the major receiving station of the cerebral cortex. It may be considered as an unloading platform where axons coming to the cortex discharge their impulses to the cells present in the layer. This is explained by the presence within the inner granular layer of a plexus of myelinated afferent fibers constituting axons that have entered the cortex. Stellate cells predominate in this layer.

e. *Inner Pyramidal Layer (Layer V).* In this layer are present the largest of the pyramidal cells. From these pyramids, axons descend to pass into the white matter. Martinotti cells are also present. In addition to these cells, a plexus of myelinated fibers is present in the deeper regions of layer V. The fibers are afferent in nature.

f. *Fusiform (Multiform) Layer (Layer VI).* This is the deepest cortical layer, lying immediately against the white matter. The most common cell type present is of the fusiform variety. Some pyramidal, stellate and Martinotti cells are also present. A prominent feature of this layer is the large numbers of fiber bundles leaving and entering the cortex.

3. Cerebellum
(Plate 52)

The cerebellum is a bilobed globular mass of nervous tissue which lies over the lower part of the brain (i.e., the pons and the medulla). It consists of a covering of **gray matter** and a core of **white matter**.

The histologic unit of the cerebellum is a narrow plate of tissue which appears **foliate** in cross section. Within each folium, a core of medullary white substance conveys myelinated and unmyelinated nerve fibers to and from the surrounding cerebellar cortex.

Three morphologically distinct layers make up the cerebellar cortex—the **granular layer**, the **layer of Purkinje cells** and the **molecular layer**.

The most internal layer, immediately adjacent to the medulla, is the **granular layer**. This is a thick zone that contains small, multipolar granule cells so densely packed that this layer has the general appearance of lymphatic tissue. Each granule cell is spherical, contains a large chromatic nucleus and displays a small peripheral covering of granular cytoplasm.

Immediately outside the granule cell layer is a narrow zone containing the **cell bodies of Purkinje neurons** in a single row. These neurons give rise to one or more dendrites which pass peripherally into the most external cortical layer, the molecular layer. The Purkinje cell body is flask shaped and many times larger than the other cells of the cerebellar cortex. It contains a clear vesicular nucleus with a single, distinct nucleolus and concentrically arranged coarse Nissl granules.

The **molecular layer** is primarily a fiber layer that serves to spread nervous excitation from one part of the cerebellum to the next. Within it is present the unique dendritic arborization of Purkinje neurons. These dendrites fan out like an espalier tree across the folium, each branch being studed with synaptic thorns. Axonic fibers of association neurons make up most of the molecular layer. Many of these run along the folium, pass through the tangles of Purkinje dendrites, and fire off these cells. From the base of the Purkinje cell a single axon arises to pass through the granule cell layer and into the white matter of the cerebellum.

4. Meninges

The 3 connective tissue coverings of the brain and the spinal cord constitute the meninges (Fig. 7-52). From without in, these coverings are the **dura mater**, the **arachnoid mater** and the **pia mater**.

The **dura mater** consists mainly of 2 layers of dense, poorly vascularized fibrous tissue. Its outer layer may serve as a periosteum, such as is the case for the cranial bones. The inner layer of the dura, which is lined by a single row of flattened cells, immediately surrounds and is adherent to the arachnoid covering of the brain and the spinal cord.

The **arachnoid membrane** is separated from the pia by a network of trabeculae. These trabeculae contain strands of connective tissue composed of delicate collagenous fibers and some elastic fibers covered by a single row of flattened cuboidal cells which extend over the pia mater. The space that separates the arachnoid from the pia mater is known as the **subarachnoid space**. This space contains many **cisterns** and is filled with **cerebrospinal fluid**. Extensions of the arachnoid, the **arachnoid villi**, penetrate the inner layer of dura to extend into the venous sinuses. These villi consist of a core of loose connective tissue lined by a row of low cells. Thus, cerebrospinal fluid is able to enter the venous circulation via the villi.

Applied directly to the surface of the brain and the spinal cord is the highly vascular, delicate, white fibrous membrane known as the **pia mater**. Since it is joined to the arachnoid, the pia and the arachnoid are often described as a single membrane, referred to as the **pia-arachnoid**.

5. Choroid Plexus (Figs. 7-53 to 7-55)

The choroid plexus constitutes a discontinuous mass of small blood vessels and covering tissues that project into the ventricles of the brain. They have to do with the production of **cerebrospinal fluid**. The covering tissue consists of connective tissue elements and a surface layer of granular epithelium. This epithelium is simple cuboidal in nature and represents a modification of the ependyma lining the ventricles.

8 · Blood Vessels

A. INTRODUCTION

The blood vessels are tubular structures in an almost perfectly closed organ system that cycles blood around the body. Blood ejected from the heart and passing to the tissues exerts considerable pressure on vessel walls. Conversely, blood slowly flowing toward the heart from the tissues exerts very little pressure on the walls of the vessels. Once again the axiom that "structure reflects function" holds true. It is possible to correlate slight variations in the rate of blood flow and the blood pressure with histologic findings at any point of the circulatory system. Although a large number of exceptions exist, a handful of histologic features can be employed to determine satisfactorily the general identity of the vast majority of blood vessels.

All blood vessels, regardless of size and of whether they are arteries or veins, are simply tubular walls that surround central spaces or lumina through which pass the formed and the dissolved elements of blood. The following general criteria are important for an appreciation of the finer histologic

PLATE 54—Blood Vessels

FIG. 8-1. Cross section through a portion of the wall of the ascending aorta, showing the structure of the tunica intima (ti) and the adjacent tunica media (tm). H & E stain. Intermediate power. (em, elastic membranes, between which are found collagen fibers, c)

FIG. 8-2. Cross section through the middle portion of the common carotid artery. Survey showing the layers. Mallory stain. Low power. (tm, tunica media; f, fat cells; v, vasa vasorum; i, internal elastic membrane)

FIG. 8-3. Intermediate-power view of section of Figure 8-2. (ti, tunica intima; tm, tunica media; ta, tunica adventitia; i, internal elastic membrane; e, external elastic membrane; em, elastic membranes; c, collagen fibers)

FIG. 8-4. High-power view of section of Figure 8-2, showing the tunica intima (ti) and the tunica media (tm). (i, internal elastic membrane; em, elastic membranes; c, collagen fibers)

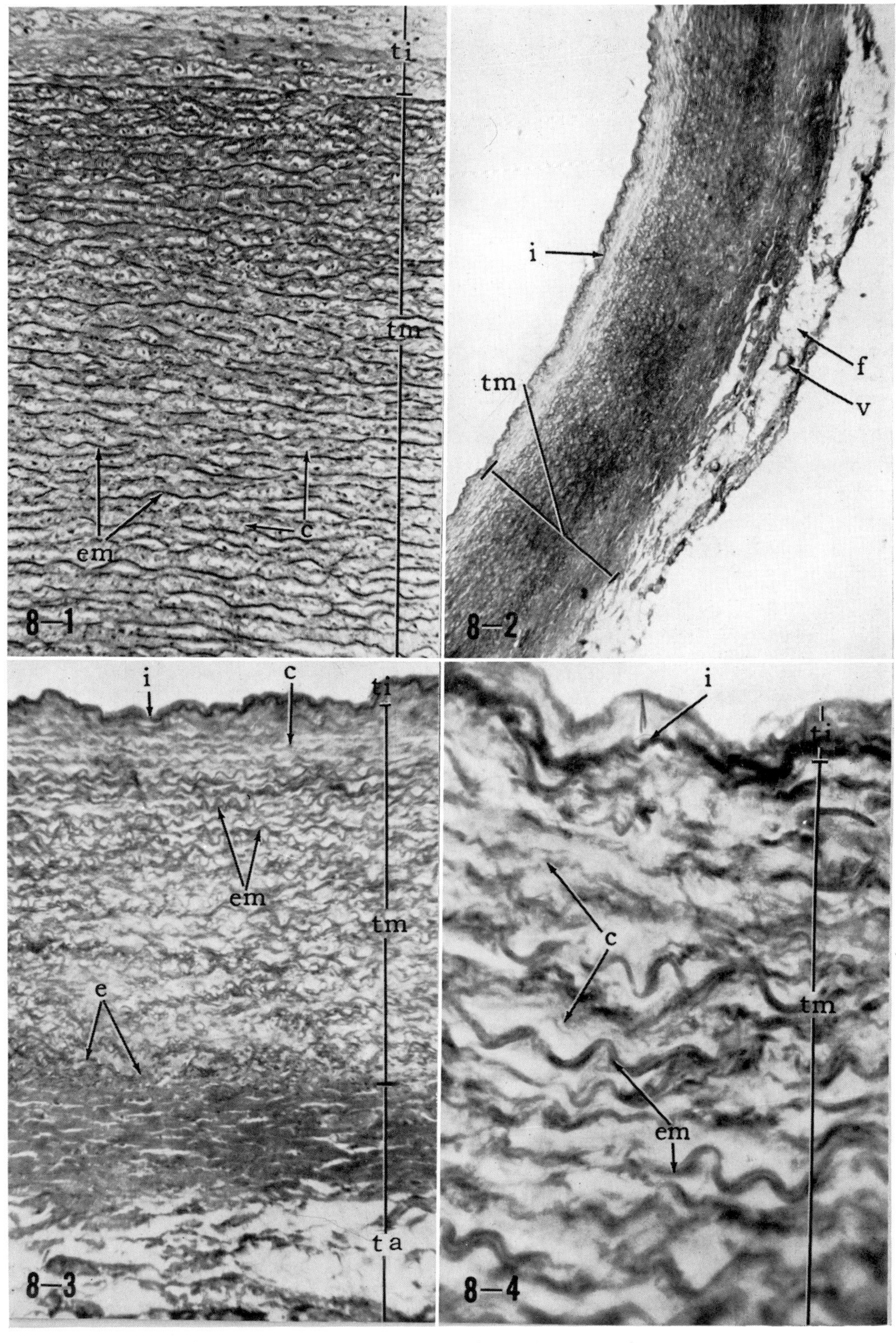
ti
tm
em
c
8—1
i
tm
f
v
8—2
i
c
ti
em
tm
e
ta
8—3
i
ti
c
tm
em
8—4

distinctions existing between the various sized vessels that will be discussed later.

1. Vessels subject to great and regular fluctuations in blood pressure—such as the arteries close to the heart—have their walls reinforced with elastic networks that provide both strength to withstand the pressure and elasticity to maintain an even rate of blood flow.

2. Vessels subject to lower and to either regular or less regular fluctuations in blood pressure—such as the arteries more distant from the heart—have within their walls relatively large numbers of smooth muscle fibers. This muscle permits the vessels to become distended when the blood pressure increases or to squeeze their lumina shut or nearly shut so as to force blood into adjacent smaller blood channels and at the same time prevent new blood from entering.

3. All blood vessels, both arteries and veins, have a lining of simple squamous epithelium upon their luminal surface which, since it lies within the vessel structure, is referred to as an **endothelium**.

4. The **wall of a typical blood vessel** is made up of 3 concentric layers referred to as tunics or coats. The innermost of these tunics is referred to as the **tunica intima (tunica interna)**, and it always includes an endothelium. The next coat outside the internal one is termed the **tunica media**. The outermost portion of the vessel wall is known as the **tunica adventitia (tunica externa)**.

5. Arterial vessels have stronger walls than venous channels, a fact that can be verified histologically by corroborating the following:

a. Arterial vessels in cross section are circular structures, whereas the corresponding venous vessels generally demonstrate irregular to collapsed outlines.

b. When examining any paired artery and vein, the artery is smaller, has a narrower lumen, a thicker wall and therefore a higher wall thickness to lumen diameter ratio. The accompanying vein is larger, has a wider lumen, a thinner wall and therefore a lower wall thickness to lumen diameter ratio.

6. In fixed histologic preparations it is much more common to find blood cells trapped in venous channels than in arterial vessels. This is so because agonal contraction of smooth muscle fibers, which are present in greatest abundance in the arteries furthest from the heart, forces most of the blood toward the venous system.

7. The tunica media is the thickest layer of the wall in a typical artery, whereas the tunica adventitia is thickest in the typical vein.

8. In the group of blood vessels visible to the naked eye, it is sometimes difficult to determine histologically whether a vessel is large or medium or small in size. This difficulty lies in the fact that in most cases there is a long transitional segment which in microscopic section is similar for the large and medium- to small-sized arteries and veins.

PLATE 55—Blood Vessels

FIG. 8-5. Section through a small artery (A) and vein (V) in the pampiniform plexus. Note that smooth muscle cells (s) arranged in concentric layers constitute the bulk of the tunica media (tm) of the artery. H & E stain. Intermediate power. (en, endothelium; ti, tunica intima; tm, tunica media; ta, tunica adventitia)

FIG. 8-6 a,b,c. Sections through small- to medium-sized arteries (A) and a vein (V). Note the internal (i) and the external (e) elastic membranes, especially in Figure 8-6c. Resorcin-Fuchsin stain. Low power.

FIG. 8-7. Section through a medium-sized artery (A) and vein (V), the femoral. Note that the tunica media (tm) of the artery appears thicker than the entire wall of the vein. The longitudinal white area (w) is an artifact of sectioning. H & E stain. Intermediate power.

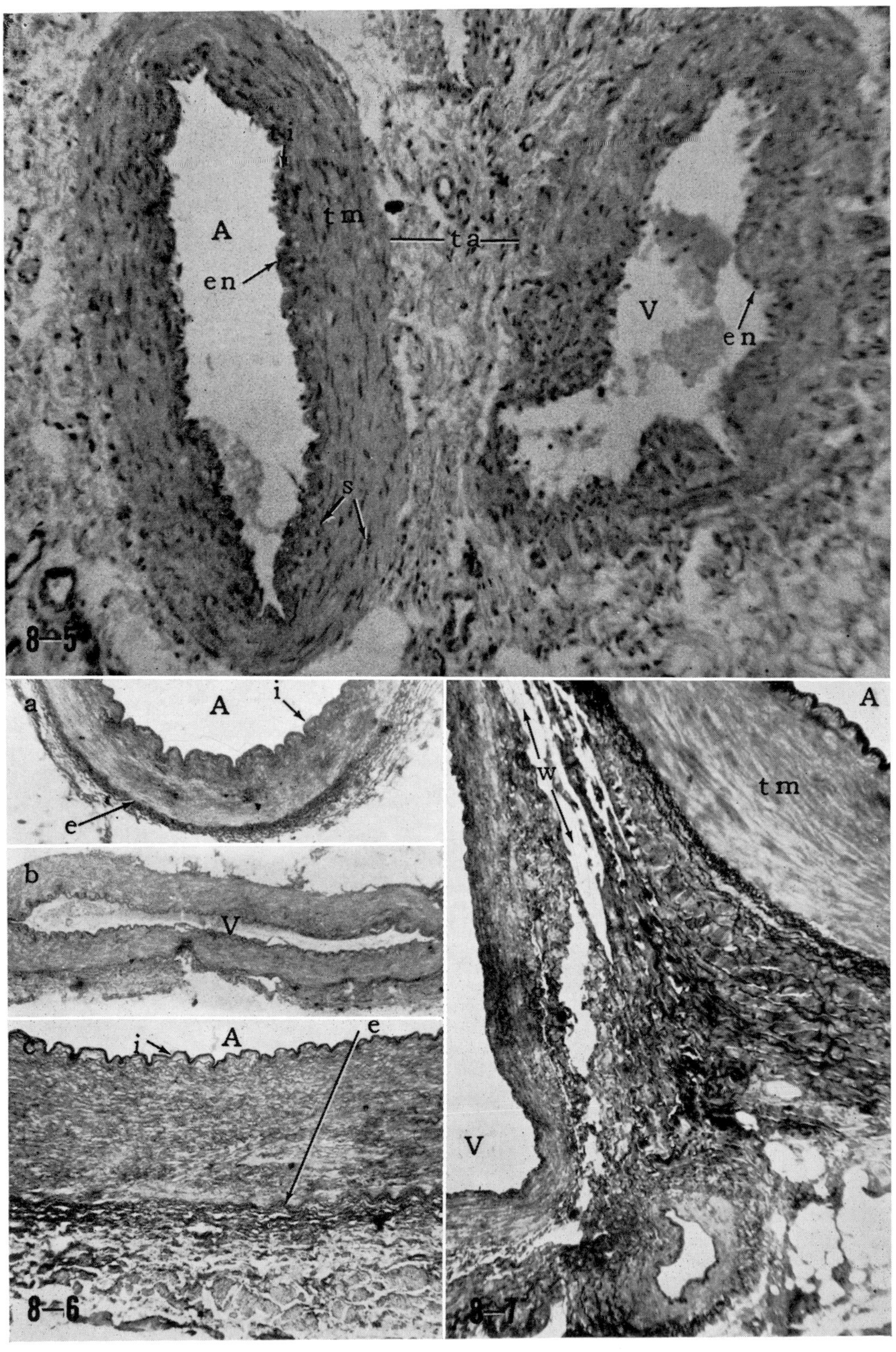
ti
A
tm
ta
en
V
en
s
8–5
a
A
i
e
b
V
c
i
A
e
8–6
A
w
tm
V
8–7

9. In fixed preparations, the agonal contraction of smooth muscle fibers results in varying degrees of vasoconstriction. This is especially true in the case of arterial vessels. The elastic membranes contract and develop longitudinal furrows and ridges which have a characteristic crinkled appearance in cross section.

10. The walls of vessels larger than 1 mm. in diameter cannot depend on the blood passing through their central channels for nourishment. These larger vessels possess tiny feeder vessels, the **vasa vasorum**, within their walls and are dependent on them for oxygen and metabolic exchanges.

The various types of arteries and veins will now be considered in the order in which blood reaches them after it leaves the left ventricle of the heart.

ARTERIES

The arterial system anatomically and histologically is divided into 3 major groups of vessels—large vessels, medium-to-small vessels and arterioles.

1. Large Arteries

These include only the pulmonary artery and the aorta and its largest branches. Because circular networks or membranes of elastic fibers are present in great numbers, this type of vessel is frequently called the **elastic type of artery**. They are also referred to as **conducting arteries** (Fig. 8-1).

a. *Tunica intima* consists of endothelium, a relatively thick subendothelial connective tissue containing both elastic and collagen fibers. The elastic tissue is arranged in the form of **concentric, discontinuous (fenestrated) membranes**. Since similar elastic membranes are present in the adjacent tunic, the boundary between intima and media is rather indefinite.

b. *Tunica media* is the thickest coat of the large artery. It consists again of elastic and collagen fibers, with numerous fibroblasts and some smooth muscle fibers. The elastic fibers are arranged concentrically into a large number of circular membranes.

c. *Tunica adventitia* is thin and more haphazardly arranged. Although fenestrated membranes are present, there is much less elastic tissue than in the other tunics. Coarse collagen bundles are arranged longitudinally or in spiral fashion.

2. Medium to Small-sized Arteries

These include practically all of the named arteries and range in size down to vessels that can just be seen with the unaided eye. Since the most prominent feature of these vessels is a thick muscular tunica media and their function is the distribution of blood to organs and tissues, these vessels are frequently referred to as **muscular** or **distributing arteries** (Figs. 8-2 to 8-8; 8-15, 8-16).

a. *Tunica intima* is similar in constitution to the tunica intima found in large arteries, except that the subendothelial connective tissue is considerably reduced, and its elastic fiber component reduced to one or two very distinct membranes known as the **internal elastic membrane**.

PLATE 56—Blood Vessels

FIG. 8-8. Section through a small artery (A) and veins (V) in the pampiniform plexus. H & E stain. Low power.

FIG. 8-9. Section through an arteriole (ar) and capillary cut longitudinally from developing finger. H & E stain. High power. (e, endothelial cells; s, smooth muscle cells)

FIG. 8-10. Section through a lymph capillary (central lacteal, cl) located in the lamina propria core of a villus of the small intestine. H & E stain. Oil immersion. (e, endothelial cells)

FIG. 8-11. Longitudinal section through a capillary from a villus of the duodenum (cat). H & E stain. Oil immersion. (e, endothelial cells)

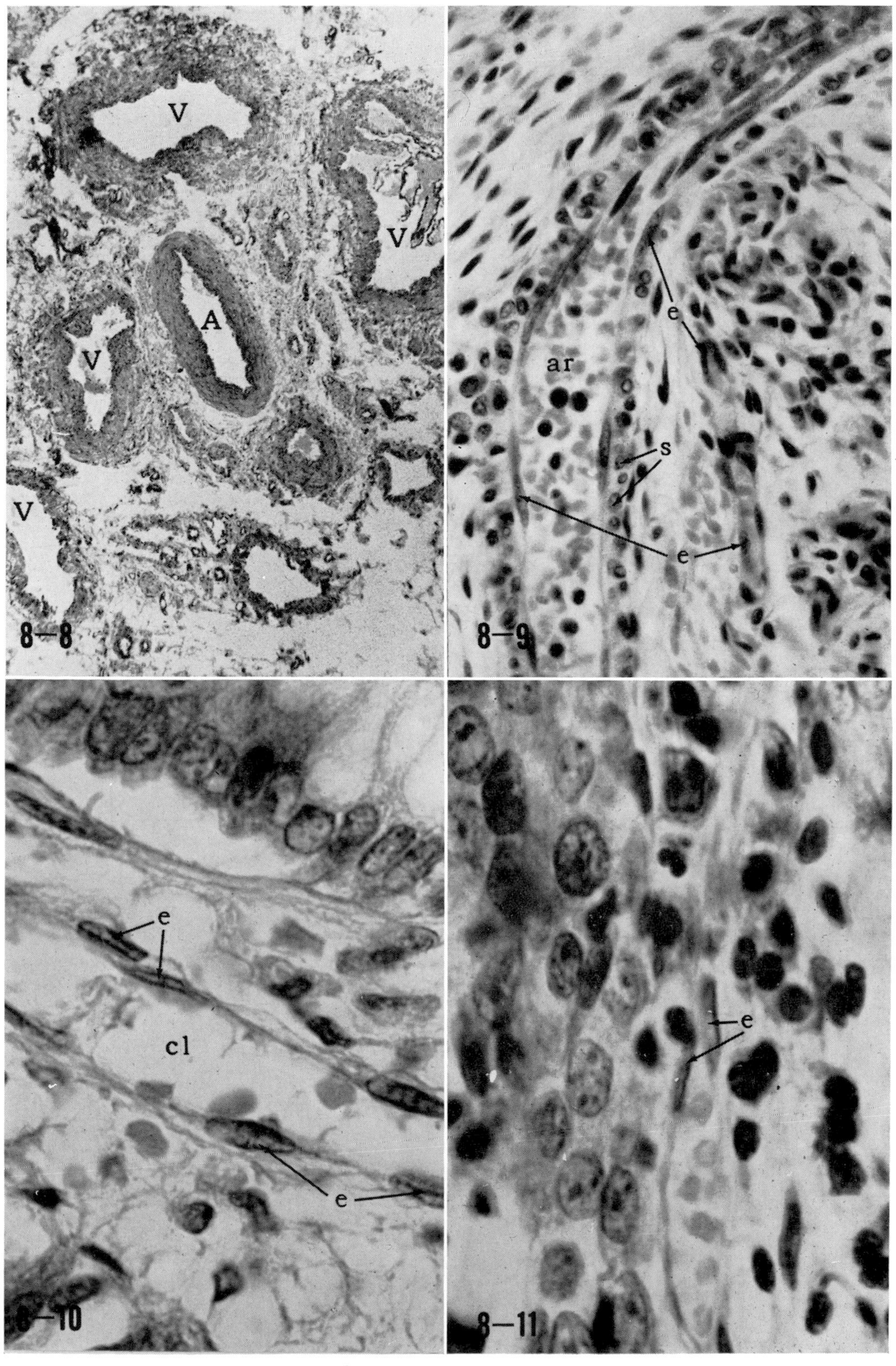
V
V
A
V
V
8—8
e
ar
s
e
8—9
e
cl
e
8—10
e
8—11

b. *Tunica media* is usually the thickest of the tunics but is similar to the tunica media of the large artery only at the very upper end of this size range of vessels. More typically, the elastic tissue seems to be dramatically reduced in amount, its place having been taken by smooth muscle elements interspersed here and there with collagen and elastic fibers. Anywhere from 5 to 40 concentric layers of smooth muscle cells may be present.

c. *Tunica adventitia* may be as thick as the media but is usually thinner. Elastic tissue is frequently present closest to the media, not uncommonly in the form of an **external elastic membrane** which represents the innermost part of the adventitia. The larger vessels in this category possess an external elastic membrane, whereas the smaller vessels lack one. Most of the fibers in this tunic are collagenous in nature, and fibroblasts and isolated smooth muscle cells are also found.

3. Arterioles

These are arteries that have diameters falling roughly between 25 and 250 μ (0.25 mm.). Although they are in the microscopic range, arterioles have, relatively speaking, the highest wall-to-lumen ratio of all arteries (Fig. 8-9).

a. *Tunica intima* seems to consist solely of endothelium and an internal elastic membrane that is usually discontinuous or absent. A subendothelial connective tissue cannot be seen with the light microscope.

b. *Tunica media* is made up of 1 to 5 concentric layers of almost pure smooth muscle. This is the thickest tunic in the arteriolar wall.

c. *Tunica adventitia* is thinner than the media and contains collagenous and elastic fibers as well as scattered fibroblasts. An external elastic membrane is absent. Observations of arterioles with the electron microscope have demonstrated the presence of pericytes (probably a specialized type of adventitial cell) applied to the outside of the smooth muscle cells.

C. CAPILLARIES

These are tiny tubular vessels, quite uniform in size, that are present in networks or meshworks between the arterial and the venous systems (arterial and venous capillaries). Histologically, they range in diameter from 8 to 12 μ, and their walls have a thickness of no more than 1 μ. The lumen of a capillary is only large enough to permit the passage of blood cells in single file.

The extremely thin capillary wall can be regarded as an endothelial tube. No more than 2 endothelial cells can be seen in a cross section through a capillary. These cells can be recognized by the marked bulges produced by nuclei as they protrude into the lumen.

The thin capillary wall represents a semipermeable membrane under normal circumstances. Under the light microscope it would appear that this wall constitutes a single layer. However, on the basis of electron microscopic and biophysical considerations, a variable number of zones are believed to intervene between blood within the capillary

PLATE 57—Blood Vessels

FIG. 8-12. Survey section of femoral vein. Weigert stain. Low power.

FIG. 8-13. Intermediate-power view of section of Figure 8-12 depicting a small number of delicate elastic fibers (e).

FIG. 8-14. High-power view of section of Figure 8-12, emphasizing the tunica intima (ti) and media (tm). Note the smooth muscle cells (s), collagen fibers (c) and elastic fibers (e).

FIG. 8-15. Section of femoral artery. Weigert stain. Low power.

FIG. 8-16. Intermediate-power view of section of Figure 8-15. Note the small amount of elastic fibers (e) present in the tunica media (tm).

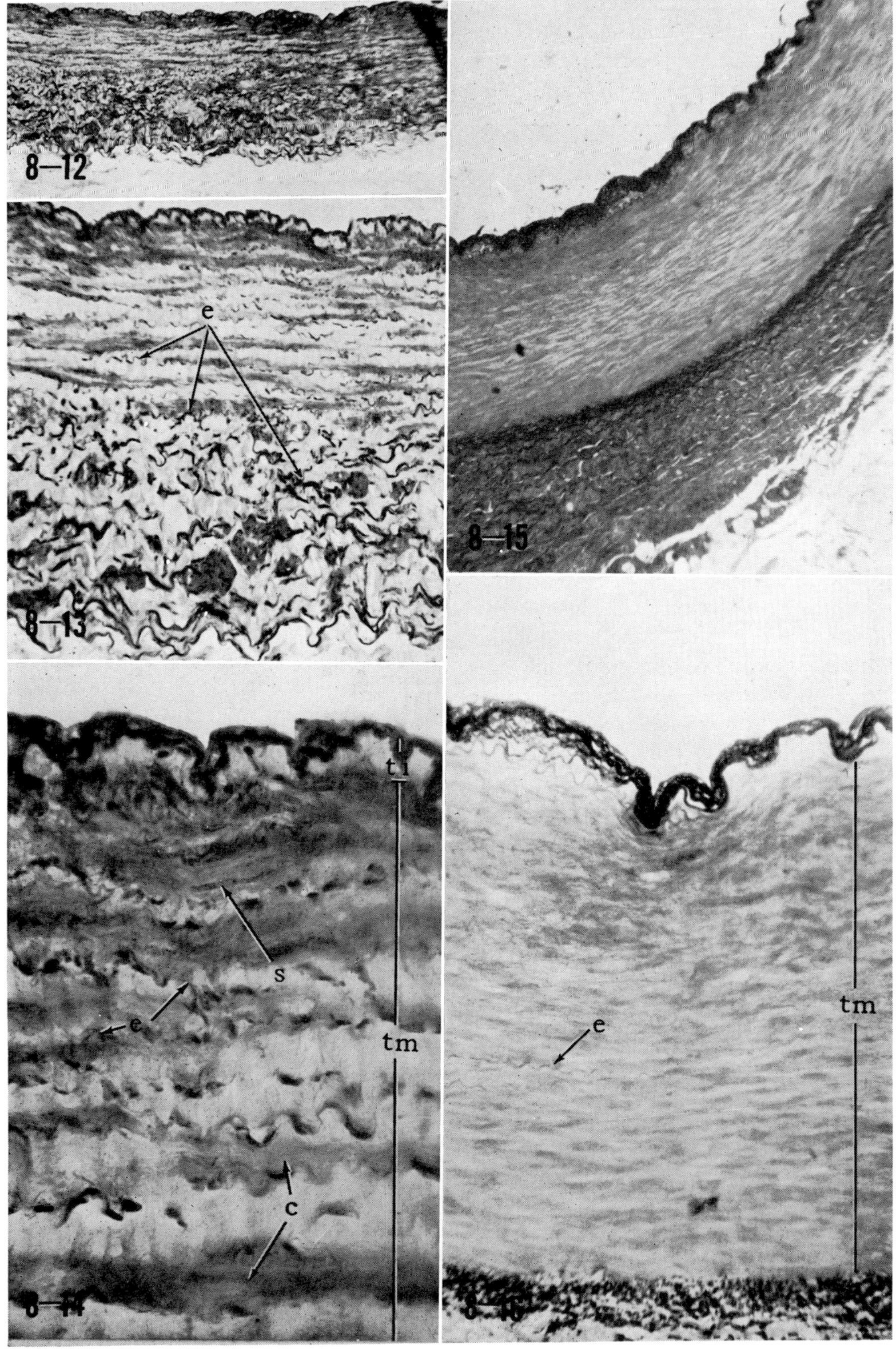
8—12
e
8—13
8—15
ti
s
e
e
tm
c
tm
e

and the tissue fluid outside the capillary (Fig. 8-11). Electron microscopic studies readily reveal the presence of pericytes and their processes closely applied to the endothelial walls of capillaries.

D. VEINS

As with the arteries, veins are subdivided according to size into 3 categories—venules, small to medium-sized veins and large veins.

1. Venules

These vessels are from about 0.25 to 1 mm. in diameter and have such flaccid walls that, in section, the outline is usually distorted (Fig. 4-9).

a. *Tunica intima* is minimal and consists solely of an endothelium. No subendothelial connective tissue or elastic membranes are present.

b. *Tunica media* is very thin in absolute terms and also as related to the media of the corresponding vessel on the arterial side, the arteriole. It consists almost entirely of smooth muscle.

c. *Tunica adventitia* is the thickest of the tunics and is composed predominantly of collagen fibers.

2. Small to Medium-sized Veins

These vessels range in size up to almost 1 cm. in diameter and include most of the named veins (Figs. 8-5 to 8-8; 8-12 to 8-14).

a. *Tunica intima* is somewhat thicker than in the venule. The only constant feature about this layer is the endothelium. A thin subendothelial connective tissue layer is present in the largest vessels of this size category and when present may contain smooth muscle, longitudinally arranged, and elastic fibers.

b. *Tunica media* is usually thin and contains, according to the size of the vessel, smooth muscle and delicate elastic membranes embedded among collagen fibers.

c. *Tunica adventitia* is thick and constitutes the greatest part of the vessel wall. Although no external elastic membrane is present, elastic fibers as well as collagen fibers are abundant. Some smooth muscle elements, usually longitudinally oriented, may also be present.

3. Large Veins

These are primarily the venae cavae, the portal vein and their major branches.

a. *Tunica intima* consists of endothelium, a somewhat thicker subendothelial connective tissue and an indistinct internal elastic membrane. Isolated cells or bundles of smooth muscle frequently are found, arranged in longitudinal fashion in the subendothelial tissue.

b. *Tunica media* is quite thin and contains less smooth muscle and more collagen fibers than it does in medium-sized veins.

c. *Tunica adventitia* constitutes roughly three quarters of the thickness of the vessel wall. There is no external elastic membrane, but the entire adventitia is very rich in coarse bundles of longitudinally arranged smooth muscle. Collagen fibers interweave throughout the muscle bundles.

9 · The Lymphatic System

A. INTRODUCTION

All lymphoid organs have a structure similar to bone marrow, being characterized by a delicate meshwork of reticular fibers for internal support and the presence mainly of lymphocytes in the interstices. In this group are the lymph nodes, the hemolymph nodes, the thymus, tonsillar tissue, solitary lymph nodules and the spleen. The **lymphoid organs**, together with the **lymphatic vessels**, constitute the **lymphatic system**. The **lymphatic vessels** consist of a collateral system of channels, lined by endothelium, which by means of their lymphatic capillaries (Fig. 8-10) collect the tissue fluid and return it by a circuitous route via larger lymphatic vessels into the thoracic and right lymphatic ducts to the venous system. The fluid in these vessels is called **lymph**. Relative to the heart, lymph is unlike blood in that it circulates in one direction only, from the periphery toward the heart. The drainage of lymph is approximately 1,000 ml. per day, and all lymph collected is restored to the blood system to help to maintain the fluid content of the

PLATE 58—Lymph Node

FIG. 9-1. Section through a lymph node. H & E stain. Low power.

FIG. 9-2. Portion of cortex bounding medulla of lymph node. H & E stain. Low power.

FIG. 9-3. Intermediate-power view of lymph node. H & E stain.

FIG. 9-4. Lymph nodule with germinal center and surrounding medium-sized lymphocytes. H & E stain. Intermediate power.

FIG. 9-5. High-power view of lymph node. H & E stain. (abbreviations for Figs. 9-1 to 9-5: c, capsule; sc, subcapsular sinus; cs, cortical sinus; n, nodules; pn, primary nodule; gc, germinal center; mc, medullary cords; t, trabeculum containing vessels; l, lymphocytes; bv, blood vessel; en, endothelium; rc, reticular cell; rf, reticular fiber)

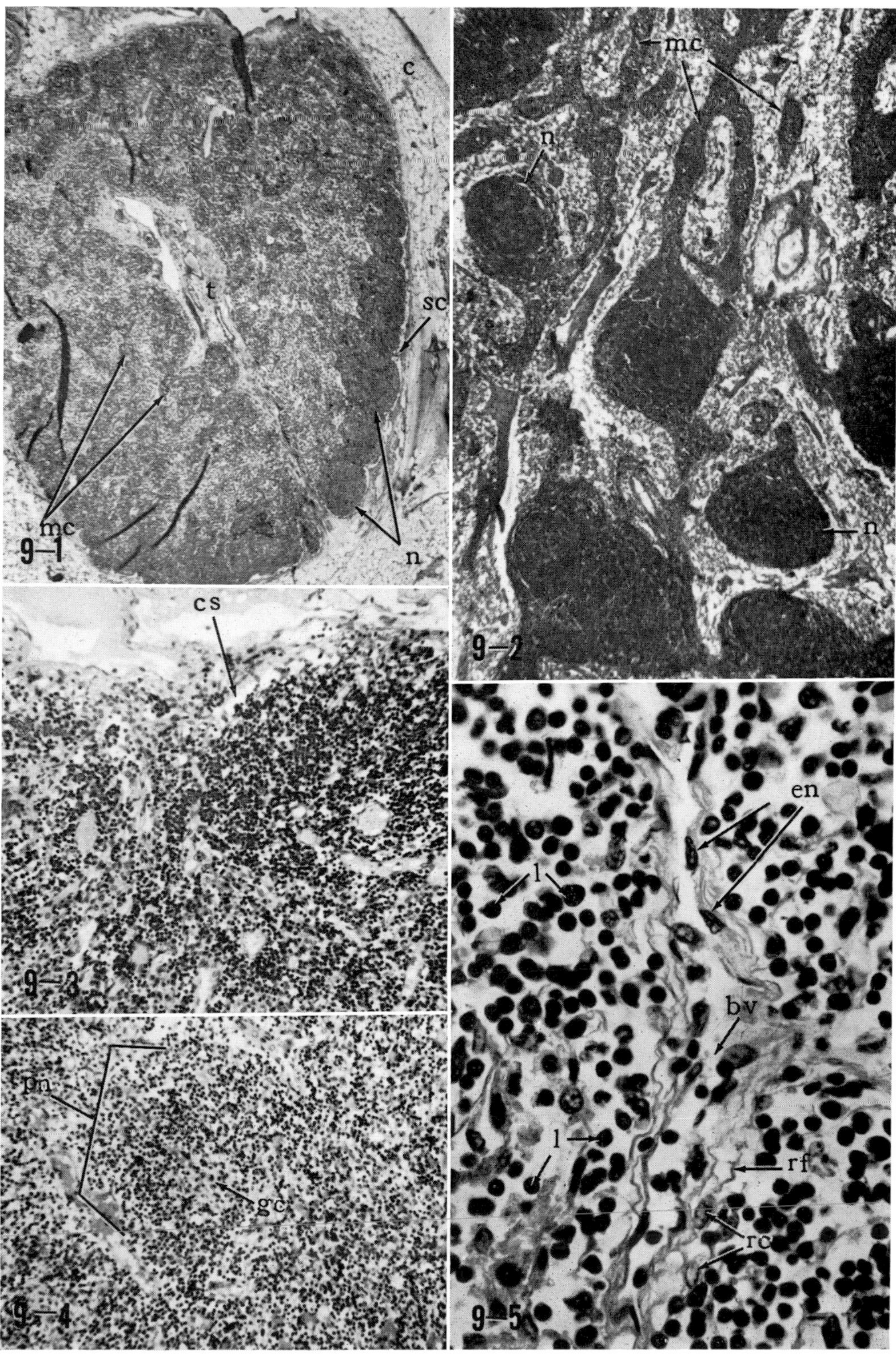

c
sc
t
mc
n
9–1
mc
n
n
9–2
cs
9–3
pn
gc
9–4
en
l
bv
l
rf
rc
9–5

blood. Lymph is similar to the plasma portion of blood, but its cellular content varies, depending on the site of collection. Generally, lymph passing through lymph nodes is characterized by a large number of lymphocytes (99%), only a few granulocytes and occasional erythrocytes being present.

B. LYMPH NODES (Plate 58)

A discussion of the lymph nodes presents a remarkable picture of variation, so that attempts to explain the deviations in structure have resulted in ascribing numerous functions to the lymph nodes. Perhaps we may simply say that the morphology of the lymph node is a reflection of its function and cellular constituents at a given time; the latter appear and almost disappear or pass through a series of cyclic changes. Generally, they are active structures that continually produce lymphocytes and act as strainers which filter lymph; they are good sign posts of various pathologic processes. Lymph nodes are widely distributed throughout the body, with many being scattered along the course of the lymph vessels. They are encapsulated, round, ovoid or bean-shaped organs of variable size (1 to 25 mm.) consisting of a peripheral portion, the **cortex**, and a central **medulla**.

Afferent lymphatic vessels pierce the capsule obliquely on the convex aspect of the node, and efferent vessels leave at the hilus. Arteries and veins, accompanied by nerves, enter and leave via the hilus. The **capsule** is composed mainly of dense collagenous fibers with some elastic fibers and a few smooth muscle cells. From the capsule, **trabeculae** penetrate the organ, separating it into compartments so that the cortex is subdivided into a number of **primary lymphatic nodules**. The primary lymphatic nodules are made up chiefly of a fine meshwork of reticular fibers with many lymphocytes, some primitive reticular cells, histiocytes and occasional granular leukocytes. Within many of the primary nodules are **secondary lymphatic nodules** or the **germinal centers** (pale areas that germinate lymphocytes). A **subcapsular sinus** is present and is visible as a zone broken up by a coarse meshwork. The lymph flows into the node via the spaces of this meshwork (subcapsular sinus) and courses into the looser parts of the lymphatic tissue, the **cortical sinuses**, surrounding the trabeculae. The medulla consists of a loose arrangement of lymphoid tissue organized into **cords.** In addition, spaces known as **medullary sinuses** are evident between the cords and the medullary trabeculae. In structure they are similar to and a continuation of the subcapsular and the cortical sinuses.

C. HEMOLYMPH NODES (HEMAL NODES)

There is still a question whether hemolymph nodes are structures *sui generis* or merely modifications of lymph nodes. These organs vary in size and, if present, are usually located in the vicinity of large blood vessels in the peritoneum. They are not con-

PLATE 59—Lymphatic Nodule

FIG. 9-6. Cross section of ileum to show Peyer's patches (Pp) consisting of many solitary nodules. H & E stain. Low power.

FIG. 9-7. Upper third of the esophagus, depicting diffuse lymphatic infiltration in lamina propria. H & E stain. Intermediate power.

FIG. 9-8. Intermediate-power view of a portion of Figure 9-6, showing a section through Peyer's patches in the lamina propria.

FIG. 9-9. Intermediate-power view of section of Figure 9-6, showing the extension of Peyer's patches to the submucosa.

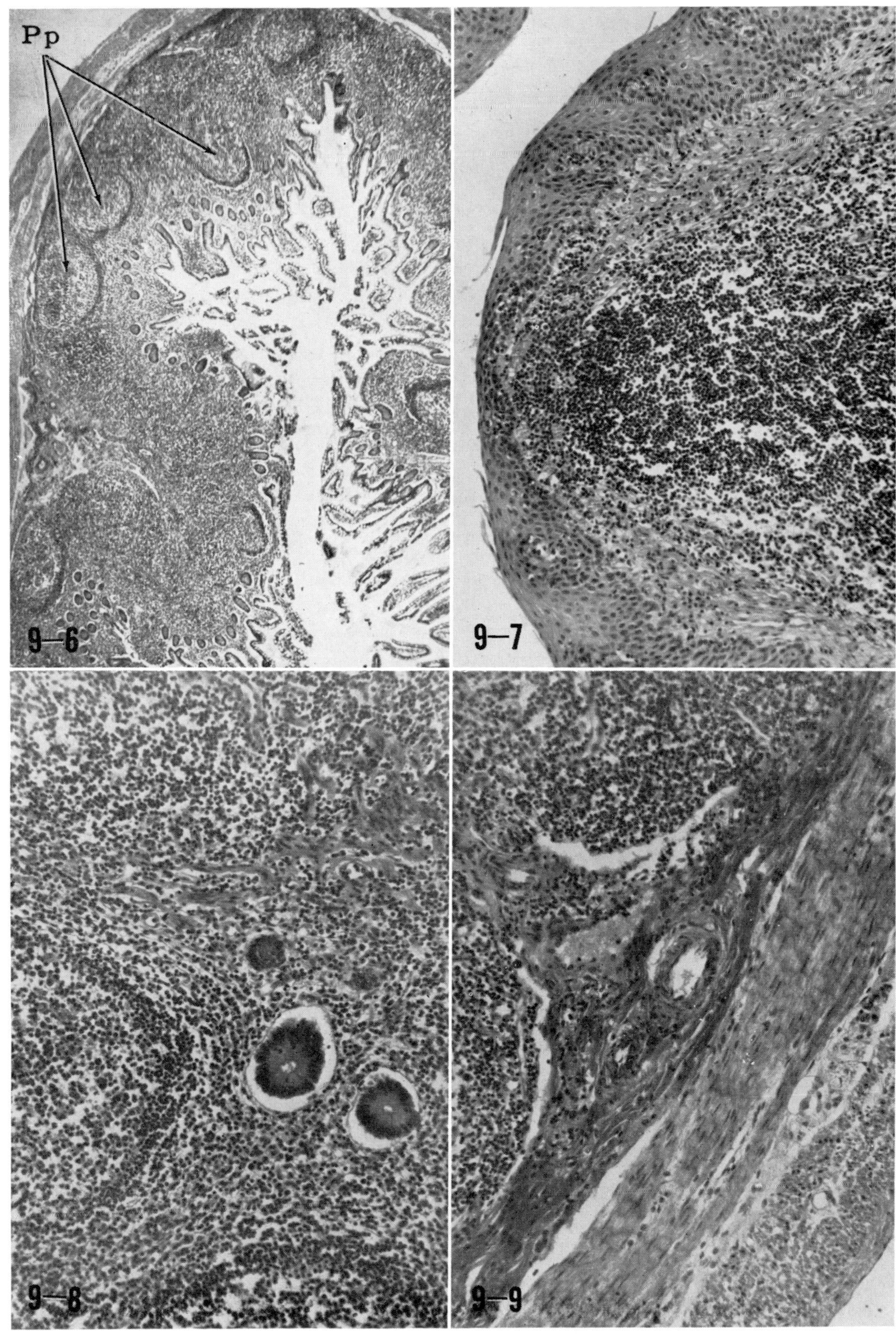
Pp
9–6
9–7
9–8
9–9

stant structures in man, although they have been described in the sheep and the ox. One of the chief differences from the lymph node is the presence of large blood sinuses revealing that this type filters blood. No afferent or efferent vessels are present.

D. SOLITARY LYMPH NODULES (Plate 59)

Solitary lymph nodules, varying from 0.6 to 3 mm. in diameter, are especially numerous in the mucosa of the intestinal tract. A layer of connective tissue surrounds the nodule and appears to blend into the internal nodular reticular framework, which tends to be obscured for the most part by a dense arrangement of lymphocytes. Thus, in H & E sections the nodule appears dark blue. Some nodules have a pale germinal center or secondary nodule which is indicative of active lymphocyte production. Afferent and efferent lymphatic vessels are absent. Besides the solitary nodules, lymphoid tissue distributed under the moist epithelial surfaces of the digestive tract and the respiratory and the urinary passages may be found as non-encapsulated structures in which lymphocytes are diffusely arranged. Typical areas are observed in the lamina propria (subepithelial connective tissue).

E. TONSILLAR TISSUES

Three types are distinguishable—**lingual**, **palatine** and **pharyngeal**. Tonsillar tissue possesses a connective tissue capsule except where the tonsil is bounded by an epithelium. In all types blood and lymph sinuses are absent. The following is a brief description of each type.

1. Lingual Tonsil (Plate 60)

This type is found on the root of the tongue as small elevations caused by aggregations of lymph nodules beneath the epithelium. The free surface of this tonsillar tissue facing the oral cavity is covered by a stratified squamous epithelium that continues down into shallow branching invaginations known as **crypts**. The ducts of mucous glands open directly into the crypts, and the glandular secretion acts to free the crypts of debris so that this type of tonsil is not prone to infection.

2. Palatine Tonsil (Plates 61 and 62)

On each side between the arching folds of the pharynx the palatine (faucial) tonsil can be recognized. Histologically, this is the type most frequently studied. The free surface of this tonsillar tissue is covered by a stratified squamous epithelium that is continued down into deep crypts. Unlike the lingual tonsils, the ducts of mucous glands do *not* open *into* the crypts but *beside* them. Therefore, the crypts are not flushed out, resulting in an accumulation of debris and ultimate infection. The lymphatic tissue appears highly diffuse, with extremely large

PLATE 60—Lingual Tonsil

FIG. 9-10. Lingual tonsil. H & E stain. Low power. (c, crypt; e, stratified squamous epithelium; l, nodular and diffuse lymphocyte concentration; g, mucous glands concentrated at the base of crypt)

FIG. 9-11. Low-power view of a deeper portion of the lingual tonsil. Note the extent of the mucous glands (g) in relation to the crypt (c) and lymphatic tissue. H & E stain.

FIG. 9-12. Intermediate-power view of a portion of section of Figure 9-10. Note the stratified squamous epithelial lining (e) of the crypt (c) with surrounding lymphoid distribution (l) and the position of the glands (g).

FIG. 9-13. Intermediate-power view of a portion of section of lingual tonsil, showing the duct (d) of the mucous glands opening into the base of the crypt (c). H & E stain.

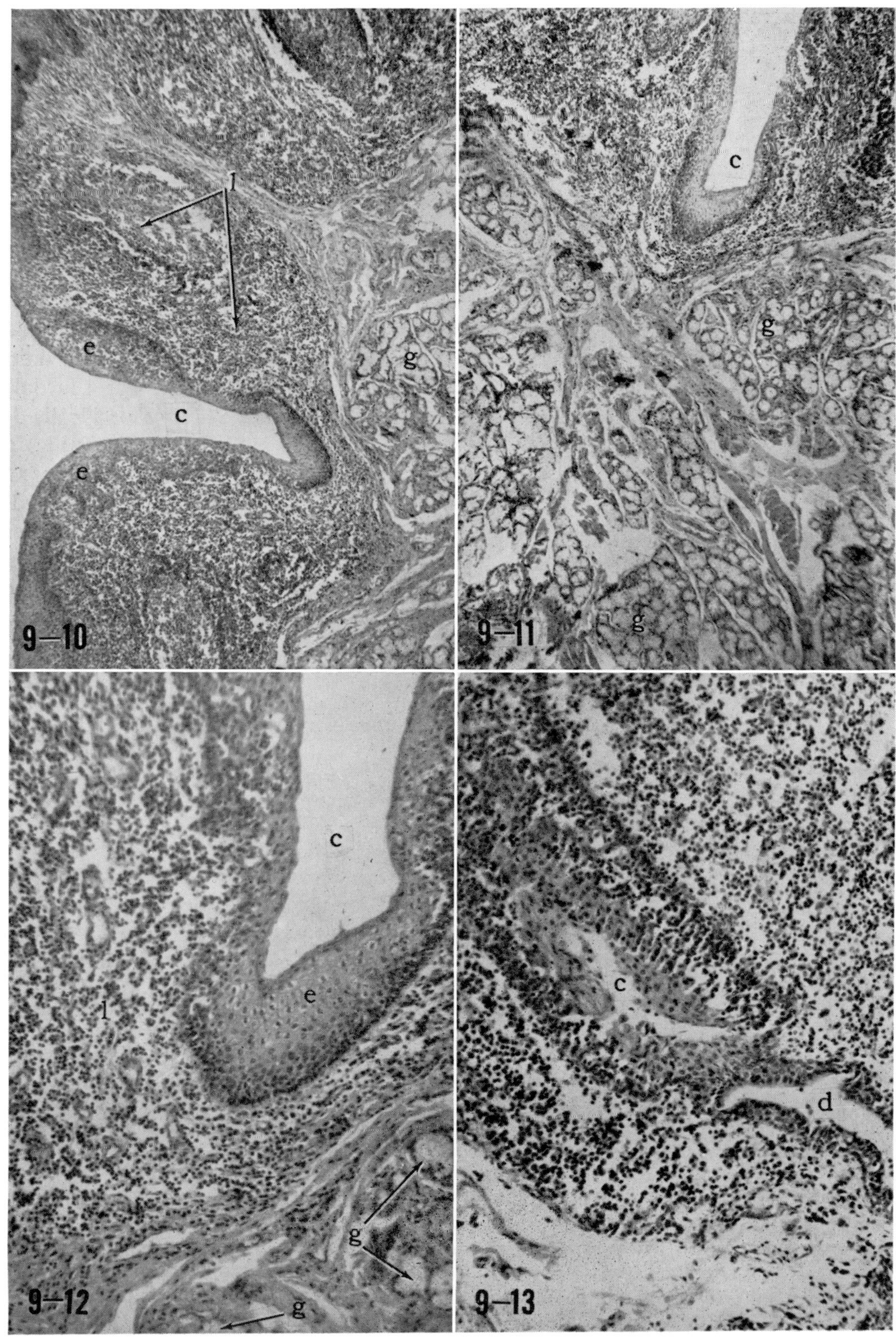
l
e
g
c
e
9–10
c
g
g
9–11
c
e
l
g
9–12
g
c
d
9–13

nodules. Migrant cells known as **salivary corpuscles** are frequently observed in the saliva of patients and represent degenerate, vesicular lymphocytes that have escaped from eroded areas of the palatine tonsillar epithelium.

3. Pharyngeal Tonsil

The pharyngeal tonsil is located in the mucous membrane that lines the median dorsal wall of the nasopharynx. Enlargement of its contained lymph nodules gives this tissue such a glandlike appearance that it is commonly known as the **adenoids** (Gk., *aden* = gland; *eidos* = form). Adenoids may result in serious obstruction of the respiratory passage and leads to mouth breathing. Although this lymphatic tissue appears to be similar to the palatine tonsil, its epithelium is arranged into numerous longitudinal folds rather than as a series of true crypts. In addition, pseudostratified ciliated columnar epithelium is present as well as stratified squamous. Seromucous glands with ducts leading into troughlike epithelial downfoldings is another differentiating feature.

F. THYMUS
(Plates 63 to 65)

We often think of the thymus gland as one of the endocrine glands, but histologically it is a lymphoid gland. This organ, located in the anterior mediastinum in close relation to the pericardium and the large veins at the base of the heart, functionally is linked with the immunity mechanisms of the body. The thymus is thinly encapsulated with fibroelastic connective tissue which gives off trabeculae dividing the organ into two main **lobes** and subsequently into many smaller **lobules**. The **cortex** of a thymic lobule is a dense, dark-staining collection of lymphocytes (**thymocytes**) suspended in a network of reticular tissue. In contrast, the **medulla** is not so dense because lymphocytes are few in number; it appears paler staining and is more vascular than the cortex. An additional histologic feature is that adjacent medullary areas may be continuous. A specifically diagnostic structure, the **Hassall's (thymic) corpuscle**, is frequently present in large numbers. Thymic corpuscles are restricted to medullary areas and are from 15 microns to over 100 microns in diameter. The component cells of a Hassall's corpuscle are epitheloid nonliving, hyalinized, coil-like or concentrically arranged structures which are eosinophilic. Afferent lymphatic vessels and lymph sinuses are not present in the thymic parenchyma. However, lymphatics are located in the interlobular connective tissue (see Figs. 9-22 to 9-28).

After puberty, the thymus gland begins to involute, presenting a different picture from the above (Figs. 9-29 to 9-33). In this condition the organ is customarily designated as **old thymus**. In this case, there is a massive infiltration of fatty and fibrous tissue which results in the retention of relatively

PLATE 61—Palatine Tonsil

FIG. 9-14. Palatine tonsil. H & E stain. Low power. (e, stratified squamous epithelium of surface; c, crypt; n, concentration of lymphatic nodules containing germinal centers, gc)

FIG. 9-15. Palatine tonsil, showing a crypt (c) lined with stratified squamous epithelium (e) infiltrated by lymphocytes from the surrounding concentration of lymphatic tissue. H & E stain. Low power.

FIG. 9-16. Palatine tonsil, showing nodules (n) with prominent germinal centers (gc) and a nest of mucous glands (g). Note the large blood vessel (b) adjacent to the glandular mass. H & E stain. Low power.

FIG. 9-17. Palatine tonsil, revealing a mass of lymphocytes in a crypt which ultimately form the salivary corpuscles. Note the stratified squamous epithelium (e) lining the crypt. H & E stain. Intermediate power.

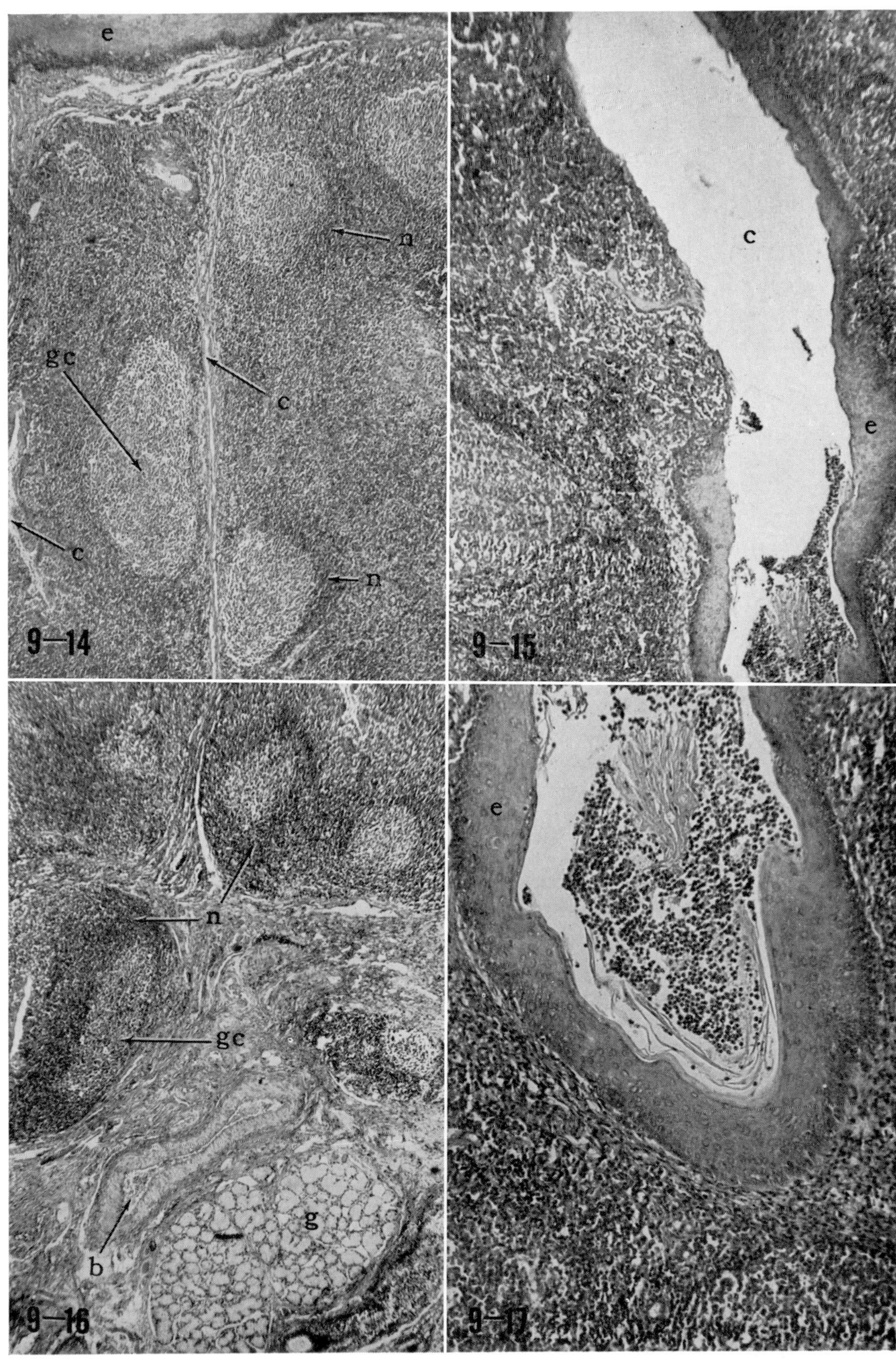
e
n
gc
c
c
n
9–14
c
e
9–15
n
gc
b
g
9–16
e
9–17

small numbers of lymphocytic elements. In the old condition, lobulation of the organ becomes indistinct, and Hassall's corpuscles become cystic, attain massive sizes, and sometimes become calcified.

G. SPLEEN

(Plates 66 to 71)

The spleen is the largest lymphoid organ in the body, approximately the size of the average adult closed fist, and is located in the shelter of the left 9th, 10th and 11th ribs. This organ exemplifies a type of lymphatic tissue that has become specialized to filter blood. Although the spleen is not essential to life, mention of some of the known functions ascribed to this gland will reveal its importance.

1. Lymphopoiesis and monocytopoiesis normally occur in the spleen. In addition, it plays a minor role in erythropoiesis during fetal life and in extramedullary erythropoiesis during certain pathologic states such as myelogenous leukemia.
2. Under various conditions such as hemorrhage, this organ serves to shunt a quantity of its stored blood into the general circulation.
3. It serves to remove old erythrocytes and, through its rich macrophagic activity, plays a substantial role in iron metabolism.
4. It acts as one of the defense mechanisms of the body.

Microscopic analysis of the spleen reveals that this organ is covered by a dense fibrous connective tissue, rich in elastic fibers and also containing a few smooth muscle fibers. Distinct trabeculae arise from the capsule, pass into the spleen and divide it into primary and secondary lobules. The **parenchyma**, between trabeculae, consists of an arrangement of lymphatic tissue which is known as **splenic pulp** and is of two types, the **white** and the **red pulp**. **White pulp** is cellular material that surrounds the arteries as a sheath and is invariably somewhat dense and nodular in arrangement. Characteristic of the white pulp is the **splenic nodule (malpighian corpuscle)** which is composed of a dense mass of lymphoid tissue around an arteriole. The **red pulp** is a looser arrangement of a vascular tissue which fills the spaces between two adjacent venous sinuses. It consists predominantly of erythrocytes, with some granulocytes, monocytes, macrophages and reticuloendothelial cells, in addition to lymphocytes; all of these cells are suspended in a reticular network. Since red pulp material is arranged in cordlike aggregates, it is often referred to as **splenic cords** or the **pulp cords of Billroth**. The red pulp gradually merges and becomes continuous with the white pulp.

The distribution of blood vessels in the spleen can be correlated with the general structure of this organ. In addition, it is of interest to note that the spleen can be considered a segmented organ on the basis of its

PLATE 62—Palatine Tonsil

FIG. 9-18. Palatine tonsil showing mucous glands (g) and two lymphatic nodules (ln). Note the prominent germinal center (gc). H & E stain. Intermediate power.

FIG. 9-19. Mucous glands and a duct (d) associated with the palatine tonsil. H & E stain. Intermediate power.

FIG. 9-20. Palatine tonsil, showing the stratified squamous lining (ss) of a primary crypt. Note the relation of lymphocytic material (l) to the epithelium. H & E stain. Intermediate power.

FIG. 9-21. Palatine tonsil, showing a small secondary crypt (c) and lymphatic nodules with germinal centers (gc). Arrow indicates a region where lymphocytes have almost obliterated the epithelial wall of the crypt. H & E stain. Intermediate power.

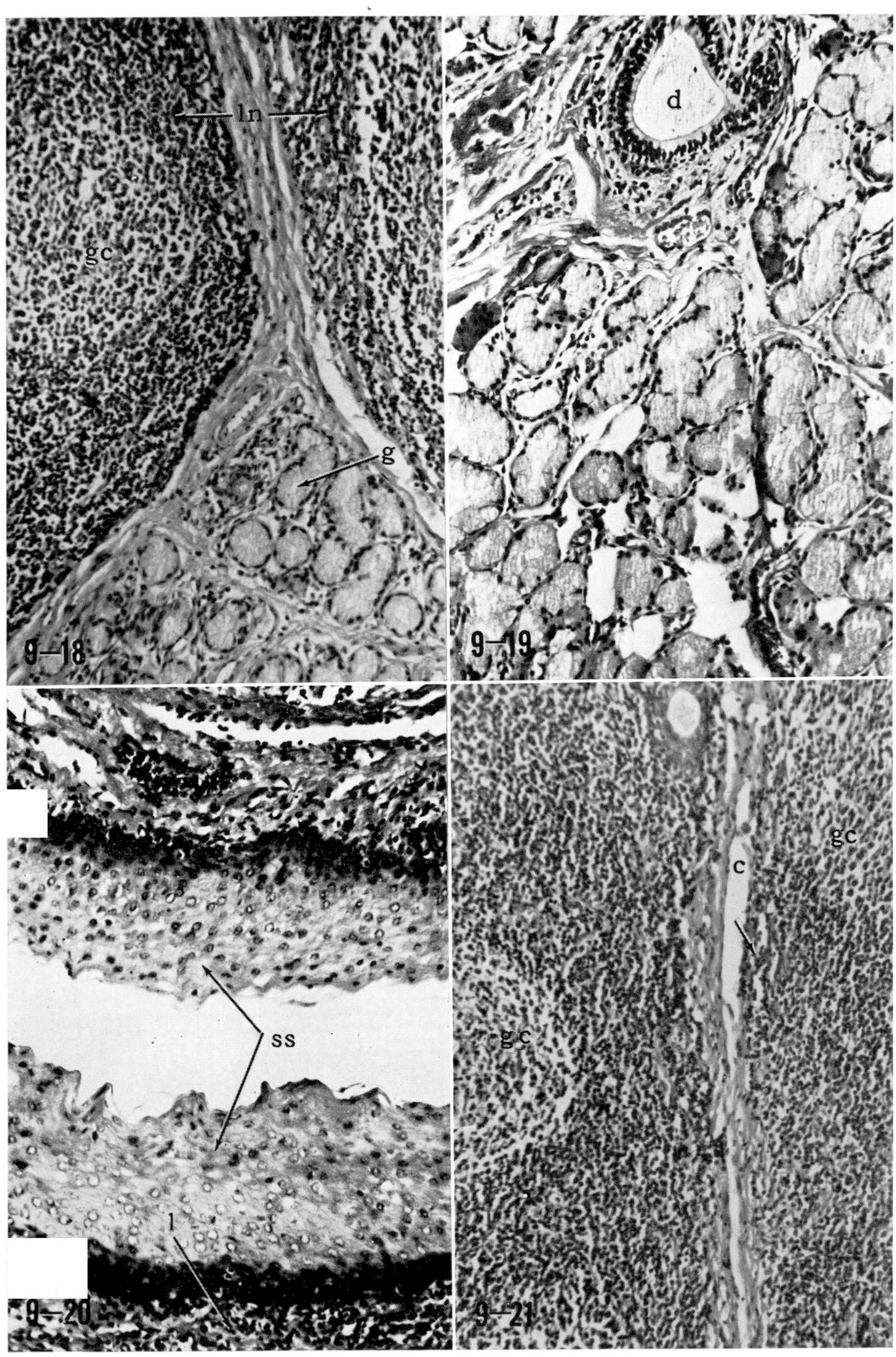
ln
gc
g
9–18
d
9–19
ss
l
9–20
gc
c
gc
9–21

vascular pattern. Basically, the entering **splenic artery branches** near the hilum pass into the trabeculae and enter the white pulp material of a lobule. From the lobules, branches enter the red pulp and further divide to form the **small penicillar arteries**, each of which consists of a pulp artery, a **sheathed artery (ellipsoid)** and **terminal capillaries.** On the venous side, there is a **plexus of venous sinuses** which unite to form the **pulp veins**. These in turn form the **trabecular veins** which ultimately combine to form the **splenic veins**. To date, a controversy still exists regarding the route by which blood cells pass from the arterial into the venous system of vessels. Three schools of thought propose the following theories:

1. The **"closed" circulation theory** maintains that the arterial capillaries connect directly with the venous sinuses.
2. The **"open" circulation theory** advocates that the arterial capillaries open into the intercellular spaces between the sinuses.
3. The **combined "open-closed" theory** proposes that both types are present at the same time. Some investigators contend that a "closed" circulation in a contracted spleen may become an "open" circulation when the spleen is distended.

PLATE 63—Thymus

FIG. 9-22. Section through a portion of thymus, depicting several lobules. H & E stain. Low power. (c, cortical tissue; m, medullary tissue; t, trabeculae with contained blood vessels)

FIG. 9-23. Section through a portion of fetal thymus. H & E stain. Low power. (c, cortical tissue; m, medullary tissue; t, trabeculae)

FIG. 9-24. Intermediate-power view of fetal thymus. H & E stain. (t, trabeculae; c, cortical tissue; m, medullary tissue; Hc, Hassall's corpuscle)

FIG. 9-25. Section of thymus to show that adjacent lobules may have a common medulla (m). Note trabecula (t) which separates adjacent lobules. H & E stain. Intermediate power.

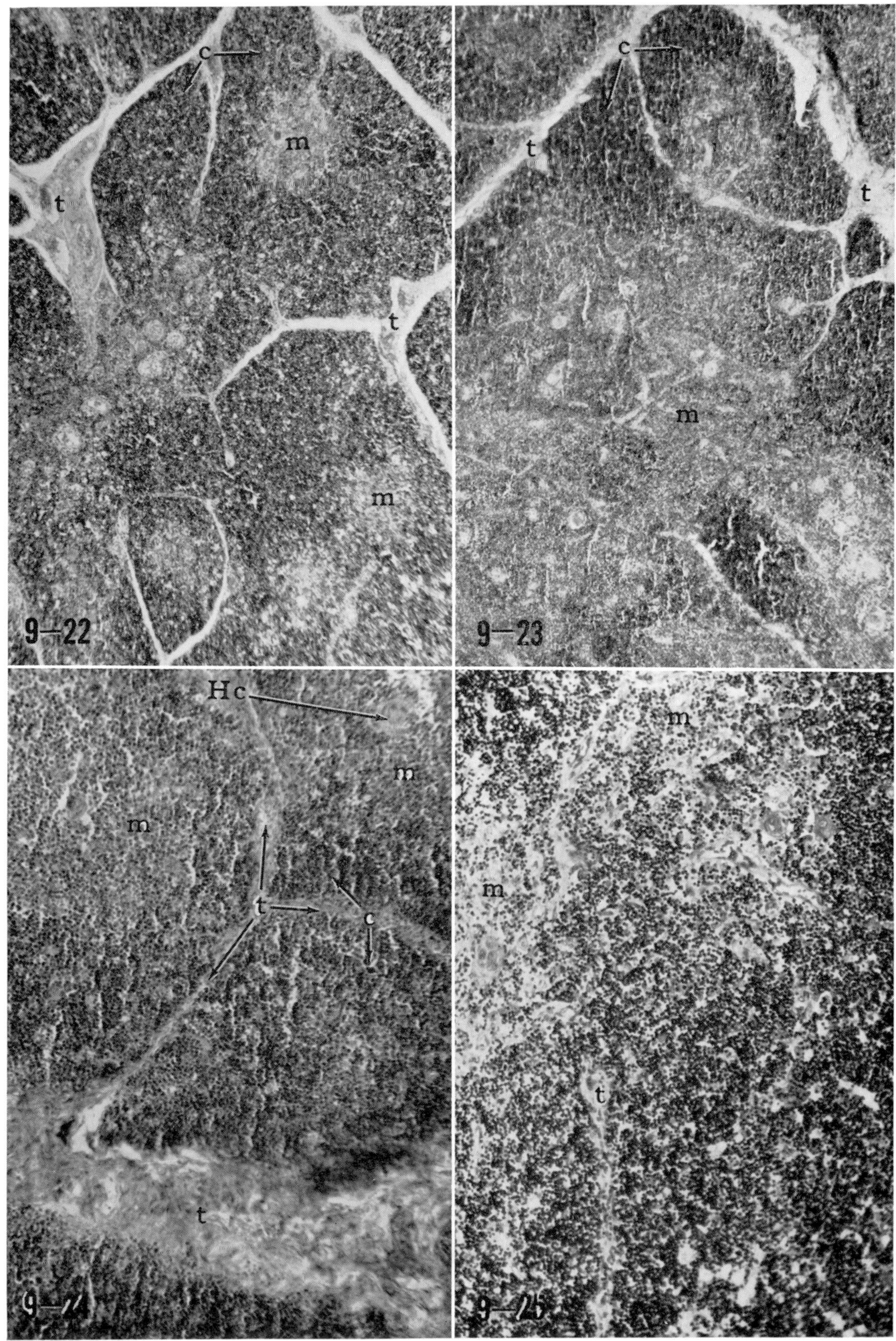
c
m
t
t
m
9–22
c
t
t
m
9–23
Hc
m
m
t
c
t
9–24
m
m
t
9–25

PLATE 64—Thymus

FIG. 9-26. Thymus, showing internal medullary tissue with a concentration of Hassall's corpuscles (Hc) and outer adjacent cortical tissue (c). H & E stain. Intermediate power.

FIG. 9-27. Thymus, showing Hassall's corpuscle (Hc) at the junction of medullary (m) and cortical (c) tissue. H & E stain. High power. (v, blood vessel in trabecula; l, lymphocytes; r, reticular cells)

FIG. 9-28. Thymus, showing a typical well-developed Hassall's corpuscle (Hc) and surrounding lymphocytes. H & E stain. High power.

FIG. 9-29. Section of old thymus. Note fibrous invasion and incomplete lobulation. Septa appear thickened. H & E stain. Low power.

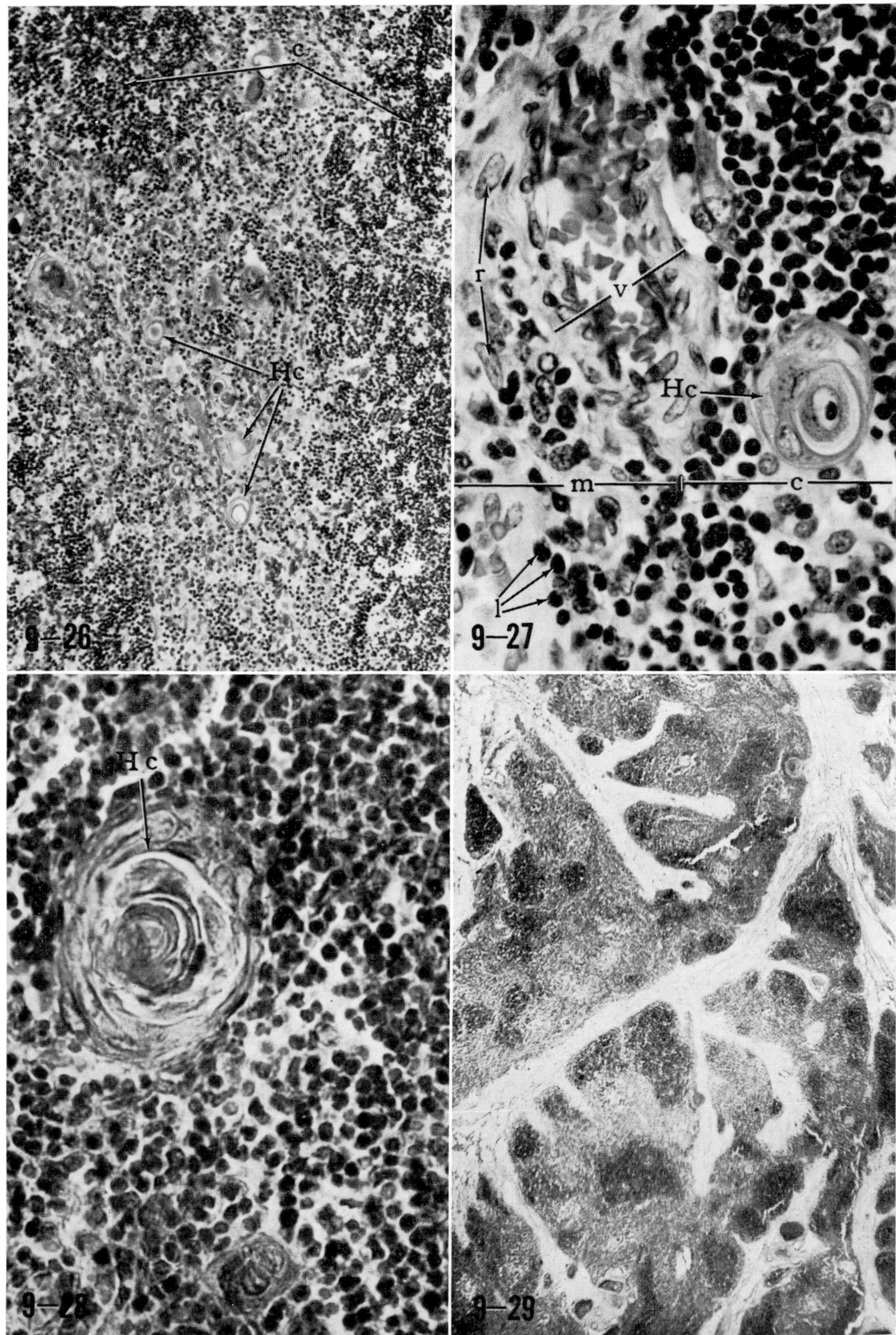
c
Hc
9–26
r
v
Hc
m
c
l
9–27
Hc
9–28
9–29

PLATE 65—Thymus

FIG. 9-30. Old thymus, showing appearance of fat (f) and thickening of trabeculae (t). H & E stain. Low power.

FIG. 9-31. Old thymus, revealing two areas infiltrated by fat (f). H & E stain. Intermediate power.

FIG. 9-32. Old thymus, showing a Hassall's corpuscle. H & E stain. High power.

FIG. 9-33. Old thymus, showing area of fat replacement. H & E stain. High power.

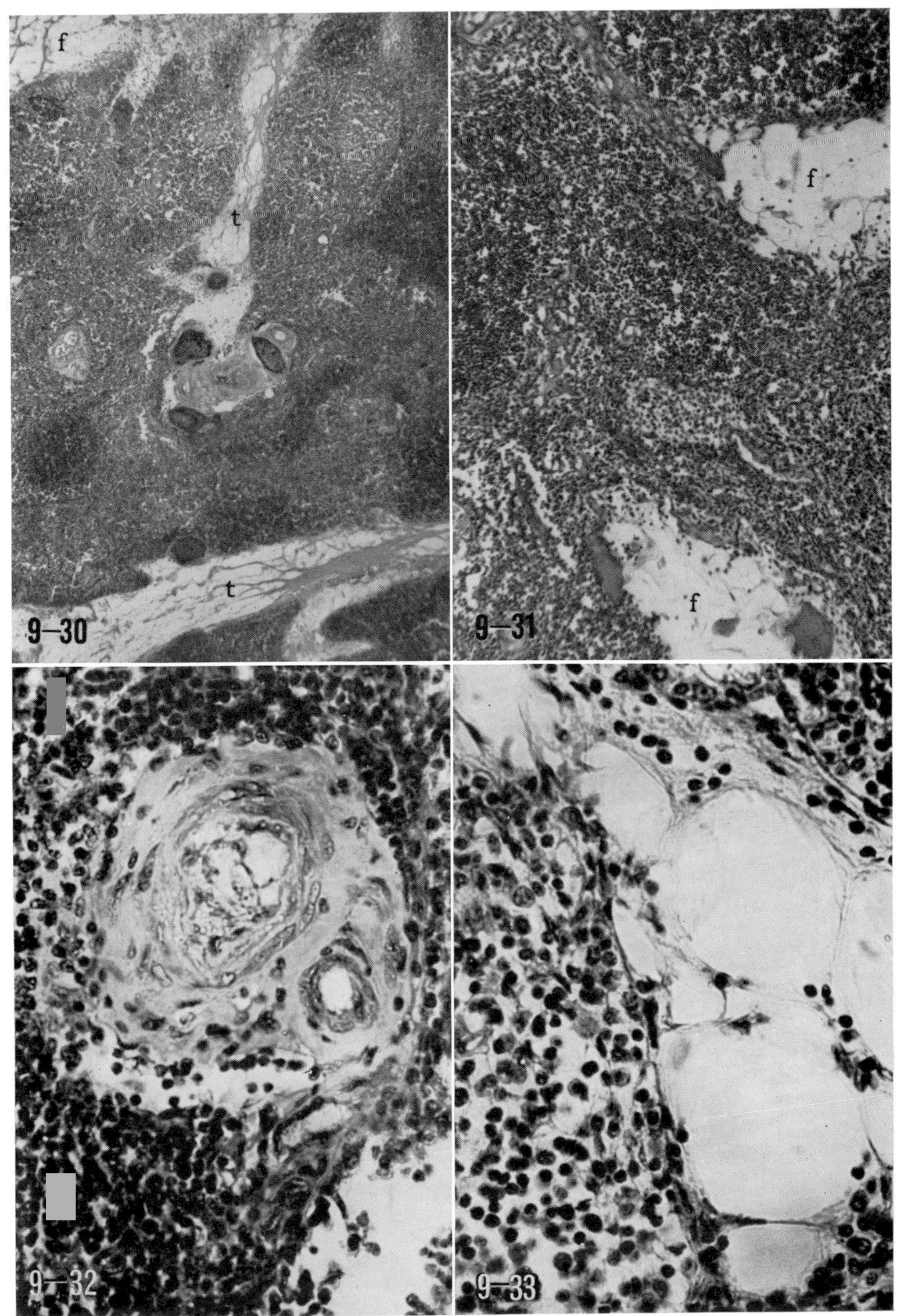
f
t
t
9–30
f
f
9–31
9–32
9–33

PLATE 66—Spleen

FIG. 9-34. Spleen showing the general structure of the pulp but especially depicting the surrounding capsule (c) and penetrating trabeculae (t). H & E stain. Low power.

FIG. 9-35. Injected animal spleen to demonstrate numerous venous sinuses of pulp (white areas). Low power. (c, capsule; t, trabeculae; ln, lymphatic nodule)

FIG. 9-36. Silver stain to demonstrate reticular fibers, especially relative to the capsule (c) and the trabeculae (t). Low power.

FIG. 9-37. Spleen cut near its center, showing trabeculae (t) with contained blood vessels. H & E stain. Low power.

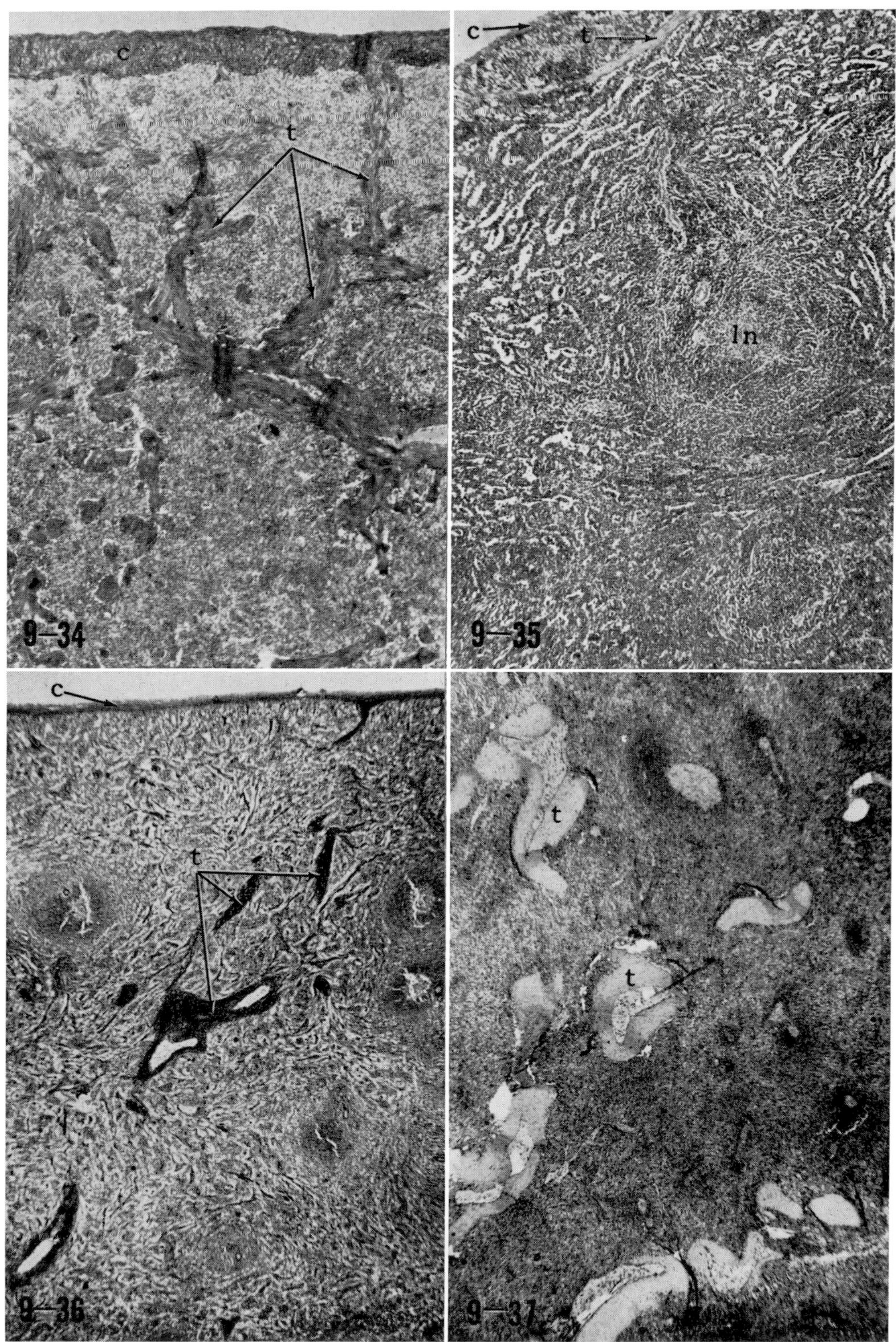

c
t
9—34
c
t
ln
9—35
c
t
9—36
t
t
9—37

PLATE 67—Spleen

FIG. 9-38. Spleen, showing the capsule (c) with a trabecula (t) coming off at right angles and penetrating the organ. Note smooth muscle cells (s) especially present in the trabecula. H & E stain. Intermediate power.

FIG. 9-39. Spleen, showing a portion of the capsule and a penetrating trabecula. Note the elastic fibers (e) between the collagen bundles. Also note the reticular fibers (r) of the pulp. Silver stain. Intermediate power.

FIG. 9-40. Spleen, showing trabecula containing a vessel (tv). Note the presence of a concentration of elastic fibers (e) in the vessel wall which indicates the vessel to be an artery. Silver stain. Intermediate power.

FIG. 9-41. Spleen, showing a trabecula containing a large vessel (tv). Silver stain. Intermediate power.

FIG. 9-42. Section showing trabeculae (t) located deep in the splenic pulp and containing a longitudinally running vessel (tv). Silver stain. Intermediate power.

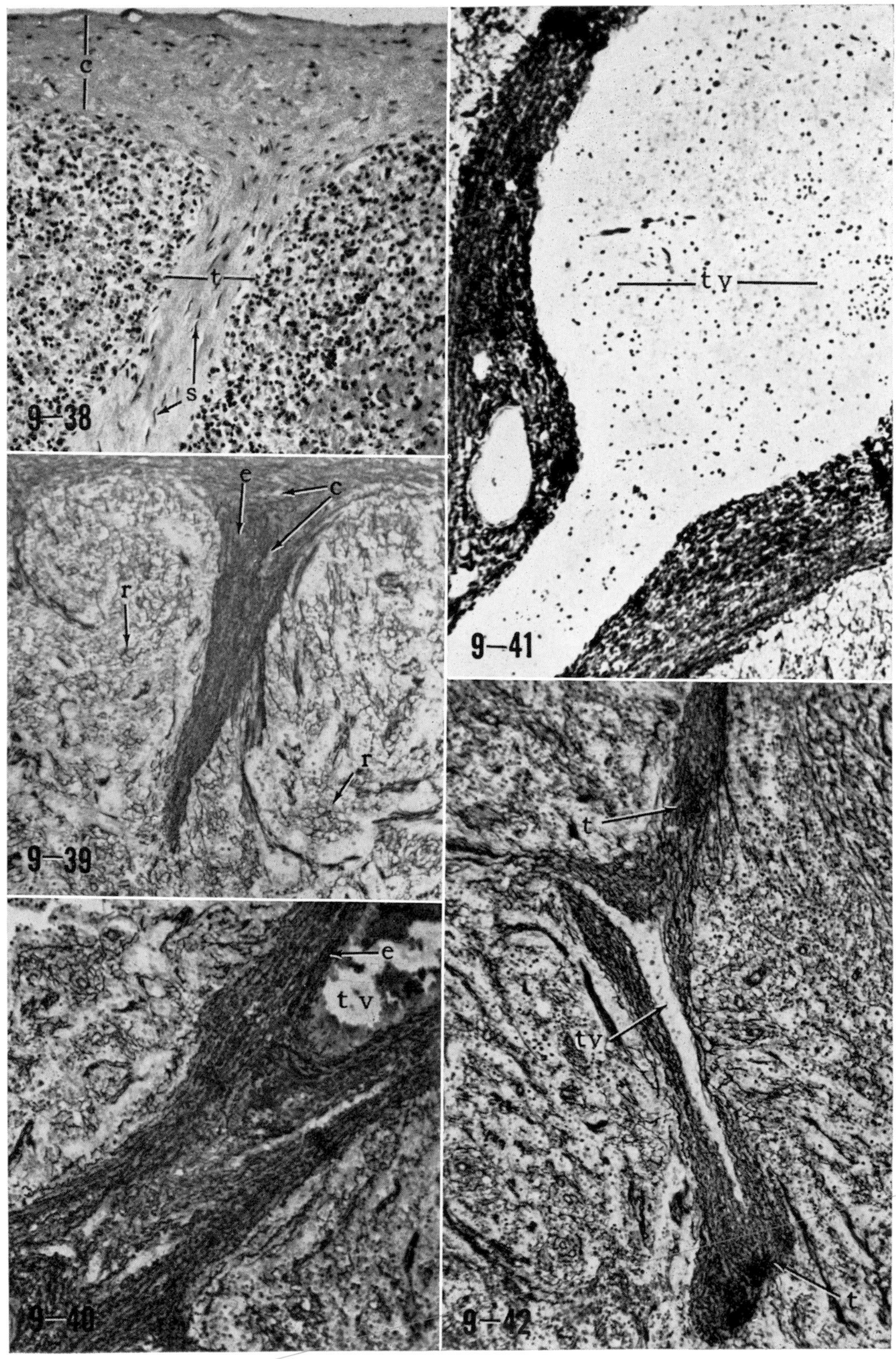
c
t
s
9–38
e
c
r
r
9–39
e
t v
9–40
t v
9–41
t
t v
t
9–42

PLATE 68—Spleen

FIG. 9-43. Section of capsule of spleen. Note the elastic fibers (e) between the collagen bundles and the presence of an occasional smooth muscle cell (s). Silver stain. High power.

FIG. 9-44. Small trabecula (t), cut longitudinally, and adjacent pulp material. Silver stain. High power.

FIG. 9-45. Trabecula (t) cut in cross section and containing a vessel. Silver stain. High power.

FIG. 9-46. Splenic pulp, showing the reticular nature of stromal fibers. Silver stain. High power.

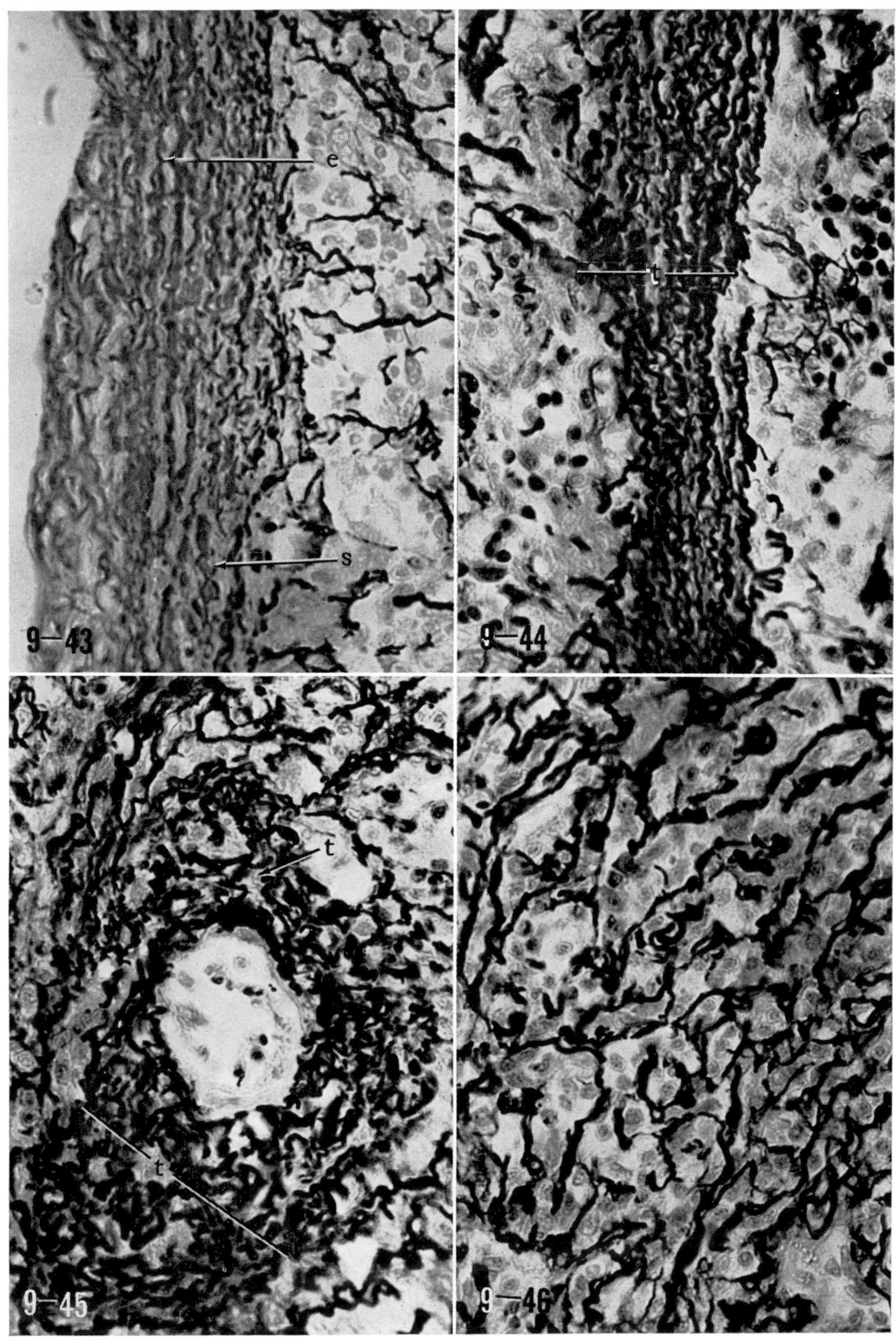
e
s
9—43
t
9—44
t
t
9—45
9—46

PLATE 69—Spleen

FIG. 9-47. Survey section showing the internal organization of the splenic pulp and contained nodules (n). H & E stain. Low power. (t, trabecula; gc, germinal center)

FIG. 9-48. Internal structure of the spleen, showing red (r) and white (w) pulp with a trabecula (t) containing a vessel. H & E stain. Low power.

FIG. 9-49. Silver stain showing a section of spleen similar to that in Figure 9-48. Low power. (r, red pulp; w, white pulp; t, trabecula)

FIG. 9-50. Intermediate-power view of the splenic pulp. H & E stain. (w, white pulp; r, red pulp)

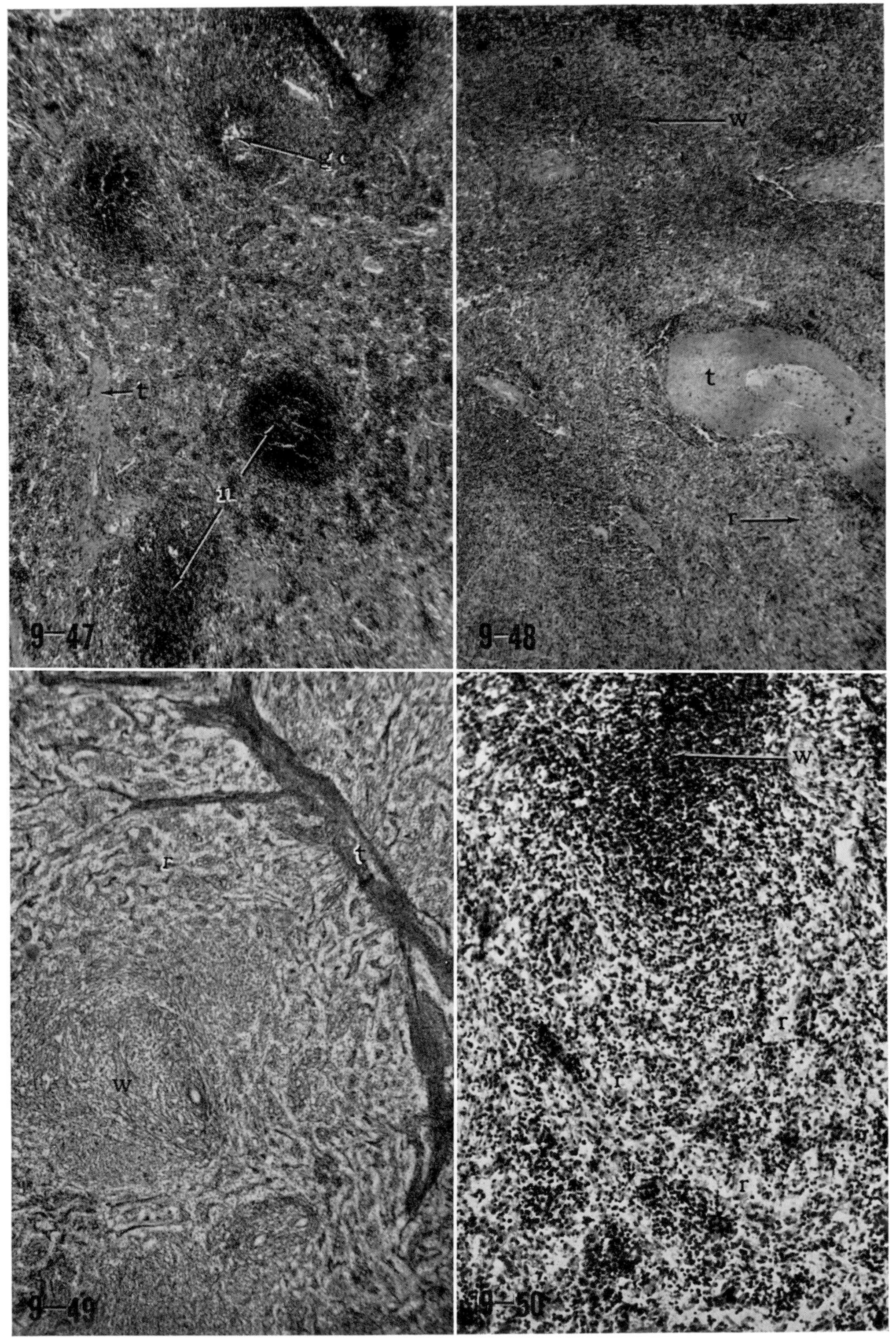
gc
t
n
9—47
w
t
r
9—48
r
t
w
9—49
w
r
r
r
9—50

PLATE 70—Spleen

FIG. 9-51. Splenic pulp, revealing a lymphatic nodule containing a so-called central artery (ca). Silver stain. Intermediate power.

FIG. 9-52. Splenic pulp, revealing a trabecula, containing an artery (ta), in the red pulp and a so-called central artery (ca) at a point of branching in a nodule of white pulp material. H & E stain. Intermediate power.

FIG. 9-53. Section revealing small trabecular nets (tn) and the reticular nature of the splenic pulp. Note the presence of venous sinusoids close to the trabecular nets, appearing as lighter, fiber-free zones. Silver stain. Intermediate power.

FIG. 9-54. Splenic pulp, showing a nodule containing a germinal center (gc) and a nodule with so-called central arteries (ca). Silver stain. Intermediate power.

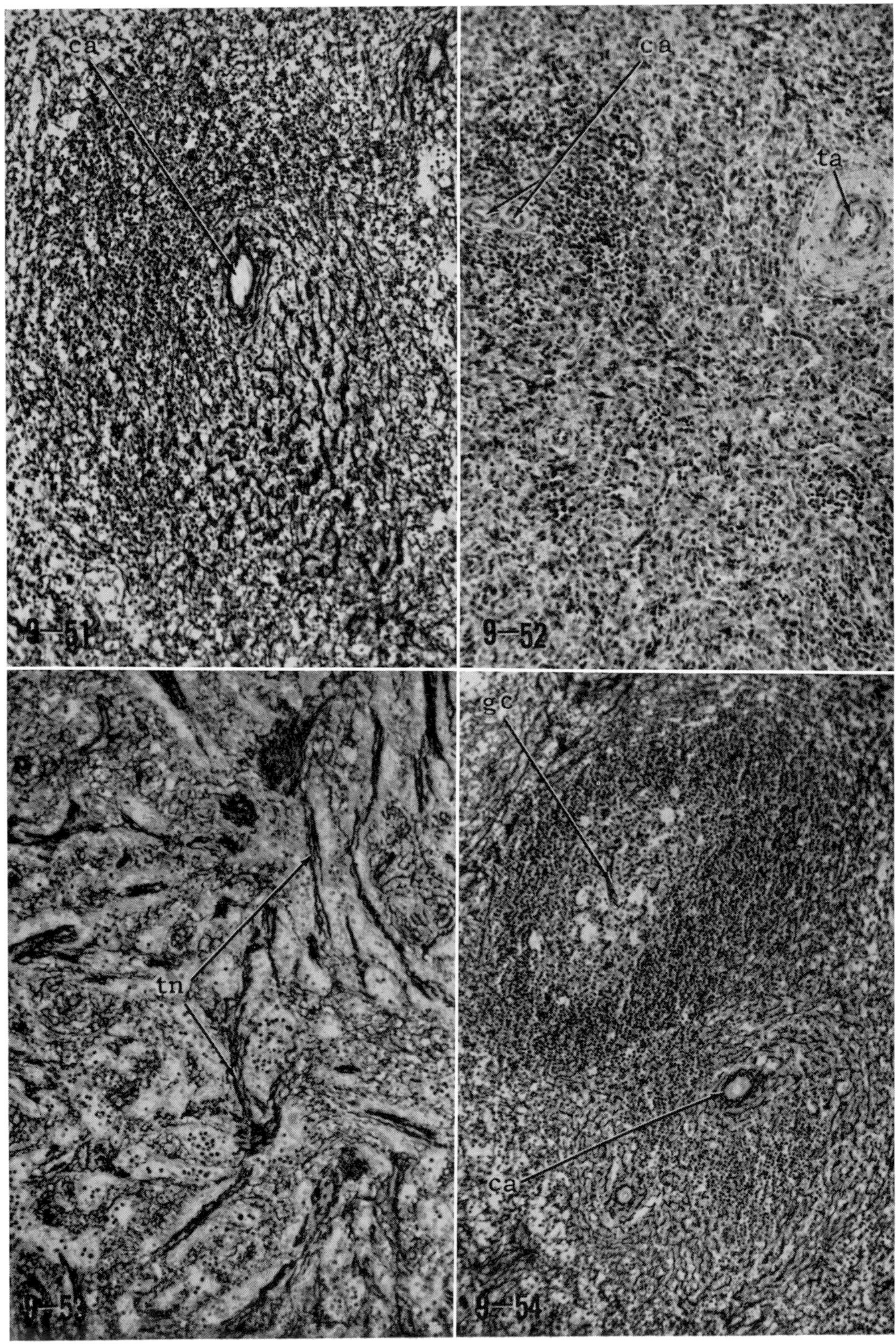
ca
9—51
ca
ta
9—52
tn
gc
ca
9—54

PLATE 71—Spleen

FIG. 9-55. Splenic pulp, revealing a nodule (n) and trabeculae (t). Venous sinusoids (vs) appear as clear areas. Silver stain. Intermediate power.

FIG. 9-56. Red pulp of spleen, revealing sheathed arteries (sa). H & E stain. High power.

FIG. 9-57. Similar to Figure 9-56. H & E. stain. High power. (sa, sheathed arteries)

FIG. 9-58. Section revealing the nature of the reticulum (black fibers) in a splenic nodule. Silver stain. High power.

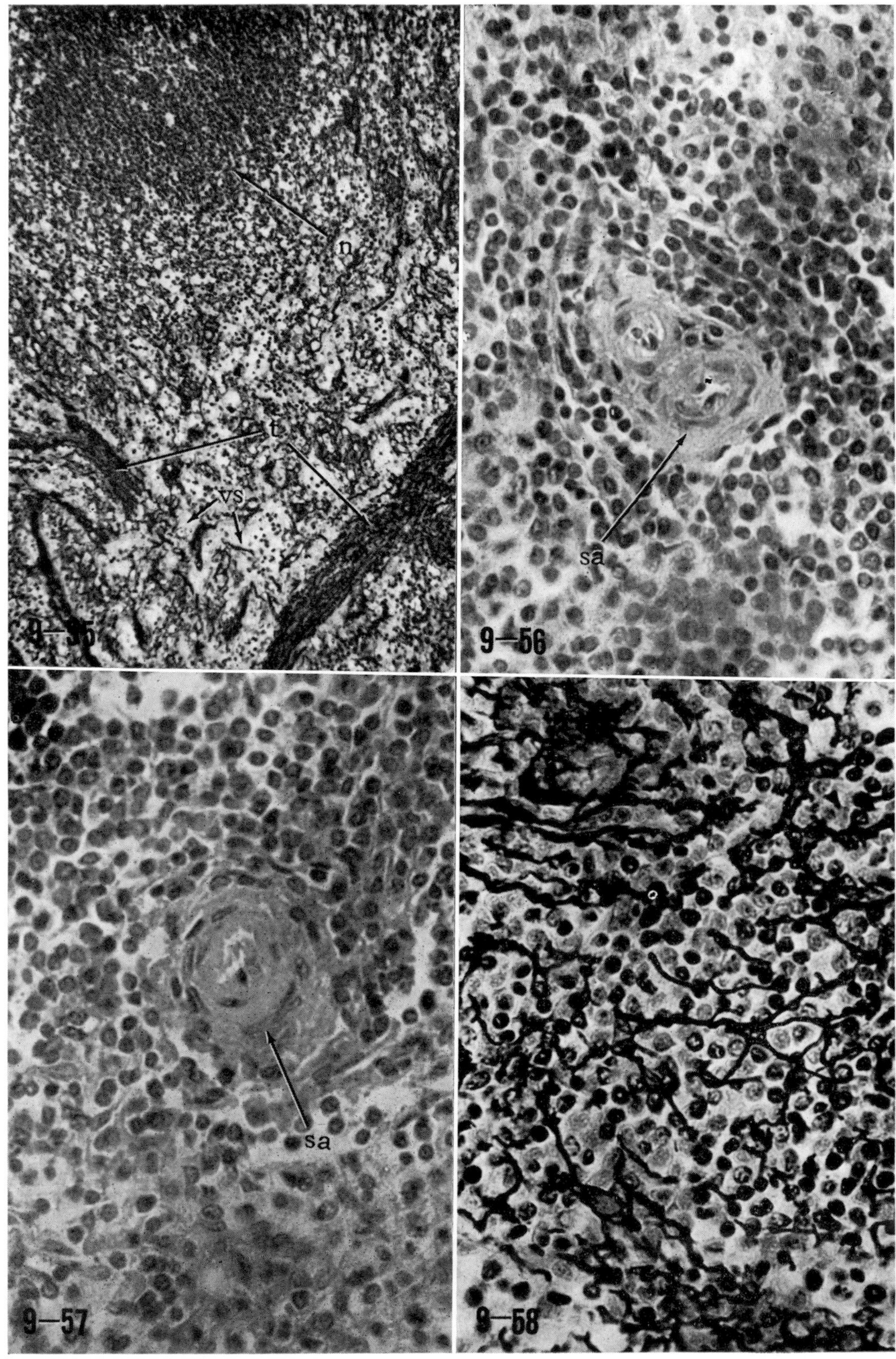
n
t
vs
9—55
sa
9—56
sa
9—57
9—58

10 · The Endocrine System

A. INTRODUCTION

Anatomically and physiologically, the glands of the endocrine system have certain features in common. These glands (glands of internal secretion) have no ducts (ductless) and pass their secretions directly, by osmosis, into the blood or the lymph circulation. Each endocrine gland produces and secretes specific chemical substances called hormones. These secretory products selectively affect some target organ, a group of tissues or the body as a whole. Hormones differ in chemical composition and include proteins, polypeptides, modified amino acids and steroids. In general, they are secreted almost as rapidly as they are formed. In some cases, however, hormones may be stored until required. Another significant feature is that only minute concentrations

PLATE 72—Pituitary Gland

FIG. 10-1. Section showing the capsule (c) and a survey of the outer mass of the pituitary gland. H & E stain. Low power.

FIG. 10-2. Survey section of the interior of the pars distalis of the pituitary gland. Mallory-Azan stain. Low power.

FIG. 10-3. Intermediate-power view of a portion of the pituitary gland showing the cordlike arrangement of the chromophilic cells (cc) of the pars distalis with its overlying capsule (c). H & E stain.

FIG. 10-4. Cords of chromophils (cc) separated by sinusoidal capillaries (s) from a section of the inner portion of the pars distalis of the pituitary gland. Mallory-Azan stain. Intermediate power.

FIG. 10-5. Intermediate-power view of a portion of the pars distalis, showing the sinusoids (s) of the pituitary gland. Mallory-Azan stain.

FIG. 10-6. Section of the pars distalis, especially showing acidophils (a) along with some basophils (b) and chromophobes (cp). H & E stain. High power.

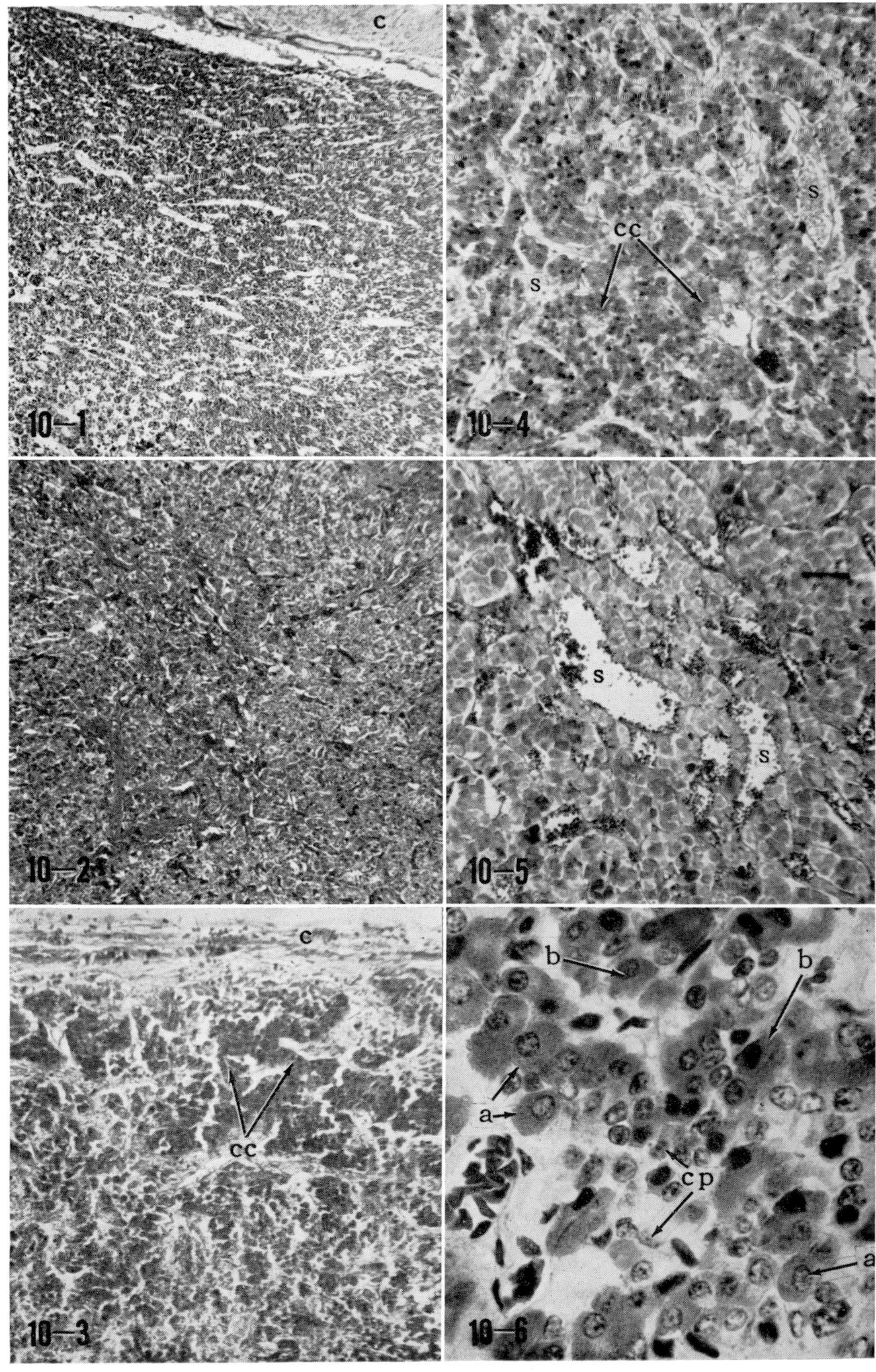
c
10—1
cc
s
s
10—4
10—2
s
s
10—5
c
cc
10—3
b
b
a
a
cp
a
10—6

of hormones in the blood are necessary to keep the various parts of the body aroused to normal activity. Their actions include morphogenesis, integration of autonomic nervous activity and the maintenance of the internal environment of the body. The glands, which strictly have no function other than that of hormone production, include the hypophysis, the thyroid, the parathyroids and the adrenals. In addition, there are endocrines which are classified as mixed glands. Such mixed glands have an endocrine portion which produces hormones and an exocrine portion that produces nonendocrine products which are passed out of the gland via a duct system. The mixed glands include the pancreas, the ovaries and the testes. Other organs are classified as endocrines of an incidental nature, since they are not entirely dissociated from the excretory ducts. This group includes the liver, the stomach and the small intestine (discussed elsewhere). Finally, other structures have been shown to function as endocrine glands; these include certain nervous tissues such as specific neurons of the hypothalamus, the pineal body and the paraganglia. The thymus, which has been discussed previously, is often classified as an endocrine gland. The structure of the thymus can undergo changes in response to alterations of other endocrine interreactions, but the actual function of thymic secretions (hormones) is unknown.

B. HYPOPHYSIS (PITUITARY GLAND)
(Plates 72 to 76)

The hypophysis is an example of an endocrine gland that has a multiplicity of reciprocal interrelations with other structures and functions, all of which are essential for the regulation of normal metabolic patterns of the body. It lies at the base of the brain, within the sella turcica of the sphenoid bone and is connected to the brain by a thin stalk, the infundibulum. The hypophysis is of dual origin, being derived partly from pharyngeal epithelium and partly from the brain wall (both ectodermal). It consists of the **adenohypophysis** (glandular epithelial part) and the **neurohypophysis** (neural part). The adenohypophysis refers to the pars distalis (anterior lobe), the pars tuberalis (upper extension of the distalis) and the pars intermedia (intermediate between the anterior part and the neurohypophysis). The neurohypophysis refers to the pars nervosa (posterior lobe) and the infundibulum.

1. Adenohypophysis

a. *Pars distalis* (Figs. 10-1 to 10-12). The anterior lobe comprises approximately 75 per cent of the gland and is composed of irregularly arranged cell cords and masses supported by a meshwork of delicate reticular connective tissue and separated by large vascular sinusoids. Two types of glandular

PLATE 73—Pituitary Gland

FIG. 10-7. Section of pars distalis of the pituitary gland, showing cords of chromophils (cc), chromophobes (cp) and red blood cells in the sinusoids (s). Mallory-Azan stain. High power.

FIG. 10-8. Pars distalis of the pituitary gland to demonstrate a large cell mass of chromophils (b, basophils; a, acidophils) and chromophobes (cp) surrounded by sinusoids (s). Mallory-Azan stain. High power.

FIG. 10-9. Pars distalis of the pituitary gland, showing chromophobes (cp) along with basophilic (b) and acidophilic (a) chromophils. Mallory-Azan stain. High power.

FIG. 10-10. Pars distalis of the pituitary gland, showing sinusoids (s) cut longitudinally and their relation to the cords of cells. Mallory stain. High power. (b, basophils; a, acidophils; cp, chromophobes)

FIG. 10-11. Pars distalis of the pituitary gland, showing sinusoids (s) cut transversely and their relation to the cords of cells. Compare with Figure 10-10. Mallory stain. High power.

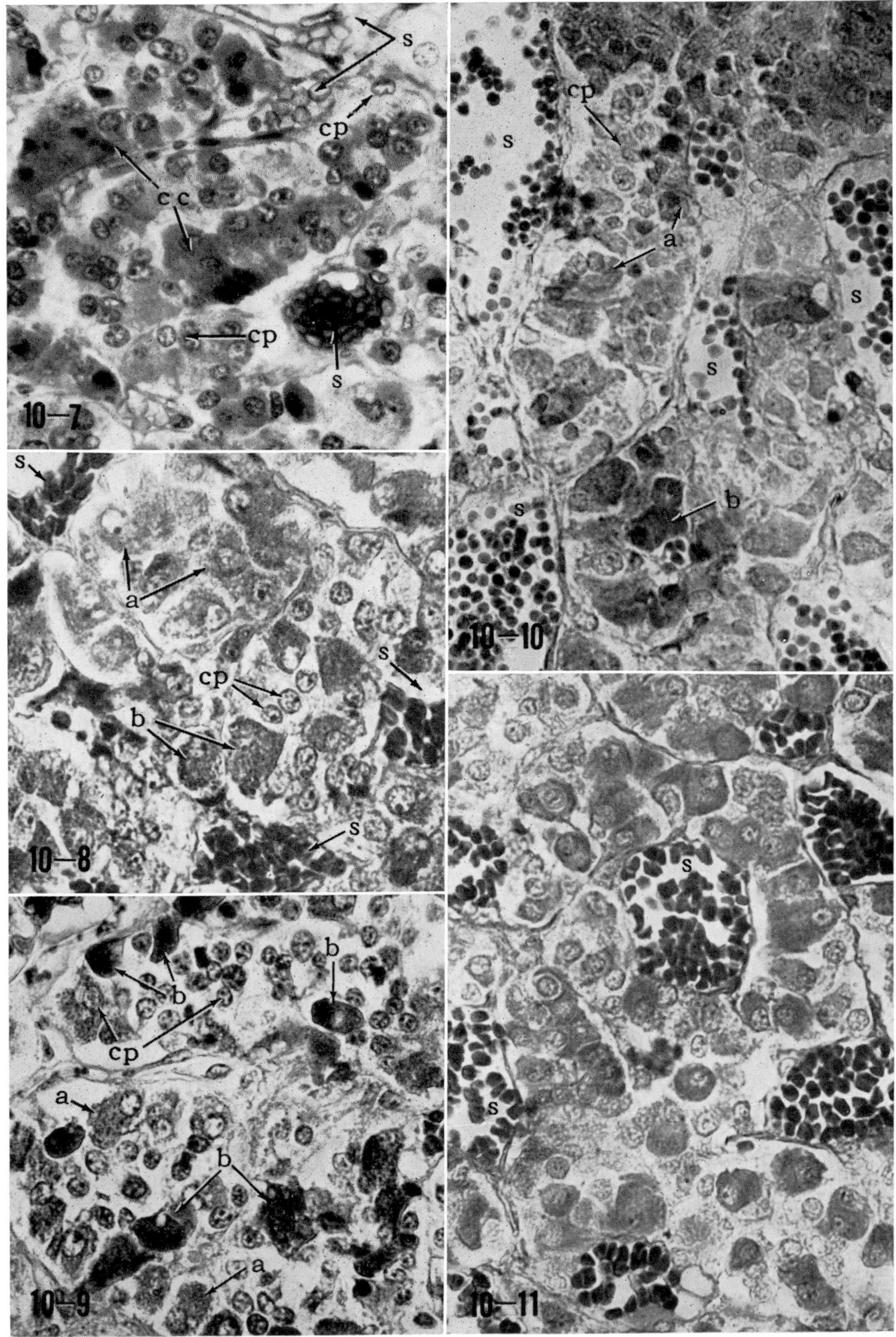

s
cp
cc
cp
s
10—7
s
a
cp
b
s
s
10—8
b
b
cp
a
b
a
10—9
cp
s
a
s
s
s
b
10—10
s
s
10—11

cells, **chromophils** and **chromophobes**, are present. These cells are so named depending on whether or not they demonstrate an affinity for dyes of various types. Employing the H and E staining reaction, the chromophils, which are highly active in the production of trophic factors (stimulate target organs), have been shown to constitute approximately half of the epithelial cells. In this group, the **acidophils** (alpha cells showing eosinophilic staining) are present in greater abundance (37%), whereas the **basophils** (beta cells with specific secretory granules that take up basic dyes) constitute the remainder (11%).

That both types of chromophilic cells are not homogeneous groups has been shown by histochemical analysis and by the use of special stains such as Mallory's trichrome stain. Acidophils stain orange with the trichrome method and are revealed to be the most numerous and also the smallest of the chromophils that are found scattered throughout the gland. Each of these cells contains a prominent nucleus and a cytoplasm that is densely packed with orange granules. Other acidophils contain large red cytoplasmic granules; these occur in cell clusters and are found predominantly in the center of the posterior portion of the pars distalis. Basophils are found predominantly in the periphery of the anterior lobe, are larger and more irregular in shape than acidophils and consist of 3 main types as demonstrated by the Mallory technic: blue basophils that contain densely packed, fine blue granules and vesicles; purple basophils with granules not forming vesicles, and pale basophils which possess a large nucleus and a foamy cytoplasm that contains granules along the cell margins.

In man, present evidence indicates that the acidophils may be the site of production of somatotrophic hormone (STH or GH) and luteotrophic hormone (LTH, prolactin or lactogenic hormone). The basophils appear to be the site of production of thyroid-stimulating hormone (TSH), follicle-stimulating hormone (FSH), luteinizing hormone (LH or ICSH) and possibly adrenocorticotropin (ACTH). Finally, it appears that the control of the production of some of the trophic hormones by the pars distalis may, in turn, be under some higher influence. In this connection the hypothalamus, which has been investigated intensively in recent years, may serve as the mediator, affecting the production and the release of the various trophic hormones.

The chromophobes (52% of the epithelial cells present) are generally regarded as precursors of the chromophils and are especially prominent near the centers of the cords of cells rather than next to the sinusoids. These chromophobic elements are the smallest of all cells in the pars distalis and possess nuclei surrounded by a diffuse light-

PLATE 74—Pituitary Gland

FIG. 10-12. Survey section of the pituitary gland, showing the pars distalis (pd), the pars intermedia (pi) and the pars nervosa (pn). Mallory-Azan stain. Low power.

FIG. 10-13. Pituitary gland, showing the junction of the pars distalis (pd), the pars intermedia and the pars nervosa (pn). Note the colloid material (c) in the follicles of the pars intermedia and the unmyelinated fibrous nature of the pars nervosa. Mallory-Azan stain. Low power.

FIG. 10-14. Pituitary gland, showing the junction of the pars tuberalis (pt), the pars intermedia (pi) and the pars nervosa (pn). Mallory-Azan stain. Intermediate power.

FIG. 10-15. Pituitary gland, showing the pars tuberalis. Note the vascularity (s) and the stromal connective tissue (ct) of this portion. Mallory-Azan stain. Intermediate power.

FIG. 10-16. High-power view of section of a portion of Figure 10-15 to show the epithelial nature of the cords and the presence of sinusoids (s). Mallory stain.

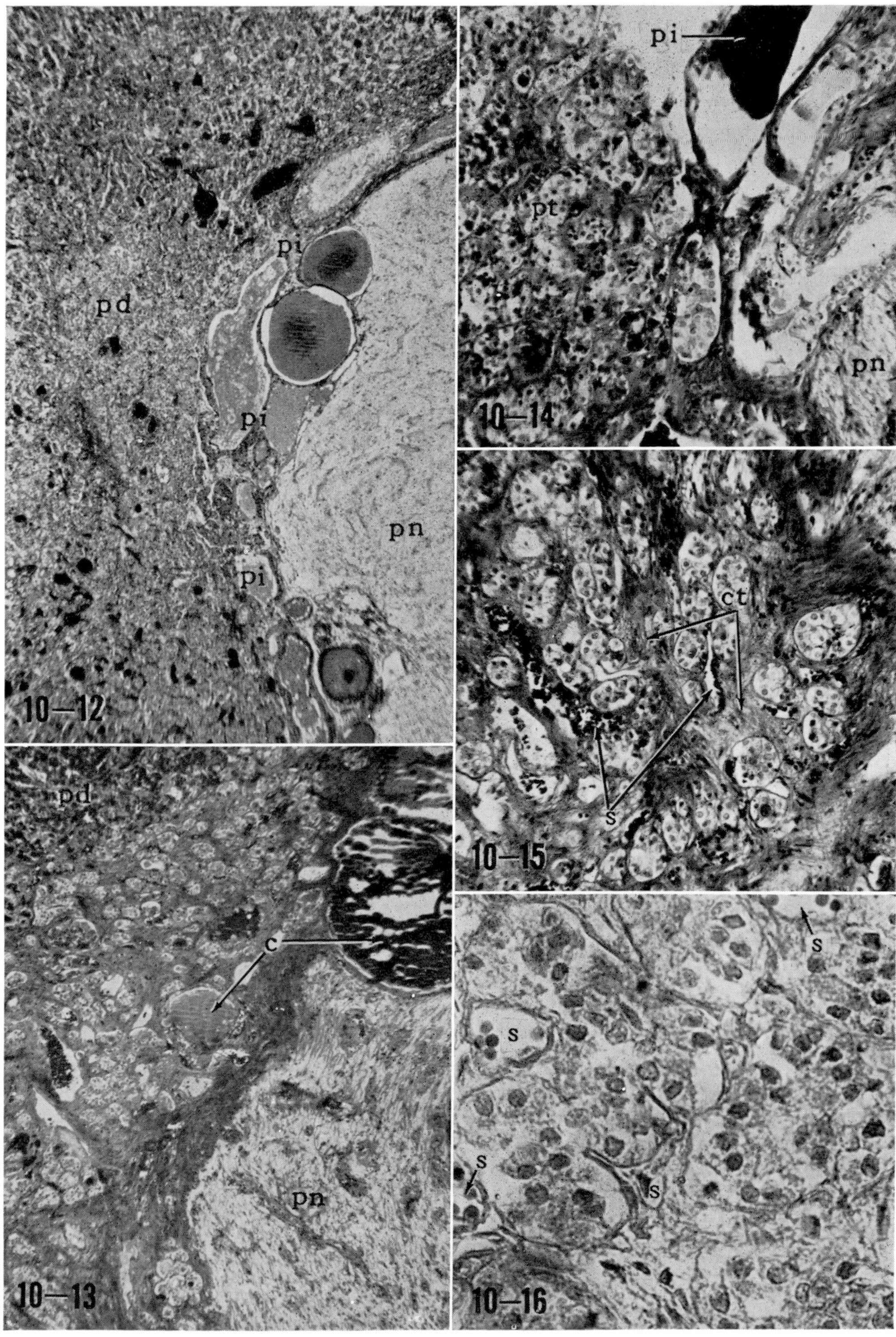
pd
pi
pi
pi
pn
10—12
pi
pt
pn
10—14
ct
s
10—15
pd
c
pn
10—13
s
s
s
s
10—16

staining cytoplasm. Because their cytoplasm is scanty and cell boundaries are indefinite, and because they usually occur in clusters, chromophobes are often referred to as nuclear heaps. Chromophobes also lack specific secretory granules, except during pregnancy when they develop into the so-called pregnancy cells which possess acidophilic granules.

b. *Pars tuberalis* (Figs. 10-13 to 10-16). This upper extension of the anterior lobe is an epithelial-like stratum which covers the neural stalk and the tuberal areas of the brain. This part of the adenohypophysis is quite vascular and contains cells which are cuboidal in shape and lightly basophilic but completely devoid of secretory granules. The function of this area is still unknown.

c. *Pars intermedia* (Figs. 10-17 to 10-21). In man, the pars intermedia is rudimentary, being composed of irregular rows of basophilic epithelial cells generally arranged into follicles which may contain a pale colloidal material.

A melanocyte-stimulating hormone is secreted by the pars intermedia of many animal forms, but at present there is no known direct action of this hormone in man.

2. Neurohypophysis (Plate 76)

a. *Pars nervosa* (Figs. 10-22 to 10-25). The posterior lobe of the pituitary is composed of a tightly arranged mass of neuroglial cells, the **pituicytes**, and blood vessels. The fibrous appearance of pituicytes is due to the presence of long, branching processes on a basic stellate or fusiform shape. These glial cells are pigmented and, in the living state, have been shown to contain refractile granules and droplets. In addition to the pituicytes, there are many unmyelinated fibers but no nerve cell bodies. Swellings or bulblike formations appearing as stained masses known as **Herring bodies** are present along the course of nerve fibers of the hypothalamo-hypophysial tracts. These bodies are often seen in routine histologic preparations as acidophilic-staining masses, but are especially evident in electron micrographs. Pigment cells, lipid and colloidal material also may often be found. It should be noted that no glandular secretory cells are observed in the pars nervosa.

The function of the posterior lobe has been shown to be the storage and the release of antidiuretic hormone (ADH) and oxytocic hormone (oxytocin, pitocin).

b. *Infundibulum*. The pituitary stalk (Fig. 10-26) serves to attach the pars nervosa to the hypothalamus and is composed of an abundance of nerve fibers from the hypothalamus and a rich plexus of blood vessels. In recent years, strong evidence has been presented to show that ADH and oxytocin are produced by the nerve cells of the supra-

PLATE 75—Pituitary Gland

FIG. 10-17. Pituitary gland, showing colloid material (c) in the follicles of the pars intermedia and the appearance of the adjacent pars nervosa (pn). H & E stain. Intermediate power.

FIG. 10-18. Survey section of the pituitary gland at the junction of the pars distalis (pd), the pars intermedia (pi) and the pars nervosa (pn). Mallory-Azan stain. Intermediate power.

FIG. 10-19. Pituitary gland, showing the junction of the pars intermedia (pi) and the pars nervosa (pn). Mallory-Azan stain. Intermediate power.

FIG. 10-20. Pituitary gland at the junction of the pars distalis and the pars intermedia. Note the lining cells (lc) and the colloid material (c) in the follicles of the pars intermedia, the masses of chromophilic cells (cc) of the pars distalis, sinusoids (s) and the stromal connective tissue (ct). Mallory-Azan stain. High power.

FIG. 10-21. Pars intermedia of pituitary gland, showing the cuboidal nature of the lining cells (lc) of the follicles, with some containing colloid material (c). Mallory-Azan stain. High power.

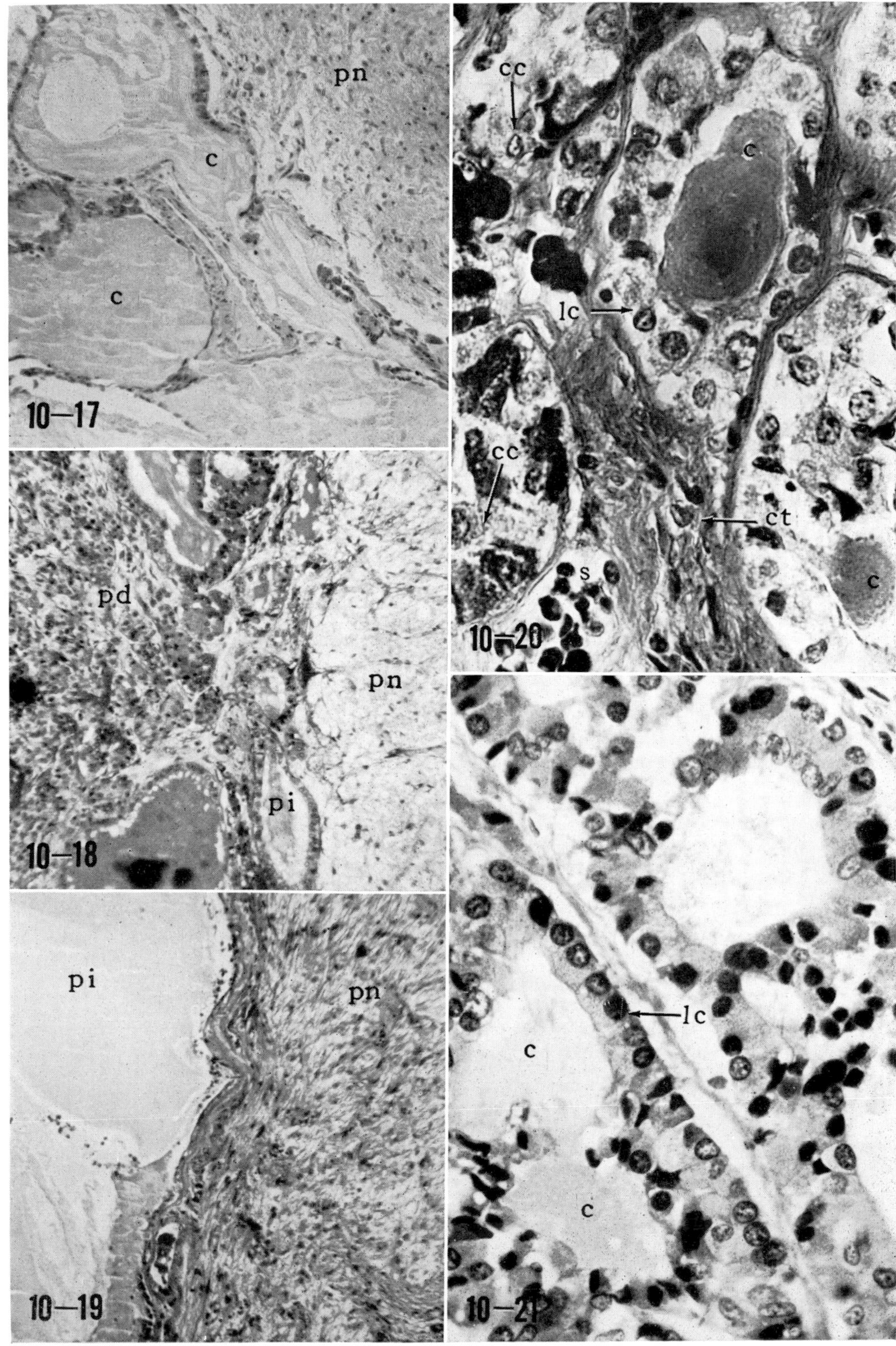
pn
c
c
10—17
pd
pn
pi
10—18
pi
pn
10—19
cc
c
lc
cc
ct
s
c
10—20
lc
c
c
10—21

optic and the paraventricular nuclei of the hypothalamus as a neurosecretion. Further, these hormones are transported via the axons through the infundibulum into the posterior lobe of the pituitary.

C. THYROID GLAND
(Plates 77 and 78)

The thyroid consists of two separate lateral lobes and a connecting part, the isthmus, lying over the superficial part of the trachea just below the larynx. The gland is derived from the midventral floor of the pharynx (endoderm). The thyroid gland is very labile and varies in size and structure in response to such factors as sex, nutrition, temperature, age, season and the iodine content of food.

Histologically, there is a capsule of fibroelastic connective tissue which continues into the surrounding pretracheal fascia. This capsular tissue sends septa into the gland, breaking it up into lobules. In addition, the connective tissue septa support the parenchymal elements and carry vessels, lymphatics and nerves. Each lobule is made up of characteristic structural units of the thyroid gland known as **follicles**. Follicles are grapelike structures that vary in size. Each follicle is the result of secretory activity of the simple epithelium of glandular cells that line its surface. With the inception of thyroid function, these glandular cells are present as a clump or nest of cells that secretes directly into a surrounding capillary network. Soon their secretory product becomes so great that intracellular storage is inadequate. As a result, all the cells of this nest pour their secretions through their plasma membranes on the side away from the capillary network. As development continues, this reservoir becomes the center of a follicle, and the glandular cells of the nest undergo mitotic division to cover the follicular surface completely.

The substance in each follicle is known as **colloid**. Colloid is a semifluid, homogeneous substance that is rich in iodine and contains the proteinaceous active principle of the gland. This hormone stimulates the rate of metabolism in tissues, according to the needs or demands of the body. In this way, the transformation of energy into forms the body can use is brought about. In the state of normal activity, the lining epithelium of the follicle is simple cuboidal or low columnar and rests on a highly vascular fibrous connective tissue that separates one follicle from the next. Generally, when the gland is in a resting state, the follicular cells are low columnar, and their secretions are transported into the follicular lumen; the result is a large lumen and an increase in its content of colloid material. On the other hand, in general, when the gland is active, the epithelium is of a tall columnar type that shows a tendency to fold upon itself. In such cases, the active principle may pass from the colloid in the lumen to the follicular cells

PLATE 76—Pituitary Gland

FIG. 10-22. Pars nervosa of the pituitary gland, to show the nerve fibers with associated glial cells (pituicytes, p). Note the endothelium (en) of a longitudinally cut arteriole. Mallory-Azan stain. High power.

FIG. 10-23. Pars nervosa of the pituitary gland, showing nerve fibers (f), pituicytes (p), sinusoids (s) and bulblike masses along some fibers, probably Herring bodies (H). Mallory-Azan stain. High power.

FIG. 10-24. Pars nervosa of the pituitary gland, showing pituicytes (p), sinusoids (s) and a Herring body (H). Mallory-Azan stain. High power.

FIG. 10-25. Section showing the fibrous nature and the vascularity of the capsule overlying the pars nervosa of the pituitary gland. Mallory-Azan stain. High power.

FIG. 10-26. Section of pituitary infundibular stalk to show the portal vessels and their arrangement. Mallory stain. Intermediate power.

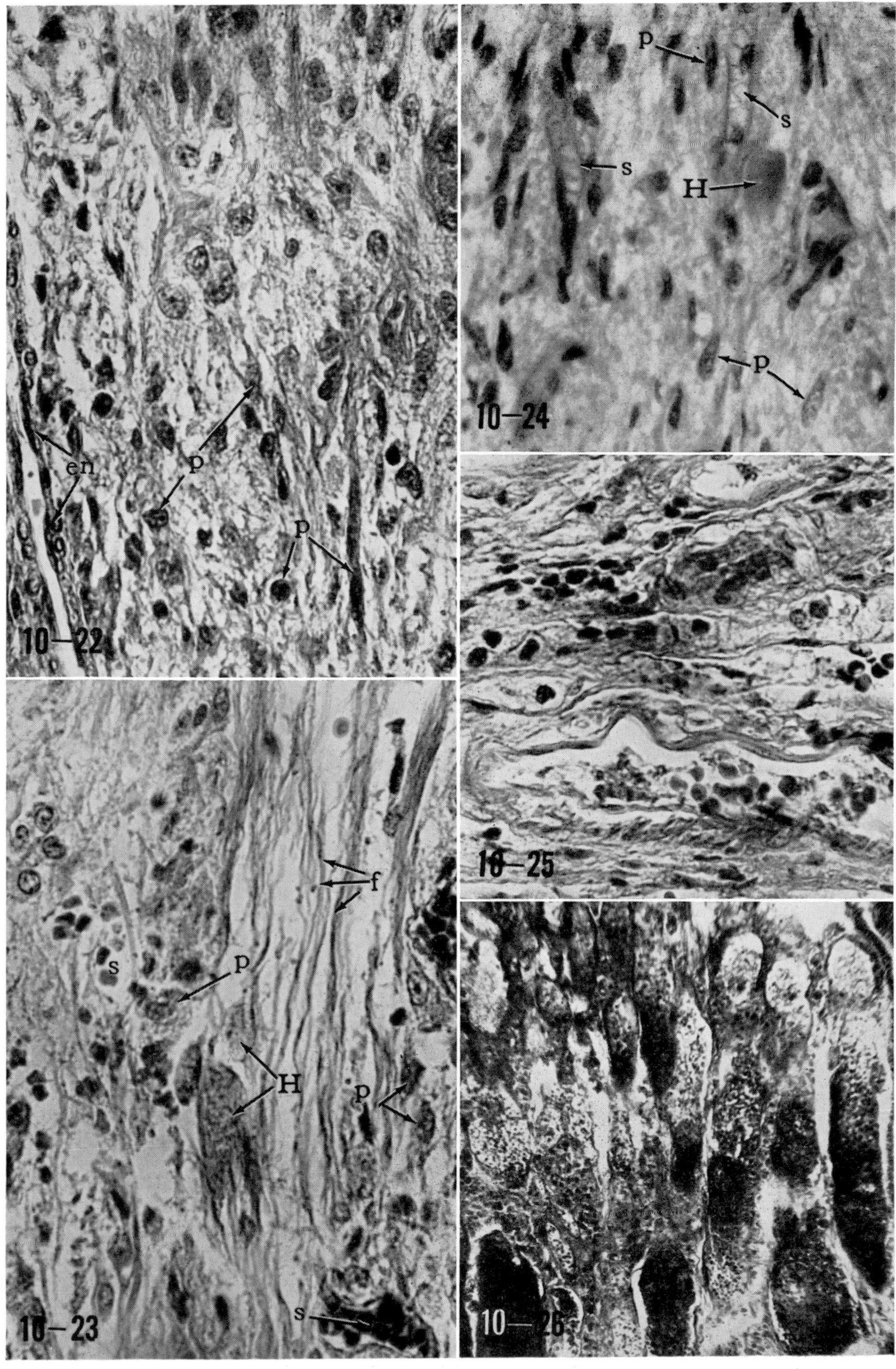
p
s
s
H
p
10–24
en
p
p
10–22
10–25
f
s
p
H
p
s
10–23
10–26

and then to the capillaries. If the gland is highly active, the secretions from the follicular cells can go directly into the capillaries.

The size and the number of mitochondria in the follicular cells increase when the gland is active. Evidence seems to indicate that this increase in mitochondria is related to the formation of colloid rather than to the release of hormone into the capillaries. Increase in the rate of release of hormone into the capillaries appears to be linked with increased size of the Golgi apparatus. Finally, it should be noted that more than one hormone is secreted by the thyroid gland; thyroxin is the principal circulating hormone, but triiodothyronine is present in smaller amounts.

D. PARATHYROIDS
(Plate 79)

In most individuals the parathyroids are 4 in number, lying in the dorsal portion of the thyroid. However, these small yellowish-red bodies may vary in number and position and may be found distributed anywhere from the base of the skull to the arch of the aorta.

Microscopic examination reveals that each gland consists of densely packed groups of vascularized anastomosing cords and clumps of cells within a capsule of thin fibrous connective tissue. Thin connective tissue septa penetrate the gland but do not divide it into distinct lobules. Two types of epithelial cells are observed, namely, the **chief (principal) cells** and the **oxyphil cells**. The chief cells are characterized by large vesicular nuclei and a pale granular cytoplasm that is rich in glycogen. These cells appear to be the most abundant type but do not stain uniformly well, some cells being present as darker, and others as lighter, staining elements. Chief cells are arranged primarily as clumps and irregular cords that are supported by reticular fibers. A rich network of large sinusoidal capillaries is present between the cells.

The oxyphil cells, which appear only after the first decade of life (postpuberty) and possibly may be a transitional form of chief cell, are usually arranged in clusters and are somewhat larger than the chief cell. The distinguishing differences are that the oxyphil cells have small chromatic nuclei and intensely acidophilic granules in their cytoplasm.

The polypeptide hormone designated as parathyroid hormone (PTH) is produced by the chief cells. This hormone plays a vital role in the metabolism of calcium and phosphorus. At the same time, the rate of parathyroid hormone secretion appears to be controlled directly by the calcium level of the blood. That is, changes in the plasma calcium level result in changes in the activity of the parathyroid glands. There appears to be no evidence for pituitary control over parathyroid activity.

E. ADRENALS (SUPRARENAL GLANDS)
(Plates 80 to 84)

The adrenal glands are paired, flattened masses in contact with the upper poles of

PLATE 77—Thyroid Gland

FIG. 10-27. Survey section of the thyroid gland, showing its capsule (c) and follicular arrangement. Note that the peripheral follicles (pf) are generally smaller than the deeper follicles (df). Mallory stain. Low power.

FIG. 10-28. Thyroid gland, showing a large vessel (v) embedded in connective tissue septa (ct) separating the gland into two lobules. Mallory stain. Low power.

FIG. 10-29. Section of thyroid gland, showing the interior of the gland with follicles in different stages of activity. Mallory stain. Low power.

FIG. 10-30. Thyroid gland, showing fat (a) and a nerve (n) in the capsule (c) surrounding the follicles. Mallory stain. Intermediate power.

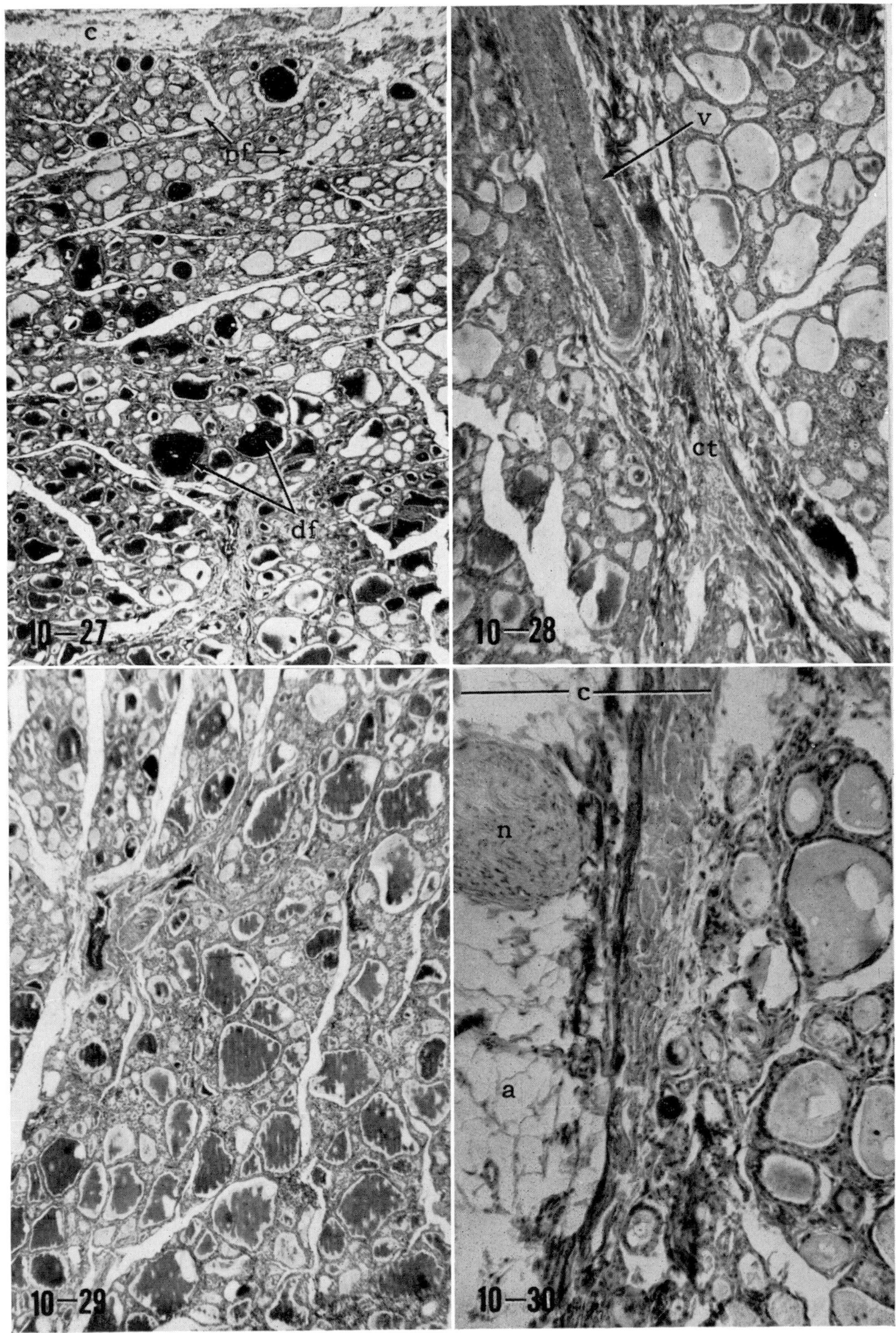
c
pf
df
10–27
v
ct
10–28
10–29
c
n
a
10–30

the kidneys. In mammals, the adrenals represent combined double organs that actually consist both structurally and functionally of two separate glands, the **adrenal cortex** and the **adrenal medulla**. The two portions are embryologically unrelated and arise from two loci quite far removed from each other. The cortex arises from coelomic mesoderm located between the urogenital fold and the dorsal mesentery. The medulla, on the other hand, is derived from neural crest ectoderm which also gives rise to the cells of sympathetic ganglia. The adrenals have a dense fibrous connective tissue capsule from which delicate trabeculae extend inward to support the cellular arrangement in conjunction with a fine reticular network that is present in the organ.

1. Adrenal Cortex (Interrenal Tissue)

Examination of a cross section of the adrenal gland reveals that the cortex occupies approximately three fourths of the width of the gland. The cortex exhibits cords of cells that border on a rich network of capillaries and sinusoids and is arranged into 3 distinct cellular zones. These 3 layers are named, from without inward, the **zona glomerulosa**, the **zona fasciculata** and the **zona reticularis**.

a. *Zona glomerulosa.* The outer zone is the narrowest and consists of ovoid groups of columnar cells that stain faintly basophilic but have deep-staining small nuclei.

b. *Zona fasciculata* (Palisade Zone; Spongy Zone). The middle zone is the widest and consists of long parallel cords of cells running toward the center of the gland. For the most part, the cells are polygonal or cuboidal and often binucleate. Especially in the outer portion of this zone the cells have a spongy or vacuolated appearance because of their high lipid content which is dissolved out during usual histologic treatment. Such cells are often referred to as spongiocytes.

c. *Zona reticularis.* The innermost zone consists of cords of cells arranged in a haphazard fashion. In general, the cells are smaller and darker than those of the zona fasciculata and exhibit various intensities of nuclear staining. The inner cells located next to the medulla are rich in pigment granules. It should be mentioned that the human infant has a 4th zone, referred to as the "fetal" X zone, which lies next to the medulla and possibly gives way to the zona reticularis as development proceeds.

The zones of the adrenal cortex, except for the zona glomerulosa, and the rates of secretion of the various hormones produced, are under the direct regulation of the adrenocorticotropic hormone. This outer portion of the adrenal gland is essential to life and elaborates a number of steroid hormones. These hormones fall into the following groups:

(1) Corticosteroids

(a) Glucocorticoids that notably affect carbohydrate metabolism, the catabolism of protein, fat metabolism, electrolyte and water metabolism, membrane permeability

PLATE 78—Thyroid Gland

FIG. 10-31. Thyroid gland, revealing vessels (v) in the interfollicular spaces and a mass of extrafollicular cells (ec). Mallory stain. High power.

FIG. 10-32. Thyroid gland, showing a group of colloid-containing follicles lined by simple cuboidal epithelium. Note connective tissue (ct) and vessels (v) between the follicles. Mallory stain. High power.

FIG. 10-33. Section showing a group of thyroid follicles with interfollicular connective tissue. Mallory stain. High power.

FIG. 10-34. Thyroid follicles, mainly lined by simple squamous epithelium. Note the vascularity of the interfollicular spaces. Mallory stain. High power.

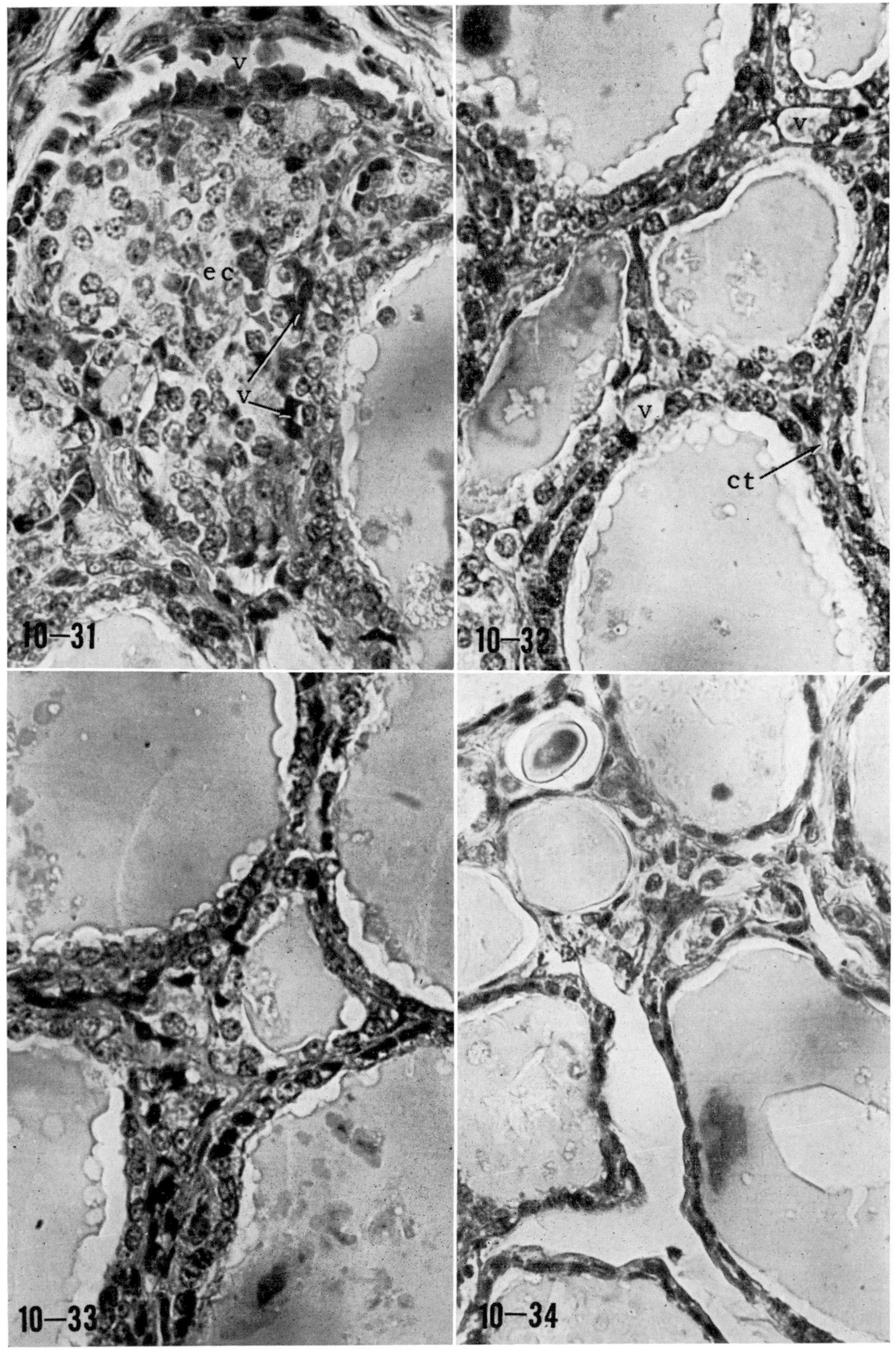
v
ec
v
10–31
v
v
ct
10–32
10–33
10–34

and other important metabolic activities of the body

(b) Mineralocorticoids that cause marked retention of sodium, chloride and water and also excretion of potassium and phosphorus

(2) Sex hormones

(a) Androgens

(b) Estrone

(c) Progesterone

2. Adrenal Medulla (Chromaffin Tissue)

The medullary cells are larger and more granular than those of the cortex. They appear as irregularly arranged cords and groups of finely granulated, basophilic cells and are found in association with vessels and sinusoids. When stained with chromic acid, the fine granules become yellowish-brown, and the cells are referred to as **chromaffin cells**. Also found in the medulla, but less numerous, are **sympathetic ganglion cells** (described elsewhere) with their axons ending around the chromaffin cells.

The adrenal medulla is not essential to life; it elaborates the amines, namely, epinephrine and norepinephrine, substances which affect circulation, respiration, carbohydrate and general metabolism, the central nervous system and other systems.

F. PARAGANGLIA

The paraganglia are small masses of cells arranged in cords within or alongside the capsules of sympathetic ganglia and along the abdominal aorta above the origin of the inferior mesenteric artery. These masses are believed to arise from sympathogonia (primitive sympathetic ganglion cells) and have the same histologic structure as the chromaffin tissue found in the adrenal medulla. Likewise, the organs of Zuckerkandl, situated on either side of the origin of the inferior mesenteric artery, and the carotid glands at the point of bifurcation of the common carotid artery contain chromaffin tissue.

G. PINEAL GLAND (EPIPHYSIS CEREBRI)

(Plates 85 and 86)

The pineal gland, which is located in the posterior end of the roof of the third ventricle lying dorsal to the midbrain, is encapsulated by connective tissue derived from the pia mater. Trabeculae penetrate into the gland, dividing it into lobules of branching parenchymal cells. These cells stain weakly and appear as irregularly shaped bodies with

PLATE 79—Parathyroid Gland

FIG. 10-35. Survey section of the parathyroid gland. H & E stain. Low power.

FIG. 10-36. Slightly higher magnification of a portion of the parathyroid gland. Note the anastomosing cordlike appearance and rich vascularity (v) associated with the glandular parenchyma. Trabeculae (t) and fat cells (f) are also present. H & E stain. Low power.

FIG. 10-37. Section of parathyroid gland showing an area of oxyphil cells (o) at the left and chief cells (c) on the right side. Note the capsule of the gland (cp) at the right with associated trabecula (t). H & E stain. Intermediate power.

FIG. 10-38. High-power magnification of a portion of the parathyroid gland, showing cords and clumps of large, highly granular oxyphil cells (o) and smaller chief cells. Note that the internuclear distances between adjacent oxyphil cells are much greater than for chief cells. Also observe vessel (v) associated with trabecula. H & E stain.

FIG. 10-39. An area of oxyphil cells, showing their arrangement as anastomosing cords of cells along with vascular channels (v) containing red blood cells. H & E stain. High power.

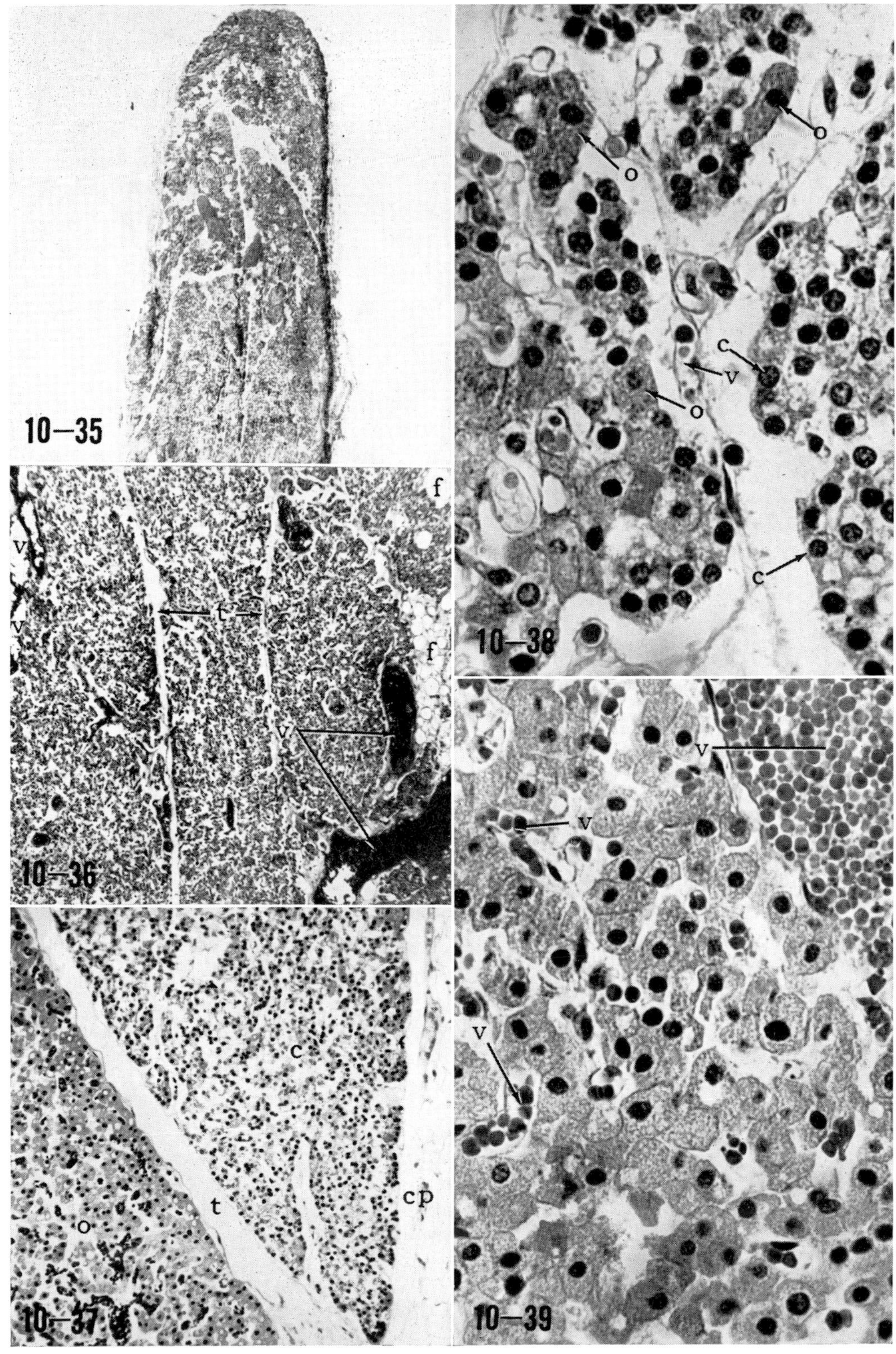
10–35
v
v
t
f
f
v
10–36
c
t
o
cp
10–37
o
o
c
v
o
c
10–38
v
v
v
10–39

long slender processes. More centrally located parenchymal cells with round vesicular nuclei and cytoplasmic processes that appear club-shaped and seem to terminate on blood vessels are often observed in special preparations. Also found scattered among the parenchymal cells are neuroglial cells, mainly of the astrocytic type, and a few microglial cells, which serve as supporting elements. A distinct histologic feature found in the capsule and at the base of the pineal gland is the presence of brain sand granules (**acervuli** or **corpora aranacea**). These are eosinophilic, mulberry-shaped, laminated, calcareous bodies.

In mammals, at present, the pineal gland is no longer considered as a functionless vestige of the median eye of certain amphibian and reptilian forms. Recently, the hormones melatonin, serotonin, norepinephrine, acetylcholine and histamine have been found as secretions of the pineal gland.

PLATE 80—Adrenal Gland

FIG. 10-40. Adrenal gland, revealing cortical (c) and medullary (m) areas. H & E stain. Low power. (v, central medullary vein; cp, portion of capsule revealing trabeculae penetrating the cortex)

FIG. 10-41. Survey of adrenal gland, revealing a portion of capsule (cp) overlying cortical (c) area with obvious delineation of zona reticularis (zr) running toward the centrally located medulla. Mallory-Azan stain. Low power.

FIG. 10-42. Adrenal gland, showing a portion of the capsule (cp) with overlying fatty investment, cordlike arrangement of cells composing the cortex (c) with a small amount of underlying medullary tissue (m). Mallory stain. Low power.

FIG. 10-43. Adrenal gland, revealing the nature of the capsule (cp) with a contained blood vessel (v). The ovoid cells of the outer zona glomerulosa (zg), and the radially running cords of cells of the broad underlying zona fasciculata are evident. Mallory stain. Intermediate power.

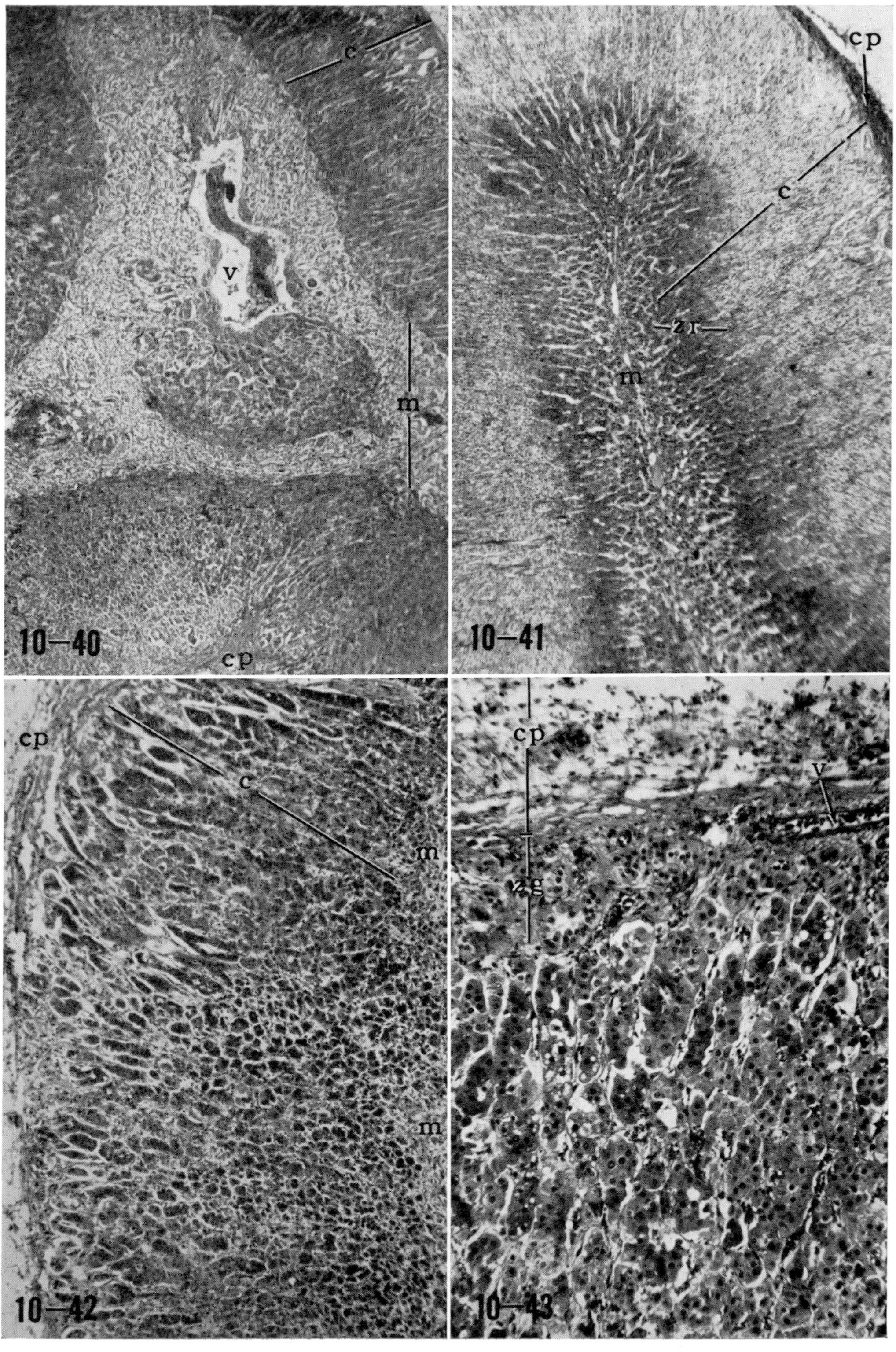
c
v
m
10–40
cp
cp
c
zr
m
10–41
cp
c
m
m
10–42
cp
v
zg
10–43

PLATE 81—Adrenal Gland

FIG. 10-44. Capsule of adrenal gland with overlying fatty investment (f). Note the dense collagenous (c) and vascular (v) nature of the capsule from which trabeculae (t) penetrate into the cortex. Mallory stain. Intermediate power.

FIG. 10-45. Section through the adrenal cortex showing a portion of the ovoid groups of cells of the zona glomerulosa (zg) and the radially coursing parallel cords of cells of the zona fasciculata (zf) which have been cut tangentially. This plane of section accounts for the broader appearance of the zona glomerulosa and the not too obvious parallel arrangement of the cords of the zona fasciculata. Note the penetrating trabecula (t) and the numerous radially disposed sinusoids(s) coursing between the cords of cells. Mallory-Azan stain. Intermediate power.

FIG. 10-46. Adrenal cortex showing the cells of the zona fasciculata. Note the typical palisade arrangement of the cords of cells separated by numerous sinusoids. Compare with Figure 10-45. H & E stain. Intermediate power.

FIG. 10-47. Adrenal gland, revealing the distal portion of the zona fasciculata (zf), the irregular network of the cords of cells of the zona reticularis (zr) and the ovoid anastomosing cords of cells of the medulla (m). Mallory stain. Intermediate power.

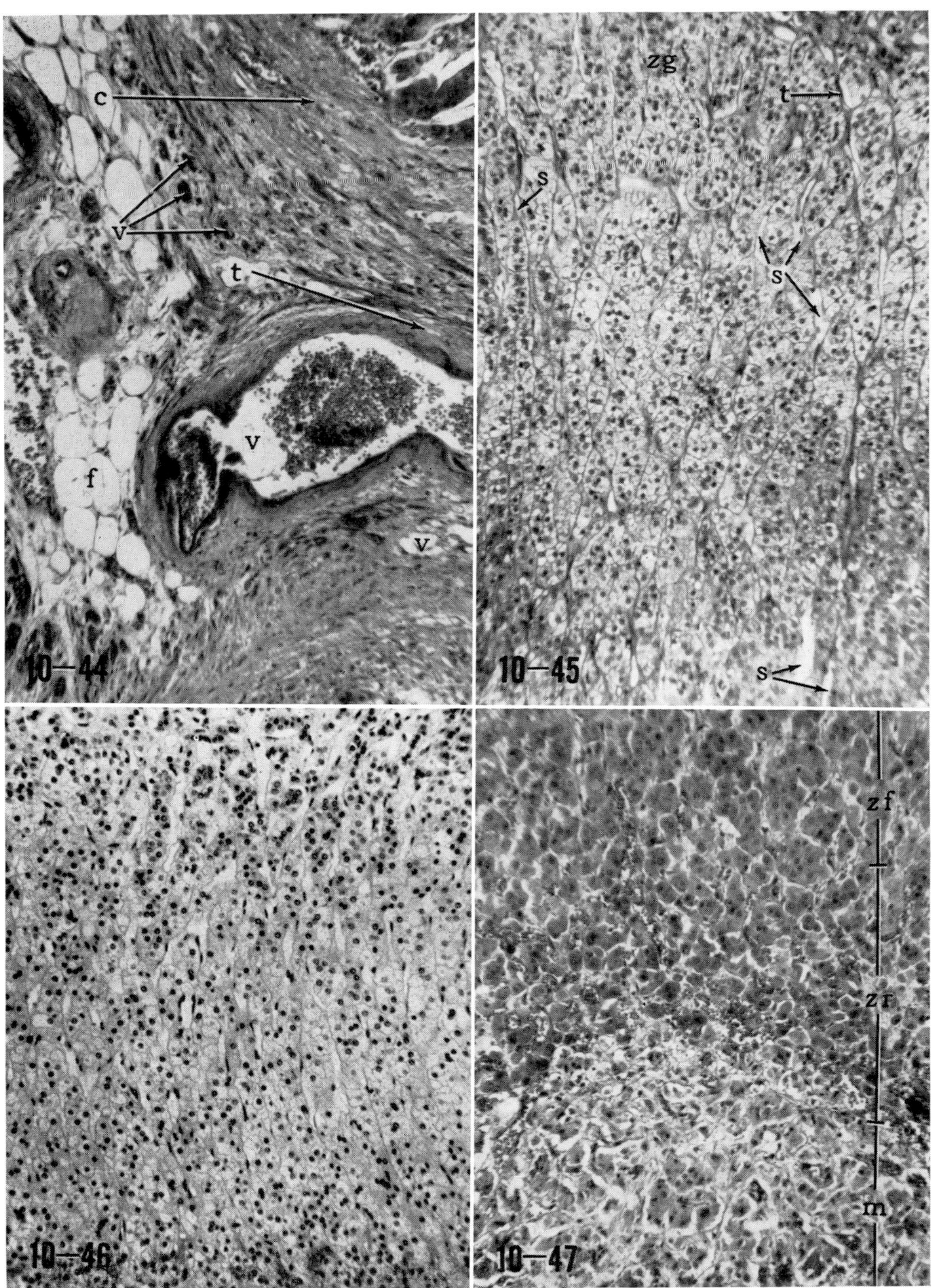
c
v
t
v
f
v
10–44
zg
t
s
s
s
10–45
10–46
zf
zr
m
10–47

PLATE 82—Adrenal Gland

FIG. 10-48. Adrenal, showing a channel (bv) filled with red blood cells penetrating the zona reticularis (zr) of the cortex and coursing toward the medulla (m). Mallory stain. Intermediate power.

FIG. 10-49. Adrenal showing a large blood-filled space (bs) in the medulla. H & E stain. Intermediate power. (m, medulla; zr, zona reticularis)

FIG. 10-50. Junction of zona reticularis (zr) of adrenal cortex and medulla (m). Note the anastomosing cords of cells and groups of cells typical of both regions. H & E stain. Intermediate power.

FIG. 10-51. Adrenal medulla (m) sandwiched between the zona reticularis (zr) of the cortex. Note the large number of blood vessels (bv) associated with the cells of the medulla. H & E stain. Intermediate power.

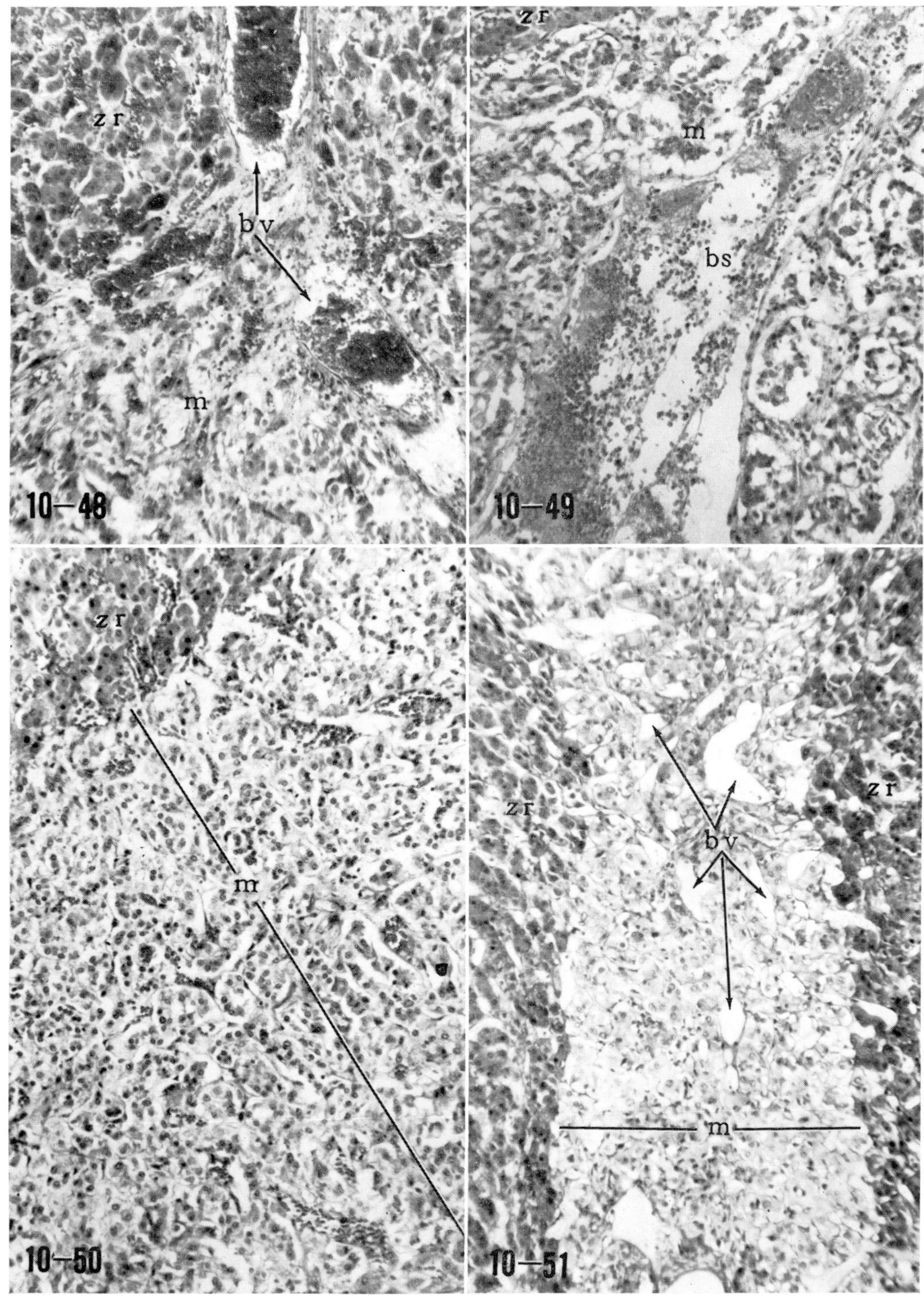
zr
bv
m
10–48
zr
m
bs
10–49
zr
m
10–50
zr
bv
zr
m
10–51

PLATE 83—Adrenal Gland

FIG. 10-52. Adrenal cortex, revealing the columnar or pyramidal nature and the closely packed ovoid arrangement of the cells of the zona glomerulosa. Also note the vascularity (v). Mallory stain. High power.

FIG. 10-53. Adrenal cortex, showing the cells of the zona glomerulosa. Mallory-Azan stain. High power.

FIG. 10-54. Adrenal cortex, showing the spongy nature of cells (spongiocytes) in the cords of the zona fasciculata. Mallory-Azan stain. High power.

FIG. 10-55. Adrenal cortex, showing the palisade arrangement of the cords of cells of the zona fasciculata. Note the secretory granular nature of the cells separated by sinusoids (s). Mallory stain. High power.

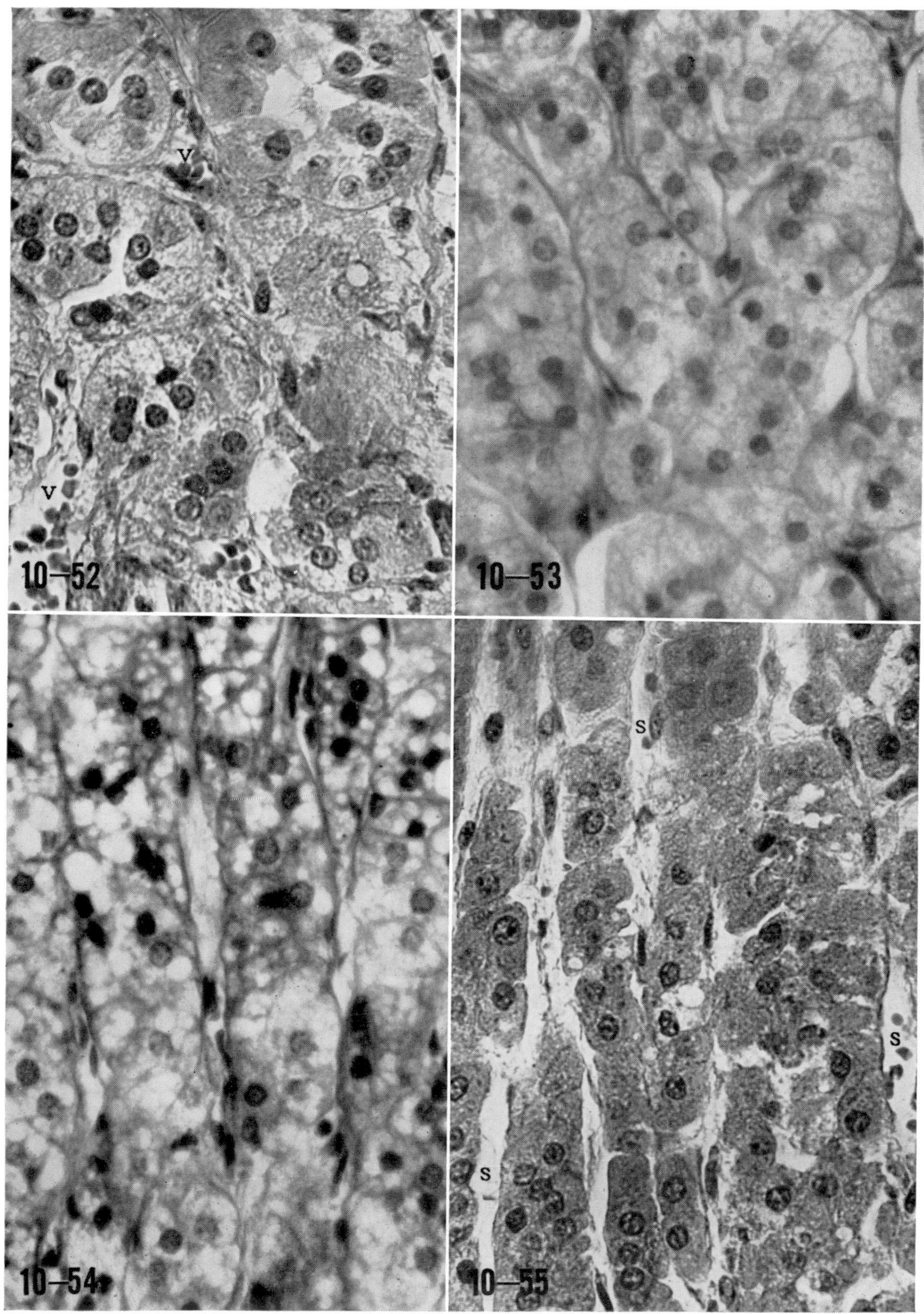
V
V
10–52
10–53
10–54
S
S
S
10–55

PLATE 84—Adrenal Gland

FIG. 10-56. Section of the zona fasciculata of the adrenal cortex showing sinusoids filled with red blood cells adjacent to the cell cords. Mallory stain. High power.

FIG. 10-57. Section of the zona reticularis of the adrenal cortex. Note the anastomosing of the cords and the sinusoidal capillaries (s). Also observe the variable type of staining of the nuclei and cytoplasm of the cells. Mallory-Azan stain. High power.

FIG. 10-58. Section of the zona reticularis of the adrenal cortex, revealing the irregular course of the cords. Mallory stain. High power.

FIG. 10-59. Adrenal medulla, showing the general arrangement of the columnar cells into clumps (cl) and cords (co). Note the blood vessel (v), which is most likely a venule. H & E stain. High power.

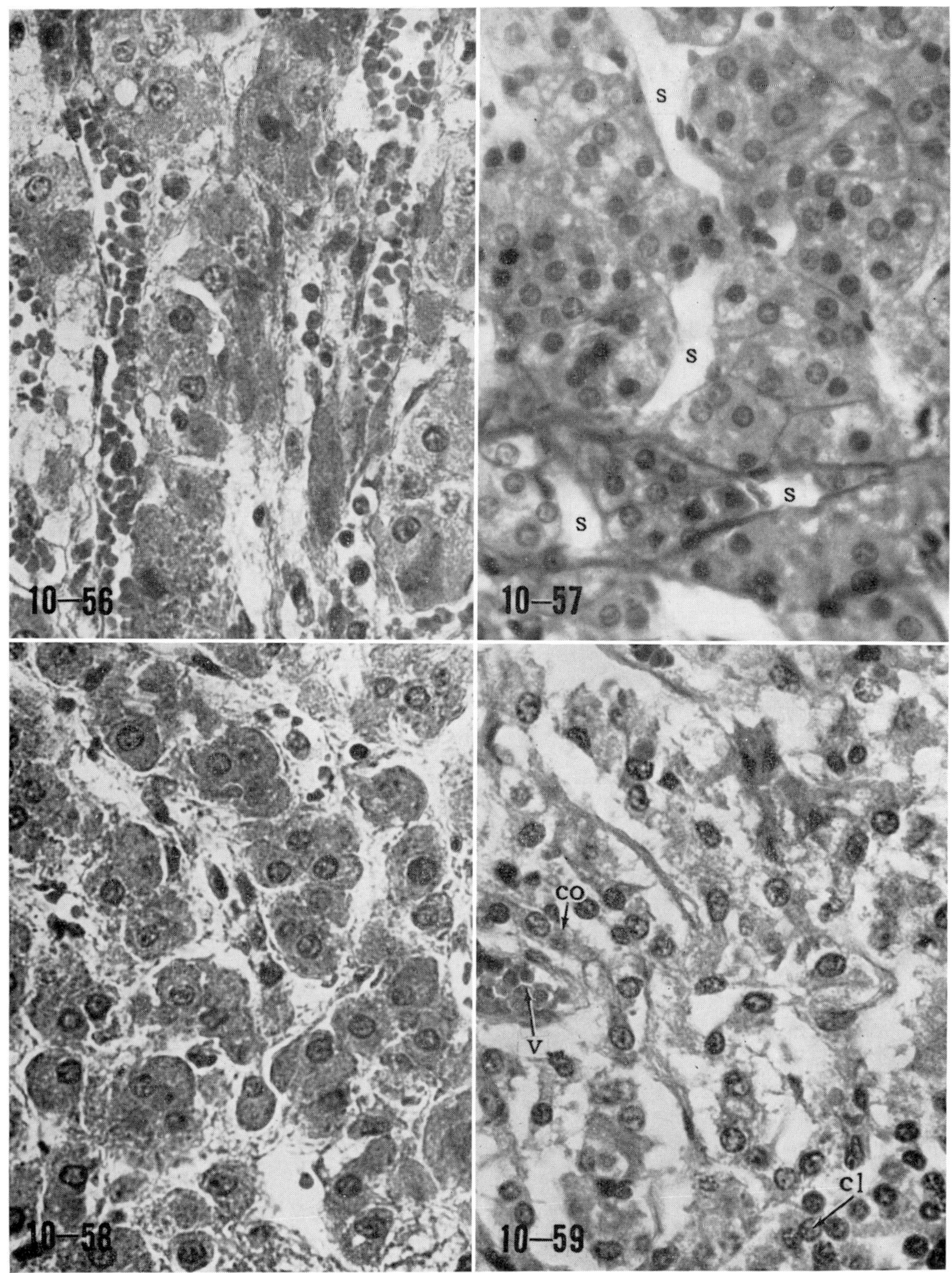
10—56
s
s
s
s
10—57
co
v
cl
10—58
10—59

PLATE 85—Pineal Gland

FIG. 10-60. Survey section of the pineal gland showing the parenchyma containing cells with little protoplasm (pl), the dark areas, and the light areas consisting of cells with much protoplasm (pm). Note calcareous brain sand granules (acervuli, a). Mallory-Azan stain. Low power.

FIG. 10-61. Survey section of the periphery of the pineal gland showing the parenchyma (pl and pm) containing small acervuli (a). Mallory-Azan stain. Intermediate power.

FIG. 10-62. Pineal gland, showing parenchymal cells (p), acervuli (a) and an interlobular trabecula (t). Mallory-Azan stain. Intermediate power.

FIG. 10-63. Section of pineal gland similar to that of Figure 10-62. Mallory-Azan stain. Intermediate power.

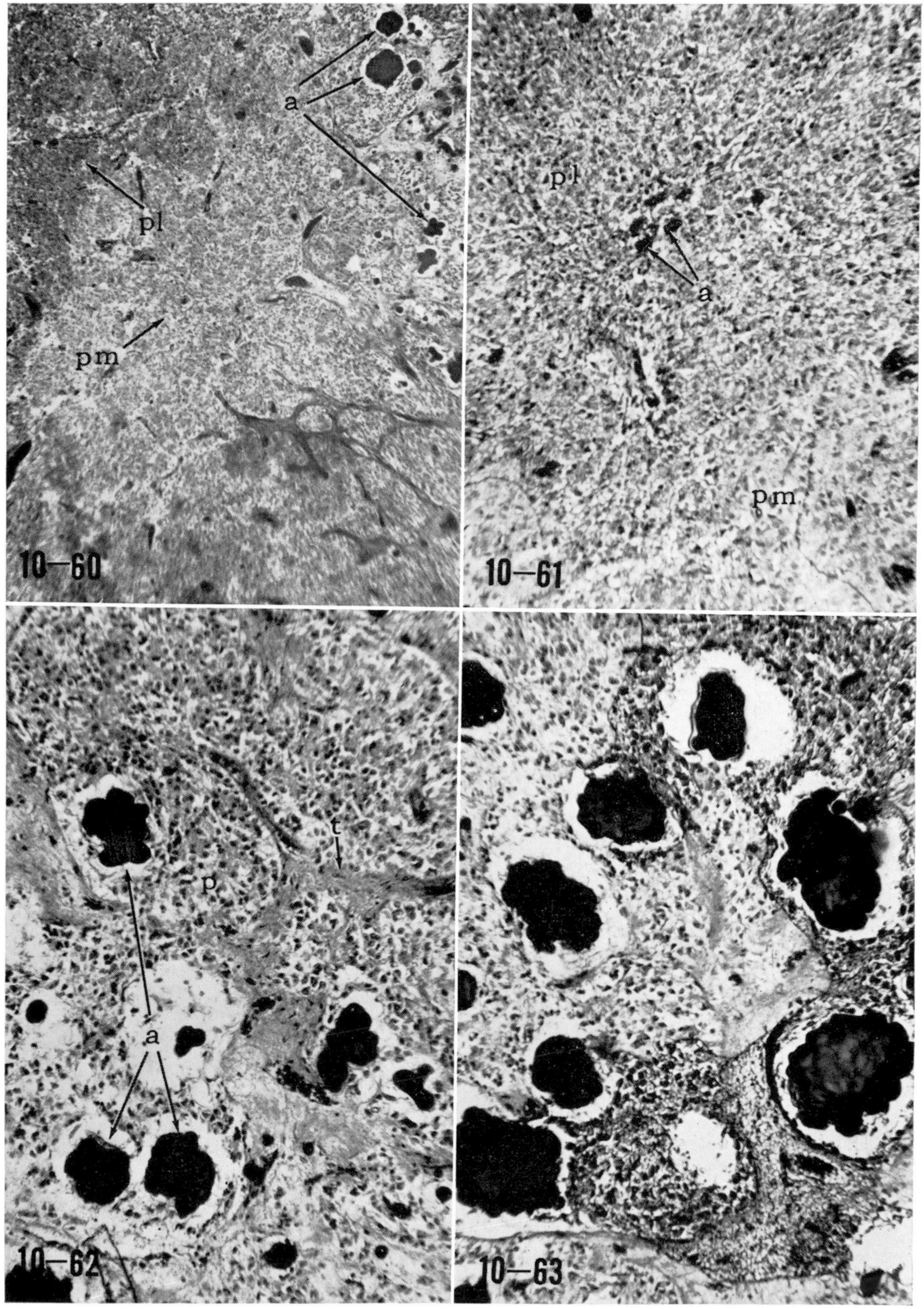
a
pl
pm
10–60
pl
a
pm
10–61
t
p
a
10–62
10–63

PLATE 86—Pineal Gland

FIG. 10-64. Pineal gland, showing irregularly shaped parenchymal cells. Mallory-Azan stain. High power.

FIG. 10-65. Pineal gland, showing parenchymal cells, a portion of an interlobular trabecula (t) with a vessel (v) and acervuli (a). Mallory-Azan stain. High power.

FIG. 10-66. Pineal gland, revealing a typical acervulus. Note the glial cell (g). Mallory-Azan stain. High power.

FIG. 10-67. Section of the pineal gland similar in type to that of Figure 10-66. Mallory-Azan stain. High power. (g, glial cell)

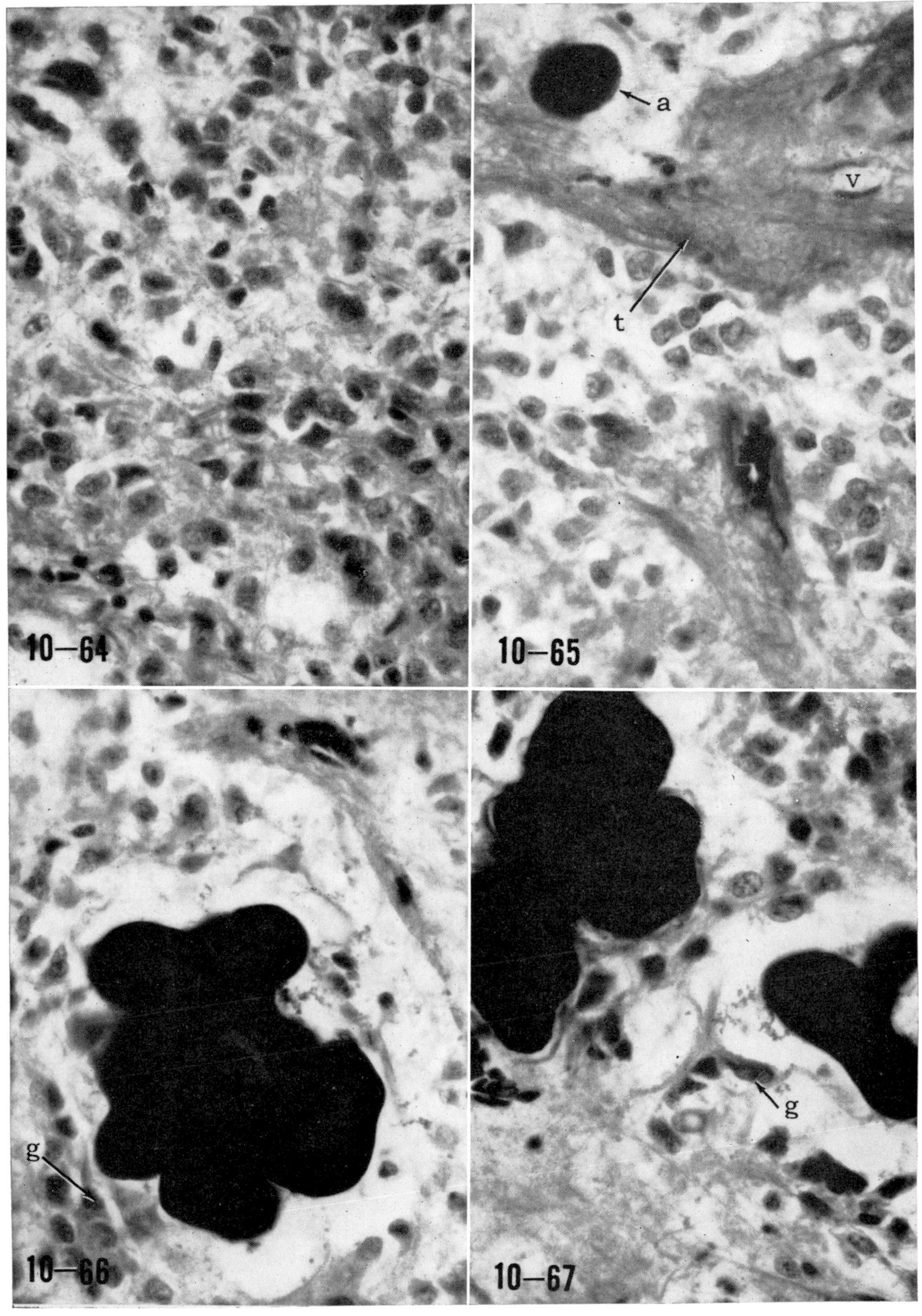
a
v
t
10–64
10–65
g
10–66
g
10–67

11 · The Digestive System

A. INTRODUCTION

The digestive system consists of a highly differentiated muscular tube, lined on its inner surface with epithelium, which passes through the body, extending from the mouth to the anus. Histologically this system is simple if one remembers that there is a general structural plan which is modified regionally to accomplish the orderly stages of digestion and absorption. Beginning at the esophagus, 4 layers or tunics are evident, namely:

1. The innermost layer or **tunica mucosa**, consisting of a lining epithelium resting on a

PLATE 87—Tooth

FIG. 11-1. Survey of a longitudinal section of developing tooth of a cat. Mallory-Azan stain. Low power. (dp, pulp of dental papilla; o, primordium of odontoblasts; d, dentin; ec, enamel cap; si, stratum intermedium; a, ameloblasts; ep, enamel pulp; ab, alveolar bone; ct, connective tissue sac)

FIG. 11-2. Relationship of the tooth to the peridental membrane (pm) and alveolar bone (ab). H & E stain. Low power. (c, cementum; d, dentin)

FIG. 11-3. Longitudinal section of developing tooth of a cat, showing the crown region. Mallory-Azan stain. Intermediate power. (d, dentin; ec, enamel cap; a, ameloblasts cut transversely and tangentially; si, stratum intermedium)

FIG. 11-4. Intermediate-power view of a portion of Figure 11-1, showing the fusion of the inner and the external enamel epithelium to form the root sheath (rs). Mallory-Azan stain. Intermediate power. (ab, alveolar bone; ep, enamel pulp; a, ameloblasts or inner enamel epithelium; si, stratum intermedium; d, dentin; o, primordium of odontoblasts; ee, external enamel epithelium; dp, pulp of dental papilla)

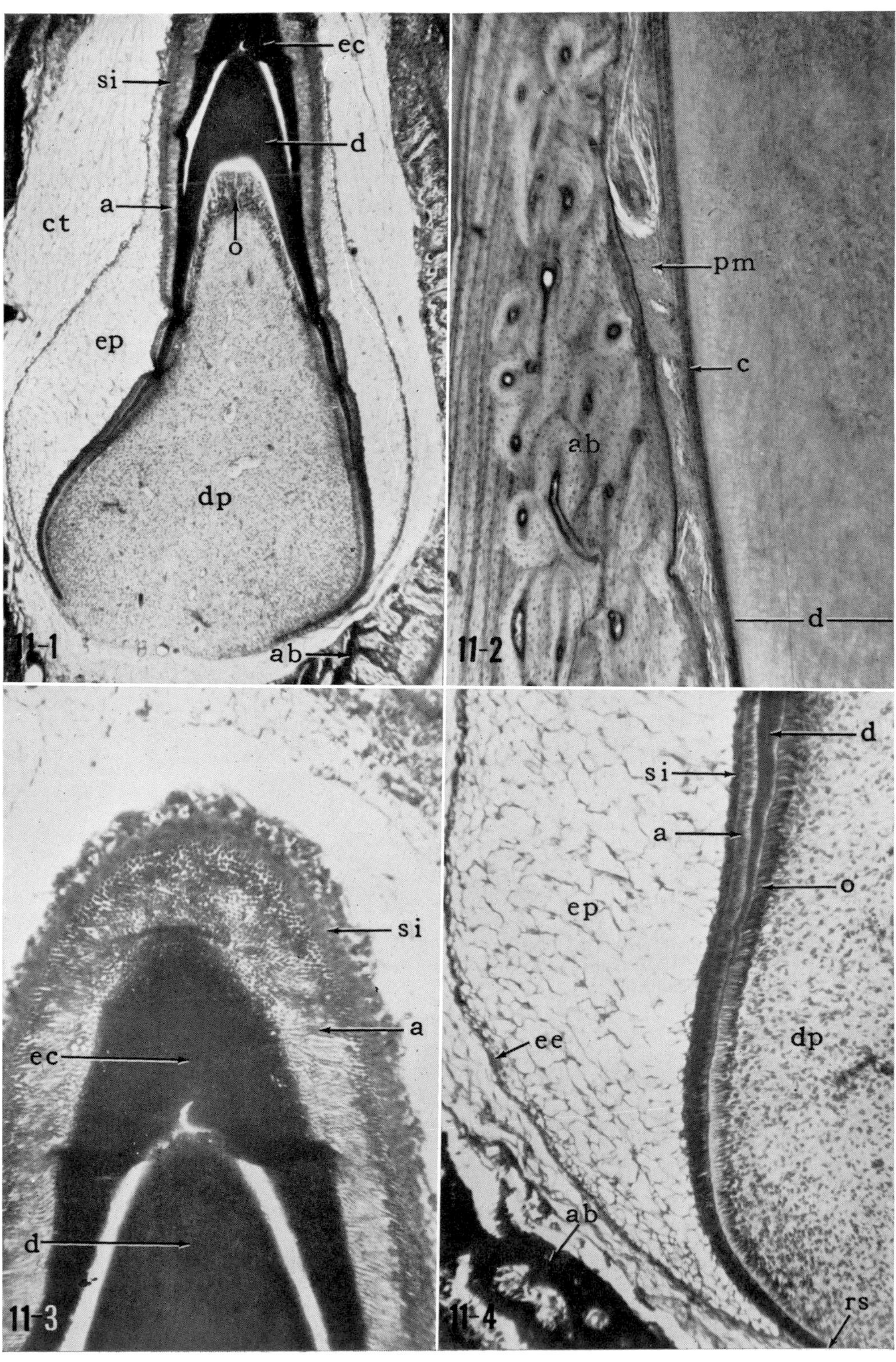
ec
si
d
a
ct
o
ep
dp
ab
11-1
pm
c
ab
d
11-2
si
a
ec
d
11-3
d
si
a
o
ep
dp
ee
ab
rs
11-4

lamina propria of loose interlacing connective tissue made up of collagenous and elastic fibers. The lamina propria contains some lymphocytes and other cells and, in most parts of the system, a glandular area. The outer limit of the tunica mucosa is defined by the muscularis mucosae. This consists usually of 2 thin strands of smooth muscle that encircle the mucosa. The fibers of the inner strand are circularly disposed, whereas the outer fibers are oriented longitudinally. Mixed in with the muscle is a thin elastic network.

2. The next layer or **tunica submucosa** is usually made up of a loose type of connective tissue with an abundance of elastic fibers. It contains a rich vascular plexus and a network of nerve fibers and ganglia (Meissner's plexus). At some levels of the digestive tract, such as the esophagus, the connective tissue is of a denser variety. Glands may be present, depending on the part under study.

3. Next is the **tunica muscularis (externa)** or muscle layer, usually exhibiting an inner circular arrangement and an outer longitudinally-disposed layer. In some regions of the digestive system, a third layer is observed. The major muscle coats are separated by a thin connective tissue in which a network of nerve fibers and ganglion cells (myenteric or Auerbach's plexus) are located.

4. Finally, an outermost layer, the **tunica adventitia** or a **tunica serosa** is evident. This tunic is composed of loose (areolar) connective tissue that is rich in blood vessels, lymphatics and nerves. Histologically, one distinguishes between adventitia and serosa by the presence of a simple squamous epithelium (mesothelium) on the latter. This represents a reflection of the peritoneum over the adventitia as the digestive tube passes from the thorax into the abdominal cavity.

It should be emphasized at this point that although the 4 tunics described exist at most levels of the digestive tract, only one, the tunica mucosa, undergoes marked histologic changes. These changes parallel alterations in the various processes of digestion that are found at each level and include increases of digestive and absorptive surfaces, variations in the types of digestive and absorptive surfaces, variations in the types of digestive glands present and changes in the amount of lymphatic material present.

B. LIPS

Each lip or labium is covered on its external surface by a thin skin which is characterized by a keratinized stratified squamous epithelium associated with relatively few low dermal papillae. Numerous short hairs, coarser in the male than the female,

PLATE 88—Tooth

FIG. 11-5. Developing tooth of cat, with the axis of the tooth oriented horizontally, showing the primordium of dental pulp (p) and root sheath (rs). Note the vascularity of the dental pulp. The primordium of dental pulp is composed of mesenchymal or young areolar tissue. Mallory-Azan stain. Intermediate power. (ab, alveolar bone; ct, connective tissue deep to the pulp)

FIG. 11-6. Tooth, showing the parallel arrangement of the dentinal tubules (dt). Thionin-picric acid stain. Intermediate power.

FIG. 11-7. High-power view of a portion of Figure 11-6, showing the dentinal tubules (dt) embedded in the matrix. Thionin-picric acid stain.

FIG. 11-8. Longitudinal section of a developing tooth of cat in the crown region. The axis of the tooth is oriented horizontally. Mallory-Azan stain. High power. (ep, enamel pulp; si, stratum intermedium; a, ameloblasts; d, dentin; e, enamel; pd, predentin; T, Tomes' processes; o, odontoblasts; p, primordium of pulp)

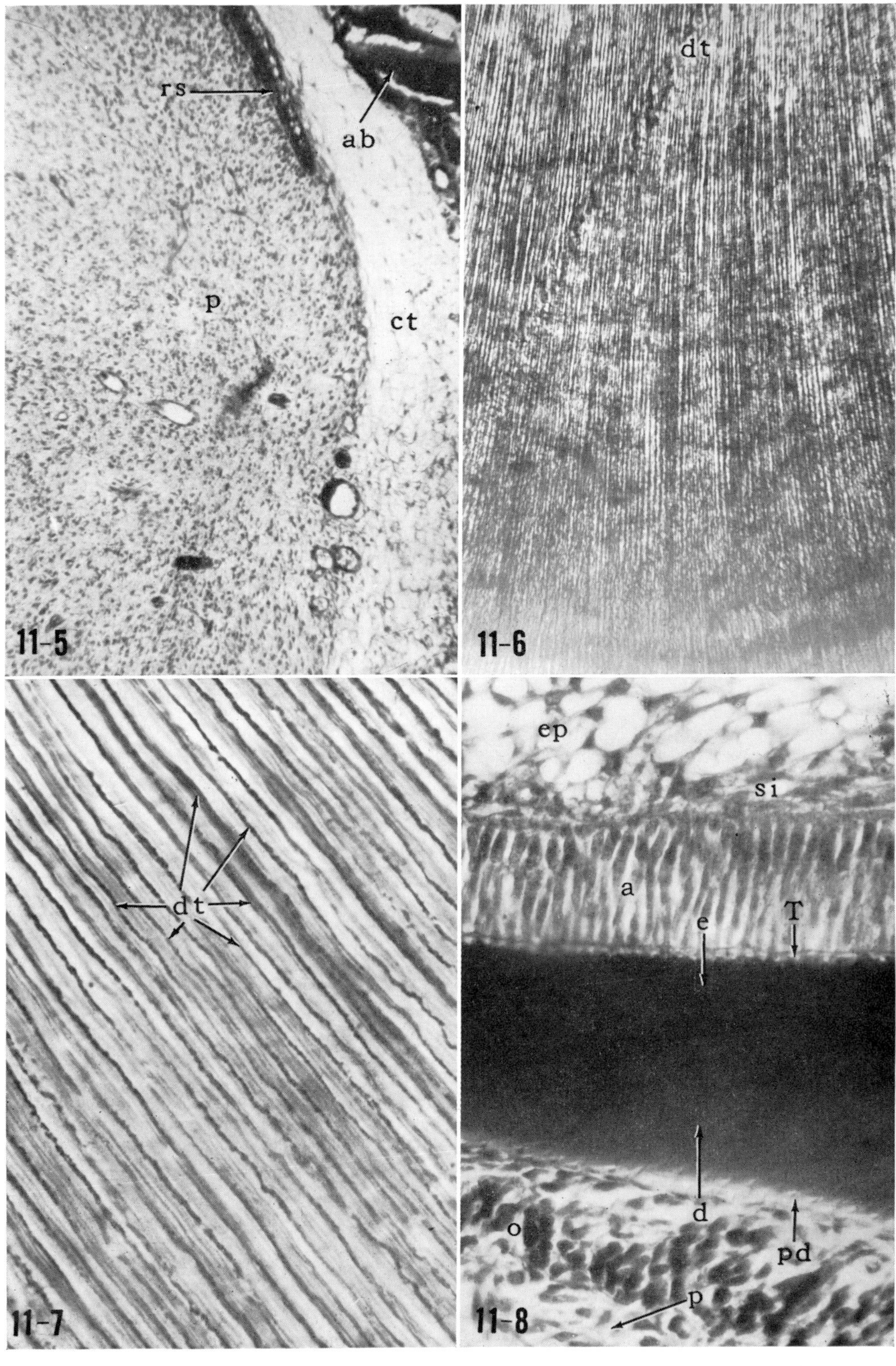
rs
ab
p
ct
11-5
dt
11-6
dt
11-7
ep
si
a
e
T
d
o
pd
p
11-8

are present, as are associated sebaceous and sweat glands.

The transitional region between the skin covering the external lip surface and the mucous membrane lining its internal surface is known as the **red portion** or **vermilion border**. The red portion is covered by a moderately thick layer of nonkeratinized stratified squamous epithelium into which project many tall branching dermal papillae of the vascular type. The presence of **eleidin** and the absence of a stratum corneum tends to make the epithelium somewhat translucent. Because of the proximity of the capillaries in the connective tissue papillae to the free epithelial surface, this transitional region of the lip has a reddish hue. Hair and glands are absent from this region, and the underlying connective tissue bed is relatively thin.

The lip surface facing the oral cavity is covered by a typical mucous membrane. The stratified squamous epithelium is thicker than elsewhere on the lip and is nonkeratinized. Dermal papillae are lower and less numerous in this region. The lamina propria of the labial mucosa consists of a dense irregular arrangement of collagen and elastic fibers, thinner in size than similar fibers in the dermis of the skin covering the anterior lip. The submucosa is made up of bandlike arrangements of collagen fibers widely separated by pockets of loose connective tissue that is rich in fat. Within this loose tissue, **labial glands**, small glandular aggregates with a compound tubulo-alveolar structure, are present in great abundance. These glands are primarily mucous in nature, but serous end-pieces may also be found. Within the lip, the internal submucosal and the external dermal connective tissues are separated by the orbicularis oris muscle, and connective tissue fibers from both sides contribute a delicate fascial covering around it.

C. TEETH

1. General

The human dentition normally consists of 2 successive sets of teeth, 20 milk teeth and 32 permanent teeth, which serve to cut, bite and grind ingested food. Since the milk teeth are temporary and are shed in early life, they are referred to collectively as the **deciduous set**.

Among the 32 **permanent teeth** are distinguished 8 **incisors**, 4 **cuspids** (**canines**), 8 **bicuspids** (**premolars**) and 12 **molars**. Despite differences in gross shape and size, each of these teeth has the same 3 basic parts. These include (1) the **crown**, that part projecting into the oral cavity; (2) a single or multiple **root**, the part that is embedded in the gum and firmly attached to a bony encasement or socket, the **alveolus**; and (3) a **neck**, the narrow segment present between the crown and the root.

The three solid parts of the tooth surround

PLATE 89—Tongue

FIG. 11-9. Survey section of the tongue. H & E stain. Low power. (p, stratified squamous epithelium of papillae; sg, serous glands; m, skeletal muscle; lp, lamina propria; mg, mucous glands; d, duct of gland)

FIG. 11-10. Section from the anterior two thirds of the tongue, showing filiform papillae and skeletal muscle. Note the slight cornification (co) of the epithelium of the papillae. H & E stain. Intermediate power. (lp, lamina propria with vessels [v]; m, skeletal muscle)

FIG. 11-11. Section from the anterior two thirds of the tongue, showing a fungiform papilla. H & E stain. Intermediate power. (e, noncornified stratified squamous epithelium; lp, lamina propria which contains many vessels [v]; m, skeletal muscle)

FIG. 11-12. Fungiform papillae, showing a taste bud (t) and the highly vascular nature of the core of the papillae (v). Also note a duct (d) coursing toward the surface, and the skeletal muscle (m). H & E stain. Intermediate power.

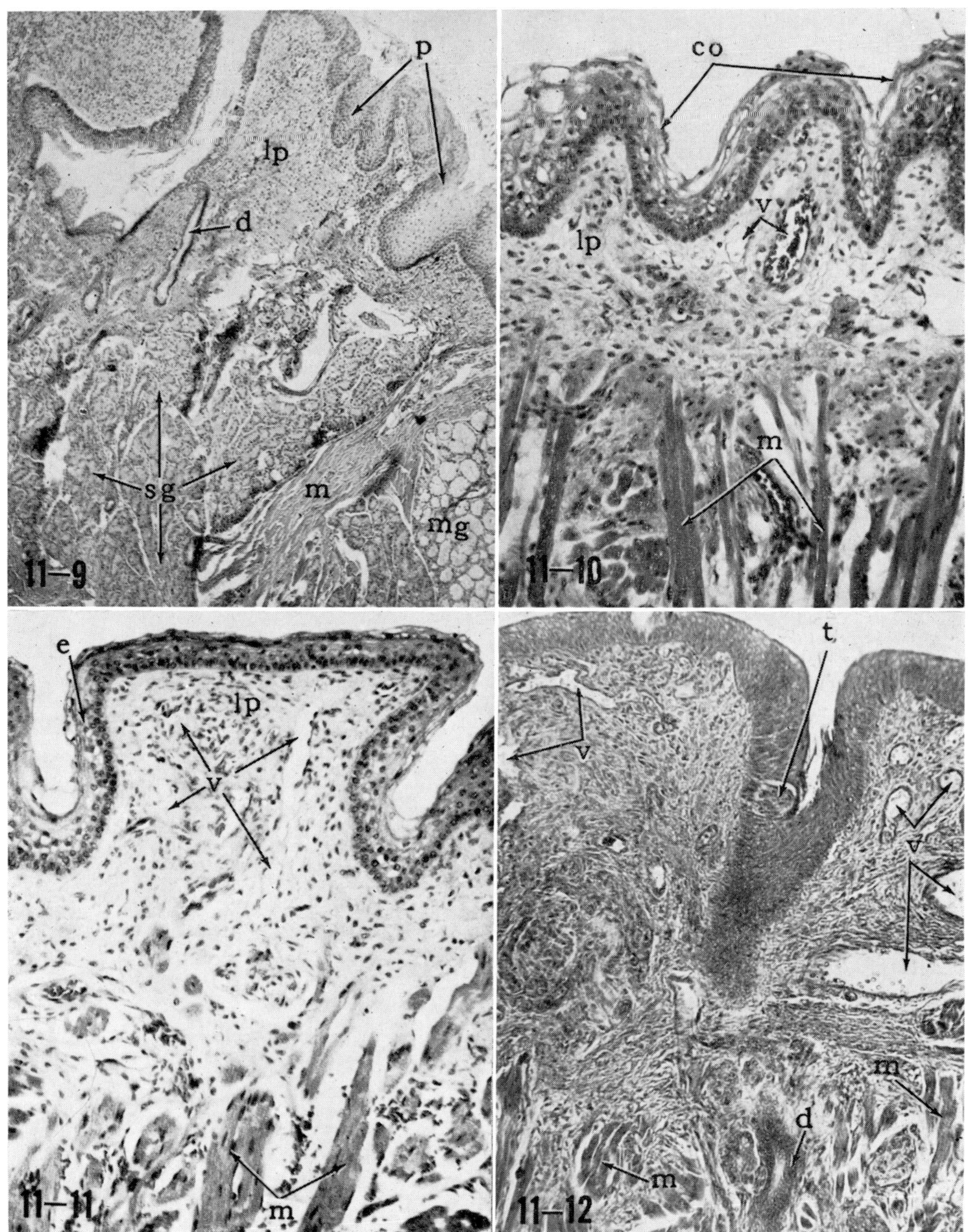
p
lp
d
sg
m
mg
11–9
co
v
lp
m
11–10
e
lp
v
m
11–11
t
v
v
m
d
m
11–12

a central mass of soft connective tissue, the **dental pulp**, which occupies a space, roughly tubular in shape, known as the **pulp chamber (cavity)**. The dental pulp is rich in connective tissue cells and fibers. Arteries, veins and nerves enter the pulp from outside the tooth by means of the **root canal**, a channel that is continuous with the pulp chamber. To reach the root canal, these soft structures pass through an opening at the apex of the root, the **apical foramen**.

2. Hard Substances of Teeth (Plates 87 and 88)

a. *Enamel.* This, the hardest material in the body, is restricted to the crown, which it covers like a cap. Enamel owes its hardness to an extremely high content (96%) of inorganic calcareous material (**apatite**). Once the crown has emerged through the gum into the oral cavity, its enamel covering becomes nonviable.

Up until the time that eruption of the tooth takes place, the enamel is both viable and fully formed. It develops by appositional growth from a layer of tall columnar epithelial cells on its external surface (**ameloblastic layer** or **inner enamel epithelium**). These **ameloblasts** constitute a portion of the **enamel organ**, a structure derived in ontogeny from the surface ectoderm of the oral cavity.

Because enamel is avital and contains a high percentage of inorganic substances, this material is quite brittle. Its integrity depends to a great extent on the integrity of another dense substance on which it is deposited, namely, the **dentin**.

Enamel is made up of elongated, rodlike or prismatic structures, the **enamel rods**. The rods are enclosed in rod sheaths and are bound together by a cementing interrod substance. In parallel fashion, the enamel rods course obliquely across the enamel layer, following the contours of the crown so that the rods are almost always oriented at right angles to the external surface of the tooth.

b. *Dentin.* This material makes up most of the hard substance of the crown, the neck and the root of the tooth. Its consistency most closely resembles that of compact bone. As in bone, collagen fibers, present in great numbers, are embedded in a calcified matrix. Dentin, however, contains more inorganic salts (about 70%) than does bone (about 46%) and therefore is slightly harder than the latter.

As with bone, dentin is a living tissue during the normal life of each tooth. The viability of this material depends on the integrity of the cells that form it. These cells, **odontoblasts**, are located at the periphery of the dental pulp, immediately adjacent to the dentin. In mature teeth, the odontoblastic

PLATE 90—Tongue and Dentogingival Junction

FIG. 11-13. Section from the anterior two thirds of the tongue, showing a circumvallate papilla with taste buds (t). Note the resemblance to the fungiform papilla although this type of papilla is larger and surrounded by a trench (tr). Two ducts (d) are seen leading to the bottom of a trench. H & E stain. Intermediate power. (lp, lamina propria showing its vascular nature; g, isolated serous glandular end-piece related to the glands of von Ebner)

FIG. 11-14. Section from the anterior two thirds of the tongue near the apex showing the glands of Nühn, mixed serous glands (sg) and mucous glands (mg), embedded in skeletal muscle. H & E stain. Intermediate power.

FIG. 11-15. Section to show the pattern of the skeletal muscle of the tongue. H & E stain. Intermediate power.

FIG. 11-16. Dentogingival junction showing the stratified squamous epithelial attachment of the gingiva (g) to the tooth (ea) and the subepithelial connective tissue attachment to the cementum of the tooth (the peridental membrane, pm). Note the extreme height of the gingival papilla. H & E stain. Intermediate power. (gc, gingival crevice; d, dentin)

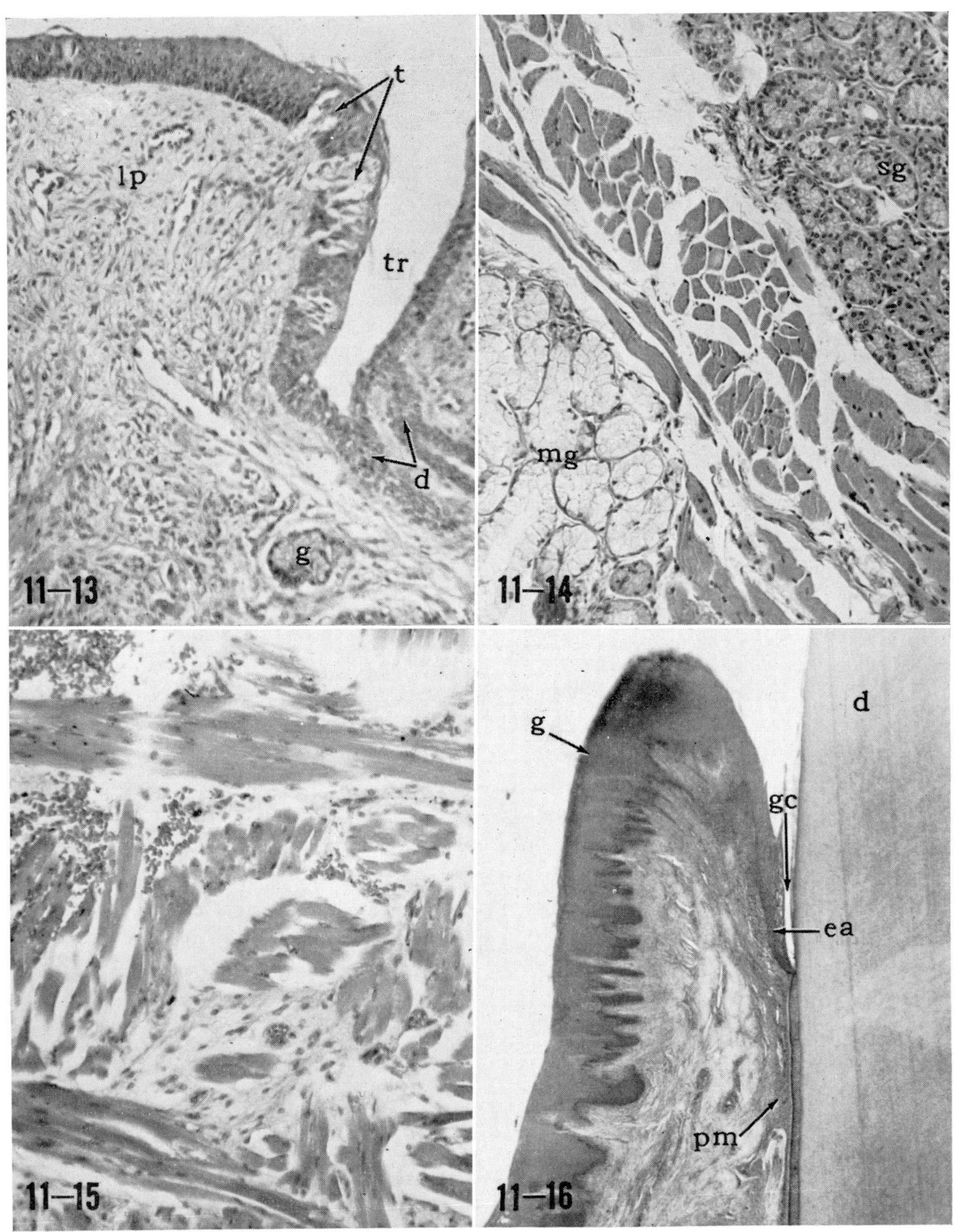
t
lp
tr
d
g
11–13
sg
mg
11–14
11–15
d
g
gc
ea
pm
11–16

cells line the surface of the pulp chamber as a simple epithelium. These cells are high columnar in the crown and the neck regions, become gradually more cuboidal in the middle of the root, and are transformed into squamous cells near the apex of the root. Odontoblasts differ from most epithelial cells in that they are derived from mesenchymal cells of the dental pulp.

Dentin is formed as a series of tubules (**dentinal tubules**) at the surfaces of the odontoblast cells furthest away from the dental pulp. In the process of dentinogenesis, large numbers of delicate reticular fibers (**Korff's fibers**), stemming from the pulp, insinuate themselves between and around the odontoblasts, forming delicate fibrous cylinders around the cells. When these precollagen fibers have reached the ends of the odontoblasts away from the pulp, they undergo differentiation into collagenous predentin. Dentin is formed by calcification of the predentin matrix. As in the case of calcification of bone, the cellular elements have high alkaline phosphatase activity and are probably responsible for the precipitation of inorganic salts around the collagen fibers of the matrix.

As dentinogenesis occurs, the odontoblasts appear to pull back slightly and, as they do so, each cell leaves a cytoplasmic process (**dentinal** or **Tomes' fiber**) trapped within the tubule of dentin that it has formed. As development continues in this fashion, the dentinal tubules become longer and the pulp mass becomes progressively reduced in size as the layer of odontoblasts moves away from the thickening dentin.

In the mature tooth, dentin consists of a calcified matrix containing fine collagen fibers and dentinal fibers present within dentinal tubules. The dentinal tubules are from 1 to 4 μ in diameter and radiate from the odontoblast layer at almost right angles.

c. *Cementum.* This calcified material, similar in composition to bone, forms a thin layer around the roots of the teeth. Its main function is to provide a dental structure to anchor the thick collagen fibers (**Sharpey's fibers**) of the peridental membrane. As in the case of compact bone, cells are present within lacunae, and a canalicular system connecting adjacent lacunae is also present. The cells of cementum, referred to as **cementocytes**, are derived from connective tissue progenitors of the peridental membrane.

3. Peridental Membrane (Ligament)

The peridental membrane consists of a fibrous investment around the roots of teeth and serves to attach the root to the surrounding alveolar bone and to gingival connective tissue. It is composed of a dense irregularly arranged connective tissue made up chiefly of coarse collagen fibers. The ends of those fibers (**Sharpey's fibers**) that anchor the hard structures are firmly embedded in bone and cementum. Fibroblasts, osteoblasts and cementoblasts are present in addition to the

PLATE 91—Esophagus

FIG. 11-17. Survey section of the wall of the upper third of the esophagus. H & E stain. Low power. (m, tunica mucosa; sm, tunica submucosa; me, muscularis externa [skeletal muscle]; a, tunica adventitia)

FIG. 11-18. A slight enlargement of a part of Figure 11-17. Low power. (e, stratified squamous epithelium; g, submucosal esophageal glands; d, ducts; mm, muscularis mucosae; ct, dense connective tissue of the tunica submucosa; me, skeletal muscle of the muscularis externa)

FIG. 11-19. Another level of the upper third of the esophagus to show solitary lymphatic nodules (l). H & E stain. Low power.

FIG. 11-20. Intermediate-power view of a portion of Figure 11-19 to show the mucous membrane lined by stratified squamous epithelium (e) and the underlying lamina propria infiltrated with lymphocytes (l). Note the thinned epithelium over the lymphatic tissue. H & E stain. Intermediate power.

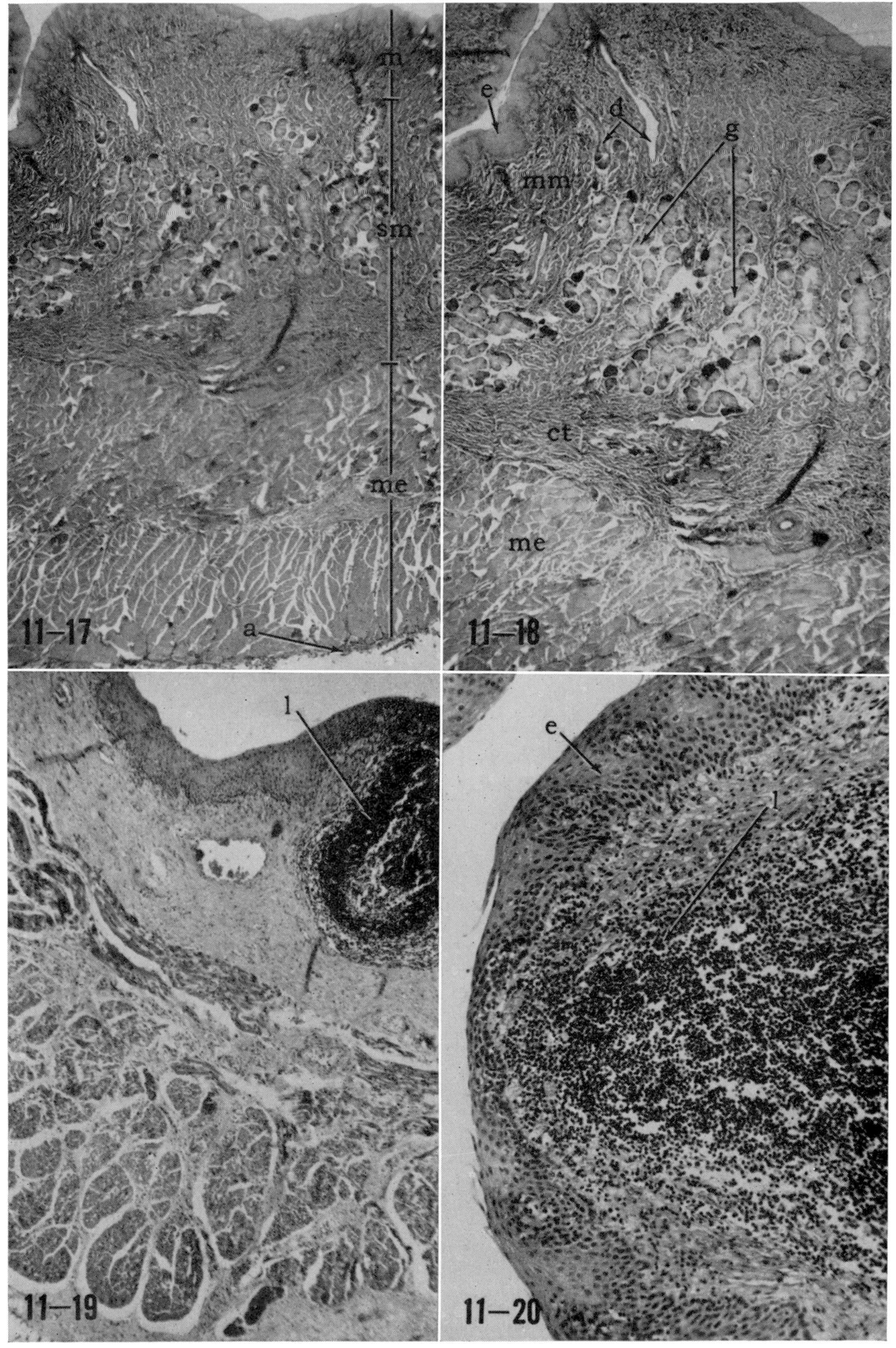
m
sm
me
a
11–17
e
d
g
mm
ct
me
11–18
l
11–19
e
l
11–20

connective tissue fibers. The peridental membrane is richly supplied with sensory nerve fibers and is quite vascular.

D. TONGUE

(Plates 89 and 90)

The tongue is one of the essential accessory structures of the digestive system. Its main mass consists of interlacing bundles of skeletal muscle fibers arranged in 3 planes, transverse, longitudinal and vertical, that cross one another at right angles. Embedded in the muscle of the anterior portion of the organ are the **glands of Nühn**. These are a paired group of mixed mucous and serous glands, with ducts opening on the underside of the tongue.

An adherent mucous membrane covers the muscular mass. The free surface of this moist covering of the tongue is lined by stratified squamous epithelium. The epithelium of the undersurface of the tongue is thin and smooth (lacks lingual papillae). On the other hand, the epithelium of the upper surface is thick and uneven due to the presence of many lingual papillae. The lamina propria is dense and fused with the interstitial connective tissue between the muscle bundles. A submucosa is present only on the undersurface of the tongue.

The **lingual papillae** (vertical projections of the mucosa) present on the tongue are of 3 distinct types—the **filiform**, the **fungiform** and the **circumvallate**.

1. The **filiform** type is the most numerous kind. These are arranged in distinct rows diverging to the right and the left of the median sulcus and parallel with the V-shaped boundary line between the anterior and the posterior parts of the dorsum. Each filiform papilla is approximately 2 to 3 mm. long and projects from the free surfaces, ending as one or more finely tapered processes. The connective tissue core bears many **secondary (dermal) papillae**. The surface of the covering epithelium may be transformed into hard scales.

2. The larger **fungiform papillae** are scattered singly among the filiform papillae and are especially numerous on the dorsum near the tip of the tongue. They resemble a button-type mushroom and have a short narrow stalk with a broader, slightly flattened, rounded top. Each of these papillae contains a connective tissue core, which is rich in blood vessels, and bears many secondary papillae. Some of these secondary papillae contain taste buds.

3. The largest of the lingual papillae, **circumvallate papillae**, are only 9 to 12 in number and are arranged in a V-shaped row just in front of the sulcus terminalis. The circumvallate papillae differ slightly from other lingual papillae in that they do not project quite as high above the surface of the mucous membrane. They are more deeply embedded within the mucous membrane and are completely encircled by a deep furrow. Only on its upper surface does the connective tissue core form secondary papillae. The lateral surfaces of each papilla contains many

PLATE 92—Esophagus

FIG. 11-21. Upper third of the esophagus showing papillae (p) of lamina propria extending up into the epithelium. Note view of papillae in cross section (cp). H & E stain. Intermediate power.

FIG. 11-22. Section similar to that in Figure 11-21. Note the interlacing arrangement and the vascularity of the connective tissue, and skeletal muscle of the muscularis externa (me). H & E stain. Intermediate power.

FIG. 11-23. Upper third of the esophagus, showing glands (g) with ducts (d) passing to the epithelial surface (e). H & E stain. Intermediate power.

FIG. 11-24. Upper third of the esophagus to show a typical nest of submucosal glands (g). Note the skeletal muscle of the muscularis externa (me). H & E stain. Intermediate power.

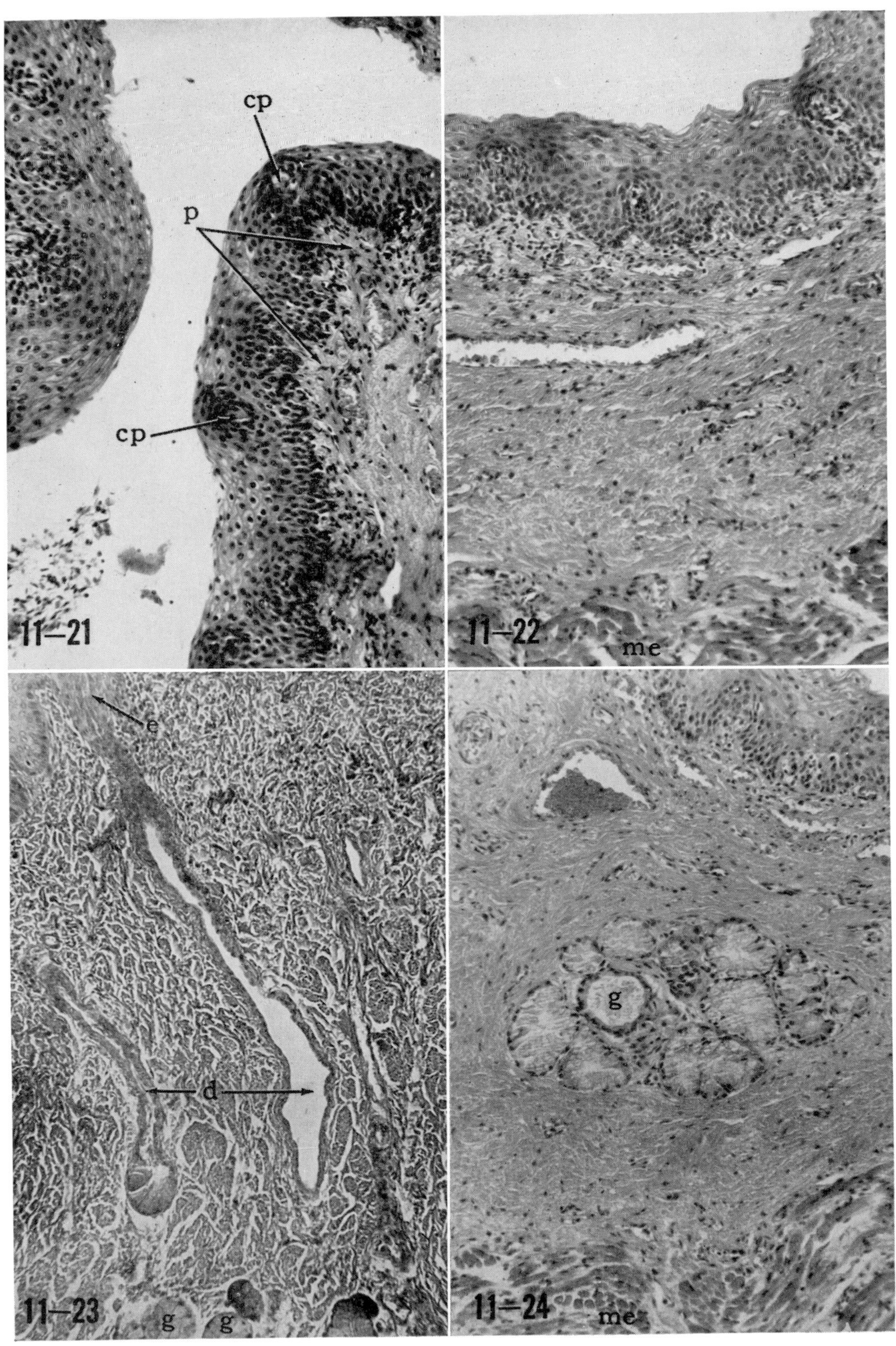
cp
p
cp
11–21
11–22
me
e
d
11–23
g
g
g
11–24
me

taste buds (approximately 250). **Taste buds** are tall, pale, oval bodies embedded in the epithelium and extending from the basement membrane almost to the surface. A small opening of the taste bud, the **outer taste pore**, pierces the epithelium. Structurally, neuro-epithelial taste cells and supporting cells are distinguished. The specialized **neuro-epithelial cell** is a slender rod-shaped element with a centrally placed, dark-staining nucleus and a short taste hair on the free surface which projects freely into the lumen of the pit. The **supporting cell** is spindleshaped and contains a light-staining peripherally located nucleus. The ends of these cells nearest the free surface surround a small opening, the **inner taste pore** which leads into a pitlike excavation. In the outer wall across the trench, fewer taste buds are present. Associated with each of the circumvallate papillae are the **glands of von Ebner**, serous (albuminous) elements which are embedded in the muscle tissue beneath these papillae. Their excretory ducts communicate with the bottom of the trench surrounding each circumvallate papilla. Found mingled with the glands of von Ebner are mucous glands associated with the root of the tongue.

E. GINGIVAE (GUMS)

The gingivae constitute the two inverted, troughlike linings of soft tissue that cover the crests of the jaws and form collars around the necks of the teeth. Most of the gingival tissue is firmly attached to the teeth and the alveolae.

Upon observing the gingiva the impression is obtained that its free surface is in the form of a scalloped line that arches across the teeth. Actually this line represents a reflection of the gum on itself against the crown of the tooth as the **epithelial attachment of the gingiva.** The line of reflection itself is known as the **free gingival margin.**

Structurally the gingivae consist of a mucous membrane resting on a submucosa. The mucosa is made up of an epithelium and a lamina propria. The former, of the stratified squamous variety, may be keratinized. Associated with this epithelium are large numbers of long, tubular papillae that project from the underlying lamina propria. The lamina propria is composed of a poorly vascularized, dense, irregularly arranged connective tissue in which thin collagen fibers predominate and elastic fibers are rare. The submucosa is made up primarily of coarse bundles of collagen fibers. These fibers attach the gingiva so firmly to the periosteum surrounding each of the bony alveoli that the gingiva, except near its free margin, is immovable (Fig. 11-16).

F. CHEEKS (BUCCAE)

The histology of the oral portion of the cheek is very similar to that of the labial

PLATE 93—Esophagus

FIG. 11-25. Survey section of the middle third of the esophageal wall. H & E stain. Low power.

FIG. 11-26. Survey section of the middle third of the wall of the esophagus showing the presence of the prominent muscularis mucosae (mm), mucous glands (g) in the tunica submucosa and both skeletal (sk) and smooth (sm) muscle in the muscularis externa. H & E stain. Low power.

FIG. 11-27. Middle third of the esophagus at the level of the trachea. Note the hyaline cartilage (c) of the trachea. Also observe the inner circular layer (ic) and the outer longitudinal layer (ol) of the muscularis externa of the esophagus. H & E stain. Low power.

FIG. 11-28. Intermediate-power view of a portion of Figure 11-26 showing the wall of the esophagus to the beginning of the muscularis externa (me). (mm, muscularis mucosae; g, mucous glands; ct, connective tissue of the submucosa showing coarser connective tissue fibers and fewer cells than found in the lamina propria, lp)

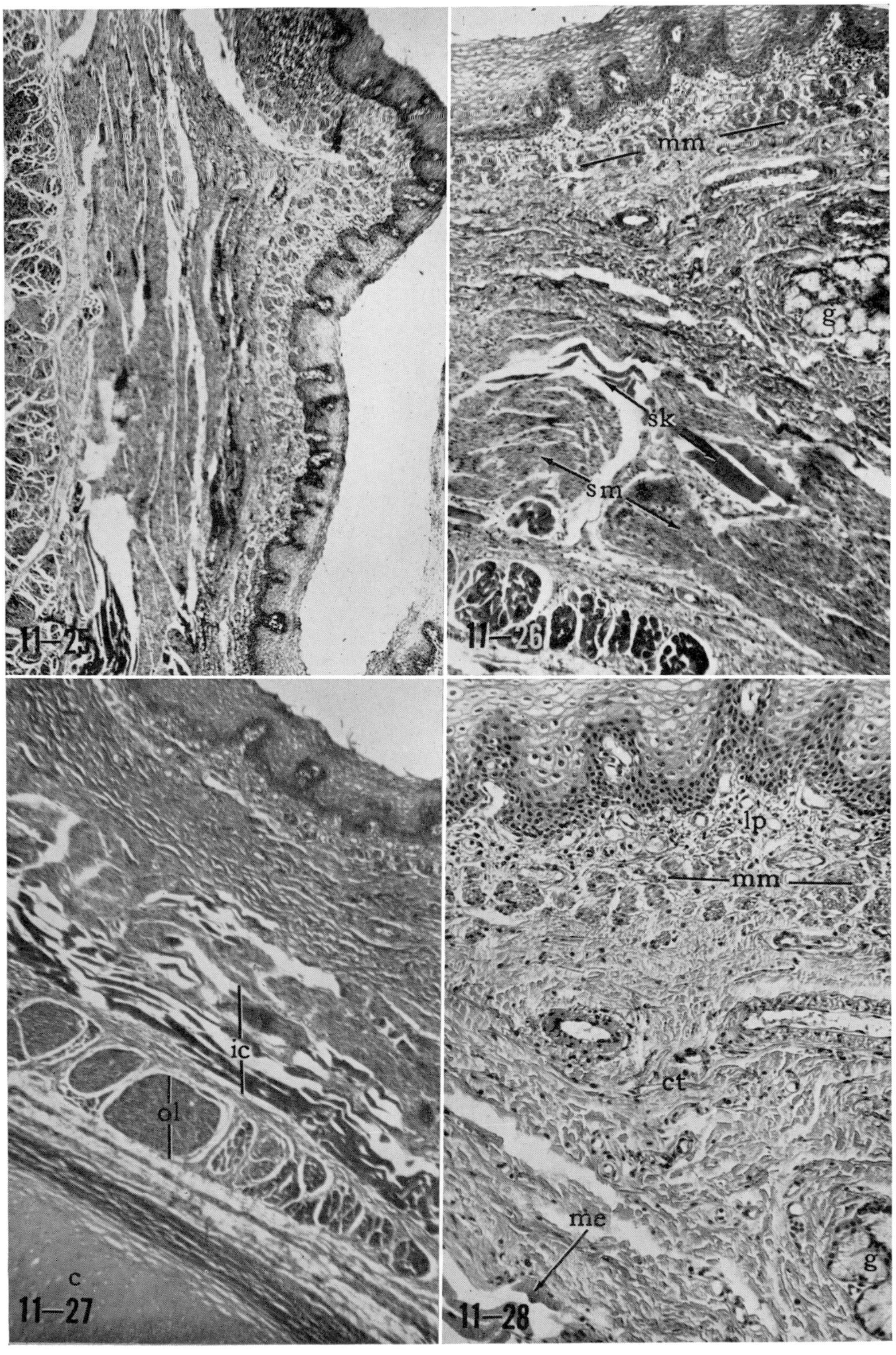

11–25
mm
g
sk
sm
11–26
ic
ol
c
11–27
lp
mm
ct
me
g
11–28

mucosa. The buccal mucosa is surmounted by a nonkeratinized stratified squamous epithelium which is penetrated by numerous connective tissue papillae. The underlying lamina propria contains a dense, irregularly arranged form of connective tissue in which collagen fibers predominate. The submucosa is a blend of both dense and loosely arranged connective tissues. The dense elements consist of coarse collagen fibers that are organized into straplike bundles that attach the buccal mucosa to the delicate underlying fascial covering of the buccinator muscle. This form of attachment prevents the buccal mucosa from folding into the oral cavity during contraction of the buccinator muscle and thereby minimizes the chances of painfully biting the internal surface of the cheek when food is being masticated.

In addition to the dense arrangement just described, unevenly distributed pockets of loose connective tissue are present in the submucosa. These contain **buccal glands**, in addition to many fat cells, fibroblasts and reticular and delicate collagen fibers. The buccal glands are mixed seromucous in nature and are small, with the exception of those located between fascicles of the buccinator muscle.

G. PALATE

The palate forms the roof of the oral cavity and separates it from the nasal cavity and the nasopharynx. The anterior portion is supported by a shelf of bone and constitutes the **hard palate**. The posterior part of the palate contains skeletal muscle rather than bone and is therefore designated the **soft palate**.

1. Hard Palate

This portion of the palate acts as a firm platform against which food is squeezed and manipulated. Because of this relationship to mastication, the histology of the soft tissues covering the undersurface of the hard palate is similar in many respects to that of the gingivae.

The palatal oral mucosa consists of a keratinized stratified squamous epithelium resting on a relatively thick lamina propria of dense, irregularly arranged collagen fibers. Projecting into the epithelium are numerous tall connective tissue papillae.

A characteristic that distinguishes the palate from the gingivae is the presence of a distinct submucosa. This layer consists of dense bundles of collagen fibers, separated

PLATE 94—Esophagus

FIG. 11-29. Middle third of the esophagus to show the denseness of the connective tissue of the tunica submucosa (sm) in comparison with that of the lamina propria portion of the tunica mucosa (m). Also observe the clear representations of papillae in cross section (cp), the richness of vessels of the lamina propria and the muscularis mucosae (mm). H & E stain. Intermediate power.

FIG. 11-30. Middle third of the esophagus, showing the muscularis externa containing both smooth (sm) and skeletal (sk) muscle. Also observe the connective tissue (ct) between the muscle layers and interspersed between the muscle bundles. H & E stain. Intermediate power. (ic, inner circular layer; ol, outer longitudinal layer)

FIG. 11-31. Survey section of the lower third of the wall of the esophagus. Note the thickness of the muscularis mucosae (mm). At this level, the muscularis externa consists entirely of smooth muscle. H & E stain. Low power.

FIG. 11-32. Intermediate-power view of a portion of Figure 11-31, showing the tunica mucosa (m), submucosa (sm) and part of the inner circular layer of the muscularis externa (me).

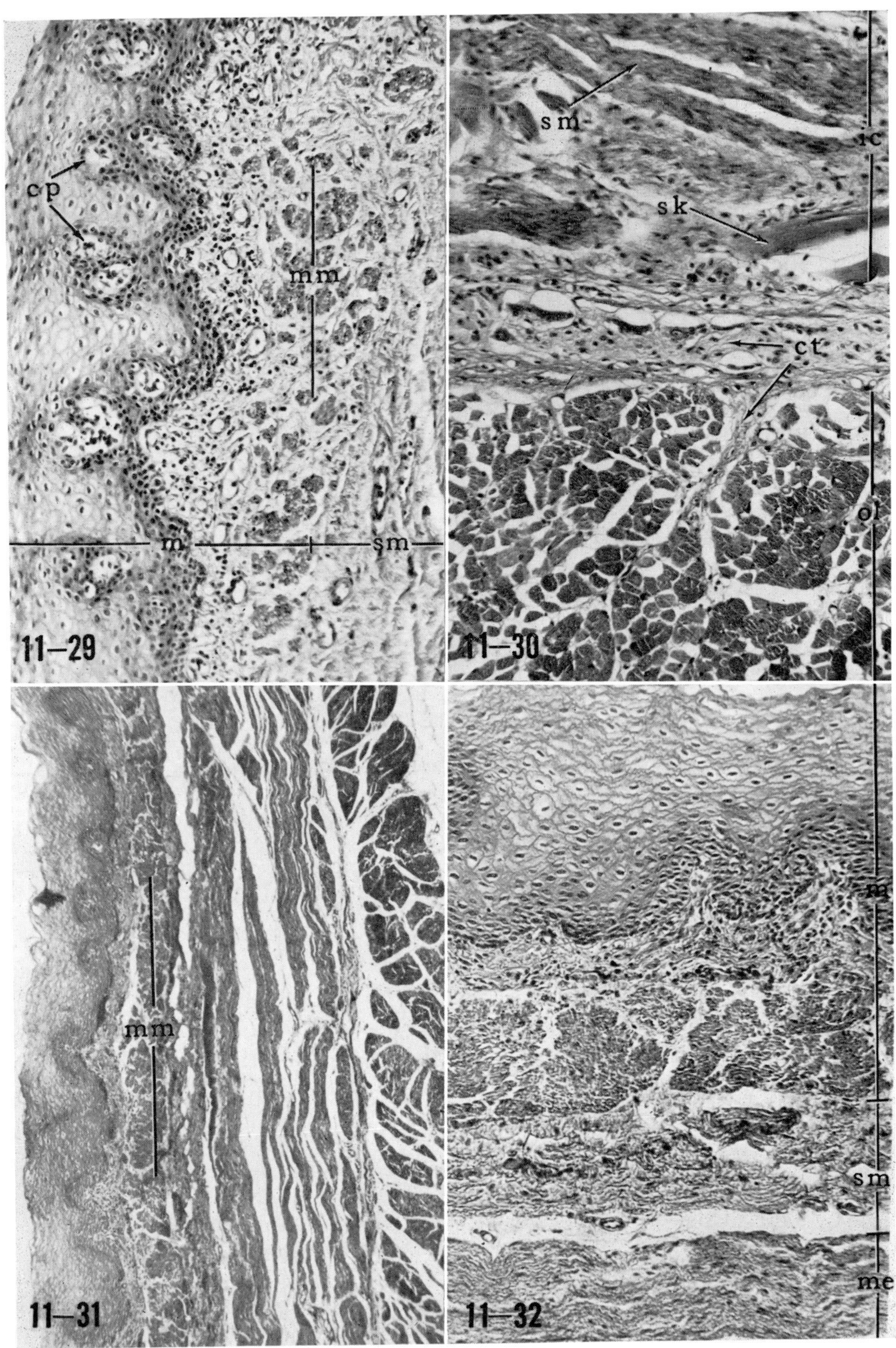
cp
mm
m
sm
11–29
sm
ic
sk
ct
ol
11–30
mm
11–31
m
sm
me
11–32

by wide gaps, which attach the lamina propria to the periosteum covering the palatal portions of the maxillary and the palatine bones. Such a mucosal attachment creates a firm, relatively immovable free surface on which masticatory manipulation of food can be effected. The wide gaps between the fiber bundles in the submucosa are filled, in the anterior part of the palate, with adipose tissue and, in the posterior portion of the hard palate, with glands. These glands are primarily mucous in nature, are organized into small lobules and, structurally, are compound tubulo-alveolar in type.

2. Soft Palate.

This flaplike portion of the palate is histologically designed to function as a valve. It consists of a fold of mucous membrane supported by a fibroelastic aponeurosis and by skeletal muscles, and exhibits a posterior projection, the **uvula**. Contraction of the musculature retracts and tightens the soft palate and at the same time raises the organ. These actions, during deglutition, effectively wall off the nasopharynx from the oropharynx and prevent food from entering the nasal passageways.

The oral mucosa of the soft palate consists of a stratified squamous epithelium resting on a thick lamina propria. This mucosa differs from that of the hard palate in several respects: the epithelium may not be keratinized, connective tissue papillae are short and less numerous, and the lamina propria is much looser in organization and contains large numbers of elastic fibers.

The submucosa is also loosely arranged. Collagen fibers are fewer in number, and elastic fibers may be present. Throughout much of this layer and extending into the lamina propria, large numbers of compound tubulo-alveolar glands are present. The majority of these glands are purely mucous in nature, but some of them, especially near the posterior surface of the soft palate, are mixed glands.

H. ESOPHAGUS
(Plates 91 to 95)

The esophagus begins at the level of the cricoid cartilage and extends below the diaphragm. This tube is 10 to 12 inches long and serves to transmit food rapidly, with the aid of gravity, from the pharynx to the stomach. Since the esophagus can be considered as a vertical tube, there is little or no time for absorption. In addition, because of the poor chewing habits of man, and his swallowing of large, coarse lumps of food, the tunica mucosa must have protection against roughage. For this reason, a stratified squamous epithelium rather than an absorptive type of columnar epithelium lines the luminal surface. Furthermore, since no absorption takes place in the esophagus and, therefore, no organisms penetrate its wall, there is little need for great amounts of lymphatic tissue to filter and cleanse the tissue

PLATE 95—Esophagus

FIG. 11-33. Lower third of the esophagus to show the presence of esophageal glands (g). H & E stain. Intermediate power.

FIG. 11-34. Lower third of the esophagus, showing glands (g) and a duct (d). H & E stain. Intermediate power.

FIG. 11-35. Survey of a section through the junctional area of the esophagus and the stomach. Especially note the abrupt epithelial change. H & E stain. Low power. (Ee, stratified squamous epithelium of the esophagus; Ge, simple columnar epithelium of the stomach; g, cardiac glands)

FIG. 11-36. Intermediate-power view of a portion of the section depicted in Figure 11-35. H & E stain. (Ee, stratified squamous epithelium of the esophagus; Ge, simple columnar epithelium of the stomach; g, cardiac glands)

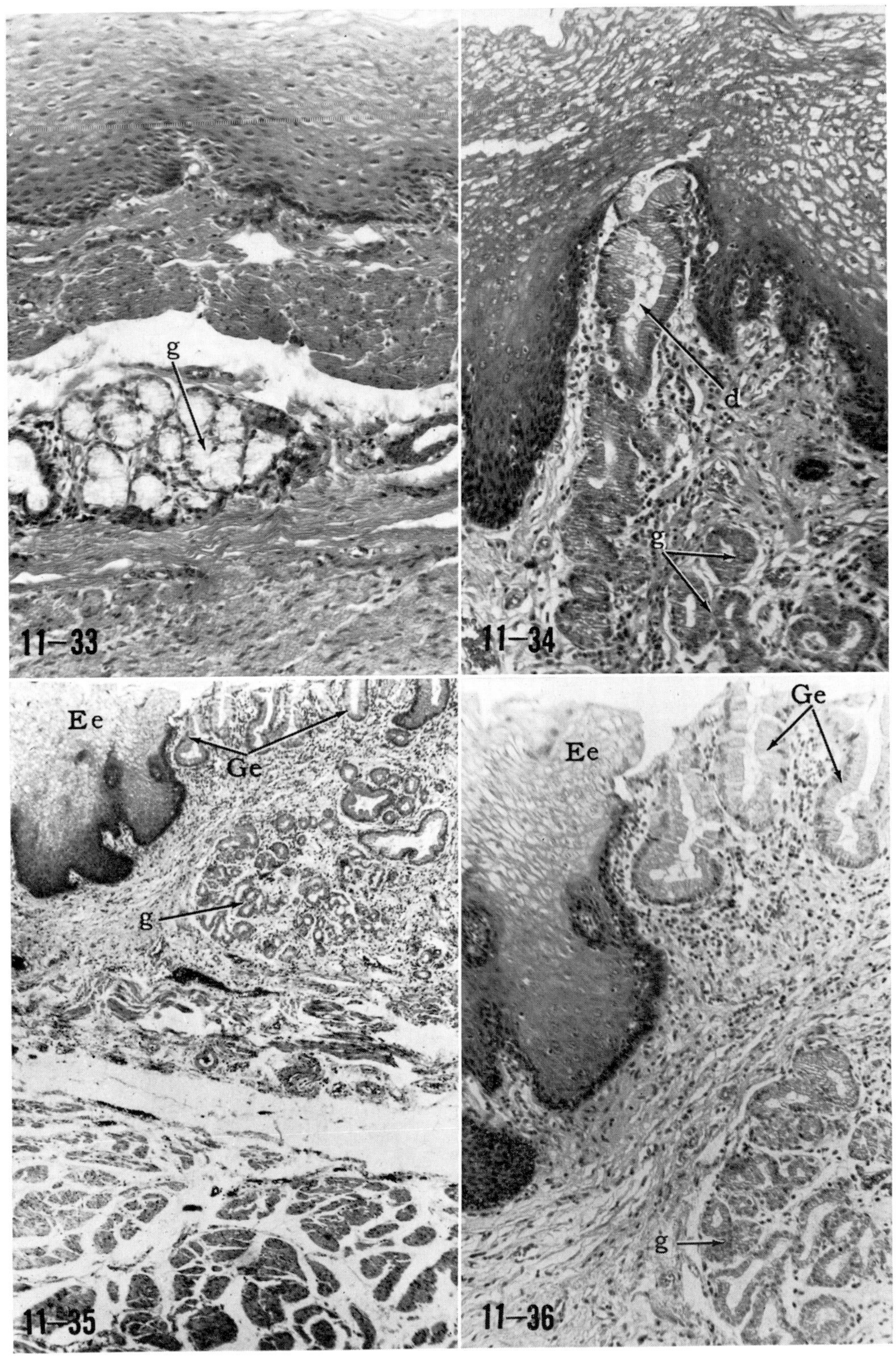

g
11–33
d
g
11–34
Ee
Ge
g
11–35
Ge
Ee
g
11–36

fluid. Because of this, lymph nodules are observed only occasionally. Likewise, since the glands of the mouth provide the necessary secretions (saliva) to lubricate food, there is no real need for glands to secrete mucus or digestive enzymes in the esophagus. Hence, small numbers of **mucous glands (cardiac)** are found in the lamina propria of the lower third of the esophagus. Regarding the muscularis mucosae, that of the lower third of the esophagus is highly developed and very thick in comparison with its development along the rest of the digestive system.

For the most part, the tunica submucosa has the appearance of a dense connective tissue but actually consists of a poorly cellular areolar connective tissue made up predominantly of coarse collagen and elastic fibers. This layer, along with the muscularis mucosa of the tunica mucosa, forms longitudinal folds, revealing an irregular lumen on cross section. During the act of swallowing, the elasticity of the tunica submucosa causes the luminal surface to become smooth. The number of **mucous alveolar glands (esophageal)** in the submucosa is variable, and usually only occasional glands of this type are observed, being restricted primarily to the upper third of the esophagus.

The esophagus is the most muscular part of the digestive system. Its muscularis externa consists of inner circular and outer longitudinal bands. The upper third of the esophagus contains muscle that is of the striated (skeletal) type only, this being continuous with the constrictors of the pharynx. As in the pharynx, in this location, there is an exception to the general rule that striated muscle is under voluntary control. The middle third of the esophagus contains both striated and smooth muscle in its muscular tunic, whereas the lower third contains only smooth muscle.

A tunica adventitia of dense connective tissue binds the esophagus to the surrounding structures but becomes serosa in the segment lying below the diaphragm.

I. STOMACH

(Plates 96 to 100)

Food passes quickly through the esophagus into the stomach where digestion and assimilation occur involuntarily. Histologically, the stomach is divisible into the **cardiac region**, located below the esophageal orifice, the **body**, including the **fundus portion**, and the **pyloric region** leading into the small intestine. In the stomach, since there is less need for the protection of the subepithelial tissue fluid, there is no stratified squamous epithelium such as is found in the esophagus. Instead, a simple columnar epithelium

PLATE 96—Fundic Stomach

FIG. 11-37. Survey section of the wall of the fundic portion of the stomach. Note the highly folded surface of the mucosa (rugae) with gastric pits (p). The glandular nature (g) and lymphocytic infiltration (1) of the mucosa are also detectable. Mallory stain. Low power.

FIG. 11-38. Survey section showing gastric pits (p), taken at a junctional region of the body and the pyloric portions of the stomach. Note the lymphocytic infiltration of the lamina propria. Masson stain. Low power.

FIG. 11-39. Fundic portion of the stomach, showing gastric pits cut in cross section. Mallory stain. Intermediate power.

FIG. 11-40. Fundic portion of the stomach, showing gastric pits cut in longitudinal section. Note the honeycomb appearance of a gastric pit cut transversely deep to the epithelial surface (hg). Mallory stain. Intermediate power.

FIG. 11-41. Tunica mucosa of the fundic portion of the stomach to show the nature of fundic (gastric) glands. Note that these simple, branched tubules are arranged perpendicular to the surface and extend to the muscularis mucosae (mm). Mallory stain. Intermediate power.

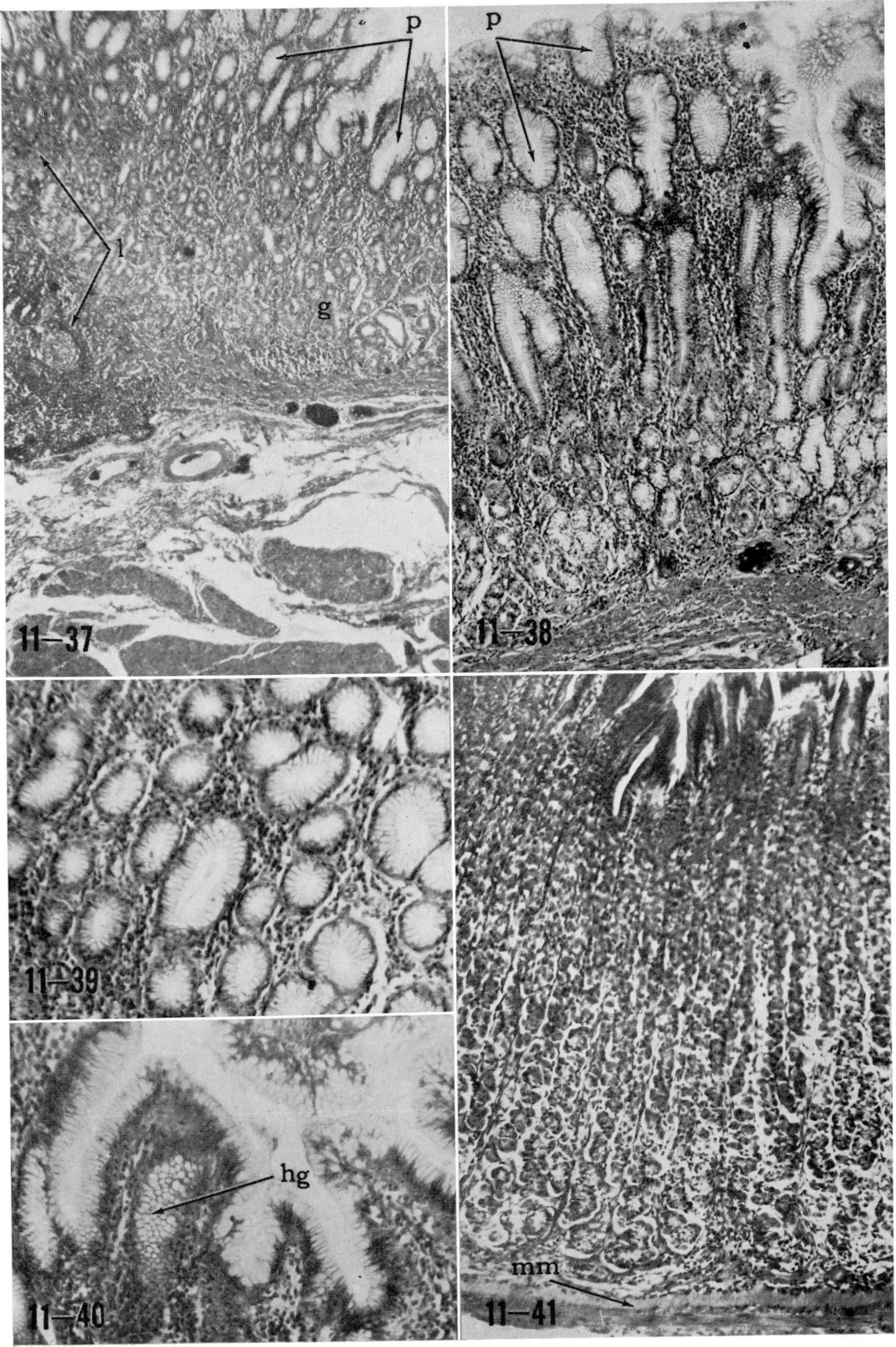
p
l
g
11–37
p
11–38
11–39
hg
11–40
mm
11–41

in which the cells are of a high, clear, mucous type is present near the surface; a lower columnar type is found in the deeper areas (pits) (Figs. 11-35, 11-36).

Examination of the entire tunica mucosa reveals a series of **ridges (rugae)** which are most prominent in the empty stomach. In addition, the entire surface is marked by grooves studded by depressions, the **gastric pits (foveolae)**, which open into and are continuous with the glands of the stomach. Functionally, these gastric pits serve as ducts for the attached glands and convey glandular secretions continuously to the surface of the stomach. This system of ridges and grooves provides for a manifold increase in the surface area as well as an increase in the number of glands. In the body and the cardiac portions, the gastric pits are shallow, whereas in the pyloric region they are deep and usually extend halfway through the tunica mucosa. Although the lamina propria of the stomach is not distinctive, it usually contains solitary lymph nodules in the pyloric region. The muscularis mucosa is thin and separates the mucosa from the submucosal layer. Distinctive glands, characteristic for each part of the stomach, are located in the tunica mucosa. These are known as cardiac, gastric and pyloric glands.

1. **Cardiac glands** are restricted to the junction of the esophagus with the cardiac portion of the stomach. They are branched tubular glands in which the cells characteristically have their nuclei flattened against the basement membrane and the cytoplasm contains mucigen granules (mucus-secreting).

2. **Gastric (fundic or principal) glands** (Plates 96 to 99) are the most numerous type and are present in approximately two thirds of the mucous membrane of the stomach. These are primarily unbranched tubular glands which have their ducts opening directly into the bases of shallow gastric pits. A typical gastric gland is divided into a mouth region which opens into a foveolae, a neck portion, the body or main part and a fundus or blind-end portion. Gastric glands are arranged in parallel, cordlike fashion. The following cell types are distinguishable:

a. **Mucoid neck cells**, located in the constricted portion of the gland immediately next to the pit, are cuboidal or low columnar elements that contain fine light-staining, granular cytoplasm and flat nuclei which are basally located. These cells secrete a mucin which is histochemically different from that secreted by the surface epithelium of the stomach and may be a carrier or a source of intrinsic factor. Intrinsic factor is normally present in gastric juice and is deficient or absent in cases of pernicious anemia. This factor interacts with vitamin B_{12} to make possible its absorption by the small intestines. A deficiency of B_{12} causes an arrest in the development of red blood cells (megaloblastic type).

b. **Chief cells** (zymogenic or peptic cells), located in the body portion of the gland, are the most numerous cell type and contain

PLATE 97—Fundic Stomach

FIG. 11-42. Fundic stomach, showing lymphatic tissue (l) in the lamina propria of the mucosa. H & E stain. Intermediate power. (fg, fundic glands; gp, gastric pits)

FIG. 11-43. Section of fundic stomach through the gastric pits (gp). H & E stain. High power. (sc, simple columnar surface epithelium of gastric pits; lp, lamina propria with diffuse infiltration of lymphocytes)

FIG. 11-44. Fundic stomach, showing varied appearance of gastric pit cells (gpc) cut in cross section. Mallory stain. High power. (lp, lamina propria)

FIG. 11-45. Fundic stomach, showing ideally sectioned fundic glands (fg) as straight radiating structures of the tunica mucosa. H & E stain. Intermediate power. (gp, gastric pits; mg, mouth of gland opening into pit; ng, neck of gland; bg, body of gland; f, fundus of gland)

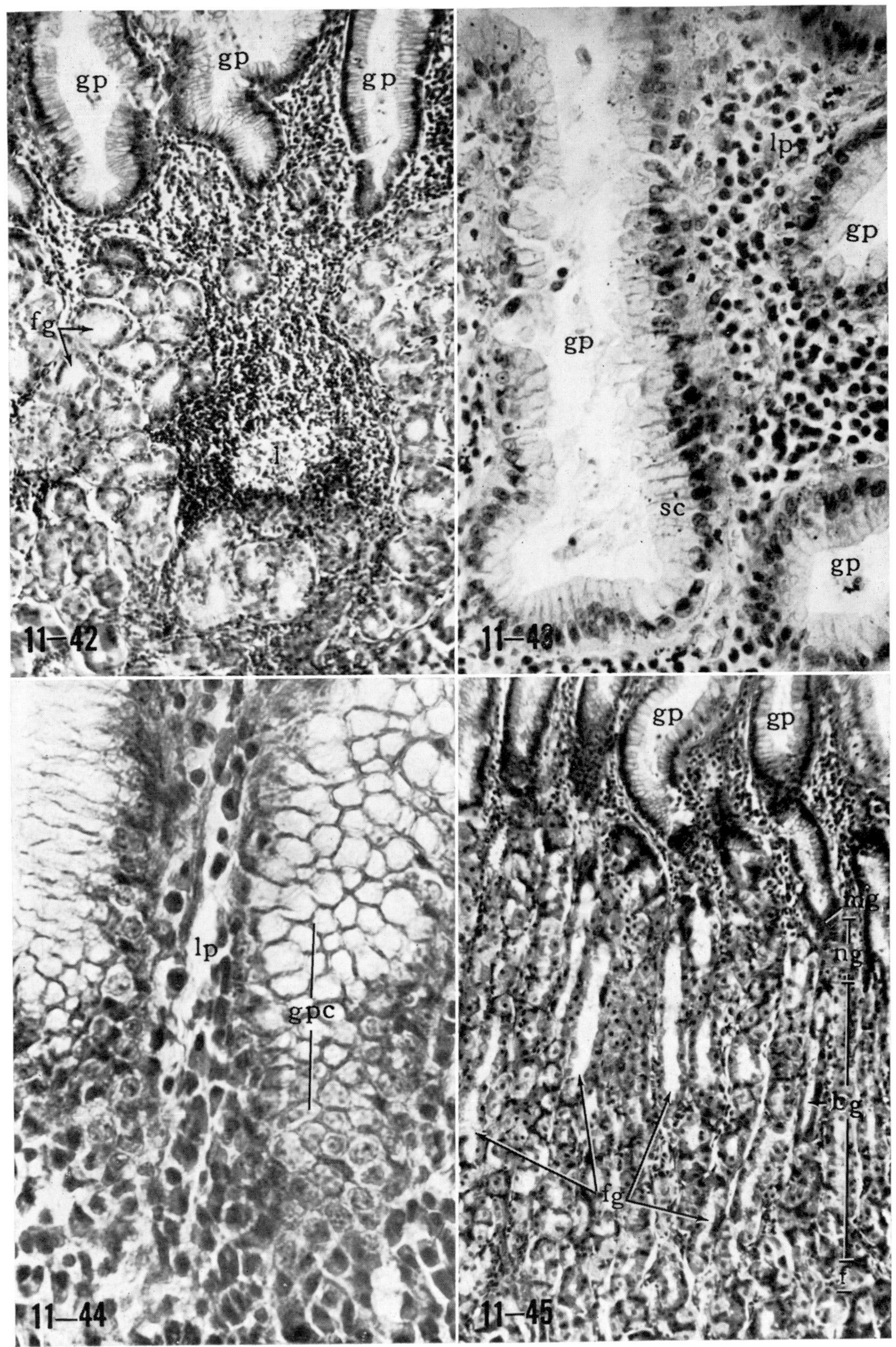
gp
gp
gp
fg
l
11–42
lp
gp
gp
sc
gp
11–43
lp
gpc
11–44
gp
gp
mg
ng
bg
fg
f
11–45

pepsinogen, the antecedent of the enzyme pepsin. Typically, these cells are square or pyramidal in shape, have spherical nuclei, generally located at the base of each cell, and usually contain a coarse brilliant, basophilic granular cytoplasm. In addition, terminal bars are present on the free surface.

c. **Parietal cells** (wall cells) occur in large numbers and serve as one of the best diagnostic features of gastric glands. These cells are found inserted between chief cells and are especially prominent in the upper body portion of the gland. They are ovoid, polygonal or wedge-shaped cells and are oriented so that the broadest or basal surface appears next to the basement membrane and the apical end is toward the lumen. The cytoplasm is strongly acidophilic, and the nucleus, which is large and centrally located in the cell, has a bloated appearance. Parietal cells communicate with the lumen by means of intercellular secretory canaliculi which are insinuated between the parietal cells and adjacent chief cells. Intracellular canaliculi are also present. Parietal cells secrete the antecedents of hydrochloric acid in a bound form to provide the necessary acid medium for the digestion of proteins.

d. **Argentaffin cells** of Heidenhein, which usually require silver stains to identify them, are present in small numbers and are located primarily at the bases of the glands between the basement membrane and the chief cells. They are flat cells with a granular chromaffin type of cytoplasm. Argentaffin cells are linked to the production of serotonin and other neurohumors. These cells possibly also contain some intrinsic factor.

3. **Pyloric glands** (Plate 100) are glands characteristic of the distal portion of the stomach. Although they secrete mucus just as do cardiac glands, they differ markedly in morphology from the latter. Pyloric glands are of a simple and branched, coiled, tubular variety and open into gastric pits which extend quite deeply into the tunica mucosa. In cross section, these coiled tubular pyloric glands appear in cartwheel or doughnut configurations.

The tunica submucosa of the stomach is not distinctive and consists of the usual arrangement of loose connective tissue.

The tunica muscularis normally consists of an inner oblique, a middle circular and an outer longitudinal layer of smooth muscle. It should be noted that the smooth muscle bundles, especially in the outer longitudinal layer, are not as uniformly arranged as elsewhere in the digestive tract. In the pyloric region the inner and the middle muscle layers thicken to form the pyloric sphincter.

The entire outer wall of the stomach is covered by a tunica serosa which is very thin.

J. SMALL INTESTINE

Because the major functions of the small intestine vary markedly from those of the stomach, it is not surprising that its histology

PLATE 98—Fundic Stomach

FIG. 11-46. Mucosa of fundic stomach, showing the simple, branched tubular fundic glands (fg) cut in a longitudinal plane. Mallory stain. Intermediate power. (gp, gastric pits; lp, lamina propria; mm, muscularis mucosae)

FIG. 11-47. Fundic stomach, showing a typical section through the fundic glands cut in a transverse plane. H & E stain. Intermediate power.

FIG. 11-48. Fundic stomach, showing the base of the fundic glands, the muscularis mucosae (mm), the submucosa (sm) and a part of the muscularis externa (me). Note that the submucosal layer consists of dense irregular connective tissue with some fat cells (f) and blood vessels (v). H & E stain. Intermediate power.

FIG. 11-49. Part of the muscularis externa (me) of the fundic stomach to show the myenteric plexus (mp). Mallory stain. Intermediate power.

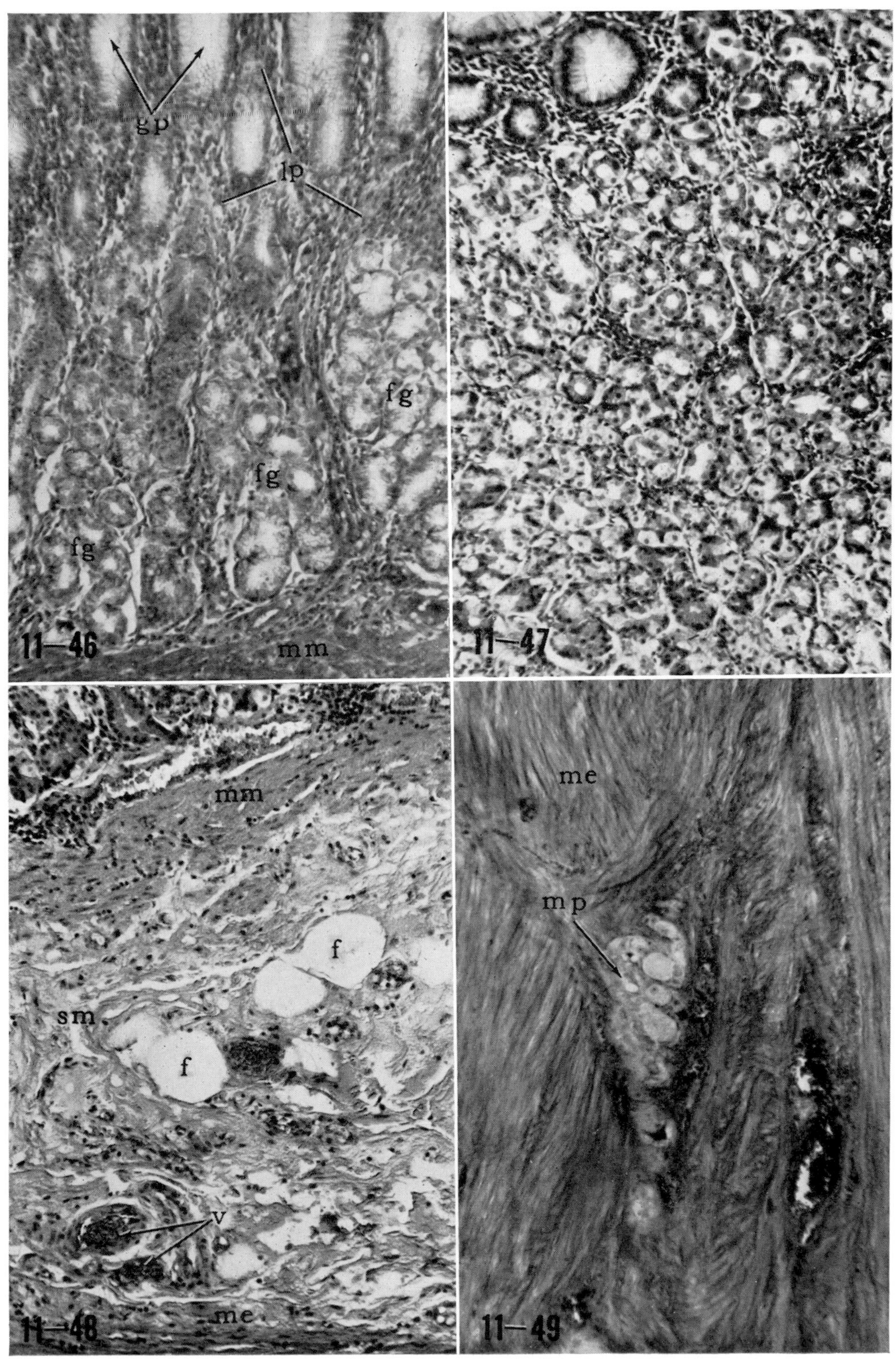
gp
lp
fg
fg
fg
11—46
mm
11—47
mm
f
f
sm
v
11—48
me
me
mp
11—49

should reflect these variations. Perhaps the most important difference is an increase in the luminal surface area of the small intestine. This is brought about in two ways. First, the mucosal and the submucosal layers are thrown into a series of circular folds analogous to the ridges or threads on a metal nut. The anatomic folds, known as **plicae circulares (valves of Kirkring)** project into the intestinal lumen and greatly increase the extent of the free mucosal surface.

A second means of increasing this surface is afforded by the presence of hundreds of thousands of delicate projections of microscopic size from the tunica mucosa into the lumen. These fingerlike or leaflike processes, known as **intestinal villi**, arise from every possible site on the surface, including the plicae circulares. Each villus is composed of a stroma of lamina propria covered by a striated, simple columnar epithelium. The stroma is a reticular meshwork of loose connective tissue and contains a central lacteal (Fig. 8-10), a capillary bed with an arteriole and a venule, an autonomic nerve net, lymphocytes and smooth muscle fibers extending into it from the muscularis mucosa. **Intestinal glands (crypts of Lieberkühn)** open into the intestinal lumen between the bases of adjacent villi and extend down into the mucosa as far as the muscularis mucosae. These crypts are lined by a simple columnar epithelium made up of absorptive cells, goblet cells, Paneth cells and a few argentaffin cells. The simple columnar absorptive cells have a fine granular cytoplasm with a cuticular (striated) border. The electron microscope has revealed that the striated appearance of the cuticular border is due to the presence of countless microvilli that greatly enhance absorption by increasing the absorptive surface many times. Water and the various breakdown products of digestion are absorbed from the lumen across this epithelial surface. The epithelium has also been shown to have a rich concentration of alkaline phosphatase next to the lumen. The goblet cells are a source of mucus that provides lubrication for the epithelial surface. Paneth cells, lying at the bases of the intestinal glands, possess coarse eosinophilic granules which are serozymogenic in nature.

Anatomically and histologically, the small intestine is divisible into the **duodenum**, the **jejunum** and the **ileum**. Apart from the general description cited, certain histologic features are evident in various regions that make identification rather straightforward.

1. Duodenum
(Plates 101 and 102)

The presence of **Brunner's** (mucous) **glands** arranged in lobules in the submucosa and the lamina propria of the mucosa, and representing an extension of the pyloric glands, are very diagnostic in the upper portion of

PLATE 99—Fundic Stomach

FIG. 11-50. Longitudinal section through the fundic glands of the fundic portion of the stomach, showing that smooth muscle fibers (sm) may be present in the lamina propria. H & E stain. High power. (cc, chief cells; pc, parietal cells)

FIG. 11-51. Section of fundic stomach, showing fundic glands (fg), cut in a longitudinal plane, and chief cells (cc) and parietal cells (pc) located within them. H & E stain. High power. (l, lumen of fundic gland)

FIG. 11-52. Section of fundic stomach, showing the fundic glands (fg) cut in cross section and demonstrating the relationship of parietal cells (pc) to chief cells (cc). H & E stain. High power. (l, lumen of fundic gland)

FIG. 11-53. Base of the mucosa and the adjacent submucosa of the fundic stomach, showing an accumulation of lymphocytes. These cells appear to be infiltrating the muscularis mucosae (mm) from the tunica submucosa (sm). H & E stain. High power. (fg, fundic glands)

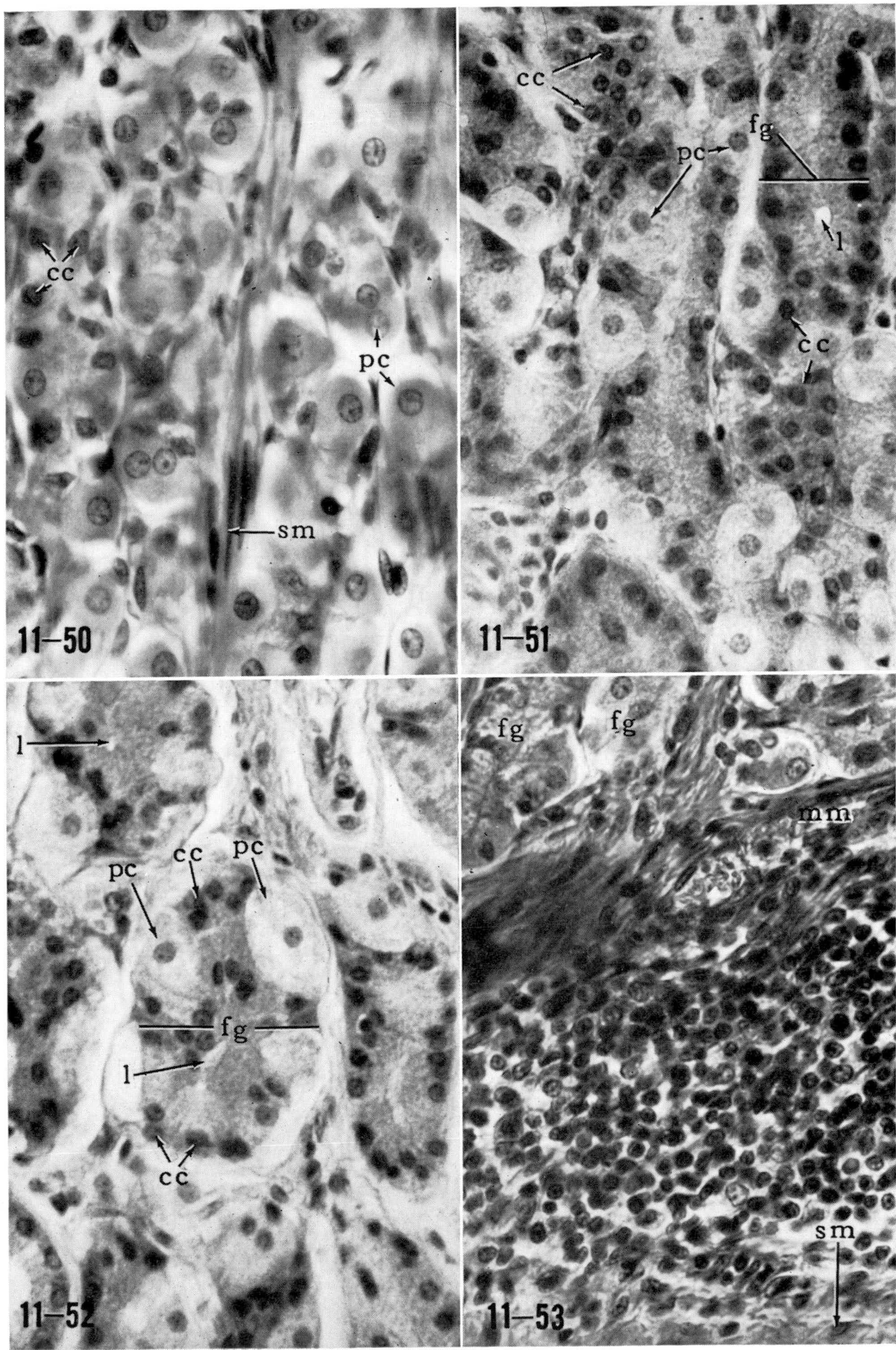
cc
pc
sm
11–50
cc
fg
pc
l
cc
11–51
l
pc
cc
pc
fg
l
cc
11–52
fg
fg
mm
sm
11–53

this region. In addition, some sections may reveal the presence of pancreatic tissue or the cholecystic duct near by.

2. Jejunum
(Plates 103 to 105)

Plicae circulares are very tall and evident especially in the proximal portion of the jejunum. An increase in the number of goblet cells and lymphocytes is less apparent.

3. Ileum
(Plate 106)

Peyer's patches (solitary lymphatic nodules) found in the submucosa and extending into the mucosa are especially diagnostic of this region. An increase in the number of goblet cells is also quite apparent in the ileum.

The tunica submucosa is distinctive only as regards the presence of Brunner's glands in the duodenum and Peyer's patches in the ileum.

The tunica muscularis is thinner than in the stomach and possesses only 2 layers, an inner circular and an outer longitudinal layer of smooth muscle. The longitudinal layer may appear slightly spiral.

Except on the retroperitoneal portion of the duodenum, a tunica serosa limits the wall.

K. LARGE INTESTINE

The architectural plan conforms to the general pattern of the digestivet ract but differs in the following details. In the large intestine the plicae circulares are absent, and the surface facing the lumen loses its corrugated appearance in long section. Also, since the contents of the lumen are rendered less fluid and become thick in consistency by the removal of water, absorption takes place in reduced amount, and villi are no longer present. The crypts of Lieberkühn (tubular intestinal glands) are longer and straighter and reveal more numerous goblet cells. There is now a need for (1) lubrication of the surface epithelium and (2) facilitation of forward movement of gradually dehydrated fecal material. An increased number of goblet cells provides a copious production of mucus which satisfies both these requirements and also gives the fecal material the proper consistency. Movements in the large intestine are slow and hesitating, resulting in the accumulation of fecal material and an increase in the width of the lumen. In addition, especially where the contents are stagnant, the lymphatic tissue becomes abundant in the lamina propria and pushes into the submucosa. In this way, nature provides a method of coping with bacterial infiltration and decomposition.

PLATE 100—Pyloric Stomach

FIG. 11-54. Survey section revealing the tunics of the pyloric stomach. H & E stain. Low power. (gp, gastric pits; pg, pyloric glands; ln, lymph nodules in the lamina propria; mm, muscularis mucosae; m, mucosa; sm, submucosa; me, muscularis externa; s, serosa)

FIG. 11-55. Survey section clearly revealing the tunica mucosa, submucosa (sm) and a portion of the muscularis externa (me). H & E stain. Low power. (gp, gastric pits; pg, pyloric glands; ln, lymph nodule; mm, muscularis mucosae)

FIG. 11-56. Tunica mucosa of the pyloric stomach, showing gastric pits (gp), pyloric glands (pg) and lymphoid tissue (l) in lamina propria. H & E stain. Intermediate power.

FIG. 11-57. Pyloric stomach, showing the simple, branched tubular pyloric glands. Note that the cells contain a pale cytoplasm with some granulation and nuclei compressed against the base. H & E stain. High power.

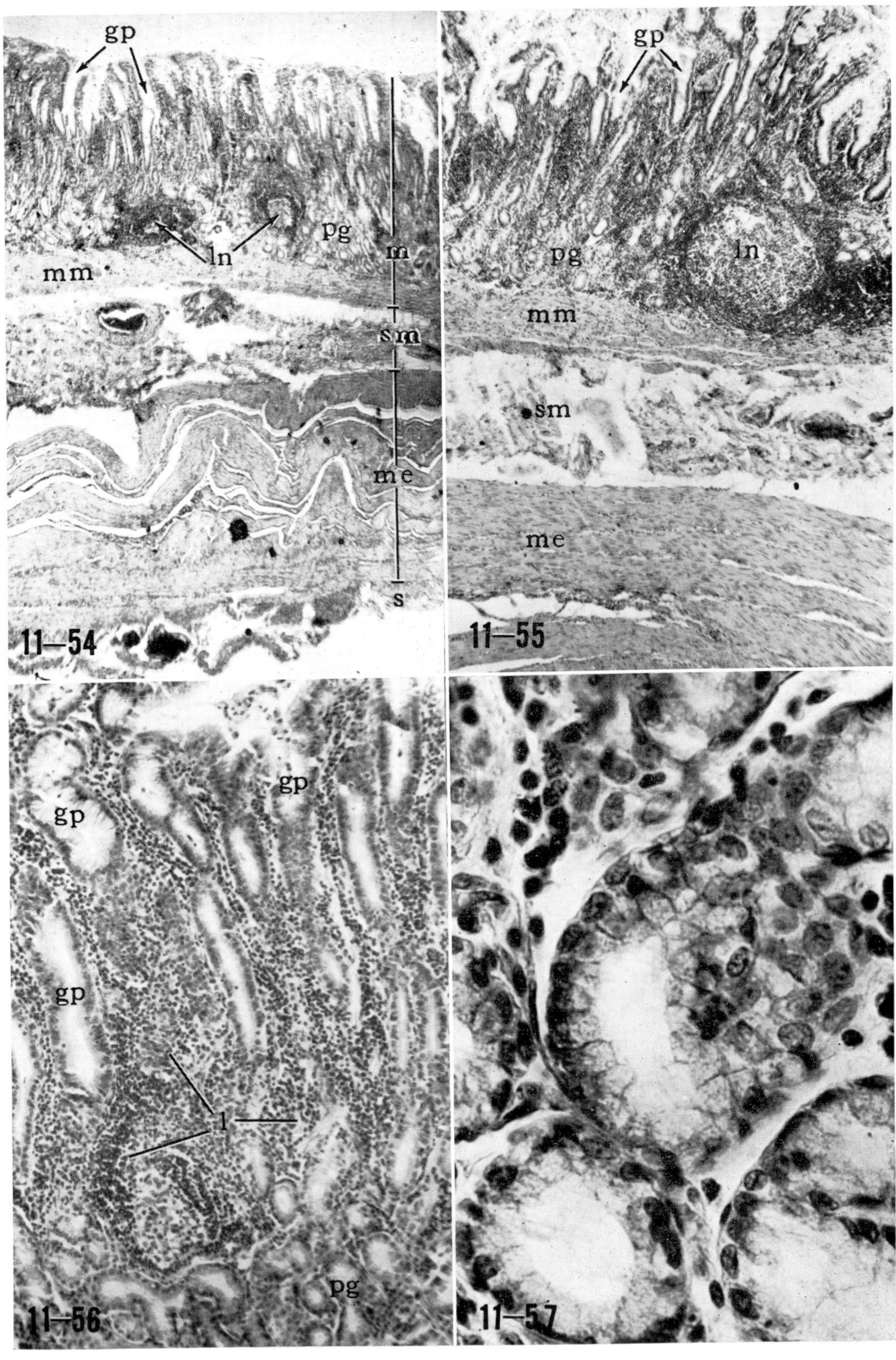
gp
ln
pg
m
mm
sm
me
s
11–54
gp
pg
ln
mm
sm
me
11–55
gp
gp
gp
l
pg
11–56
11–57

The main parts of the large intestine include the **cecum** with the **vermiform appendix**, the **colon**, the **rectum** and the **anal canal**.

1. Cecum

This blind pouch hangs downward below the level of the ileocecal sphincter. The tunics are essentially similar to those of the colon (see Section 3).

2. Vermiform Appendix
(Plate 107)

This wormlike process, which is attached to the cecum, has a mucosa which is essentially like that of the colon. However, certain features are diagnostic. The glands of Lieberkühn are not as developed and are found to radiate from the lumen which is angular, narrow or occluded and contains masses of dead cells and free lymphocytes. The lamina propria has a greater concentration of lymph nodules and tends to be fibrous. The tunica submucosa tends to be fatty and contains a plentiful amount of lymphatic tissue extending into it from the mucosa. Although the pattern of the tunica muscularis is maintained, there is a definite reduction in this layer. A serosa is present but may show degenerative changes.

3. Colon
(Plate 108)

The mucosa in the colon is smooth and, as in the intestine up to this point, is lined by epithelium. Although most epithelial cells are of the mucus-secreting goblet variety, some are absorptive cells and have a thin, striated border. The crypts of Lieberkühn are straight, and they extend to the surface. Numerous goblet cells are present in these glands, but no Paneth cells are apparent. Considerable diffuse lymphatic tissue is present throughout the lamina propria, and lymph nodules may also be found. In some instances the lymphatic tissue may be so abundant that it penetrates through the muscularis mucosae into the submucosa. The tunica submucosa is distinctive in the abundance of lymphatic tissue, and fat cells are often found.

The tunica muscularis consists of an inner layer which, together with the tunica mucosa and the submucosa, forms crescentic folds. The outer longitudinal muscle has the unique arrangement of being massed into 3 thick flat bands, the **taenia coli**. Although not continuous around the wall of the colon, these bands, which are often as wide as 1 cm., appear to be evenly set in cross section. Along

PLATE 101—Duodenum

FIG. 11-58. Survey section revealing the tunics of the upper part of the duodenum. H & E stain. Low power. (m, mucosa; sm, submucosa; cm, circular smooth muscle layer of the muscularis externa; lm, longitudinal smooth muscle layer of the muscularis externa; v, villi projecting from the plica circulares; c, crypts of Lieberkühn; Bg, Brunner's glands)

FIG. 11-59. Survey section of the descending duodenal wall traversed by the ductus choledochus (dc). Note the absence of Brunner's glands at this level. H & E stain. Low power.

FIG. 11-60. Deep part of the mucosa and adjacent submucosa of the upper portion of the duodenum. Note the crypts of Lieberkühn (c), the muscularis mucosae (mm) and Brunner's glands (Bg). H & E stain. Intermediate power.

FIG. 11-61. Ductus choledochus in the submucosa of the duodenum, showing its tall simple columnar epithelial lining (sc) which has an obvious striated border on the luminal surface of the cells. H & E stain. Intermediate power. (lp, lamina propria)

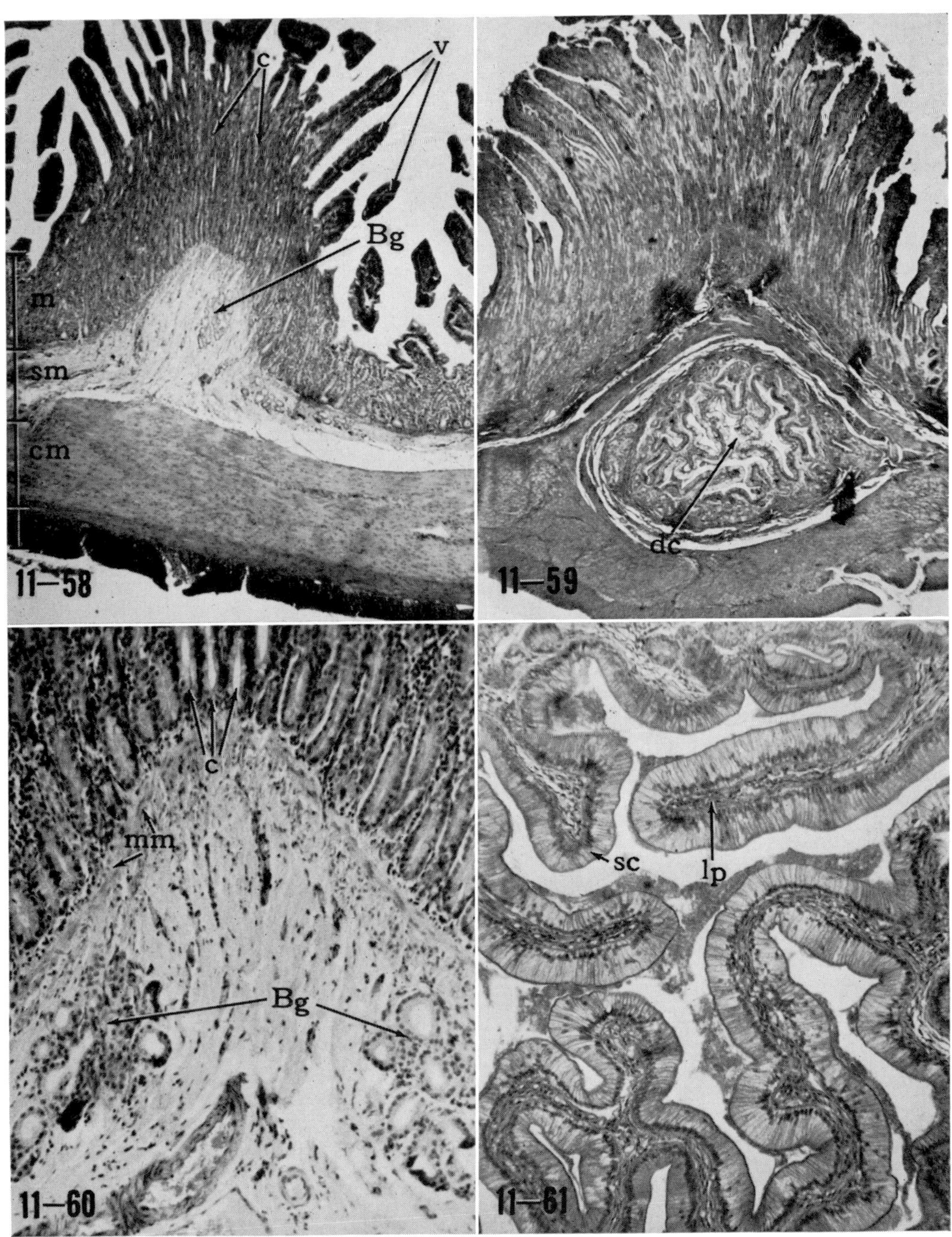
v
c
Bg
m
sm
cm
11–58
dc
11–59
c
mm
Bg
11–60
sc
lp
11–61

with the contractions of the inner muscle, the action of the taenia coli is to form the characteristic sacculations of the colon (**haustra**).

The colon has a distinctive tunica serosa because the latter contains swellings, the **appendices epiploicae**. These are protuberances of fat and cells of the omentum.

4. Rectum
(Plate 109, Figs. 11-91 and 11-92)

This is the straighter part of the large intestine which extends to the anus. The rectum proper is 5 to 7 inches in length and, with a few modifications, is histologically similar to the colon. Glands of Lieberkühn are still present but are decidedly increased in length as a result of thickening of the tunica mucosa and are spaced farther apart. Although there are no sacculations in the wall of the rectum, the lower part of the rectum, when empty, demonstrates 8 longitudinal folds known as the **rectal columns of Morgagni**. Three permanent transverse folds of mucosa, submucosa and circular muscle, the **rectal valves**, are also present and project into the lumen. These valves serve to hold back feces.

The tunica submucosa has no conspicuous amount of lymphoid tissue in the lower part of the rectum. A striking feature is the presence of large hemorrhoidal arteries and veins.

The taenia coli are absent, and the tunica muscularis appears thickened, ultimately forming the internal anal sphincter in the lower part of the rectum.

A tunica serosa is absent.

5. Anal Canal
(Plate 109, Figs. 11-93 and 11-94)

Here, there is a strikingly sudden change in the epithelium lining the mucosa from a simple columnar to a stratified squamous variety. The glands of Leiberkühn abruptly become shortened and ultimately disappear.

The tunica submucosa has prominent blood vessels, as noted in the lower part of the rectum.

Likewise, the internal sphincter of smooth muscle extends into the muscularis of the anal canal. However, in addition, an external sphincter of skeletal muscle is formed around the internal sphincter.

Hair follicles, sebaceous and large sweat glands (the circumanal glands) are present and appear outside the anal canal.

PLATE 102—Duodenum

FIG. 11-62. Duodenum showing the leaflike villi and the crypts of Lieberkühn (c) at the bases of the villi. Note the core of loose connective tissue (lp) infiltrated by lymphocytes and also containing some smooth muscle cells from the muscularis mucosae. Simple columnar epithelium (sc) having a striated border and containing many goblet cells covers the lamina propria core of the villi. H & E stain. Intermediate power.

FIG. 11-63. Crypts of Lieberkühn (c) from the duodenum with surrounding lamina propria (lp). H & E stain. High power. (gc, goblet cells)

FIG. 11-64. Cross section of duodenum, showing the base of the crypts of Lieberkühn (c), lamina propria (lp), inner circular (ic) and outer longitudinal (ol) smooth muscle layers of the muscularis mucosae and the submucosa (sm). H & E stain. High power. (Pc, Paneth cells)

FIG. 11-65. Brunner's glands (Bg) located in the submucosa (sm) of the upper part of the duodenum. Note their branched tubular nature and, for the most part, the pale appearance of these mucous cells. H & E stain. High power.

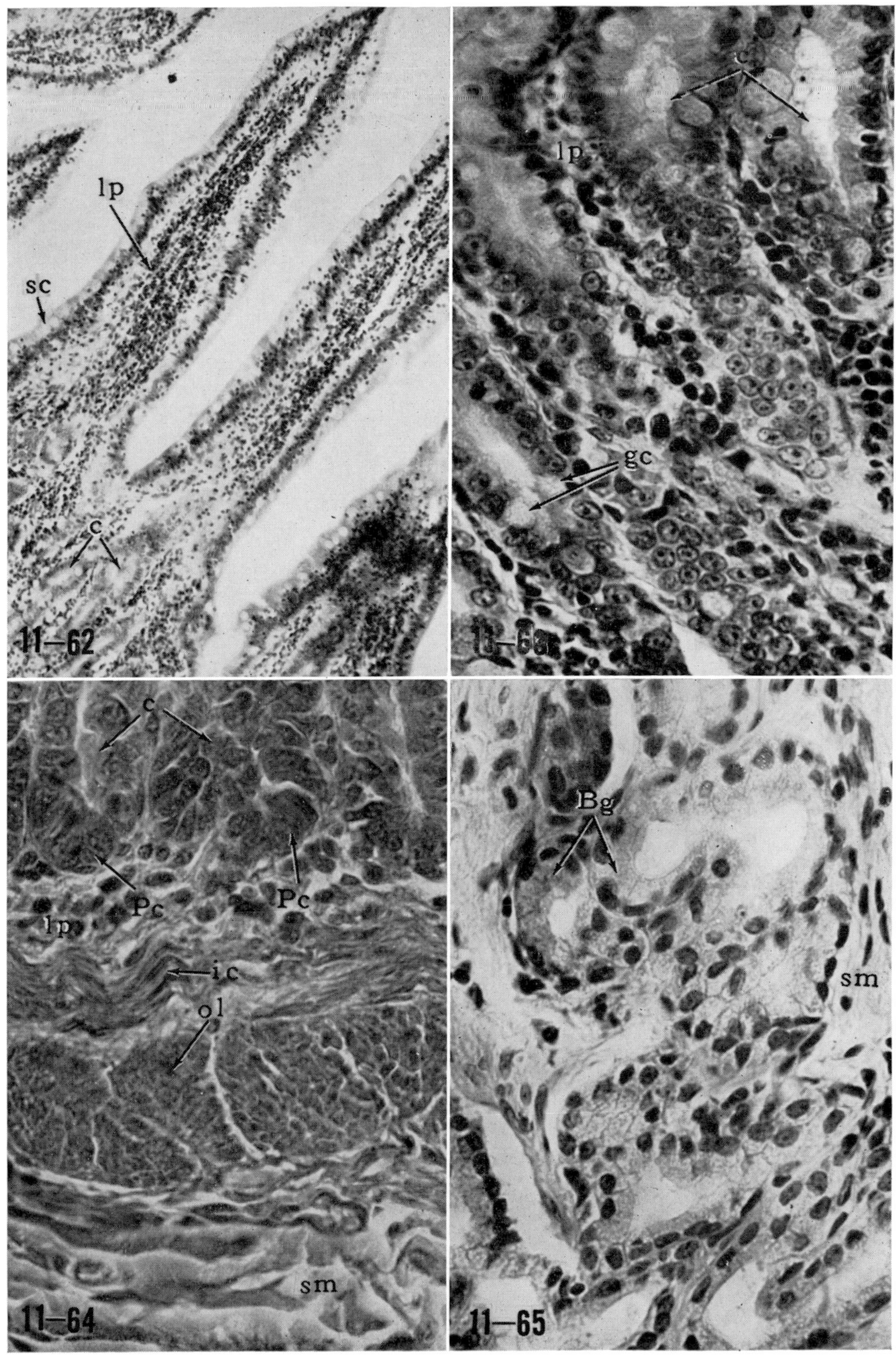

lp
sc
c
11–62
c
lp
gc
c
Pc
Pc
lp
ic
ol
sm
11–64
Bg
sm
11–65

PLATE 103—Jejunum

FIG. 11-66. Wall of the jejunum. Note that the villi (v) have been cut transversely and parallel with their long axes. H & E stain. Low power. (c, crypts of Lieberkühn; sm, submucosa; cm, circular smooth muscle layer of the muscularis externa; lm, longitudinal smooth muscle layer of the muscularis externa; s, serosa)

FIG. 11-67. Longitudinal section of the wall of the jejunum (dog), showing the extension of the submucosa (sm) into the tall plicae circulares (pc). Note the numerous villi (v) projecting from the plicae circulares into the lumen. Masson stain. Low power. (c, crypts of Lieberkühn; me, muscularis externa)

FIG. 11-68. Villi of the jejunum. H & E stain. Intermediate power. (sb, striated border of simple columnar epithelium; gc, goblet cells; lp, lamina propria core; sm, smooth muscle cells)

FIG. 11-69. Crypts of Lieberkühn (c) of the jejunum at the base of villi (v) revealing their simple tubular nature. Note the lamina propria between the crypts. H & E stain. Intermediate power.

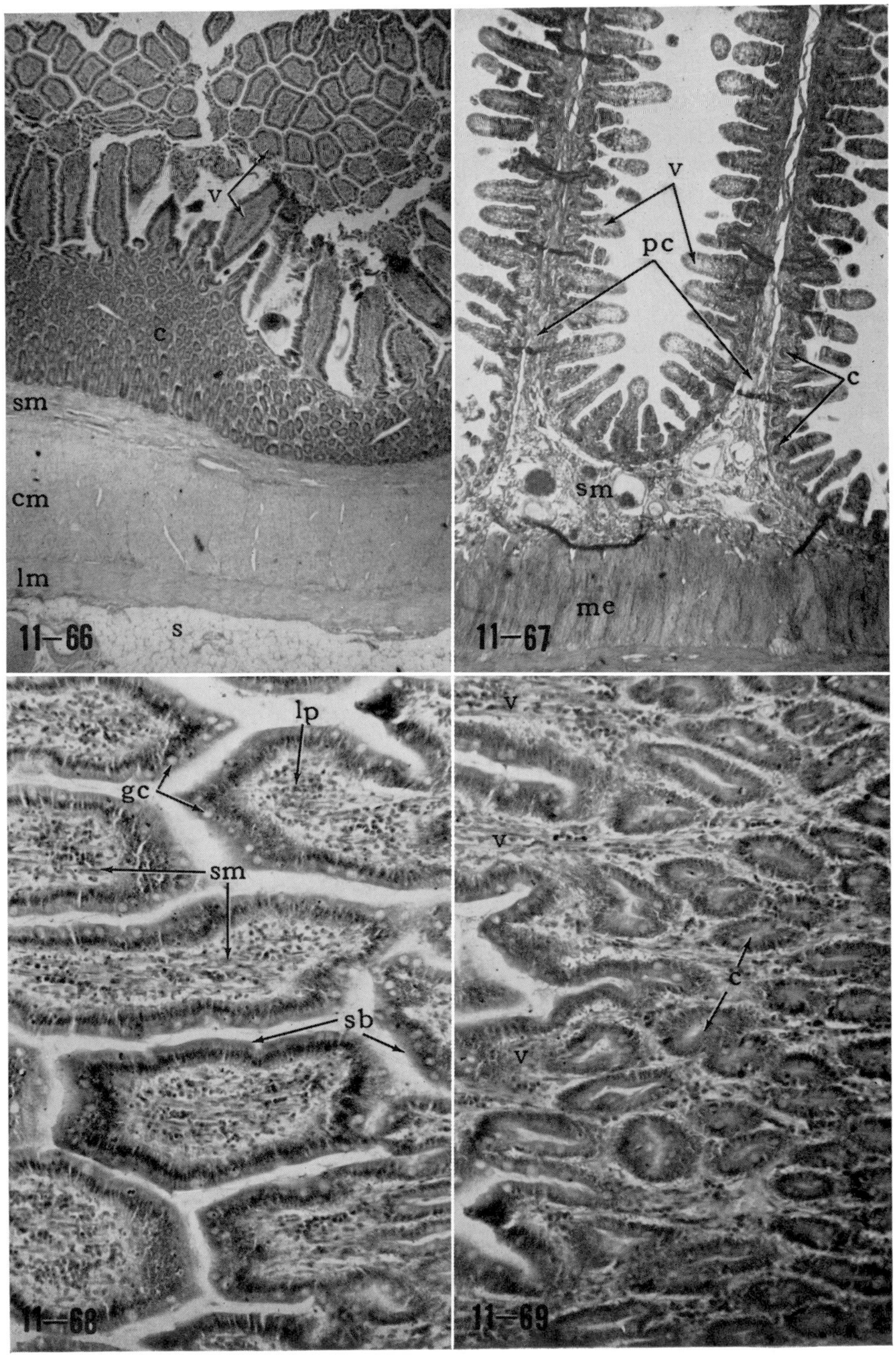
v
c
sm
cm
lm
s
11–66
v
pc
c
sm
me
11–67
lp
gc
sm
sb
11–68
v
v
c
v
11–69

PLATE 104—Jejunum

FIG. 11-70. Injected section of the mucosa of animal jejunum, showing the vascularity of villi (v) and crypts of Lieberkühn (c). Intermediate power.

FIG. 11-71. Injected section of the wall of animal jejunum complementing Figure 11-70 showing the vascularity of the crypts of Lieberkühn (c), the submucosa (sm) and the muscularis externa (me). Intermediate power. (mm, muscularis mucosae)

FIG. 11-72. Deep part of the mucosa (m) of the jejunum, showing crypts of Lieberkühn and the muscularis mucosae (mm). H & E stain. Intermediate power.

FIG. 11-73. Part of the muscularis externa (me) of the jejunum and the underlying serosa revealing fat cells (f) and blood vessels (v). H & E stain. Intermediate power.

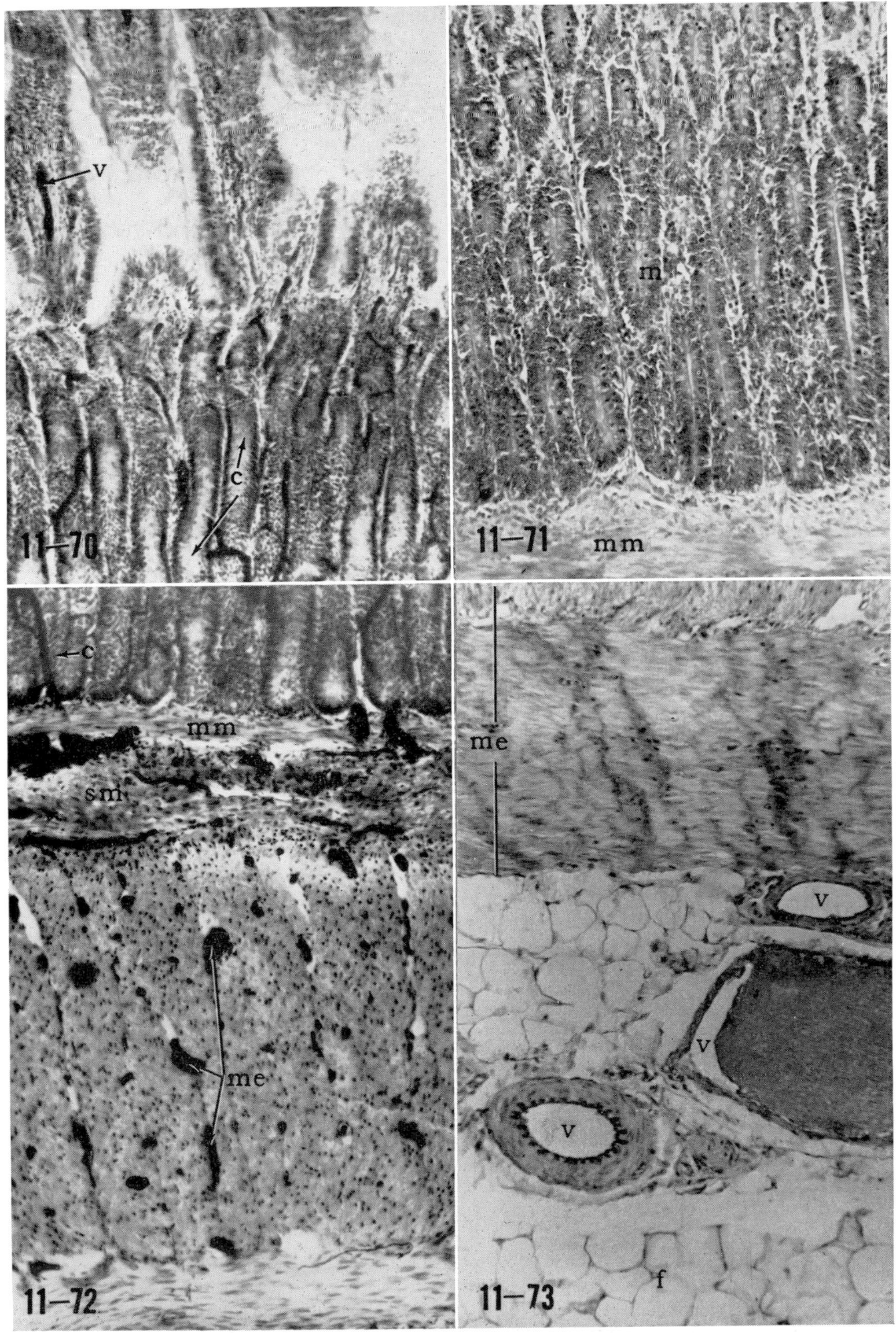
v
c
11–70
m
11–71
mm
c
mm
sm
me
11–72
me
v
v
v
f
11–73

PLATE 105—Jejunum

FIG. 11-74. Longitudinal section of a villus of the jejunum. H & E stain. High power. (sb, striated border of columnar cells; tw, terminal web; g, goblet cells; lp, core of lamina propria with smooth muscle fibers [m] arranged with their long axes parallel with that of the villus)

FIG. 11-75. Cross section of a villus of the jejunum. Masson stain. High power. (sb, striated border of columnar cells; g, goblet cells; lp, core of lamina propria; m, smooth muscle fibers; v, blood vessel; bm, basement membrane)

FIG. 11-76. Cross section of crypt of Lieberkühn located between the bases of adjacent facing villi (vi) in a section of dog jejunum. Note the Paneth cells (Pc), the lumen of the crypt (l) and the surrounding cellular lamina propria (lp). Masson stain. High power.

FIG. 11-77. Longitudinal section of dog jejunum at the base of a plica circularis (valve of Kerkring). Masson stain. Intermediate power. (mm, muscularis mucosae; lp, lamina propria; vi, bases of two adjacent villi; v, vessels associated with the submucosa)

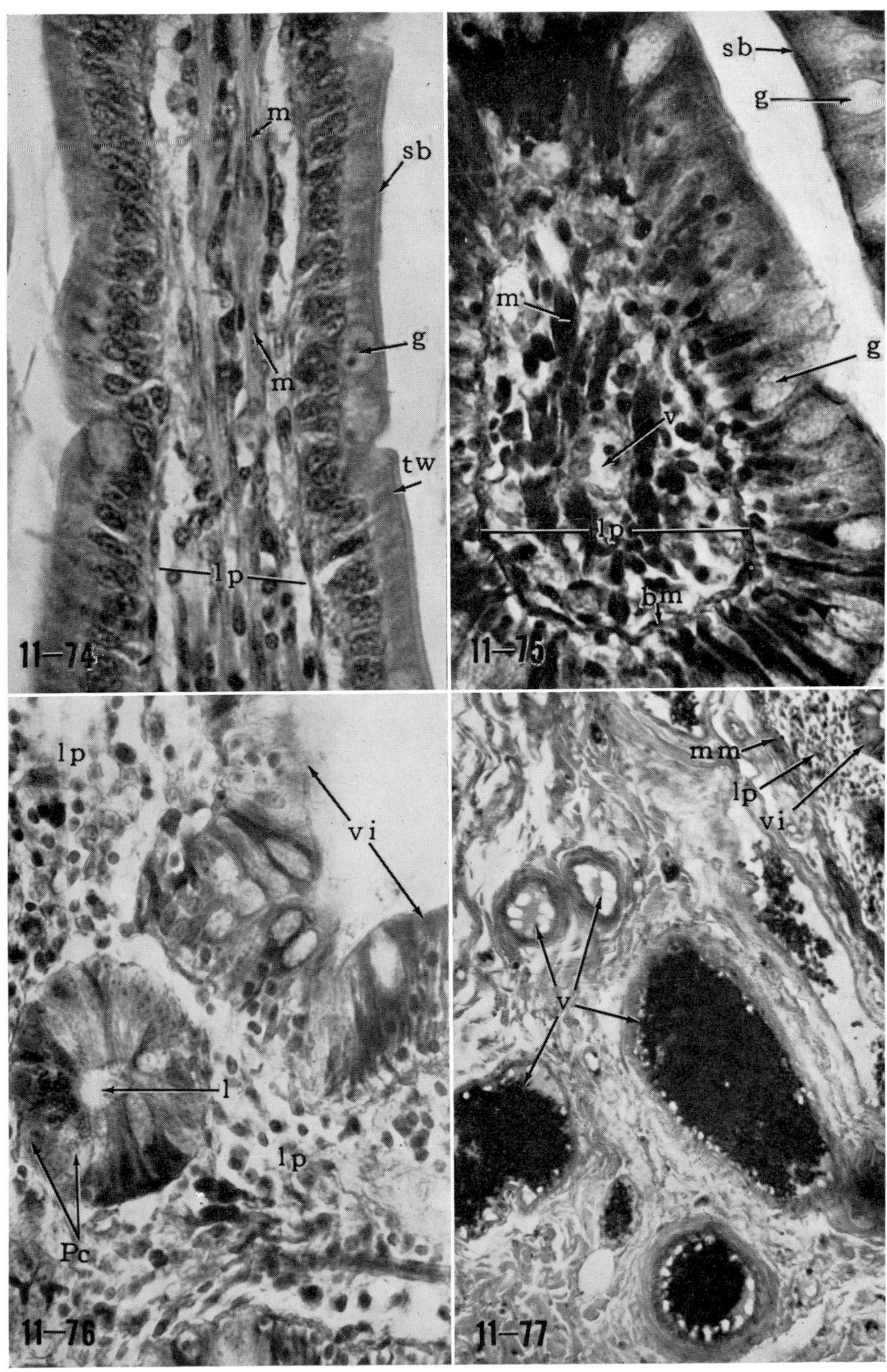
m
sb
g
m
tw
lp
11–74
sb
g
m
g
v
lp
bm
11–75
lp
vi
l
lp
Pc
11–76
mm
lp
vi
v
11–77

PLATE 106—Ileum

FIG. 11-78. Survey of a transverse section of the ileum to demonstrate especially the aggregations of solitary nodules (Peyer's patches, Pp) which are found in the lamina propria of the mucosa (m) and extend into the submucosa (sm). H & E stain. Low power.

FIG. 11-79. A slightly higher magnification of the ileum, showing a high concentration of lymphoid nodules in a region of the wall that is opposite the attachment of the mesentery. Arrows indicate the pear-shaped apices of two Peyer's patches (Pp) which are directed toward the lumen (l). H & E stain. Low power.

FIG. 11-80. Portion of the ileum near the mesenteric attachment to show that lymphoid material may be absent. Compare with Figure 11-79. Shorter, clublike-shaped villi (v) are usually characteristic of this region of the small intestine. Also note the crypts of Lieberkühn (c), the lamina propria (lp), the submucosa (sm) and the muscularis externa (me). H & E stain. Intermediate power.

FIG. 11-81. A slightly higher magnification of a villus of the ileum. Note the presence of numerous goblet cells (g) between the epithelial cells and observe the cellular lamina propria core (lp) of the villus. H & E stain. Intermediate power.

FIG. 11-82. Ileum, showing a mass of diffuse lymphatic tissue occupying the entire thickness of the mucosa and extending into the submucosa. H & E stain. Intermediate power.

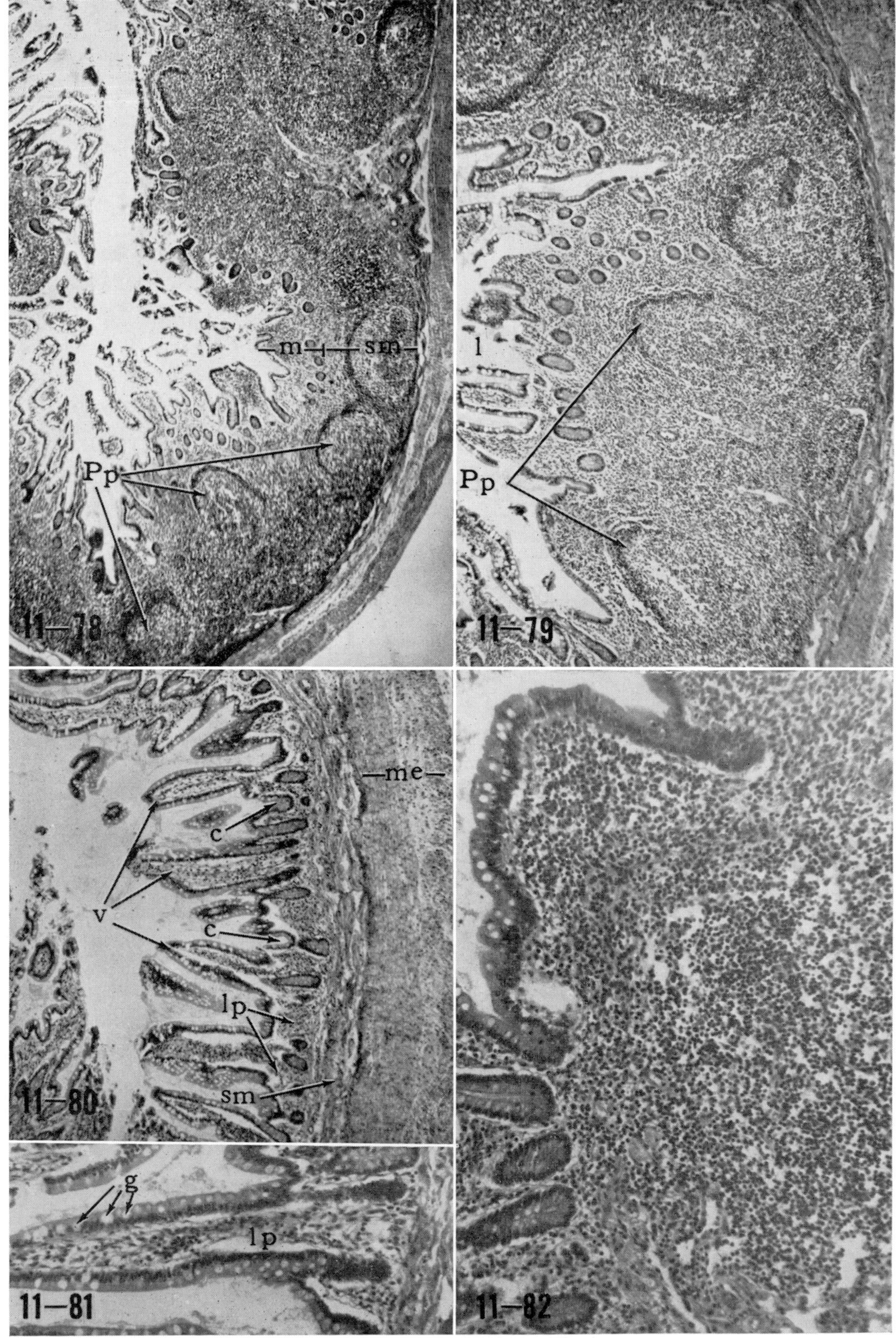

m
sm
Pp
11—78
l
Pp
11—79
me
c
v
c
lp
sm
11—80
g
lp
11—81
11—82

PLATE 107—Appendix

FIG. 11-83. Survey section of the appendix. H & E stain. Low power. (l, lumen with debris; c, crypts of Lieberkühn; sm, submucosa which is edematous; me, muscularis externa; lt, lymphatic tissue)

FIG. 11-84. Survey section of the appendix, especially to depict the extensive lymphatic tissue (lt) and the submucosa containing blood vessels (v) and fat lobules (f). H & E stain. Low power. (ln, lymph nodules; c, crypts of Lieberkühn)

FIG. 11-85. Intermediate power of a portion of Figure 11-84. (c, crypts of Lieberkühn; ln, lymph nodule; f, fat lobules; v, blood vessels)

FIG. 11-86. A portion of the mucosa of the appendix, showing the crypts of Lieberkühn (c), the muscularis mucosae (mm) and a large lymphatic nodule (ln). H & E stain. Intermediate power.

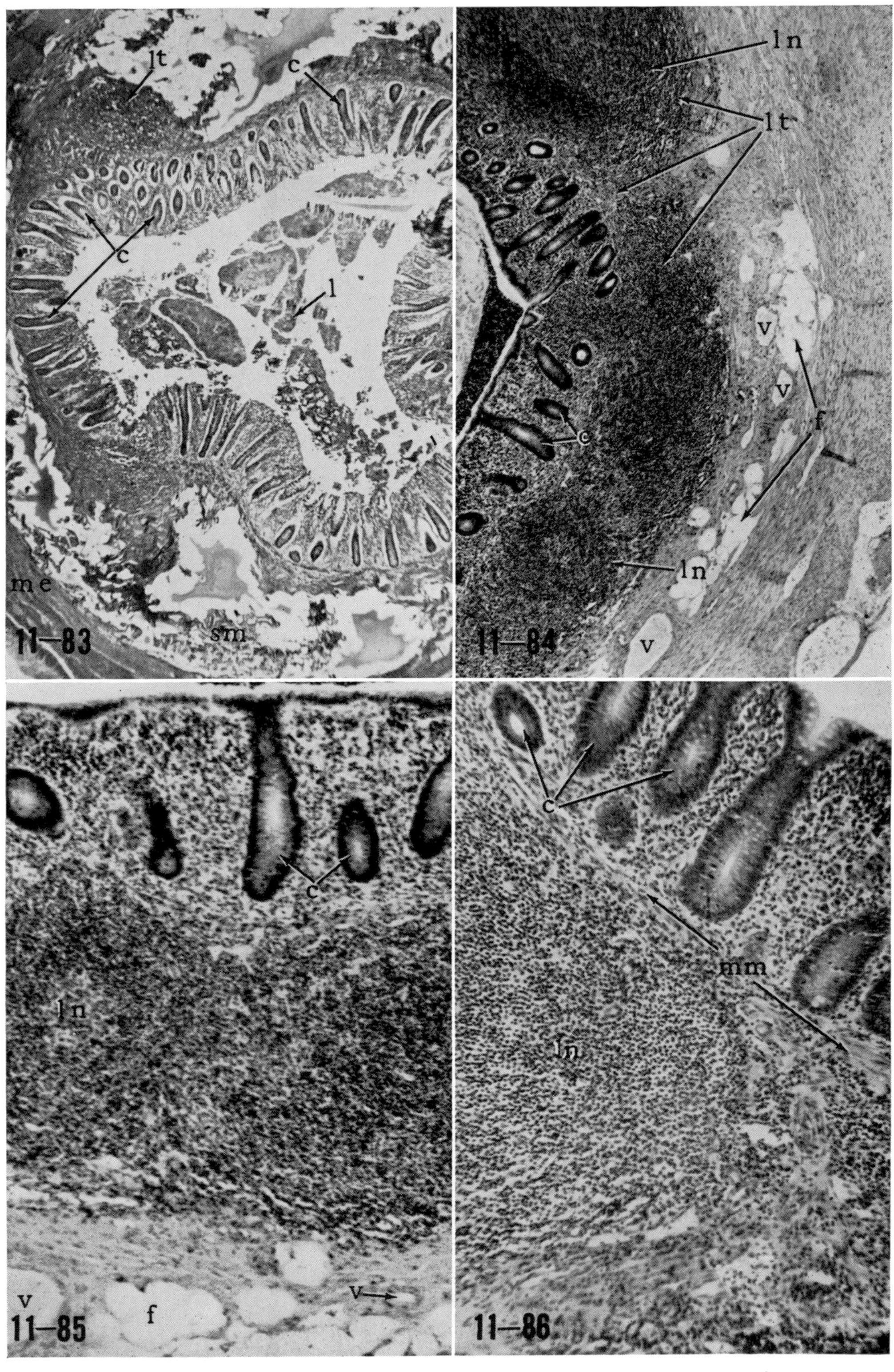
lt
c
c
l
me
sm
11–83
ln
lt
v
v
f
c
ln
v
11–84
c
ln
v
f
v
11–85
c
mm
ln
11–86

PLATE 108—Colon

FIG. 11-87. Survey of longitudinal section of the wall of the colon. H & E stain. Low power. (c, crypts of Lieberkühn; lp, lamina propria; mm, muscularis mucosae; ln, lymphatic nodule; sm, submucosa; me, muscularis externa)

FIG. 11-88. Portion of wall of colon showing structures similar to those seen in Figure 11-87 at a slightly higher magnification. Note the vascularity of the submucosa. H & E stain. Low power. (c, crypts of Lieberkühn; lp, lamina propria; mm, muscularis mucosae; sm, submucosa; me, muscularis externa)

FIG. 11-89. Colon showing straight, radiating crypts in the tunica mucosa. Note the large numbers of goblet cells. H & E stain. Intermediate power.

FIG. 11-90. Colon showing crypts in cross section. H & E stain. Intermediate power.

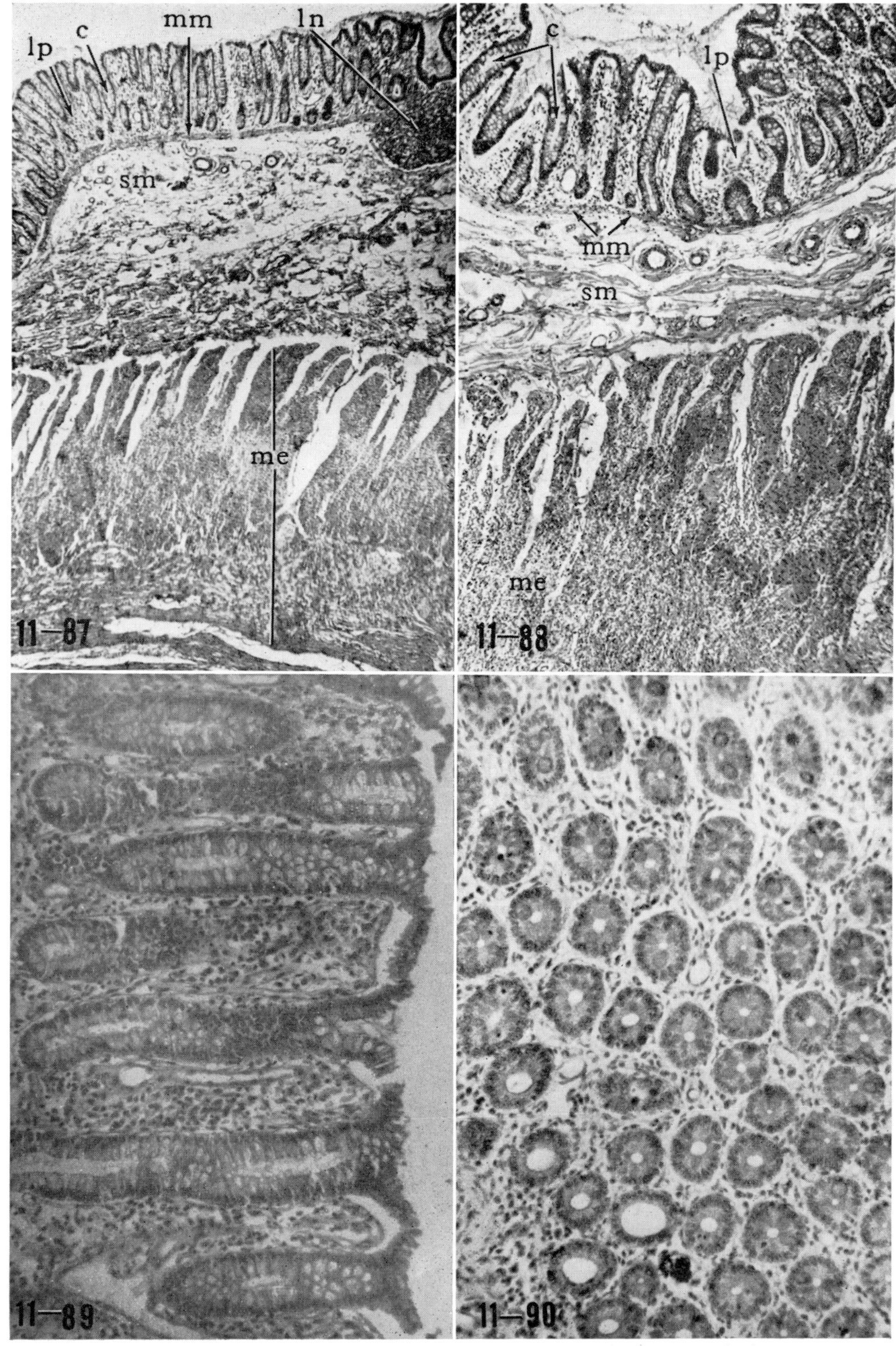
lp
c
mm
ln
sm
me
11-87
c
lp
mm
sm
me
11-88
11-89
11-90

PLATE 109—Rectum and Anal Canal

FIG. 11-91. Rectum. Note the rich plexus of blood vessels in the submucosa. H & E stain. Low power. (c, crypts of Lieberkühn; mm, muscularis mucosae)

FIG. 11-92. Rectum, showing the crypts of Lieberkühn (c) richly lined by goblet cells. Note the well-developed muscularis mucosae (mm) and the rich vascularity of the submucosa. H & E stain. Low power.

FIG. 11-93. Upper portion of the anal canal at the level of the anal valves. Note that the epithelium changes to the stratified squamous type (ss) and that the muscularis mucosae is no longer apparent. H & E stain. Low power. (me, muscularis externa)

FIG. 11-94. Lower portion of the anal canal. Note that the stratified squamous epithelium (ss) is becoming cornified and that the connective tissue deep to the epithelium looks less like submucosa and more like dermis. This transition occurs close to the anal orifice. H & E stain. Intermediate power.

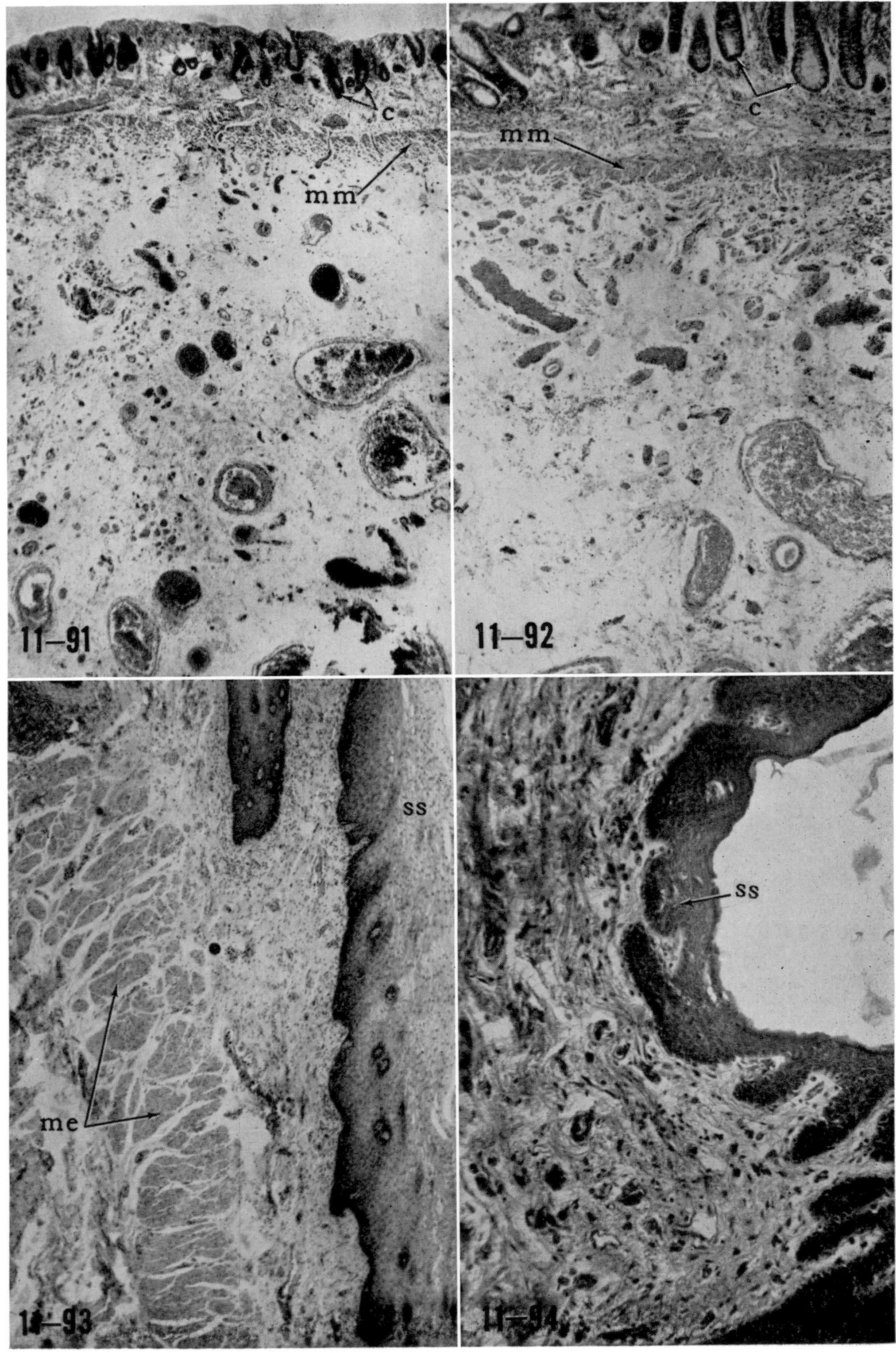
c
mm
11–91
c
mm
11–92
ss
me
11–93
ss
11–94

12 · Some Associated Glands of the Digestive System

A. Salivary Glands *B. Pancreas*

All the glands in this group are located outside the gastrointestinal system but are connected with it by ducts or a duct system. This category includes the salivary glands, the pancreas and the liver. The liver will be considered in Chapter 13. The salivary glands and the exocrine pancreas produce enzymes and mucus which are discharged at different levels onto a surface related to the digestive system.

A. SALIVARY GLANDS

These include 3 major pairs or groupings of glands as well as many lesser glands. On each side, the major salivary glands are the parotid, the submaxillary and the sublinguals. The lesser glands of the oral cavity include the labial glands, the buccal glands, the glossopalatine glands and the lingual glands.

1. Parotid Gland (Plate 110)

a. *Organization of Gland.* This large glandular mass is superficially located in front of the ear and produces a watery secretion which is discharged via Stensen's duct into the oral cavity opposite the upper second molar tooth. Morphologically it is a compound tubulo-alveolar gland in which the secretory end-pieces are, in man, almost entirely serous in nature. The gland is sur-

PLATE 110—Parotid Gland

FIG. 12-1. Parotid gland. Note the serous nature of the end-pieces (sa). H & E stain. Low power. (id, intralobular ducts; ld, interlobular ducts; f, fat cells)

FIG. 12-2. Parotid gland, showing intralobular ducts (id) and fat (f). H & E stain. Intermediate power.

FIG. 12-3. Section of the parotid gland which is similar to that of Figure 12-2. H & E stain. Intermediate power. (id, intralobular ducts; f, fat cells)

FIG. 12-4. Parotid gland showing serous alveoli (sa) and an intralobular duct (id). H & E stain. High power.

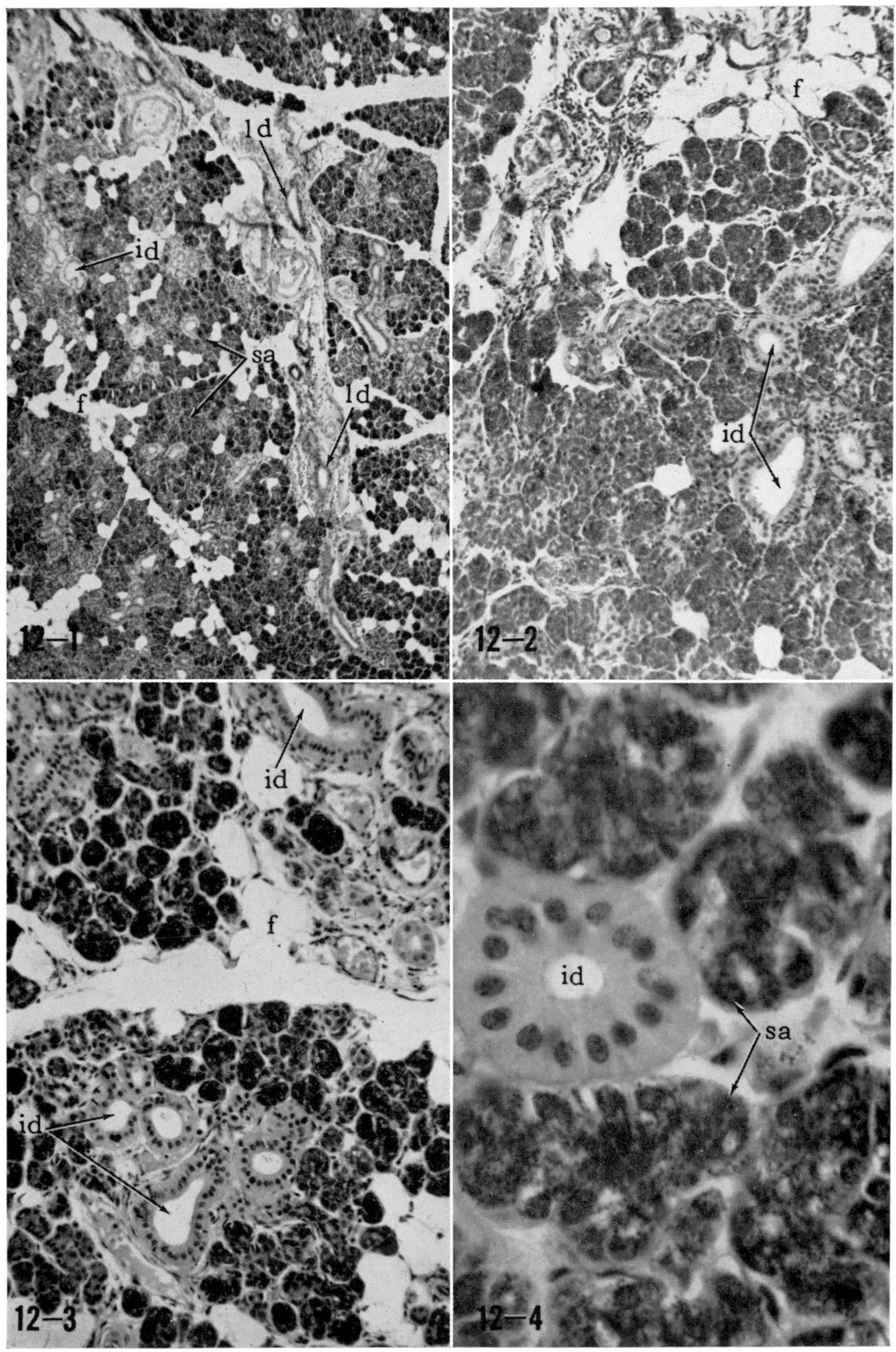
ld
id
sa
f
ld
12—1
f
id
12—2
id
f
id
12—3
id
sa
12—4

rounded by a capsule composed primarily of collagen and reticular fibers; from the capsule, connective tissue septa penetrate the parenchymal mass, breaking it up into lobes and lobules. Commonly, adipose tissue can be found in varying amounts in the capsule and penetrating into the stroma via the connective tissue septa.

b. *Secretory End-Pieces (100% Serous).* These alveolar and tubular structures are organized into lobules separated by the connective tissue septa. With the light microscope, it is almost impossible to distinguish a transversely sectioned tubular end-piece from an alveolus, and the description that follows holds true for both.

In section, each end-piece is circular or oval and is made up of pyramidal (modified simple columnar) cells that have molded themselves around a very tiny central lumen. Since the gland cells secrete an albuminous fluid, the lumen may be quite minute.

The cells constituting an end-piece rest against a basement membrane; myoepithelial or basket cells are found between the two. Each gland cell has a single round nucleus that is basally located. The cytoplasm present between the nucleus and the apex of the cell takes a heavy basophilic stain. In this region, and depending on the stage of secretion of the cell, a few or many coarse, basophilic zymogen granules will be found. These granules are the precursors of enzymes. The basal portion of each cell has been shown by electron microscopy to contain a well-developed endoplasmic reticulum associated with mitochondria. These elements are arranged so as to give this region, as seen with the light microscope, a vaguely striated appearance, the **basal striations.**

During secretion, which is of the merocrine type, material can pass into the lumen either directly or indirectly. If direct, secreted material passes through the cell membrane at the apex of the cell. More commonly, secretions pass through the plasma membrane covering the sides of the cell into intercellular canaliculi, which in turn discharge into the lumen.

c. *The Duct System.* The excretory duct system present in all salivary glands is unusual in that certain of the smaller ducts lying not far from the secretory end-pieces also serve a secretory function. These **secretory ducts** do not generally demonstrate zymogen granules but have well-developed basal striations. It is assumed that these ducts merely add fluid and perhaps ions to the secreted material passing by. These ducts are lined by a simple columnar epithelium and are most numerous (but not longest) in the parotid gland.

Interposed (intercalated) between the secretory end-pieces and the secretory ducts are the first elements of the excretory system. These, the **intercalated ducts**, are lined by a simple squamous or low cuboidal epithelium and begin at the external surface of the secretory end-pieces. Among the salivary

PLATE 111—Submaxillary Gland

FIG. 12-5. Survey section of the submaxillary gland. H & E stain. Low power. (sa, serous alveoli; ma, mucous alveoli; mt, mucous tubules; lct, interlobar connective tissue; sct, interlobular connective tissue; f, fat cells)

FIG. 12-6. Submaxillary gland showing serous alveoli (sa), mucous alveoli (ma), mucous tubules (mt), intralobular ducts (id) and fat cells (f). H & E stain. Intermediate power.

FIG. 12-7. Submaxillary gland showing a mucous alveolus (ma) surrounded by serous alveoli. H & E stain. High power.

FIG. 12-8. Connective tissue septa of the submaxillary gland, revealing the junction of two large interlobular ducts (sd) lined by pseudostratified epithelium to form a larger interlobar duct (ld). Note the presence of vessels (v) and fat cells (f). H & E stain. Intermediate power.

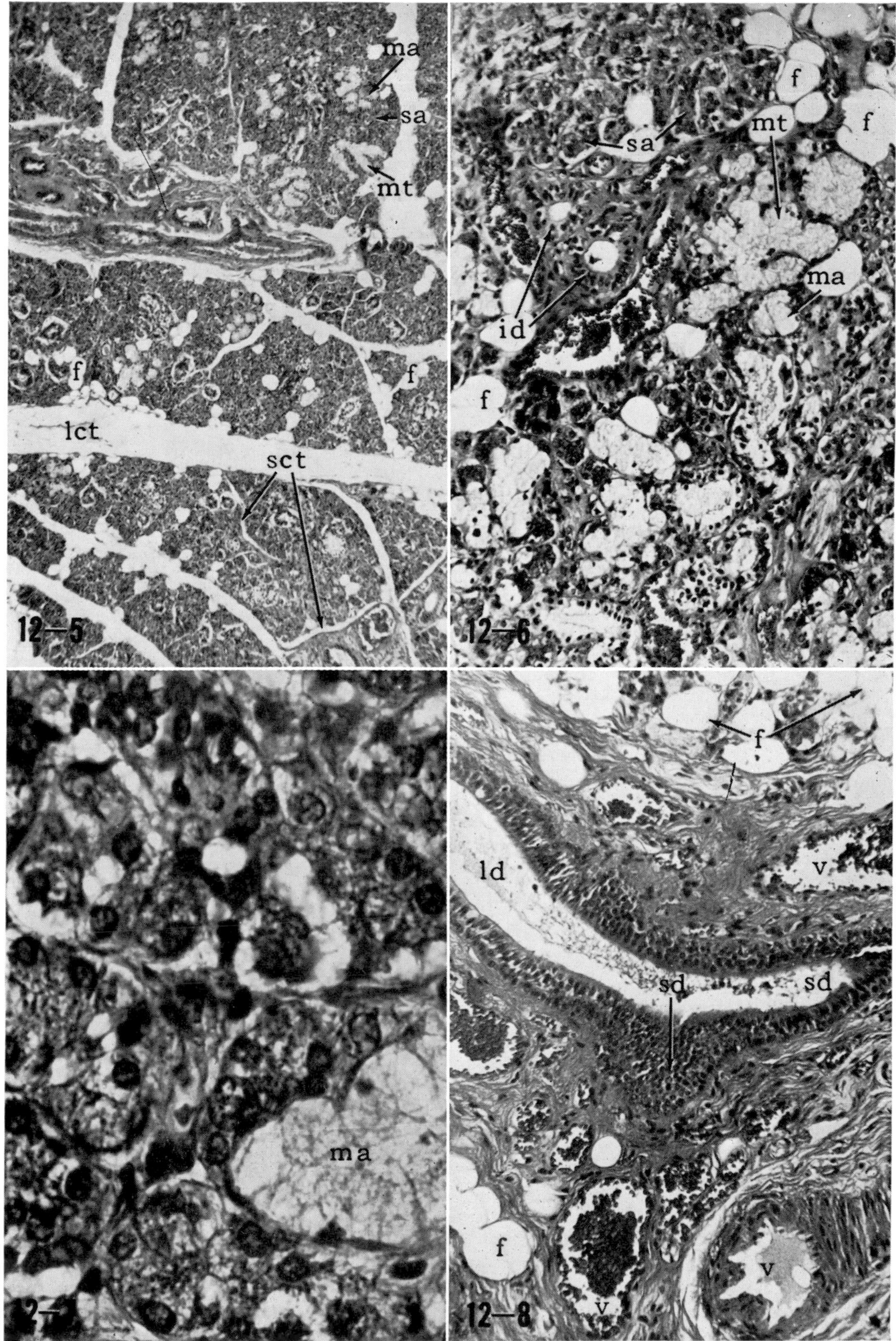
ma
sa
mt
f
f
lct
sct
12—5
f
f
sa
mt
f
ma
id
f
12—6
ma
12—7
f
ld
v
sd
sd
f
v
v
12—8

glands, **intercalated ducts are longest in the parotid gland, intermediate in length in the submaxillary gland and shortest in the sublingual glands**.

Intercalated and secretory ducts, since they lie so close to the secretory end-pieces, are often referred to as **intralobular ducts**. Most of the other elements of the duct system run along the connective tissue septa between gland lobules and hence are referred to as **interlobular ducts**. As the excretory ducts combine and recombine into larger and larger passageways, the lining epithelium alters from a simple columnar type to a pseudostratified type and finally to a stratified squamous type. The last-mentioned epithelium becomes continuous with that of the oral cavity.

2. Submaxillary Gland
(Plate 111)

a. *Organization of Gland.* Each of the two glands is submandibular in location. The secretion elaborated is mainly serous, but a small amount of mucus is also produced. The secreted material is discharged into the oral cavity via Wharton's duct, which opens onto the frenulum of the tongue. The gland is compound tubulo-alveolar in structure and is surrounded by a connective tissue capsule which sends septa inward, breaking up the parenchyma into lobules.

b. *Secretory End-Pieces (80% Serous, 20% Mucous).* The alveolar and the tubular end-pieces are mostly serous in nature. However, a smaller number of end-pieces are mucous in nature and have groups of serous cells attached at the end furthest removed from the intercalated duct. The light-microscope appearance of a mucus-secreting alveolus or tubule is somewhat different from that of a serous end-piece. The lumen of the mucous end-piece is slightly larger than that of a serous end-piece, which is in keeping with the more viscous nature of the secretion. The cells lining the end-piece are similar in shape to their serous counterparts. Water-soluble mucigen droplets, a precursor to mucus, accumulate in the cytoplasm before active secretion occurs. When this mucigen material is dissolved out during preparation of histologic material, the cytoplasm assumes a faintly reticulated appearance, the particulate elements of which take basic dyes.

When stored mucigen is abundant, the nucleus is flattened against the basal surface of the cell. Since active secretion occupies only a small part of the secretory cycle, the nuclei of mucous cells tend to be compressed against the basal cell surfaces most of the time.

If serous cells are present in a mucous end-piece, they occur together as a group of cells that caps the blind end of the structure. When present, these caps are referred to as **serous demilunes** (of Heidenhain) or **crescents** (of Gianuzzi).

c. *The Duct System.* The branched duct system is similar to that of the parotid gland

PLATE 112—Sublingual Gland

FIG. 12-9. Survey section of the sublingual gland. Note the presence of preponderantly mucous alveoli (light staining areas). H & E stain. Low power.

FIG. 12-10. Sublingual gland, showing the mixed glandular nature of this organ and the presence of a series of ducts (d). Mallory-Azan stain. Low power.

FIG. 12-11. Intermediate-power view of sublingual gland, demonstrating its preponderantly mucous nature. Note the presence of an intralobular duct (id) and an interlobular duct (ld) as well as the numerous tubular (mt) and alveolar (ma) end-pieces. H & E stain. Intermediate power.

FIG. 12-12. Sublingual gland, showing typical mucous alveoli (ma), mucous tubule (mt), serous alveolus (sa), serous demilunes (sd) and an intralobular duct (id). Mallory-Azan stain. High power.

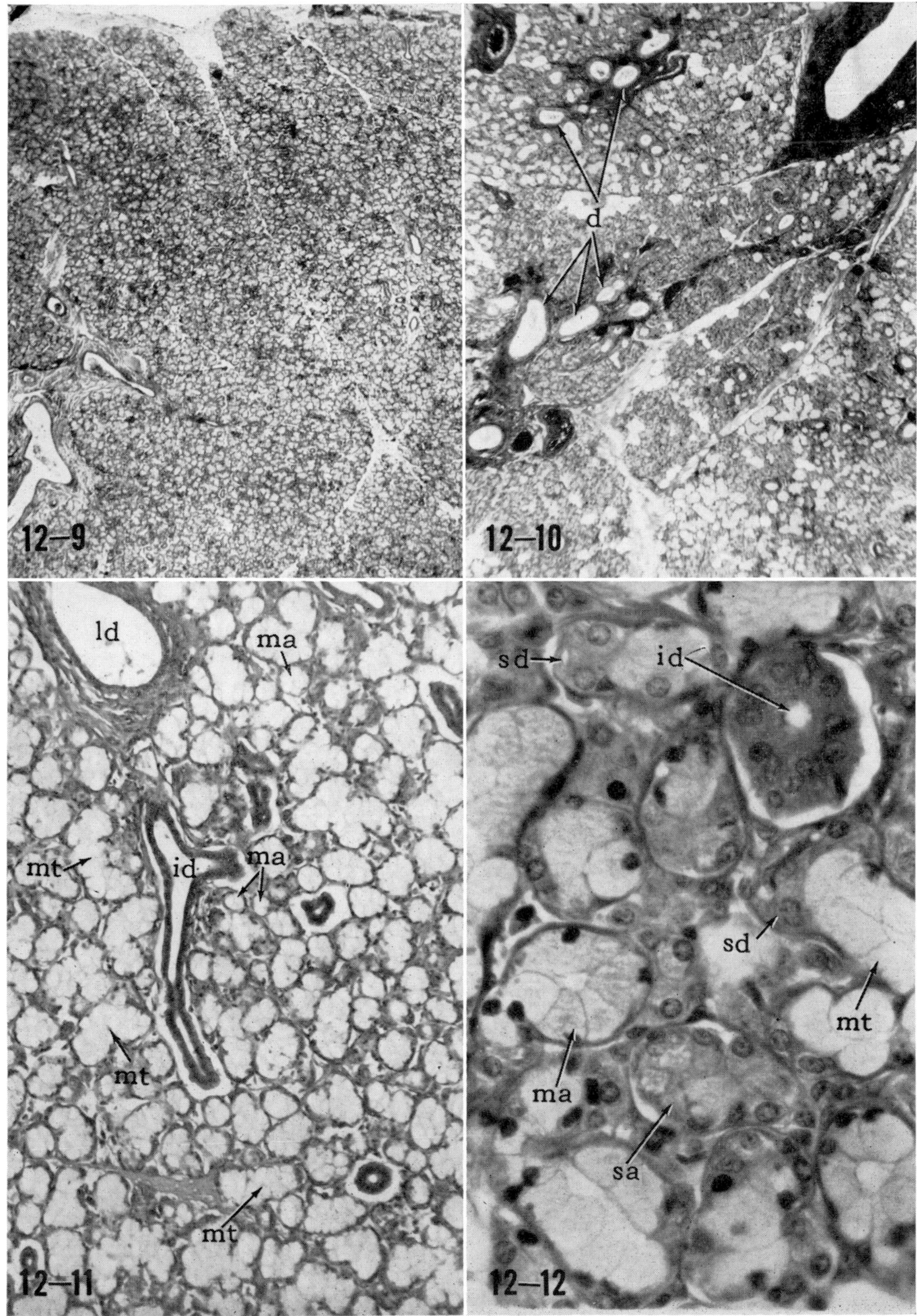
12–9
d
12–10
ld
ma
mt
id
ma
mt
mt
12–11
sd
id
sd
mt
ma
sa
12–12

except that intercalated ducts are shorter, secretory ducts are longer, and intralobular ducts are generally less numerous.

3. Sublingual Glands (Plates 112 and 113)

a. *Organization of Gland.* A sublingual gland actually consists of groupings of from 6 to 16 compound tubulo-alveolar glands, each of which opens onto the floor of the mouth by its own duct. The most anterior of these glandular elements is referred to as the **major sublingual gland**; its duct (Bartholin's duct) opens into the oral cavity next to the submaxillary duct. The remaining glandular elements constitute the **minor sublingual glands**, and their ducts (Rivinian ducts) open up, one behind the other, into the trenchlike space in the floor of the mouth adjacent to the root of the tongue. The secretion from this group of glands is primarily mucus.

b. *Secretory End-Pieces* (Predominantly Mucous). Most of the alveoli and the tubules are mucus-secreting. Few purely serous end-pieces are present, and most serous cells occur as demilunes or crescents grouped around the blind end of a mucous element.

c. *The Duct System.* Intralobular ducts are few in number in contrast with the other salivary glands. This is because both intercalated and secretory ducts are very short and will be found only with great difficulty. Interlobular ducts are quite apparent, and their lining cells undergo the same changes in type that takes place in the other salivary glands.

B. PANCREAS (Plates 114 and 115)

1. Introduction

Embryologically, the pancreas develops from 2 duodenal diverticulae. The straightened out, comma-shaped structure in the adult reflects this dual origin. That part of the pancreas which is analogous to the head of the comma contains the accessory excretory duct of Santorini. Fittingly, this region is referred to as the head of the pancreas. It is continuous with the more attenuated portions, the body and the tail. The major excretory duct, the duct of Wirsung, runs through these parts and usually joins the accessory duct in the head region.

Actually, the pancreas is a double gland. Its main bulk is a tubulo-alveolar exocrine gland concerned with producing digestive enzymes. Scattered throughout its mass are isolated cells, cell nests and large islands of cells, the **islets of Langerhans**, which secrete hormones directly into contained blood capillaries. Both exocrine and endocrine elements have a common developmental origin. However, a sizable number of the terminal ducts degenerate, leaving isolated end-pieces without ducts into which to secrete. To compensate for the missing ducts, these end-pieces become highly vascularized and are modified into end-pieces or glands of internal secretion.

2. Exocrine Structure of Pancreas

a. *Organization of Gland.* The pancreas is invested by a loose connective tissue

PLATE 113—Sublingual Gland

FIG. 12-13. Sublingual gland, showing mucous alveoli (ma) and tubules (mt), serous demilunes (sd) and serous alveoli (sa). Mallory-Azan stain. High power.

FIG. 12-14. Sublingual gland, showing a nest of typical serous alveoli and an intralobular duct (id). Mallory-Azan stain. High power.

FIG. 12-15. Sublingual gland, showing typical serous alveoli with an unusual section of a tubular serous end-piece (st) and serous demilunes (sd). Mallory-Azan stain. High power.

FIG. 12-16. An intralobular duct (id) surrounded by mucous alveoli of the sublingual gland. H & E stain. High power.

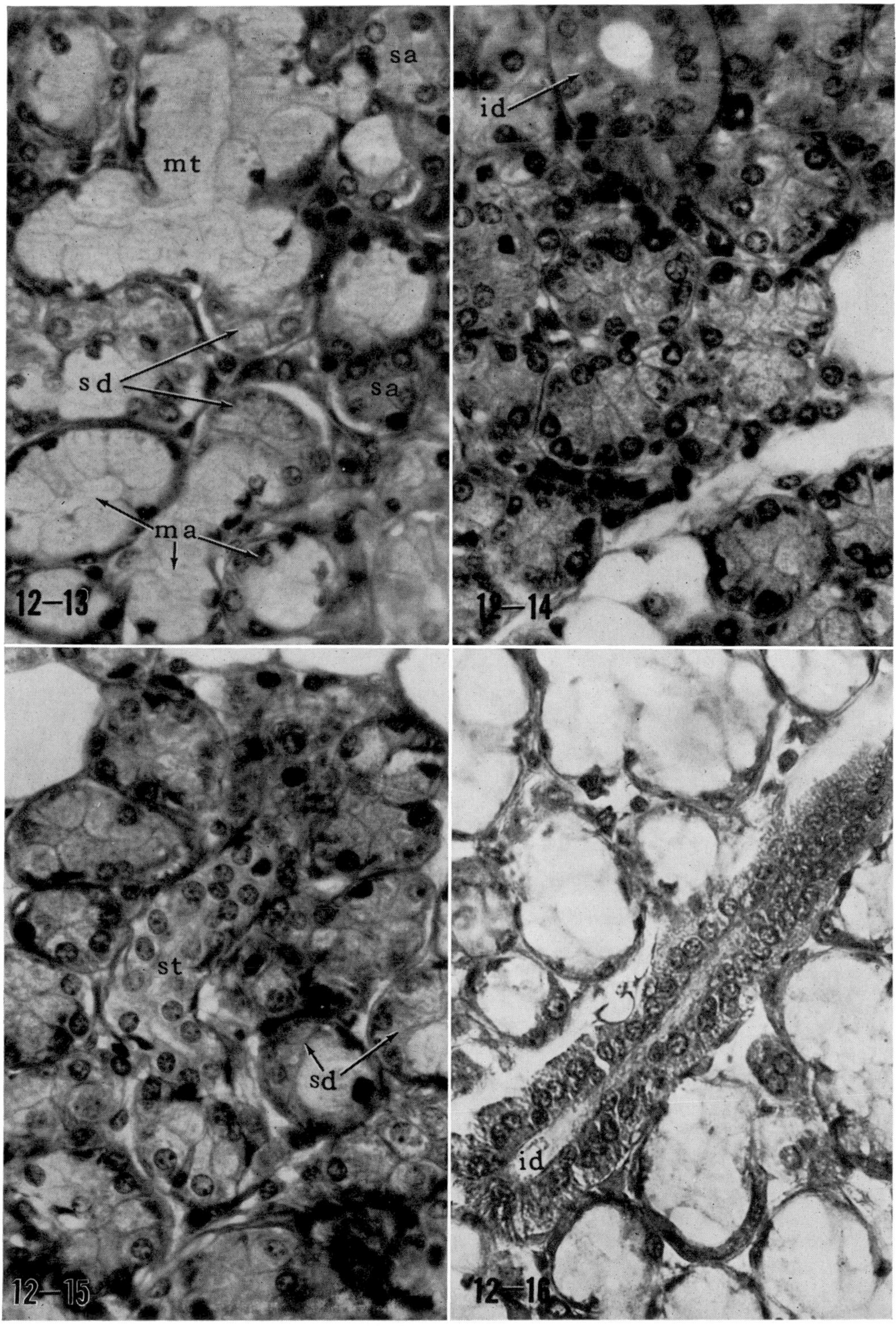

sa
mt
id
sd
sa
ma
12–13
12–14
st
sd
id
12–15
12–16

which is more delicate than that found around most of the salivary glands. Septal projections of collagen and reticular fibers penetrate the gland and break it up into fairly distinct lobules. The gland is compound tubulo-alveolar in structure, but both the ducts and the secretory end-pieces differ somewhat from those previously described for the salivary glands.

b. *Secretory End-pieces (100% Serous).* These elements exhibit greater variety of 2-dimensional shapes in section than do end-pieces of the salivary glands. The alveoli and the tubules are uniformly made up of pyramidal serous cells, a feature which the pancreas has in common with the parotid gland. Nuclei are round and basally placed, basal striations can be seen, and zymogen granules are prominent. In addition, the lumen of the typical end-piece is small, and intercellular canaliculi are present. In the central regions of end-pieces, however, superfluous nuclei appear to be present. These will be explained in the next section.

c. *The Duct System.* The major duct of Wirsung gives off collateral ducts at fairly regular intervals and at right angles to its course. These side ducts are interlobular in nature, since they pass between lobules and are invested in the septal connective tissue. These offshoots of the duct of Wirsung, in turn, give off a smaller number of intralobular branches which pass into the exocrine parenchyma. Within each lobule, the intralobular channels give rise to a large number of quite long intercalated ducts, which divide and become associated with the secretory end-pieces.

Because the pancreatic lobules contain *no* secretory ducts and few sizable intralobular ducts, the student may receive the impression that the secretory end-pieces lack a duct system. However, careful microscopy will reveal the presence of a rich distribution of intercalated ducts. These smallest elements of the duct system are lined by a simple epithelium ranging in size from squamous to cuboidal. In contradistinction to similar passageways in the salivary glands, intercalated ducts in the pancreas penetrate the walls of the secretory end-pieces to establish continuity with the lumina located therein. The presence of duct cells within pancreatic alveoli and tubules is apparent as groupings of nuclei in the center of those elements. Such representations of the lining cells of intercalated ducts within an end-piece are referred to as **centro-alveolar** or **centro-acinar cells**.

3. Endocrine Structure of Pancreas—Islets of Langerhans

Small nests or islands of cells, isolated from the exocrine elements only by delicate reticular fibers, collectively form the structural basis of the vital endocrine elements of the pancreas. The secretions of these nests, the **islets of Langerhans**, are extremely important for normal body utilization of carbohydrates.

The size and the number of islets vary considerably from one part of the pancreas

PLATE 114—Pancreas

FIG. 12-17. Survey section of the pancreas, showing islets of Langerhans (i) scattered among the acinar tissue. Mallory-Azan stain. Low power.

FIG. 12-18. Survey section of pancreatic acini and interlobular connective tissue (it) with ducts (d) and blood vessels (v). Note the septa (s) which divide the pancreatic tissue into lobules. H & E stain. Low power.

FIG. 12-19. Pancreas, showing the interlobular connective tissue (it) with 2 ducts (d). Note the surrounding acinar tissue. H & E stain. Intermediate power.

FIG. 12-20. Pancreas, showing several islets (i) and the surrounding acinar tissue. H & E stain. Intermediate power.

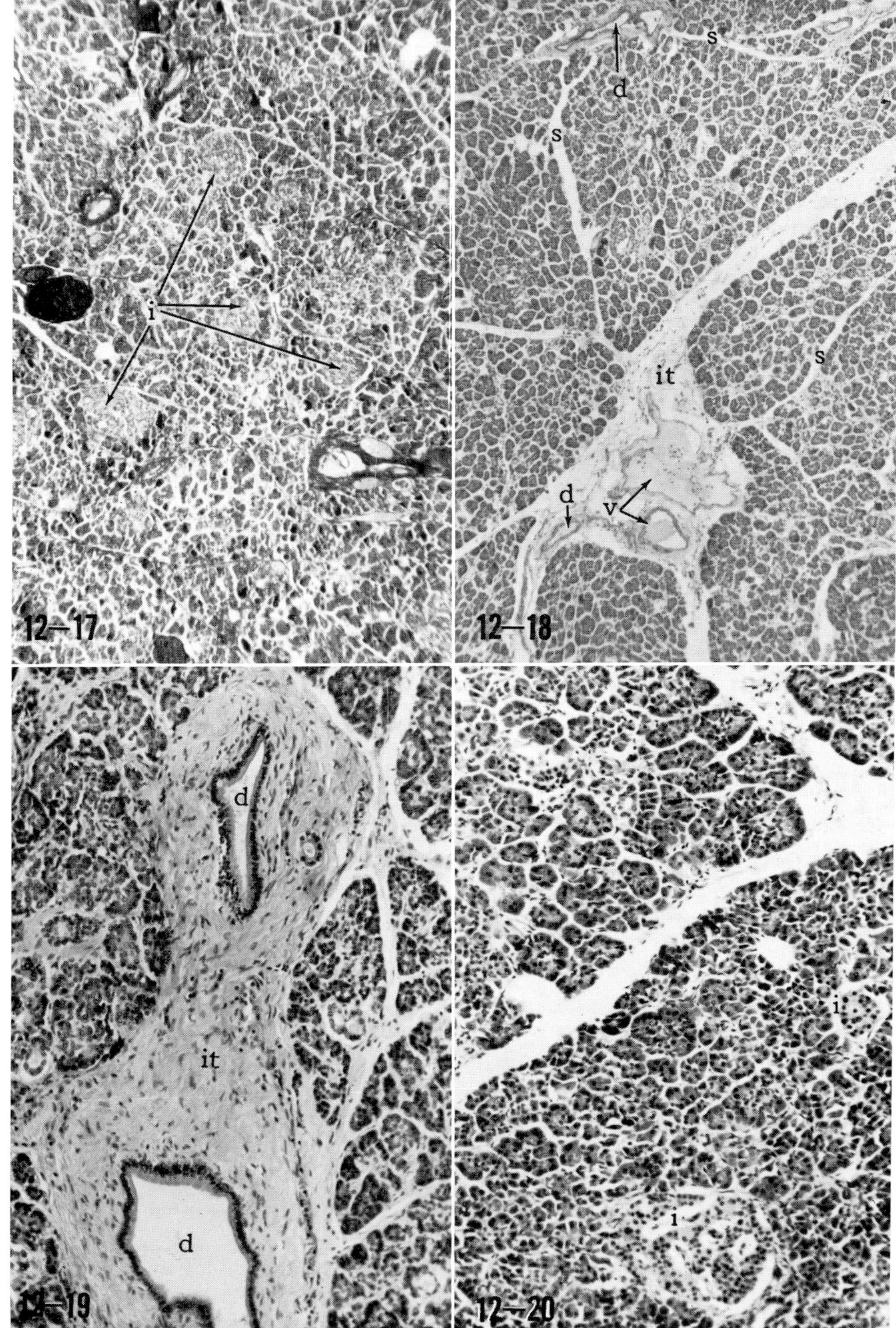
i
12—17
d
s
s
it
s
d
v
12—18
d
it
d
12—19
i
i
12—20

to the other. It is difficult, therefore, to assign any definite description to islet shape. However, within an islet, the cells are arranged as irregular cords separated from each other by a rich and irregular distribution of blood capillaries.

Two cell types make up almost the entire population of each islet, **alpha cells** and **beta cells**. By far the most numerous (approximately two thirds) is the beta cell. This large cell has a diameter that is 4 to 6 times that of an erythrocyte. Speaking generally, beta cells are larger; they have larger round to oval nuclei, more distinct plasma membranes, and in addition they contain larger and coarser cytoplasmic granules than do alpha cells.

With routine histologic stains it is often difficult to distinguish between the alpha cell and the beta cell. Only by using special staining methods is it possible to demonstrate coarse basophilic granules in the beta cell and finer acidophilic granules in the alpha cell. It is fairly well established that the beta cell produces insulin. Less well established is the association of alpha cells with the hyperglycemic-glycogenolytic factor (H.G.F.) or glucagon.

PLATE 115—Pancreas

FIG. 12-21. Pancreas, showing an intralobular duct (id) and surrounding acinar tissue. H & E stain. High power. (ca, centro-acinar cells; sc, secretory cells)

FIG. 12-22. Pancreas, showing the origin of an intralobular duct (id) from an interlobular duct (ld) and surrounding acinar tissue. H & E stain. High power.

FIG. 12-23. Pancreas, revealing an intercalated duct (icd) leading into an acinus (a). Note the presence of numerous centro-acinar cells (ca). H & E stain. High power.

FIG. 12-24. Pancreas, showing the component cells of a large islet of Langerhans and associated blood capillaries (c). Mallory-Azan stain. High power. (A, alpha cells; B, beta cells)

FIG. 12-25. Pancreas, showing a branching interlobular duct (ld) and acini. H & E stain. High power.

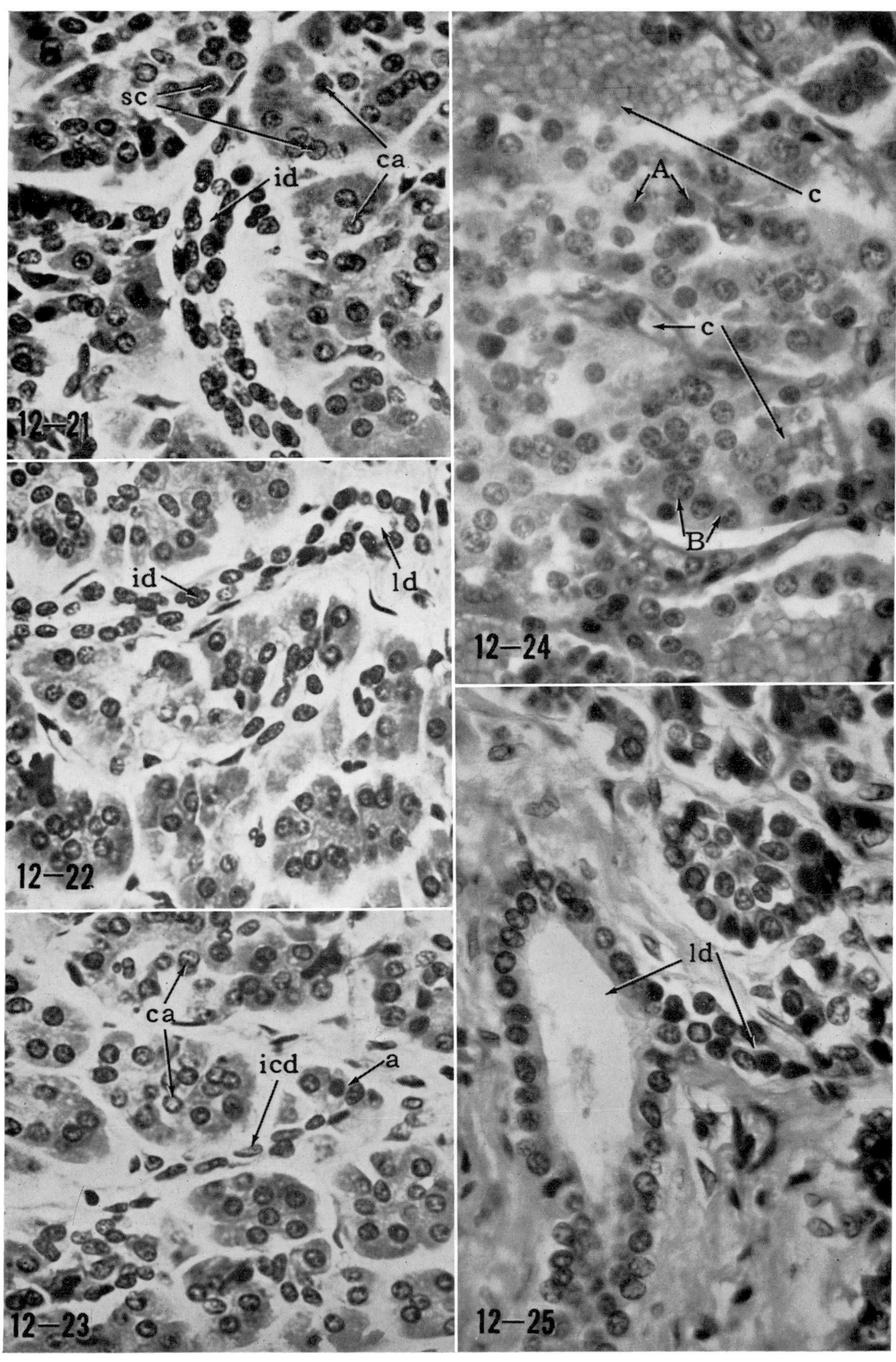
sc
ca
id
12—21
id
ld
12—22
ca
icd
a
12—23
A
c
c
B
12—24
ld
12—25

13 · The Liver

A. INTRODUCTION

The liver is an accessory gland of digestion that produces bile and possesses a duct system which conveys this secretion to the duodenum. In addition, the liver serves as a temporary storage depot for glycogen, enzymes, certain vitamins and hormones, heparin and fibrinogen, and it excretes metabolic breakdown products such as bile pigments, cholesterol and urea. Although the subject of many intensive investigations, the modus operandi of liver function is far from resolved. Its complexity is probably second only to that of the brain.

Structurally, the liver is the largest viscus of the body and has the appearance of a compound tubular gland. This structure can be appreciated if it is recalled that (1) the branching system of hepatic excretory ducts (ducts conveying bile) as well as the associated "tubular" secretory end-pieces arise as an endodermal diverticulum from the fetal duodenum and that (2) this diverticulum becomes intimately associated with the hepatic artery and the portal vein, dividing and subdividing at regular intervals, faithfully paralleling the course taken by those vessels.

The liver consists of 4 poorly separated lobes whose surfaces are covered by a thin but distinct fibrous capsule (**capsule of**

PLATE 116—Liver

FIG. 13-1. Survey section near the surface of the liver showing Glisson's capsule (G). Mallory-Azan stain. Low power. (c, central vein with radiating hepatic cords)

FIG. 13-2. Glisson's capsule (G) covering the surface of the liver. H & E stain. Intermediate power. (c, central veins with radiating hepatic cords [hc]; hepatic sinusoids are seen as white areas between the cords)

FIG. 13-3. Survey section of liver (pig) showing a tangentially sectioned hepatic lobule sharply delineated by connective tissue (ct) from adjacent lobules. Mallory-Azan stain. Low power. (c, central vein; p, portal canal)

FIG. 13-4. Liver from an animal injected with India ink. Refer to Figure 13-10. H & E stain. Low power. (c, central veins; p, portal canals)

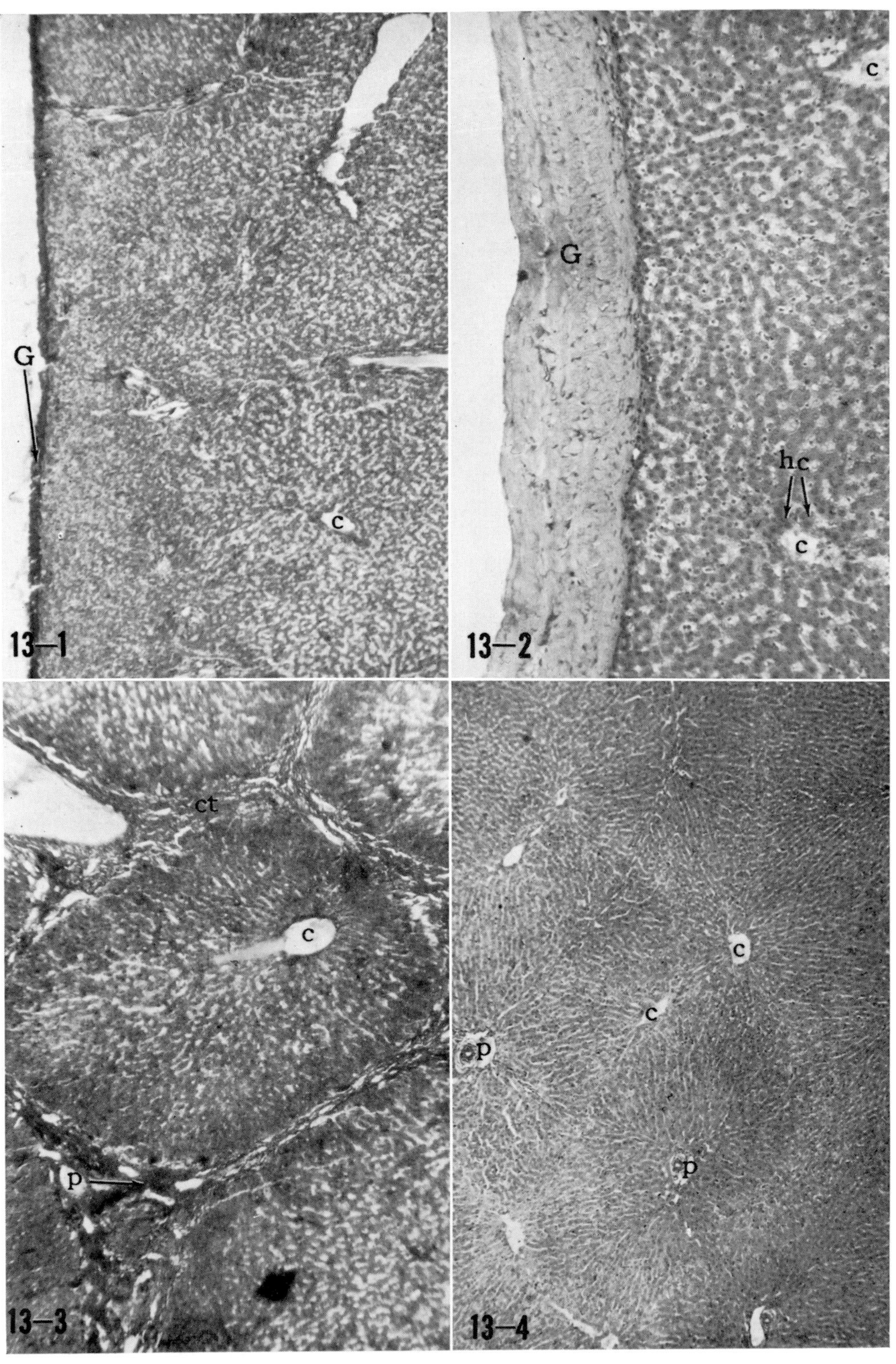
G
c
13—1
c
G
hc
c
13—2
ct
c
p
13—3
c
c
p
p
13—4

Glisson). The capsule of Glisson is itself overlayed on most surfaces by a reflection of the peritoneum. In addition, the liver has **a hilus** or **porta hepatis** into which pass the **bile duct**, the **portal vein** and the **hepatic artery** as well as draining lymph channels. All of the structures are invested in connective tissue, and this supporting stroma also enters the porta after being reflected inwardly from the liver surface.

See Plates 116 to 119.

B. THE HEPATIC LOBULE

In conjunction with extensions of Glisson's capsule, the **hepatic triad** of structures (hepatic artery, portal vein and bile duct) branch repeatedly after entering the porta hepatis. Eventually, terminal branches of these structures come into relationship with surfaces of each of the millions of histologic units of structure of the liver, the **hepatic (classic or traditional) lobules.**

Hepatic lobules measure about 1 × 2 mm. and appear as irregular, polygonal elements that vary in shape from elongated hat boxes to pyramids. It is useful for the student to visualize the average lobule as having the shape of a 5- or 6-sided polygon, twice as tall as it is wide. Running along each of the 5 or 6 edges of a hepatic lobule will be found the radicles of the hepatic triad invested in a small amount of loose connective tissue. These structures together constitute the portal canal or portal area. In this location the branch of the hepatic artery is usually arteriolar in size, the portal vein, venular in size; the small bile duct element is lined by a simple cuboidal epithelium. Running lengthwise through the middle of the lobule is a large vascular space known variously as the **central vein**, the **central canal** or the **central space**. In each lobule the central vein represents the beginning of the hepatic vein. If one were able to see an ideal hepatic lobule in cross section, it would be possible to find a portal area at each of the 5 or 6 corners and also a centrally placed central canal. Unfortunately, such diagrammatic areas cannot be found on most sections.

When a cross section of the hepatic lobule is examined with the light microscope, a distinct impression is obtained that the liver parenchyma consists of **cords of cells** radiating from the periphery of the lobule to the central canal. These radiating cords are separated from each other by narrow spaces, the **hepatic sinusoids**.

Based on 3-dimensional reconstructions of hepatic lobules and on electron microscopy, Hans Elias has introduced the concept that the appearance of radiating cords of cells leads to a misinterpretation of the actual arrangement of the liver parenchyma. Such a misconception is based on the fact that a microscopic preparation has only 2 dimensions. Perhaps a simple familiar example will clarify this point. If one were to section a cylindrical structure, such as a large blood vessel, in a plane parallel with its long axis, the resulting slide representation would usually appear as a pair of paral-

PLATE 117—Liver

FIG. 13-5. Liver, showing a central vein (cv), the hepatic cords (hc) and sinusoids (s). H & E stain. Intermediate power.

FIG. 13-6. Injected section of animal liver, showing a portal canal with its portal vein (pv), bile duct (b) and branches of the hepatic artery (ha). Note the adjacent three hepatic lobules, one of which contains a central vein (cv). Intermediate power.

FIG. 13-7. Liver (animal), showing interlobular connective tissue with contained vein (v) and artery (a) and surrounding hepatic lobules. H & E stain. Intermediate power.

FIG. 13-8. Rio-Hortega stain of a section of liver to demonstrate the abundant framework of reticular fibers within the hepatic lobules. Intermediate power. (cv, central vein; hc, hepatic cords)

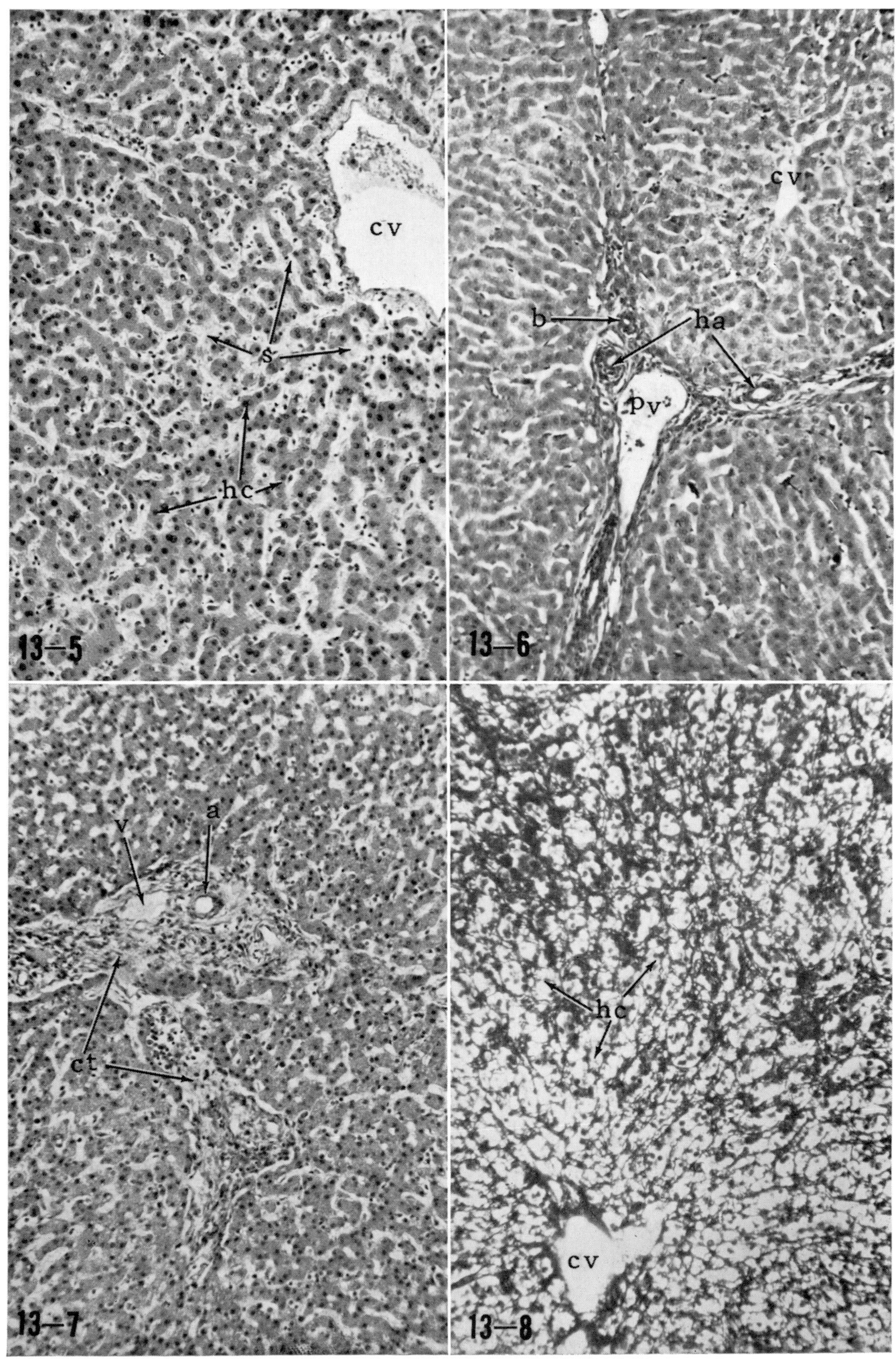
cv
s
hc
13—5
cv
b
ha
pv
13—6
v
a
ct
13—7
hc
cv
13—8

lel walls. Unless it were possible to reconstruct the vessel serially from many adjacent sections, or unless previous knowledge of the 3-dimensional shape were available, it would be almost impossible to interpret the structure's shape from its 2-dimensional appearance on a slide. Based on this type of approach, Elias feels that radiating cell cords in the liver exist only so far as they relate to the 2-dimensional image. Three-dimensional reconstructions have led him to propose that hepatic lobules are not made up of cords at all but rather of **communicating plates of cells.**

Elias' concept of the structure of the hepatic lobule can be understood by mentally constructing a lobule, using the following steps as a guide:

1. Start with a series of plates (laminae) of cells, each having surface dimensions of 1 × 2 mm. and only 1 cell in thickness. Imagine a hundred or more of these plates standing upright like two decks of cards so that each is separated from the plate adjacent to it by a narrow space (**interplate** or **interlaminar space**).

2. Divide these plates into 3 groups and rearrange them so that, when looking down on the 3 groups, they have the appearance of a triangular structure surrounding a large angular central space.

3. Now bend all of the plates lengthwise somewhere near their midline and arrange them around the central space.

4. Imagine now that each of the laminae (plates) is not solid but is perforated by holes to such an extent that it resembles a slice of Swiss cheese. As a result, assume that the surface of each plate is now 50 per cent solid and 50 per cent perforated.

5. Now imagine that because of the weakening effect of the perforations on the solid portions of each plate, it becomes necessary to strengthen them. This is accomplished by connecting adjacent laminae to each other by means of tubular bridges of cells (**interlaminar bridges**). The tubular wall of each bridge is only 1 cell in thickness and extends across the interlaminar space from perforation to perforation.

6. The resulting structure as seen from above is identical with the 2-dimensional microscopic picture of the hepatic lobule in cross section. The interlaminar spaces are in communication with each other via the perforations in the laminae, and, together, these constitute the sinusoids which radiate to the central space of the model.

According to Elias, the parenchyma of adjacent hepatic lobules, in the region of each portal canal, forms a somewhat thinner, perforated plate, the **limiting plate (lamina limitans)**. Through the perforations in the limiting plate the blood vessels within the portal canal communicate with the sinusoids of adjacent hepatic lobules.

It is important to realize that this newer concept of lobule structure is based on laminae that are 1 cell in thickness. Since the intercommunicating sinusoids that course centrally between the plates are filled with blood that drains from the vessels in the

PLATE 118—Liver

FIG. 13-9. Hepatic cords, showing the liver cells. Numerous binucleated cells (b) are present. H & E stain. High power. (sc, stellate cells of von Kupffer; s, sinusoids)

FIG. 13-10. Liver from an animal injected with India ink to show the phagocytic properties of the stellate Kupffer cells (sc) lining the sinusoids. H & E stain. High power. (bc, bile canaliculus)

FIG. 13-11. Liver (animal), showing the central vein (c). Note the communication of a sinusoid (s) with the central vein. H & E stain. High power. (hc, hepatic cords; lc, lining cells of sinusoid)

FIG. 13-12. Liver from an animal injected with India ink to clearly demonstrate the central vein (c) with its endothelial cells (e). H & E stain. High power.

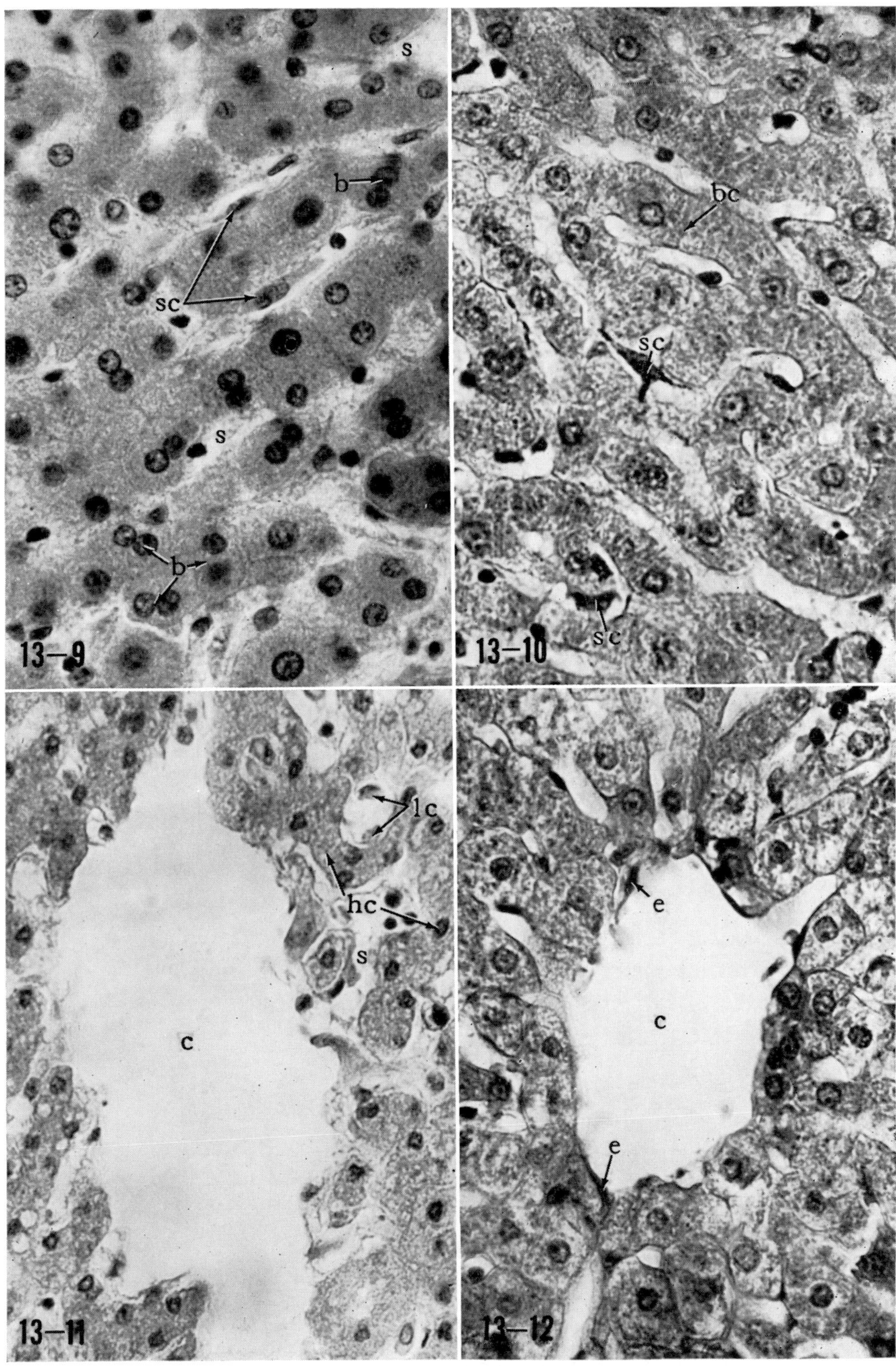
s
b
sc
s
b
13—9
bc
sc
sc
13—10
lc
hc
s
c
13—11
e
c
e
13—12

portal canals to the central vein, the question arises how does bile secreted by the cells making up the laminae pass peripherally to the bile ducts? The answer lies in a modification of the plasma membranes of adjacent cells in each plate. Halfway through the sheet of cells making up each lamina and also between each row of adjacent cells in the lamina, the plasma membranes become grooved. The grooves in the surface membranes of any two adjacent cells fit together to form a tiny channel. Thousands of these minute channels join to form a system of bile canaliculi which serve as excretory ducts. Bile flows peripherally in these canaliculi through the hepatic lobule toward a bile duct located within a portal canal. If it is remembered that the liver cells arose embryologically as buds stemming from the system of bile ducts, then the continuity of structure of the bile-conducting channels can be understood. Slightly modified liver cells at the periphery of a lobule constitute the canals of Hering. These form short channels that convey bile from the canaliculi through the limiting plate of cells around a portal canal into a bile duct contained therein.

C. PORTAL LOBULE (FUNCTIONAL LOBULE)

In considering the exocrine function of the liver (**bile secretion**), it should be realized that bile secreted by the parenchymal cells in a hepatic lobule passes peripherally toward the nearest bile duct. This duct receives the secretions from wedge-shaped segments of all of the hepatic lobules that surround it.

To convey the functional concept of bile drainage, one must be able to visualize a hypothetical lobule. To do this, one must imagine that he is looking down on the surface of a group of 3 neighboring hepatic lobules, each of which has a 6-sided appearance. Imagine that these lobules are arranged so that one of the portal canals located near the middle of the arrangement is common to all 3 hepatic lobules. By projecting imaginary lines between the 3 central veins, a triangular surface is outlined which has at its center a draining bile duct. Such hypothetical 3-sided or wedge-shaped structures are referred to as portal lobules. The following scheme indicates how such a lobule might appear.

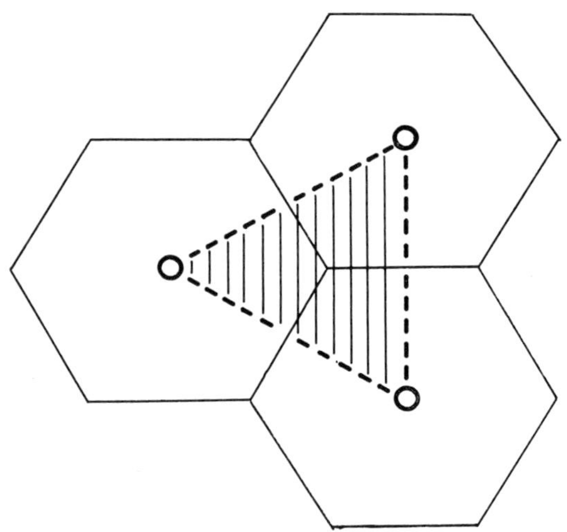

PLATE 119—Liver

FIG. 13-13. A portal area at the juncture of three lobules of the liver which contains branches of the portal vein (v), the hepatic artery (a) and the bile duct (b). This portal area is unusual in that lymphocytes are present in large numbers. Note the limiting plate of cells (lp) of adjacent hepatic lobules. H & E stain. High power.

FIG. 13-14. A portal area with surrounding limiting plate and hepatic cord cells. H & E stain. High power. (v, portal vein; a, hepatic artery; b, bile duct; lc, lymphatic channel)

FIG. 13-15. Electron micrograph showing a liver cell. Note the fine microvilli projecting into the bile canaliculus (bc). × 5,500. (n, nucleus of hepatic cell; m, mitochondria; e, cisternae of endoplasmic reticulum; cb, cell boundary)

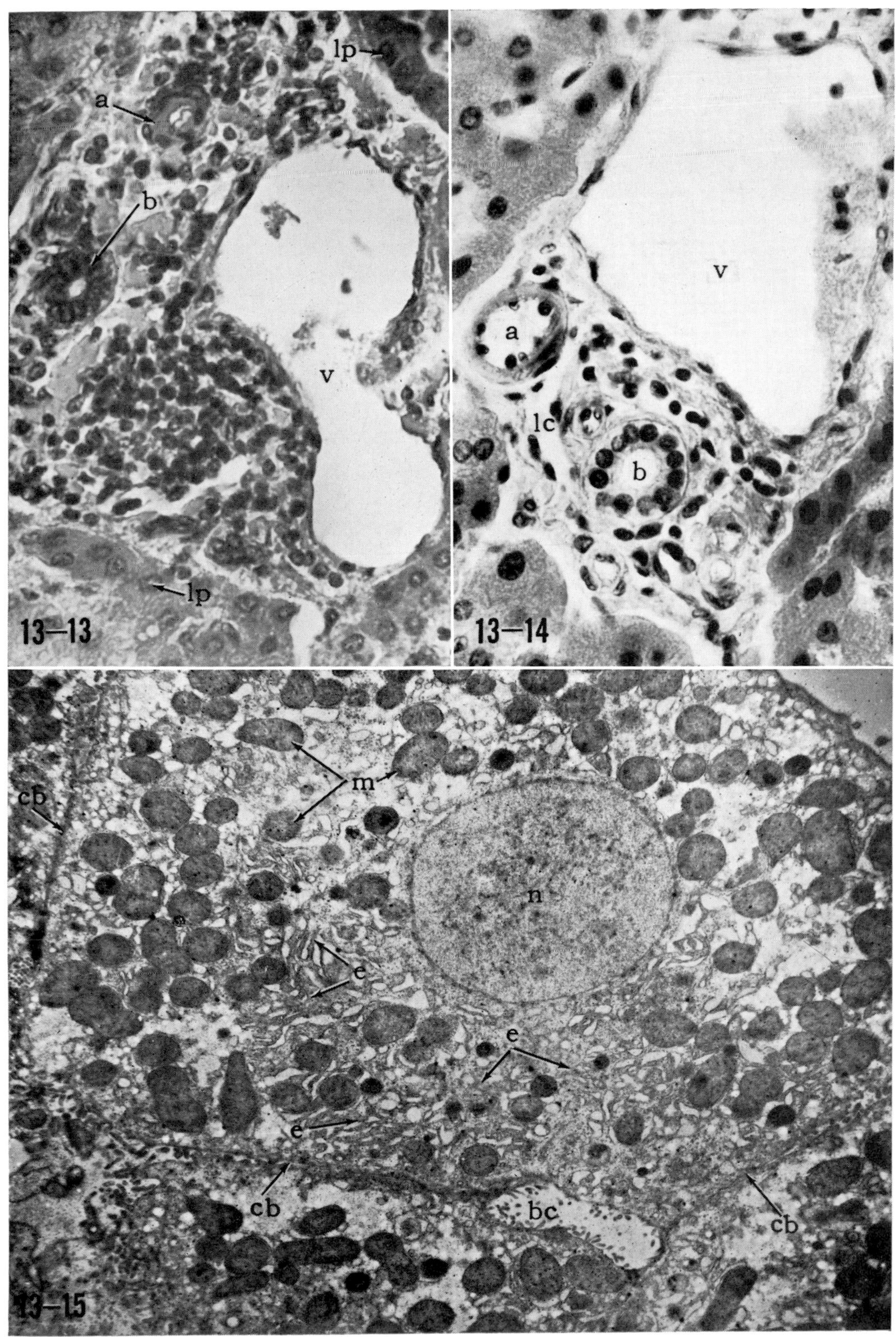
lp
a
b
v
lp
13–13
v
a
lc
b
13–14
m
cb
n
e
e
e
cb
bc
cb
13–15

D. FINER STRUCTURE OF THE LIVER

1. Hepatic Cells

The cells that constitute the parenchyma of the liver lobules are large and polygonal, having a diameter 3 to 4 times that of the erythrocyte. They contain 1 nucleus, and not infrequently 2 nuclei, placed near the center of the cell. One or more distinct nucleoli may be found. Plasma membranes between adjacent cells are rather delicate. The cytoplasm is granular and contains a high lipid and glycogen content. Because these constituents are dissolved out when routine histologic methods are applied, the cytoplasm of liver cells appears rather washed out.

2. Hepatic Sinusoids

Within a liver lobule, the narrow spaces present between laminae (or between what appear to be cords) of liver cells are termed **hepatic sinusoids**. These anastomosing channels have lumina that are slightly wider than the diameter of the red blood cell. The sinusoids connect the central vein and the blood vessels located in the portal canals.

Supporting the hepatic cells is an impressive network of reticular fibers. This network covers the surface of the parenchymal elements. These reticular fibers not only support the liver parenchyma, but also serve to form the fibrous walls of the complex system of intercommunicating sinusoidal spaces. Present among the reticular fibers are many lining cells. These elements are found in various stages of differentiation between **primitive reticular (stem) cells** and fully differentiated macrophages. The stem cells are smaller, attenuated, show scanty cytoplasm and contain elongated, deeply staining nuclei. The macrophages, known as **stellate cells of von Kupffer**, are larger, contain plumper, more vesicular nuclei and have a more abundant cytoplasm that may demonstrate many processes. Kupffer cells represent the liver's contribution to the widespread cellular reticuloendothelial system. It seems probable that within the liver, these cells, in addition to general phagocytic activity, are also responsible for the salvaging of bile pigment. This is accomplished by degradation of old erythrocytes that were not broken down by the spleen and the bone marrow.

14 · Gallbladder and Extrahepatic Biliary Passages

A. INTRODUCTION

The gallbladder is a saccular diverticulum from the bile-conveying duct system. It is thin-walled when distended and relatively thick-walled when constricted. It serves not only as a reservoir for bile coming from the liver but as an organ that can concentrate this fluid. The sac has a shape somewhat like that of a drumstick in which the broad end portion constitutes the **fundus** (blind end), the meaty part of the drumstick constitutes the **body portion**, and the more elongated portion makes up the **neck** of the organ. The neck becomes continuous with the **cystic duct**, present at the beginning of the diverticulum.

PLATE 120—Gallbladder

FIG. 14-1. Survey section of the wall of the gallbladder in a contracted state. H & E stain. Low power. (e, epithelium of mucosal folds; lp, lamina propria; ct, fatty connective tissue between the muscularis [m] and the serosa [s])

FIG. 14-2. Intermediate-power view of a portion of the gallbladder in a contracted state to show the nature of the folds of the mucosa. Note that the major and the minor folds are covered by tall columnar epithelium (e) and contain a core of lamina propria connective tissue (lp). H & E stain. (m, smooth muscle bundles with connective tissue interspersed between the bundles)

FIG. 14-3. Gallbladder, showing the mucosal and the muscularis layers. H & E stain. Intermediate power. (e, tall columnar epithelium with striated border; lp, lamina propria; ct, connective tissue between muscle bundles [m])

FIG. 14-4. Mucosa of gallbladder. Note the tall columnar epithelium revealing some terminal bars (tb). Subepithelial connective tissue (lp) extends into the folds of epithelium. H & E stain. High power.

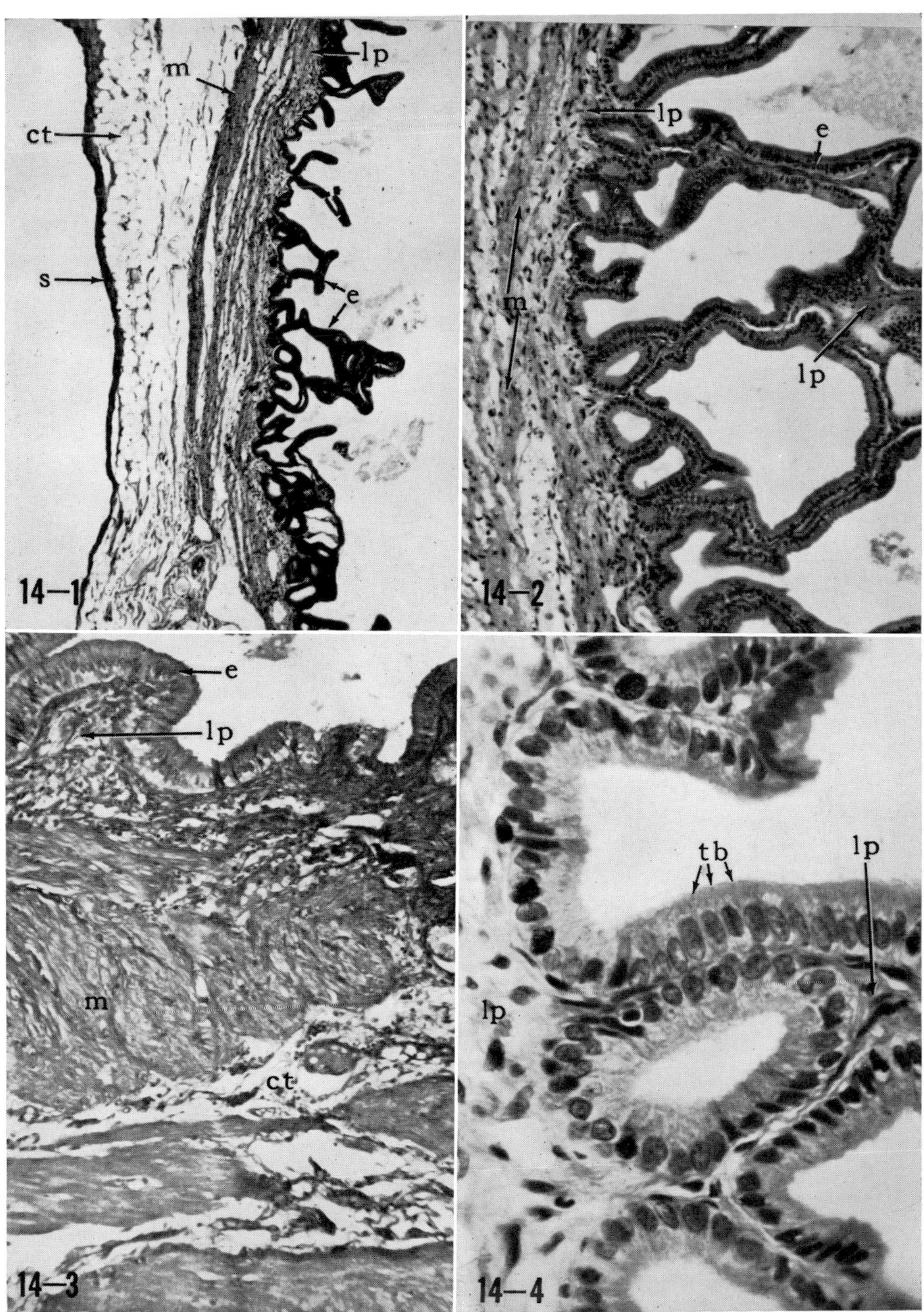
lp
m
ct
s
e
14–1
lp
e
m
lp
14–2
e
lp
m
ct
14–3
tb
lp
lp
14–4

B. HISTOLOGY OF GALLBLADDER

(Plate 120)

The histology of the gallbladder differs somewhat from that of other hollow organs of the digestive system in that certain of the layers of its wall—the muscularis mucosae and the tunica submucosa—are absent. In addition, the muscle layer is thinner, is more broken up by connective tissue and has a less orderly arrangement than is found in the gastrointestinal tract.

1. Mucosa

In the contracted condition of the organ, the mucosa projects into the lumen as a complicated system of small and large branching folds that have no particular spatial orientation. In section, these folds often give the impression of being large walled-off spaces or sinuses. This appearance is explained in the same way that one explains the chamberlike appearance of a hair follicle in the epidermis of skin when it is cut in cross section. When the gallbladder is full or distended, most of these folds disappear.

The epithelium that lines the mucosa is of a very tall simple columnar type. The nuclei are elongate and basally placed, and the abundant cytoplasm usually takes acid stains only feebly. These cells are regarded by many as being somewhat similar to the lining cells of the stomach in that they produce mucus, although in lesser quantities. At the same time, these cells are covered by a very thin cuticle which usually cannot be seen with the light microscope. The cuticular border represents a similarity with the lining cells of the small intestine and is also associated with microvilli and absorption.

An obvious basement membrane is not present, and the epithelium appears, with the light microscope, to rest directly on the connective tissue of the lamina propria. As elsewhere in the digestive system where this supporting layer is present, the fibers are primarily reticular in nature. The lamina propria is well provided with vessels and lymph spaces and may contain diffuse aggregations of lymphatic tissue as well as isolated smooth muscle fibers. Glands in the lamina propria are found only in the neck region of the gallbladder. In this restricted area the glands have an unbranched (simple) duct system associated with tubular and alveolar end-pieces that secrete mucus.

2. Muscularis

The muscular layer consists of a thin, irregular network of smooth muscle fibers. Individual muscle fibers may run circularly, obliquely or longitudinally, although most of the fibers appear to be circularly oriented. Isolated groups of fibers are frequently separated by gaps filled with elastic and collagen fibers. Presumably these connective tissue fibers between muscle bundles, in conjunction with the connective tissue of the lamina propria and the fairly dense connective tissue external to the muscularis, all serve to transform the apparently poorly organized muscle into a useful functional unit.

3. Serosa

This mesothelium-covered connective tissue is present on all surfaces of the gallbladder that are not in contact with the posterior surface of the liver. The connective tissue elements consist mainly of collagenous fibers. Also present between the serosa and the underlying muscularis is a fairly thick layer of loose, highly vascularized connective tissue known as the subserosal or perimuscular connective tissue.

C. SPECIAL FEATURES OF GALLBLADDER

1. Spiral Valve of Heister

In the neck of the gallbladder the mucous membrane is thrown into a series of very long folds. These folds produce irregular troughs or trenches that spiral around the mucosal surface. More smooth muscle is present in the neck than elsewhere in the gallbladder, and this muscle tends to be oriented mainly in a circular direction. Muscular contraction prevents distention of the neck as bile passes through.

2. Cystic Duct

This tubular structure is a continuation of the neck of the gallbladder and permits communication between that organ and the major conducting passageway of bile. Its mucosa is thrown into a discontinuous spiral arrangement of folds, and circularly arranged smooth muscle once again is very abundant. That part of the cystic duct adjacent to the neck region contributes to the spiral valve of Heister.

D. MAJOR BILIARY PASSAGEWAYS

A major hepatic duct drains each of the two primary lobes of the liver. These combine in the porta hepatis to form what can be termed the **hepatic duct proper**. By union of the **hepatic** and the **cystic ducts**, the (**common**) **bile duct** or **ductus choledochus** is formed. This enters the wall of the duodenum. As the bile duct contacts the muscularis externa of the duodenum, a special sphincter of smooth muscle, the **sphincter of Boyden**, develops around it. Deeper in the duodenal wall, the bile duct commonly fuses with the pancreatic duct to form an expanded space known as the **ampulla of Vater**. A smaller accumulation of smooth muscle fibers around the ampulla constitutes the **sphincter of Oddi**. The presence of the ampulla and its surrounding muscle causes a moundlike elevation (papilla) to project from the mucosal surface of the duodenum. Bile and pancreatic juices are released into the duodenal lumen at the apex of this **duodenal papilla**.

15 · The Respiratory System

A. Nose
B. Pharynx
C. Larynx
D. Trachea
E. Lungs

The respiratory system consists of a series of passageways whose walls are histologically modified to condition inspired and expired air. These modifications include:

1. A cartilaginous skeleton to hold open the lumina of certain of the passages
2. A vascular, moist surface to humidify and warm inspired air as well as to remove foreign particulate matter that otherwise would cause respiratory embarrassment
3. Smooth muscle that contracts to retain inspired air in microscopic pockets of the lung in which respiratory exchange occurs.

A. NOSE

(Plate 121)

This hollow organ consists of 2 nasal cavities (separated by a septum) and their walls and is composed of bone, cartilage,

PLATE 121—Nose

FIG. 15-1. Survey section of the nasal conchae of a dog. Mallory-Azan stain. Low power. (e, ciliated pseudostratified columnar epithelium; v, blood vessels; b, bone; ct, connective tissue)

FIG. 15-2. Olfactory epithelium of the nasal concha from an embryo. H & E stain. Low power. (e, lining epithelium; v, blood vessels in connective tissue; g, glands of Bowman; c, hyaline cartilage)

FIG. 15-3. Intermediate-power view of a section of the nasal conchae of a dog, similar to Figure 15-1. Mallory-Azan stain. (e, ciliated pseudostratified columnar epithelium with goblet cells; v, vessels in connective tissue; b, bone)

FIG. 15-4. High-power view of a section of a portion of Figure 15-3, showing the nature of the epithelium and the underlying vascularized connective tissue. Note the cilia (c) on the surface of the pseudostratified columnar epithelium.

FIG. 15-5. Thin area of the nasal wall, revealing the ciliated pseudostratified columnar epithelium (e) with distinct basement membrane (bm), underlying connective tissue (ct) and a strip of bone (b). Mallory-Azan stain. High power.

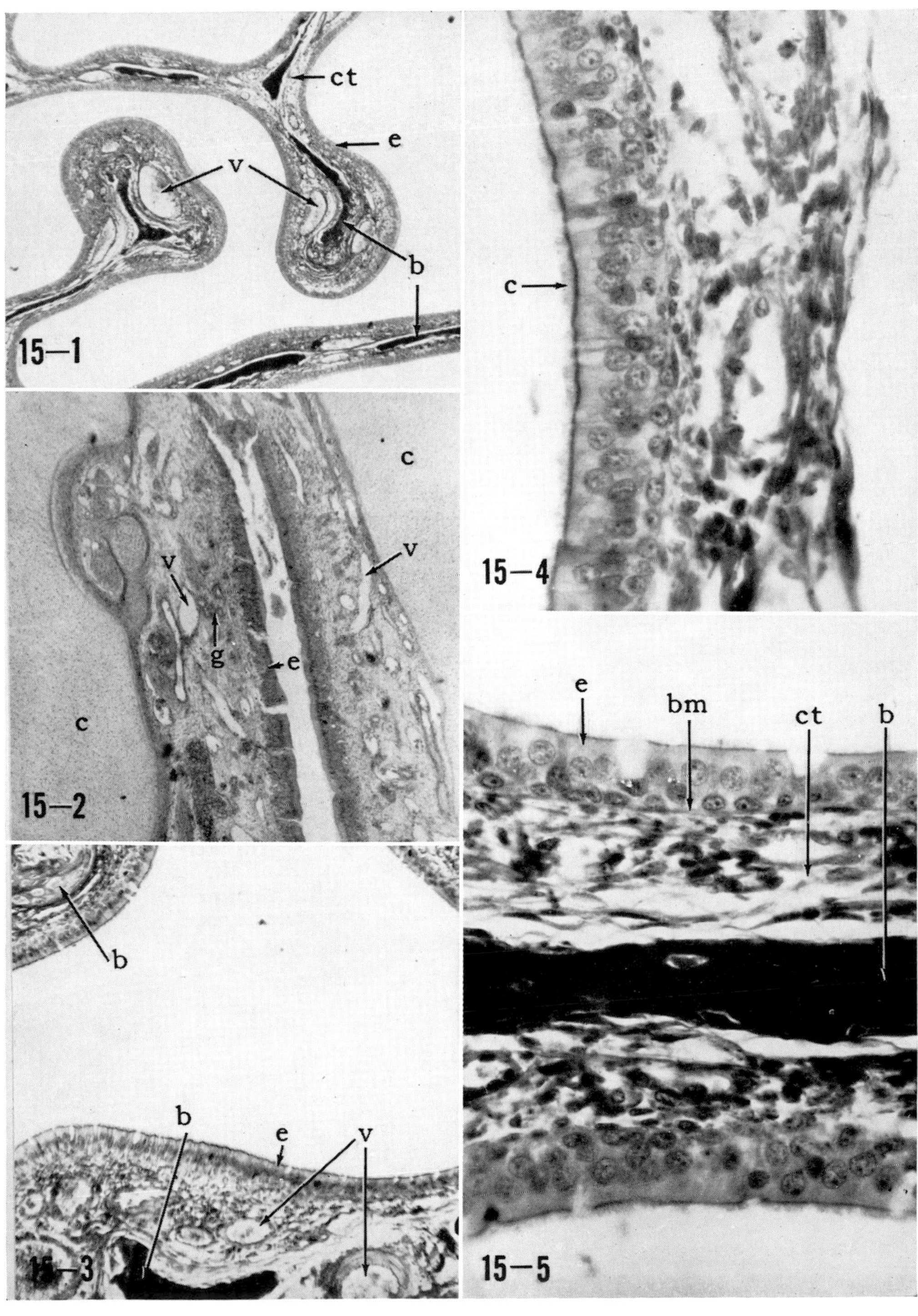
ct
e
v
b
15—1
c
v
g
e
15—2
b
e
v
15—3
c
15—4
e
bm
ct
b
15—5

muscle, connective tissue and epithelium. Each nasal cavity funnels air into the nasopharynx and is divided into **vestibular, respiratory** and **olfactory portions**. The vestibule is that portion lying posterior to the nares; it is supported by hyaline cartilages on its medial side. The olfactory area consists of the sides and the roof of the superoposterior portion of each nasal cavity. The remainder of each nasal cavity constitutes the respiratory portion and includes parts of the septum and the lateral walls.

1. Epithelial Coverings of Nose

The external nose is covered by a thin skin which is continuous through the nares with the mucous membrane lining the nasal cavity.

a. *External Nose.* The skin of the nose includes a typical stratified squamous epithelium and a dermis which contains large sebaceous glands and fine hairs. At the reflection of the skin into the vestibule, hairs (**the vibrissae**) become coarser and more numerous to serve as a trap for dust particles present in the inspired air.

b. *Vestibule and Respiratory Area.* Where the vestibule of the nasal cavity borders on the respiratory part, a transformation from stratified squamous epithelium to a pseudostratified ciliated columnar epithelium takes place. This ciliated epithelium contains numerous goblet cells which secrete the mucous material present on the surface of the mucous membrane. The respiratory mucoperiosteum often is referred to as the **schneiderian membrane**. A rich vascular bed beneath the epithelium provides warmth which radiates from the surface to warm and humidify inspired air.

c. *Olfactory Area.* In the olfactory region of the nasal cavity, the lining epithelium has been described alternately to be of either a pseudostratified, nonciliated or a stratified columnar type.

The mucous membrane of this restricted region is covered by an epithelium made up of 3 types of cells, **supporting, basal** and **olfactory**. The **supporting** or **sustentacular cells** are tall and cylindrical, contain ovoid nuclei and have present in their superficial cytoplasm yellowish-brown pigment granules. The presence of pigment within the supporting cells gives the mucous membrane its typical brownish color. The **basal cells** consist of a single layer of small conical elements lying between the bases of the supporting cells. These small cells contain dark-staining nuclei and have branching cytoplasmic processes. The third cell type in the olfactory epithelium is the **sensory element** that responds to olfactory stimuli. These spindle-shaped **olfactory cells** are actually **bipolar nerve cell bodies.** From a

PLATE 122—Larynx and Trachea

FIG. 15-6. Section of the larynx from a 9-month-old fetus. Masson stain. Low power. (e, epithelium; lp, lamina propria; g, tubulo-acinar mixed glands; d, duct)

FIG. 15-7. Survey of full thickness through the anterior wall of the trachea. H & E stain. Low power. (e, ciliated pseudostratified columnar epithelium; lp, lamina propria; g, seromucous glands of the submucosa; c, hyaline cartilage; f, fibroelastic layer passing into the perichondrium)

FIG. 15-8. Survey of the wall of the trachea through the open end of its cartilage (c) near the posterior region. Note the fibroelastic membrane (f) extending across from the end of the cartilage. Compare the thickness of the glandular area here with that seen in Figure 15-7. H & E stain. Low power. (e, surface epithelium; lp, lamina propria; g, submucosal glands; p, perichondrium)

FIG. 15-9. Intermediate-power view of a section of a portion of Figure 15-7. (e, ciliated pseudostratified columnar epithelium with underlying basement membrane; lp, lamina propria; g, seromucous glands of the submucosa; p, perichondrium; c, hyaline cartilage; f, fibroelastic membrane)

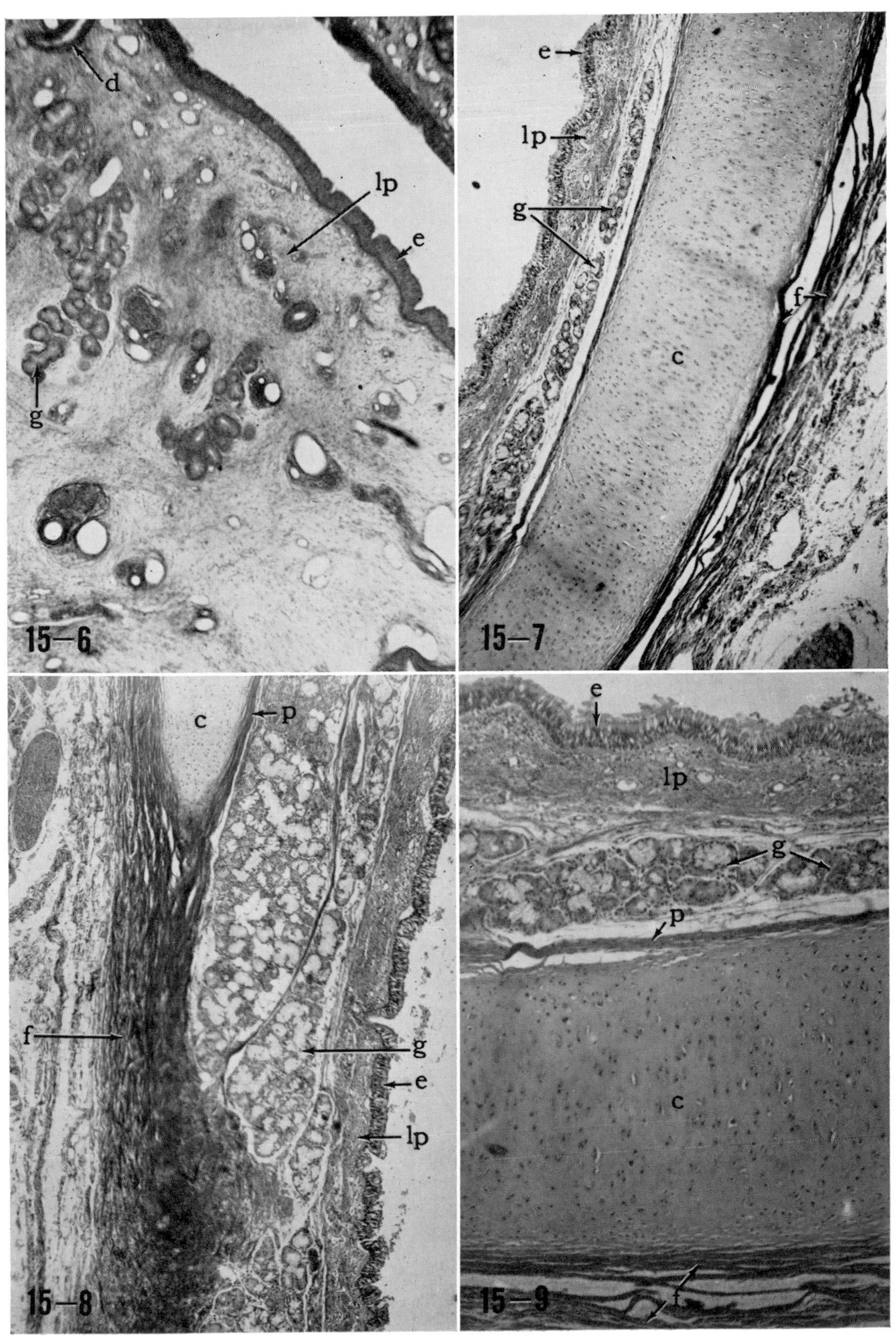
d
lp
e
g
15—6
e
lp
g
f
c
15—7
c
p
f
g
e
lp
15—8
e
lp
g
p
c
f
15—9

vesicle present in the superficial part of these cells a tuft of **olfactory hairs** takes origin and projects from the surface of the mucous membrane. Each tuft of hairs can be considered to be the functional dendrite of the olfactory cell. A single axonic process leaves the deeper part of each olfactory cell and courses through the connective tissue (lamina propria) beneath the epithelium as an olfactory nerve fiber.

2. Connective Tissue of the Nasal Mucosa

The ciliated epithelium of the respiratory portion of the nasal cavity rests on a distinct basement membrane. Underneath this membrane is a layer of connective tissue, the lamina propria, rich in elastic and collagen fibers and laden with glands that have seromucous end-pieces. The secretions from these nasal glands moisten the mucosal surface of the nose and serve to trap airborne foreign matter that has been inhaled. This foreign material is moved toward the throat by ciliary action. The lamina propria also contains rich venous plexuses which, by means of heat transfer from the blood passing through them, aid in warming and humidifying the air as it passes through the nasal cavity. Lymphocytes and other leukocytes also infiltrate the lamina propria.

In the olfactory region, the lamina propria contains the **olfactory glands of Bowman**. These are branched tubulo-alveolar glands with serous end-pieces whose secretions moisten the mucosal surface.

3. Supporting Tissues of the Nose

In addition to small cartilages in the alae of the nose, the lateral wall of the nose is supported by bone and fibrous tissue richly infiltrated with fat. From each lateral wall 3 scroll-like plates of bone, arranged one above the other, project into the nasal cavity; these are the **conchae** or **turbinates**. The nasal septum is also supported by bone and cartilage.

4. Paranasal Sinuses

Four paranasal air sinuses are associated with each nasal cavity. They are the **frontal**, the **ethmoidal**, the **sphenoidal** and the **maxillary (antrum of Highmore) sinuses**, named for the bones in which they are predominantly located. Their delicate mucosa is lined with a pseudostratified ciliated columnar epithelium similar to that found lining the nasal cavity. However, goblet cells and glands are present, although venous plexuses are lacking.

B. PHARYNX

The pharynx is the posterior continuation of the oral cavity, with an upper portion constituting the nasopharynx and a middle portion the oropharynx.

1. Epithelium

Most of the nasal portion of the pharynx is covered with a pseudostratified ciliated columnar epithelium containing many gob-

PLATE 123—Trachea

FIG. 15-10. Trachea, showing the distribution of the mixed glands of the submucosa with a duct (d) opening on the free surface of the epithelium. H & E stain. Intermediate power.

FIG. 15-11. Trachea, emphasizing the nature of the tracheal glands and the hyaline cartilage with its perichondrium (p). Note that serous glandular end-pieces are present as alveoli (sa) and as demilunes (sd) and that mucous glands are present as alveoli (ma) and tubules (mt). H & E stain. Intermediate power.

FIG. 15-12. Section of the posterior portion of the trachea between the ends of the cartilage plate. Note the presence of smooth muscle bundles and the abundance of tracheal glands. H & E stain. Intermediate power. (tm, transversely sectioned smooth muscle; lm, longitudinally sectioned smooth muscle)

FIG. 15-13. High-power view of the tracheal glands. Mallory-Azan stain. (sa, serous alveoli; ma, mucous alveoli; mt, mucous tubules; sd, serous demilunes; f, fat cells)

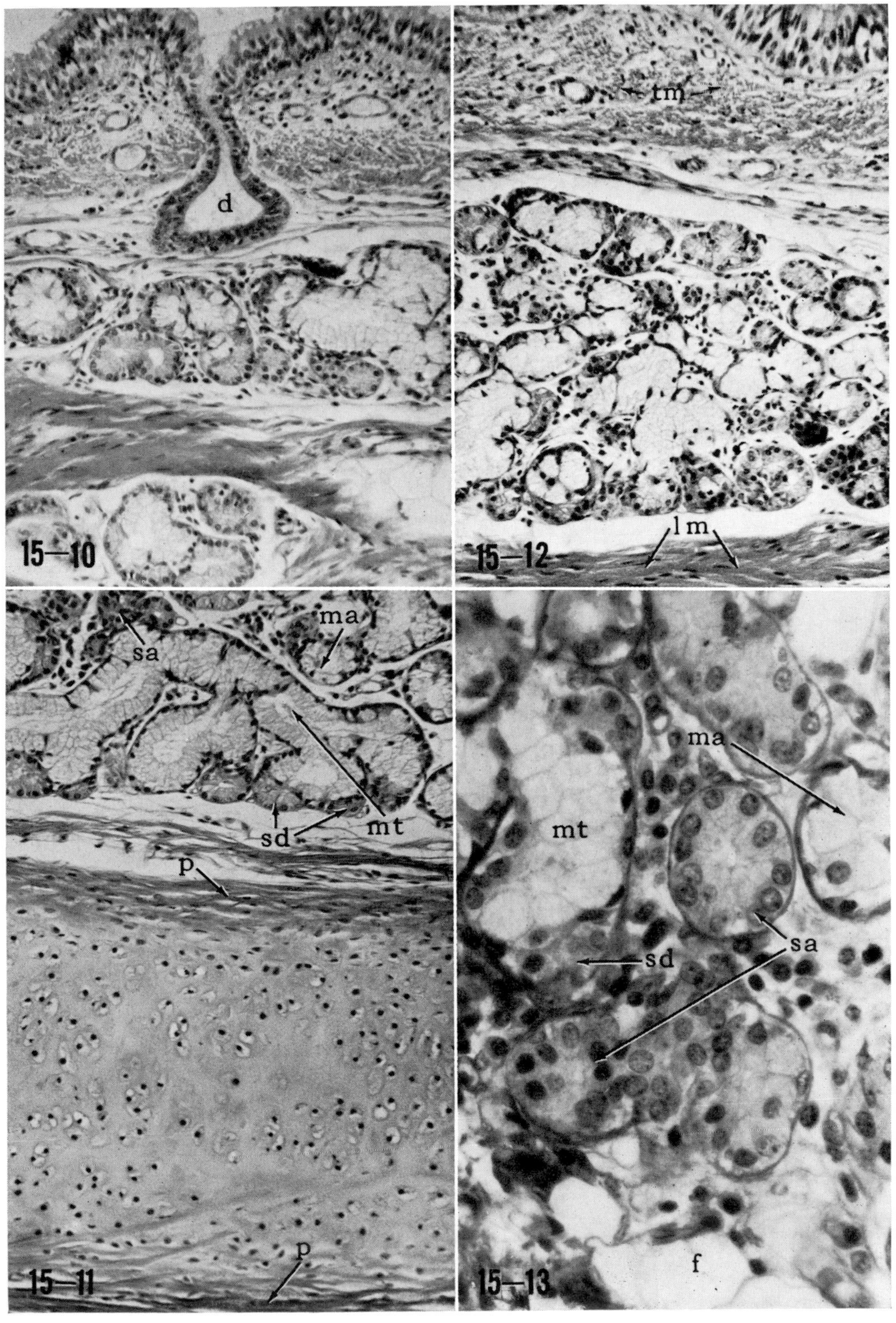
d
15—10
tm
lm
15—12
sa
ma
mt
sd
p
p
15—11
ma
mt
sa
sd
f
15—13

let cells. On the other hand, the oral part is lined by a stratified squamous epithelium resembling that of the esophagus.

2. Lamina Propria

The lamina propria of both regions consists of a thick network of elastic fibers and glands. The glands of the nasopharynx contain tubulo-alveolar end-pieces of mixed serous and mucous nature. The glands of the oropharynx are entirely mucous in nature.

3. Submucosa

A well-developed submucosa of loose connective tissue (areolar) is found in the lateral wall of the nasopharynx and where the pharynx continues into the esophagus.

4. Muscularis

Except where a submucosa exists, the mucous membrane is adjacent to the muscularis. This tunic consists of an inner longitudinal and an outer oblique layer of striated muscle; strands of elastic fibers are found mixed between the muscle bundles.

C. LARYNX (Fig. 15-6)

The larynx is an elongated, firm tubelike structure supported by 9 hyaline and elastic cartilages, to which are attached the laryngeal skeletal musculature. The larynx connects the pharynx with the trachea and also contains the vocal cords.

1. Epithelium

The anterior and upper half of the posterior surfaces of the epiglottis, the aryepiglottic folds and the vocal cords are covered with stratified squamous epithelium. Pseudostratified ciliated columnar epithelium containing goblet cells constitutes the rest of the lining epithelium of the larynx. The cilia move foreign particulate matter and mucus toward the pharynx.

2. Lamina Propria

The lamina propria of both regions is rich in elastic fibers and contains tubulo-alveolar glands that have a mixture of serous and mucous end-pieces. Lymph nodes and lymphocytes are scattered throughout the lamina propria. The true vocal cords are folds of the mucous membrane which enclose a band of elastic tissue (the **vocal ligament**) and are bordered laterally by the thyroarytenoid muscle (the **vocal muscle**).

3. Supporting Tissue of the Larynx

The supporting framework of the larynx consists of large **plates of hyaline cartilage** (thyroid, cricoid and lower part of arytenoids) and smaller **elastic cartilage plates** (corniculate, cuneiform, epiglottic and upper part of arytenoids).

PLATE 124—Lung

FIG. 15-14. Lung, showing a bronchus (b), with some hyaline cartilage plates (c), conducting (cbr) and respiratory (rbr) bronchioles, alveolar ducts (ad) in transverse and longitudinal section, and surrounding alveoli. Mallory stain. Low power.

FIG. 15-15. Section through a bronchus (b) and surrounding alveolar ducts (ad) and alveoli. H & E stain. Low power. (c, hyaline cartilage plates; e, ciliated pseudostratified columnar epithelium; m, circular smooth muscle; g, mixed glands)

FIG. 15-16. Lung, showing a bronchus (b) and a section through a terminal bronchiole (tbr). H & E stain. Low power. (rbr, respiratory bronchiole; ad, alveolar duct; a, alveoli; v, blood vessel)

FIG. 15-17. Section showing several alveolar ducts (ad). Note the portion of a small bronchus (b) with adjacent cartilaginous plate (c). H & E stain. Low power.

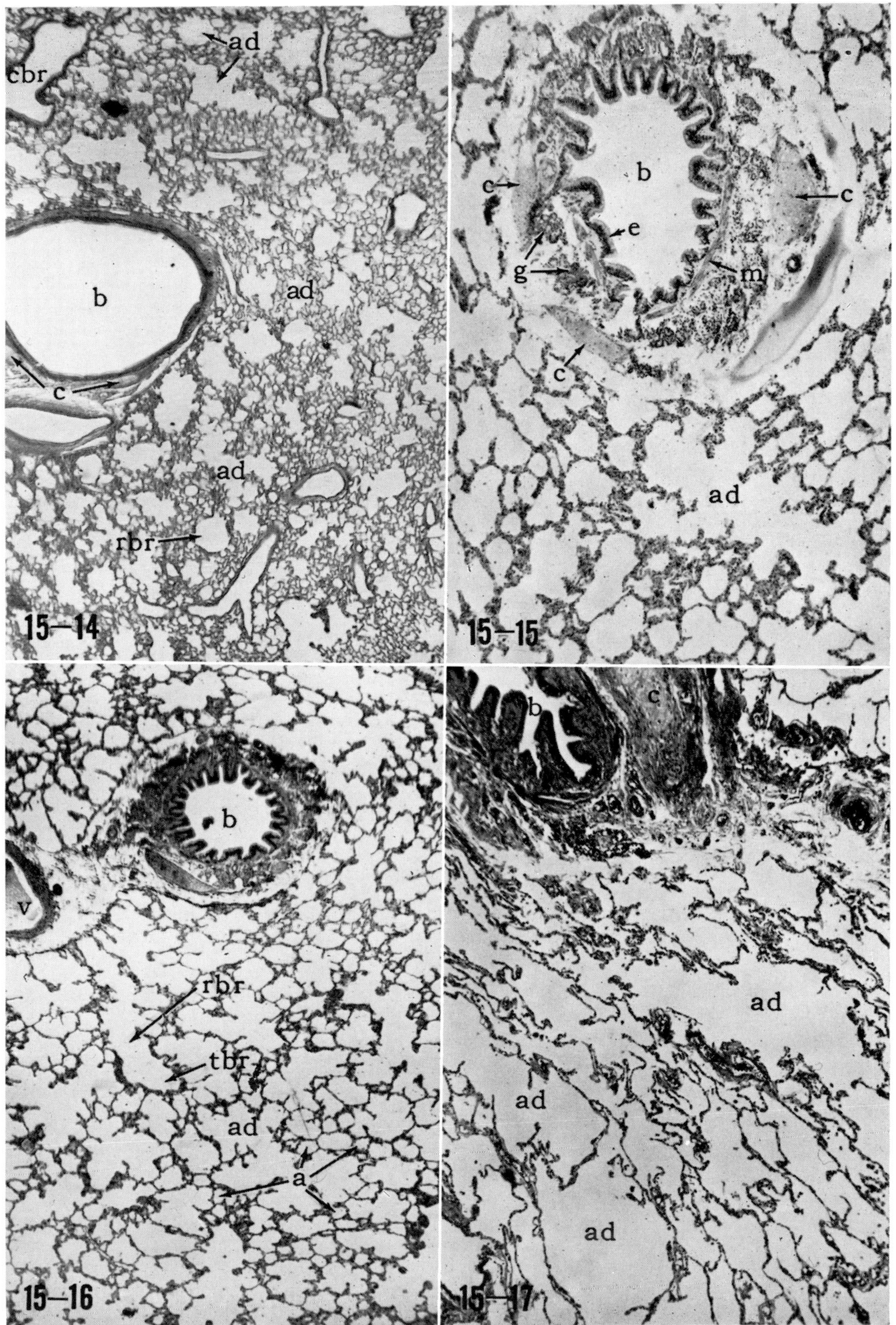
ad
cbr
b
ad
c
ad
rbr
15—14
b
c
c
e
g
g
m
c
ad
15—15
b
v
rbr
tbr
ad
a
15—16
b
c
ad
ad
ad
15—17

4. Functional Aspects of Musculature

Extrinsic pharyngeal constricter muscles (skeletal) act on the cartilages of the larynx during deglutition and pull down the epiglottis so as to prevent ingested material from passing into the respiratory tract. Intrinsic skeletal muscle in the larynx attaches the laryngeal cartilages to each other and to the laryngeal mucous membrane. This intrinsic musculature therefore plays a major role in phonation by controlling tension on the vocal cords.

D. TRACHEA

The trachea is a thin-walled, rigid membranous tube which is continuous with the larynx and bifurcates into two primary bronchi near the lungs (Figs. 15-7 to 15-13).

1. Epithelium

The luminal surfaces of the trachea and the primary bronchi are lined with a pseudostratified ciliated columnar epithelium, containing numerous globlet cells and rests on a distinct basement membrane.

2. Lamina Propria

The lamina propria is made up principally of reticular connective tissue and contains accumulations of lymphocytes and many elastic fibers, especially in the deeper zones (in place of the muscularis mucosa).

3. Submucosa

The submucosa is made up of loose connective tissue (areolar) and contains many small **seromucous glands (tracheal)** which extend through the muscle layer present in the posterior portion of the trachea. Short ducts from these glands penetrate the mucosa to open on the free surface.

4. Adventitia

Perhaps the most characteristic feature of the trachea is found in the **adventitia**. Here 16 to 20 C- or Y-shaped **hyaline cartilages** are present in the anterior and the lateral parts of this membranous tube. The cartilages are separated from one another by fibroelastic tissue. This arrangement affords the tube greater plasticity. The posterior part of the wall facing the esophagus is occupied by a thick layer of smooth muscle (transversely running trachealis muscle) and a dense fibroelastic tissue membrane.

The structure of the main bronchi is basically identical with that of the trachea.

E. LUNGS

(Plates 124 to 127)

The structural plan of each lung is such that the serous membrane covering (visceral pleura) turns inwardly so that there is a division of the lungs into lobes. Thus, there are 3 major lobes in the right lung and a division of 2 lobes in the left lung, so that the right and the left main bronchi (primary) entering the right and the left lungs, respectively, give rise to 3 secondary bronchi in the right lung and 2 in the left lung. These secondary bronchi are segmentally distributed (segmental and terminal bronchi) so

PLATE 125—Lung

FIG. 15-18. Injected lung (animal), showing a longitudinal section of a conducting bronchiole (cbr) giving rise to two terminal bronchioles (tbr) and a respiratory bronchiole (rbr). Low power. (a, alveoli; d, alveolar duct; v, blood vessels)

FIG. 15-19. Lung (cat) injected with carmine to show the vascular nature of the alveoli. Low power.

FIG. 15-20. Section of an alveolar duct, showing concentrations of smooth muscle (m) around the openings of the alveoli. Mallory-Azan stain. Intermediate power. (v, blood vessels)

FIG. 15-21. Intermediate-power view of a section of a portion of Figure 15-19, showing the rich plexus of capillaries (black) which form part of the alveolar wall.

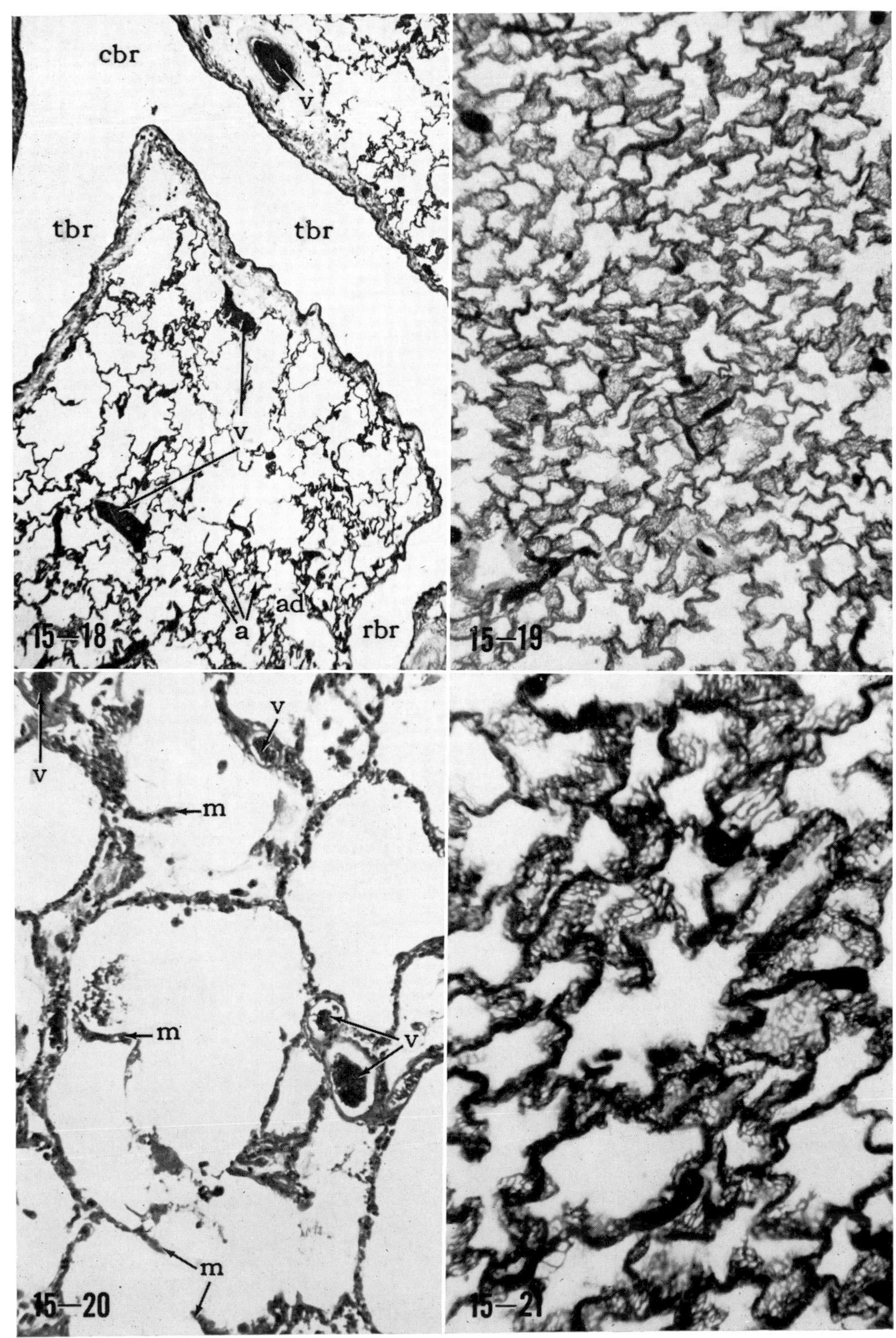

cbr
v
tbr
tbr
v
a
ad
rbr
15–18
15–19
v
v
m
m
v
m
15–20
15–21

that the right lung, which consists of 10 bronchopulmonary segments, receives 10 such bronchi, while the left lung, which consists of 8 segments, is supplied by 8 of these bronchial passages. From the segmental and the terminal bronchi arise the bronchioles; 50 to 80 terminal (lobular) bronchioles are present in each secondary lobule. The terminal bronchioles each give rise to 2 to 5 respiratory bronchioles, which in turn give rise to 2 to 11 alveolar ducts covered with alveoli (air cells). The alveolar ducts lead into alveolar sacs (air sacs), each of which terminates in numerous alveoli. It is in the alveoli that the exchange of respiratory gases takes place.

1. Primary Bronchi (Extrapulmonary)

These air passages present basically the same histologic picture as described for the trachea.

2. Secondary Bronchi (Intrapulmonary; Lobar Bronchi)

Microscopically, the epithelium is of the pseudostratified ciliated columnar type with goblet cells still present but not as abundant as in the primary bronchi. As these secondary bronchi become smaller, the epithelium becomes ciliated simple columnar with goblet cells still persisting. Unlike the situation found in the trachea and the primary bronchi, the lamina propria, which gradually decreases in thickness, is encircled by muscularis mucosae which becomes relatively thicker as the size of the bronchi decreases.

Seromucous glands, which decrease in number as the bronchi become smaller, are found in the submucosa.

A look at the adventitia reveals irregularly shaped cartilage plates instead of the cartilage rings.

3. Segmental and Terminal Bronchi

The segmental bronchi become progressively smaller in diameter (terminal bronchi) and reveal increasingly thinner walls. Associated with these changes, it will be noted, microscopically, that most prominently there is a reduced amount of cartilage and glandular material along with a relative increase in smooth muscle.

4. Bronchioles

Finally, when the passages are reduced to a diameter of 1 mm. or less, the most prominent changes noted are the gradual disappearance of goblet cells and seromucous glands and the complete absence of cartilage. Actually, the lack of cartilage signals the end of the bronchi, and the passages now are referred to as bronchioles. Except at the level of the respiratory bronchioles, the muscularis mucosae dominates the lamina propria.

5. Terminal Bronchioles (Lobular)

The smallest of the conducting bronchioles, the terminal bronchiole, is about 0.5

PLATE 126—Lung

FIG. 15-22. Transverse section through an alveolar duct (ad) and alveoli. Note the smooth muscle bundles (s) around the openings of the alveoli (a). H & E stain. Intermediate power.

FIG. 15-23. Lung, showing the alveolar walls. H & E stain. High power. (as, alveolar septae; c, capillaries; s, smooth muscle; ae, alveolar epithelial cells; sc, septal cells)

FIG. 15-24. Section through a terminal bronchiole (tbr), showing the transition to a respiratory bronchiole (rbr), an alveolar duct (ad) and surrounding alveoli. Mallory stain. Intermediate power. (v, blood vessel)

FIG. 15-25. Section through a bronchus with cartilage not shown. H & E stain. Intermediate power. (e, pseudostratified ciliated columnar epithelium with goblet cells; m, smooth muscle)

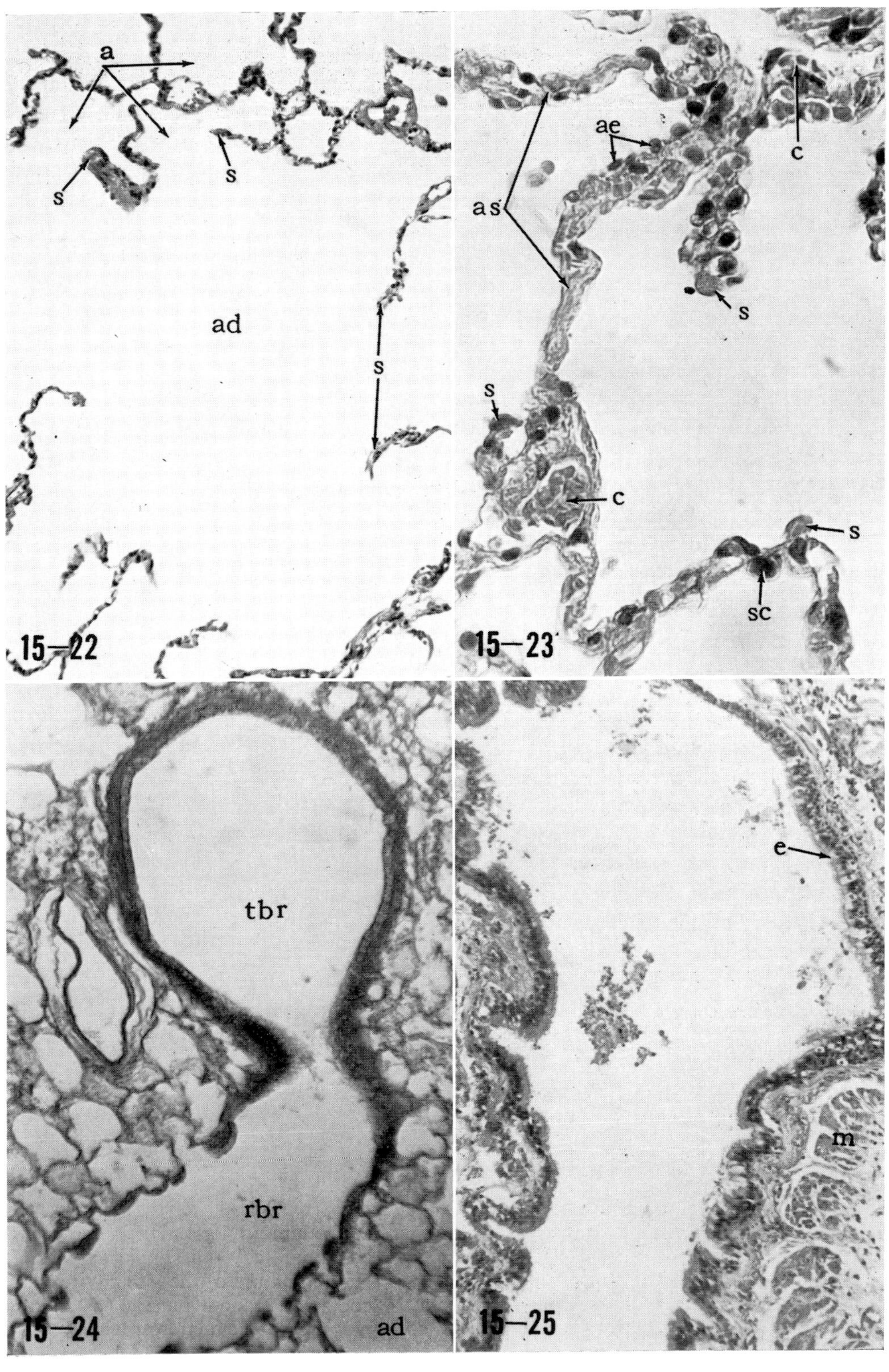
a
s
s
ad
s
15–22
ae
c
as
s
s
c
s
sc
15–23
tbr
rbr
ad
15–24
e
m
15–25

mm. in diameter. Except for reduction of the epithelial height to a cuboidal type and the complete disappearance of goblet cells, the microscopic picture is similar to that encountered in the larger bronchioles.

6. Respiratory Bronchioles

These short branching tubes of the lung may contain cilia (absent in tubes of smallest diameter). Here the main support is provided by collagenous fibers forming an interlacing network with some smooth muscle and elastic fibers. A few alveoli appear as outpocketings from the side of the bronchiole. Hence, the name respiratory bronchiole is applicable. The alveolar duct and the parts of the conducting system distal to it, including the surrounding tissue structures, are often referred to in the literature as a **primary lobule**.

7. Alveolar Ducts

The respiratory bronchioles branch to give rise to the alveolar ducts. These long thin-walled branching tubes have a thin epithelial lining characteristic of the alveolar walls. In addition, they consist of fibroelastic connective tissue and some spirals of smooth muscle cells which often appear knoblike. Perhaps the most characteristic feature of the alveolar ducts is the alveolar sacs (2 to 5) which bud off their sides, opening into the ducts. It can be seen, therefore, that the major mass of the lung consists of "air spaces."

8. Alveolar Sacs and Alveoli

An alveolar sac (air sac) is somewhat or approximately polyhedral in shape and is in communication proximally with an alveolar duct and distally with alveoli. The sac walls do not contain smooth muscle but are composed mainly of elastic and reticular fibers, moistened internally by a thin film of fluid, and enmeshed in numerous anastomosing capillaries of the pulmonary artery. Surrounding the openings (mouths) in the walls of the alveolar sacs, wavy wreaths consisting mainly of elastic fibers are often apparent.

The wall of an alveolus consists of blood capillaries along with elastic and reticular fibers. Recent electron microscopic studies reveal that there is a continuous flat epithelium covering the alveolar walls. Free macrophages characteristically found within the alveoli and alveolar ducts have also been observed on the epithelial covering of the alveolar walls. These cells, often referred to as **dust cells** or **alveolar phagocytes**, are actively phagocytic and serve to remove foreign and harmful matter. Another cell type which is often described in association with the alveoli is the so-called **septal cell**. One must also remember that the alveoli are not closed sacs; they open into alveolar ducts. Also, adjacent alveoli may be connected by means of perforations (**alveolar pores**) of the septum. In this way there is the free diffusion of air into the interior of the alveoli.

PLATE 127—Lung

FIG. 15-26. Injected animal lung to demonstrate the walls between adjacent alveoli. High power.

FIG. 15-27. Alveolar wall, showing the presence of dust cells (d). H & E stain. High power.

FIG. 15-28. Section through a bronchus, showing its pseudostratified ciliated columnar epithelial lining with goblet cells and the underlying lamina propia. H & E stain. High power.

FIG. 15-29. Section through a conducting bronchiole, showing varied types of epithelium in its lining (simple ciliated columnar [cc] and simple cuboidal [sc]) and the nature of the lamina propria with contained smooth muscle (m). Note the presence of cellular elements and debris in the lumen (l). H & E stain. High power.

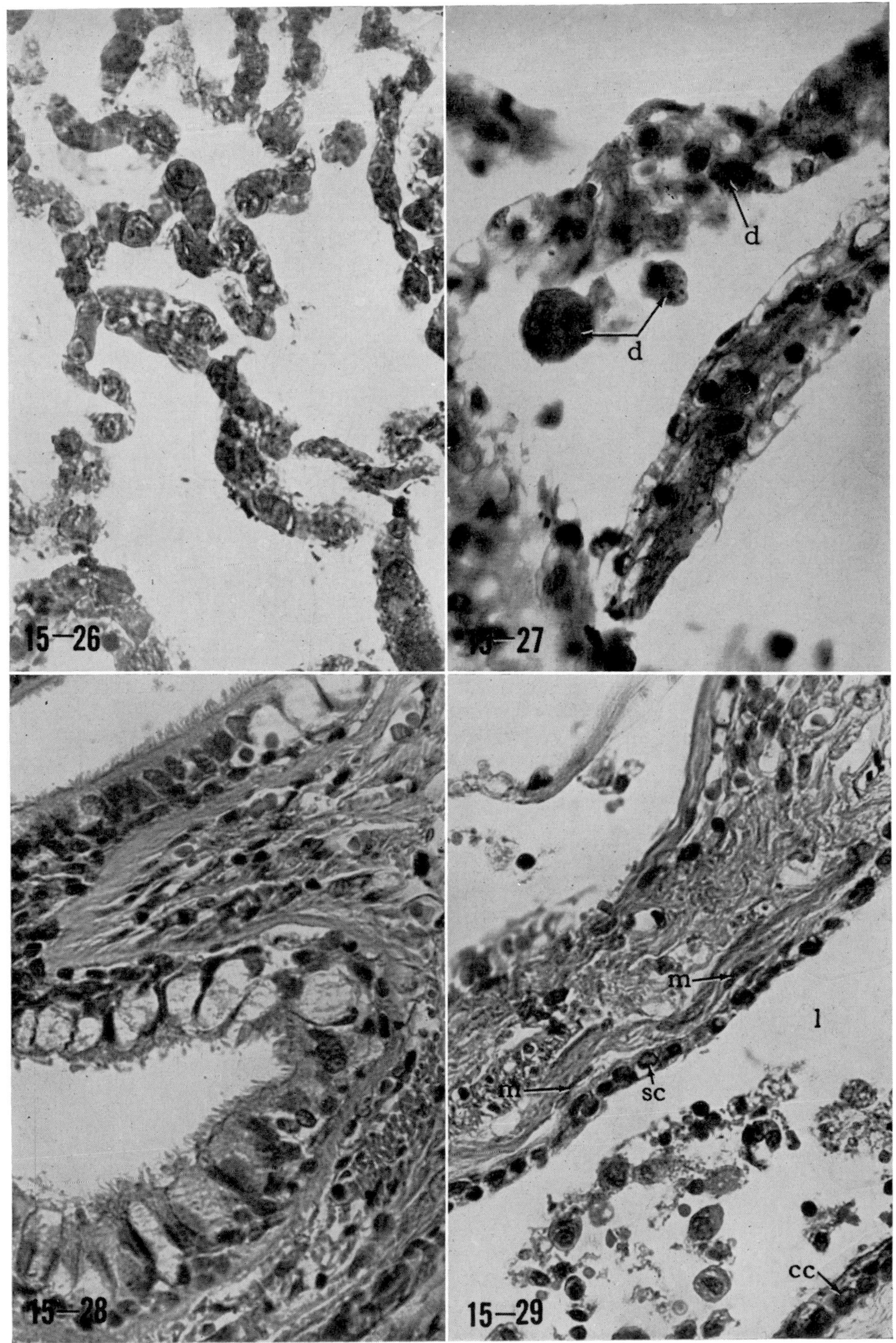
d
d
15—26
15—27
15—28
m
l
m
sc
cc
15—29

16 • Integument and Accessory Structures

A. Introduction
B. Epidermis
C. Dermis
D. Accessory Structures of the Integument
E. Some Special Aspects of Integument

A. INTRODUCTION

The integument or skin is the largest organ of the body and represents a blanket of variable thickness (about 0.5 to 5 mm.) that covers the entire body. It becomes continuous through a number of orifices with moist (mucous) membranes that line the gastrointestinal, the respiratory and the genitourinary tracts. It serves primarily as a protective encasement but also serves important functions related to the maintenance of a constant body temperature (homeothermy) and water balance as well as to excretion and insensible perspiration. Skin contains components that are clearly related to each of these functions.

The integument consists of an external

PLATE 128—Skin

FIG. 16-1. Skin of back (embryo) showing young connective tissue (ct) and the origin of hair rudiments (hr) from the surface epithelium (e). H & E stain. Low power.

FIG. 16-2. Skin of back (embryo), showing the early appearance of stratified squamous epithelium of the epidermis (ep) and young connective tissue (ct). H & E stain. High power.

FIG. 16-3. Thick skin from the palm. H & E stain. Low power. (ep, epidermis; dct, dermal connective tissue; sct, subcutaneous connective tissue; sc, stratum corneum; sl, stratum lucidum; sgr, stratum granulosum; sg, stratum germinativum; p, papillary layer of dermis; r, reticular layer of dermis; d, duct of sweat glands; g, sweat glands; f, fat cells)

FIG. 16-4. High-power view of section of thick skin from the palm, revealing the nature of the stratum corneum (sc), the stratum granulosum (sgr), the stratum germinativum (sg) and the underlying papillary layer (p) of the dermal connective tissue. The stratum lucidum does not stand out clearly in this section. H & E stain.

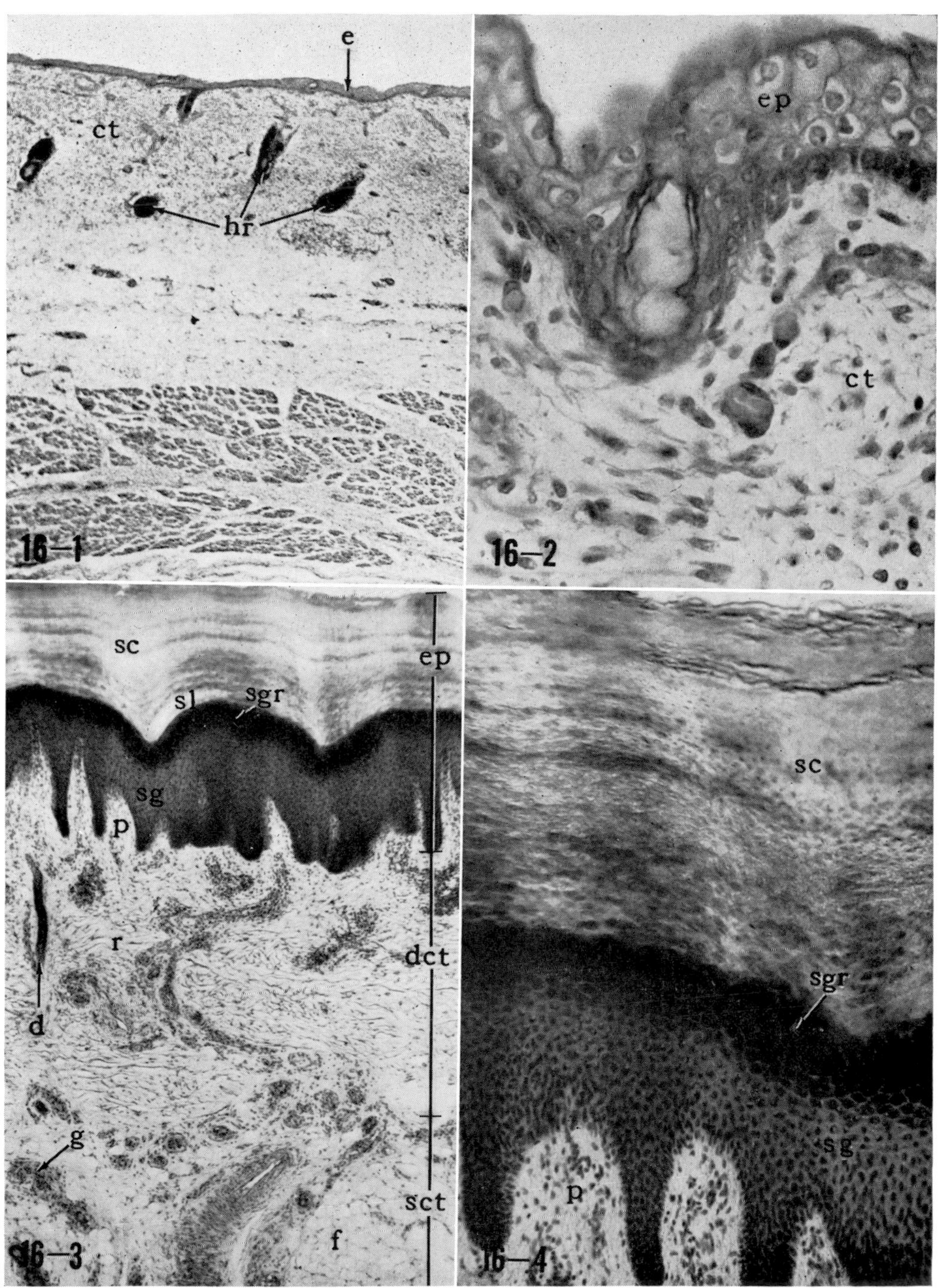
e
ct
hr
16—1
ep
ct
16—2
sc
ep
sl
sgr
sg
p
r
dct
d
g
sct
f
16—3
sc
sgr
sg
p
16—4

epithelial portion, the **epidermis**, and a deeper, connective tissue portion, the **dermis** (corium or cutis vera). These two layers everywhere are sandwiched together by an extremely thin cementing material, the **basement membrane (membrana propria)**. Further attachment between the epithelial and the connective tissue components of skin is effected at this boundary by the interdigitation of downgrowths from the epithelium (**rete pegs**) with upward extensions from the connective tissue (**dermal papillae**). This dermo-epidermal junction in section appears quite wavy and represents a strengthening of the attachment between the overlying protective epithelium and the underlying vascular connective tissue. Thus, it is understandable that skin surfaces that are subjected to much abrasion or stretching during daily activities have longer projections (up to 500 μ) and more of them (up to 70,000/sq. in.) than skin surfaces that are protected or do not move much.

Wide variations in the thickness of skin exist, with the thickest examples being found on the palms and the soles and the thinnest on the eyelid. The skin is attached to underlying muscles by another, nonintegumentary layer, the subcutaneous connective tissue (superficial fascia). Again, the nature of this attachment determines whether the overlying skin has great or slight mobility. In most instances the skin is only loosely bound to the structures that lie deep to it and generally is quite movable.

B. EPIDERMIS

(Figs. 16-1 to 16-6)

This is an avascular layer and consists of a stratified squamous epithelium. The free surface or squamous cover of the epidermis is usually keratinized (cornified, stratum corneum, horny cell layer). In the thickest epidermis (palm and sole), 5 distinct epithelial layers can be distinguished. These are:

1. *Stratum basalis* (*stratum cylindricum*, sometimes referred to in a narrow sense as the *stratum germinativum*). This represents the deepest layer and consists of a single row of columnar or cylindrical cells which are placed immediately upon the basement membrane. These cells are the most actively mitotic elements of the epidermis; their division creates daughter cells which push upward into the other epithelial strata. In this process of migration, the cells undergo morphologic changes and become part of the other epithelial layers. Because of their high

PLATE 129—Skin and Hair

FIG. 16-5. Thin skin of body. Note that the epidermis (ep) appears as a thin homogeneous band at this magnification, with the underlying dermal connective tissue revealing an irregular arrangement of coarse fibers. H & E stain. Low power.

FIG. 16-6. Thin skin of body, revealing that the thin epidermis consists of a stratum corneum (sc), a stratum granulosum (sgr) and a stratum germinativum (sge). Masson stain. Low power. (p, papillary layer of dermis; r, reticular layer of dermis; f, fat cells)

FIG. 16-7. Scalp, showing a portion of a hair and its follicle sectioned longitudinally. H & E stain. Low power. (ep, epidermis; d, dermis; cts, connective tissue sheath of hair follicle; hs, hair shaft; oe, outer epithelial root sheath; ie, inner epithelial root sheath; sg, sebaceous gland; sf, subcutaneous fat cell)

FIG. 16-8. Scalp, showing hairs and their follicles cut in oblique section. H & E stain. Low power. (ep, epidermis; d, dermis; hs, hair shaft; sg, sebaceous glands; sf, subcutaneous fat)

FIG. 16-9. Scalp, showing hair follicles cut in almost a cross-sectional plane. H & E stain. Low power. (ie, inner epithelial root sheath; oe, outer epithelial root sheath; cts, connective tissue sheath of hair follicle; f, follicle containing hair; g, sweat glands; ep, epidermis; d, dermis; sf, subcutaneous fat)

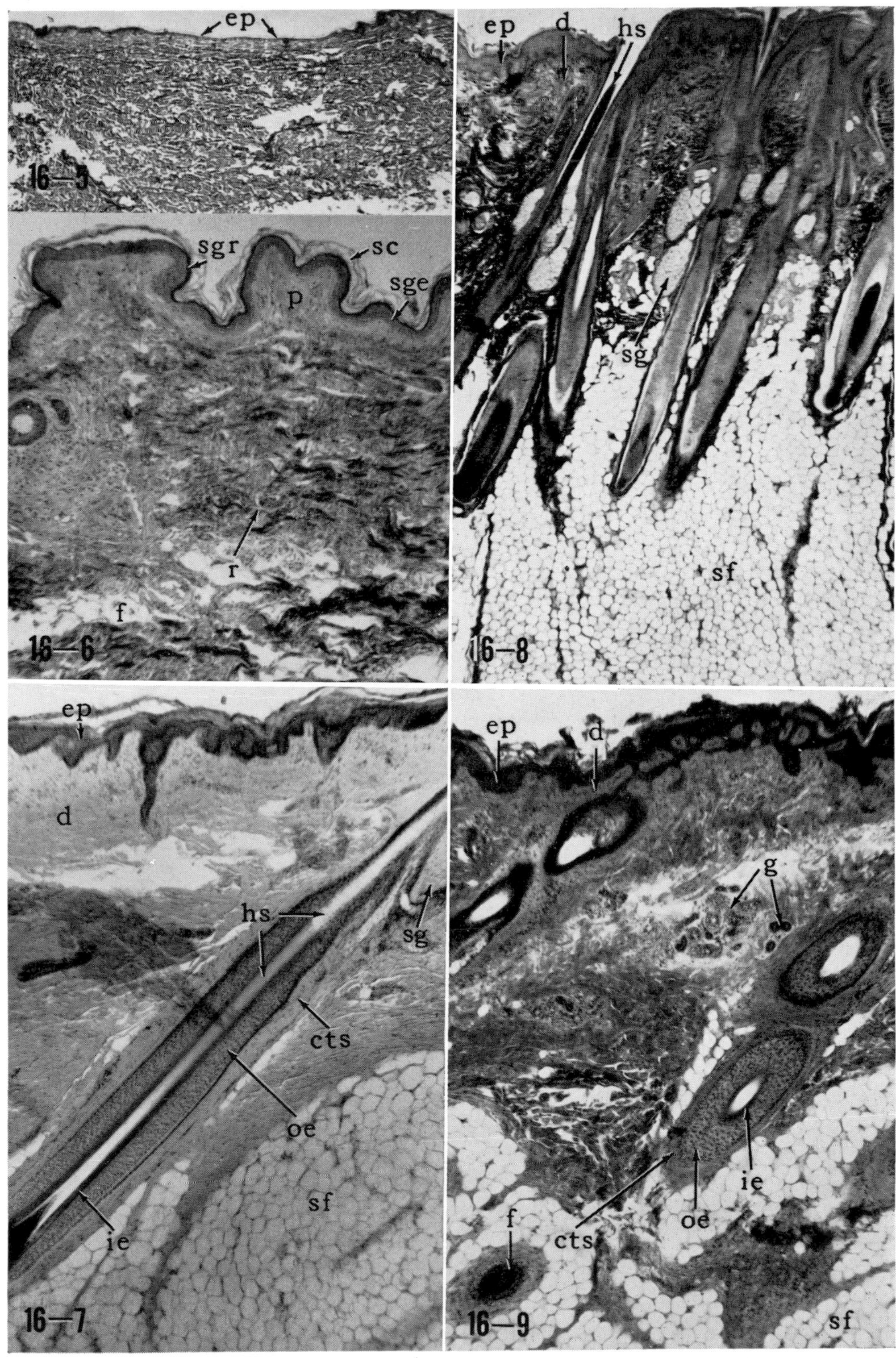
ep
16—5
sgr
sc
p
sge
r
f
16—6
ep
d
hs
sg
sf
16—8
ep
d
hs
sg
cts
oe
sf
ie
16—7
ep
d
g
ie
oe
cts
f
16—9
sf

metabolic activity, the cells of the stratum basalis take on a deeper basophilic stain than the cells in the other layers of the epidermis.

2. *Stratum spinosum* (*spinous or prickle cell layer; this layer, together with the stratum basalis*, is referred to in its broadest sense as the *stratum germinativum*). This stratum, many cells in thickness, lies immediately above the stratum basalis. The deeper cells in it are polygonal in shape, but toward the more superficial aspects of the layer the cells become oval or flattened in a plane parallel with the skin surface. All of the cells in this zone are less intensely basophilic in their staining properties than the cells in the stratum basalis. Also, this decreasing basophilia progresses from the deepest region of the stratum spinosum to the most superficial one. Adjacent cells in this layer appear slightly separated from one another by a narrow intercellular gap that is filled with a homogeneous cementing substance. Across these narrow gaps, fine hairlike connections, the **desmosomes (intercellular bridges)**, can be seen and appear to anchor the cells together. Long cytoplasmic filaments known as **tonofibrils**, which are usually not visible in ordinary preparations, sweep toward and converge at the beginning of the desmosomes. Recent electron microscopic findings indicate that tonofibrils do not cross the desmosomes. If one of the polygonal cells of this zone could be microdissected out with its desmosomes still attached, the cell would look like a thistle. This appearance gives the stratum spinosum its name.

3. *Stratum granulosum.* As the cells of the stratum spinosum move into this zone, they are too distant to receive adequate nourishment from feeding capillaries in the connective tissue underlying the epidermis. Degenerative changes of the nuclei begin to occur, the cells assume a rhomboidal or squamous shape, and the cytoplasm becomes filled with coarse, refractile keratohyalin granules that take a dense basophilic stain. **Keratohyalin** is one of the protein molecules formed in the process of keratinization. This process simply means the creation of keratin, a protein material that covers practically all stratified squamous epithelial surfaces that are exposed to air. Some investigators feel that keratohyalin may be a transformation product related to the tonofibrils that exist in the cytoplasm of cells in the deeper parts of the epidermis.

4. *Stratum lucidum.* This layer in ordinary preparations appears to be a thin homogenous shiny band which has only slight acidophilic staining properties. The outlines of squamous cells can be seen in favorable sections, but nuclei generally are not found. The cells of this layer can be considered nonviable. The cytoplasmic area of these dead cells contains **eleidin**, a compound that represents a semiliquid transformation product of the keratohyalin granules of the stratum granulosum.

5. *Stratum corneum* (stratum disjunc-

PLATE 130—Hair

FIG. 16-10. Origin of the hair from the bulb and papilla (p). H & E stain. Intermediate power. (hc, hair cortex; c, cuticle; ie, inner epithelial root sheath; oe, outer epithelial root sheath; cts, connective tissue sheath of hair follicle)

FIG. 16-11. Section showing the walls of two hair follicles. H & E stain. Intermediate power.

FIG. 16-12. Longitudinal section of hair and follicle immediately above the papilla region. H & E stain. Intermediate power. (hs, hair shaft; ch, cuticle of hair; ci, cuticle of inner root sheath; Hu, Huxley's layer; He, Henle's layer; oe, outer epithelial root sheath)

FIG. 16-13. Part of wall of a hair follicle cut obliquely, deep to the sebaceous glandular portion. H & E stain. High power. (hs, degenerating nuclei of cells of hair shaft; er, epithelial root sheath; gm, glassy membrane; ct, connective tissue)

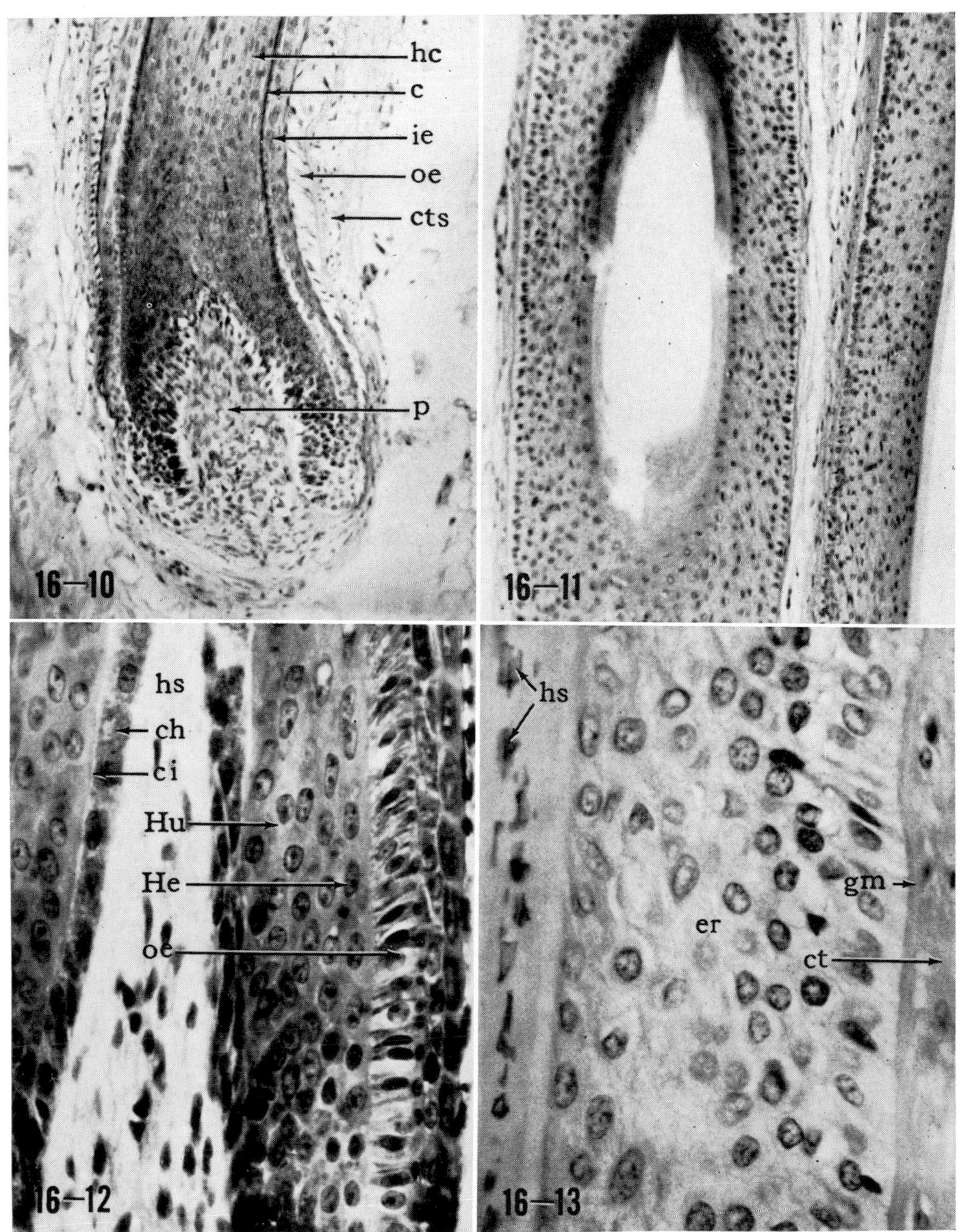
hc
c
ie
oe
cts
p
16—10
16—11
hs
ch
ci
Hu
He
oe
16—12
hs
gm
er
ct
16—13

tum). This is the most superficial layer of the epidermis in thick skin. Frequently the cells of this stratum are reduced to squamous, fused and scalelike elements. Less frequently, although the elements are closely packed, the outlines of dead squamous cells can be seen. The stratum corneum contains **keratin** in and around the cellular remains. Keratin results from the chemical transformation of eleidin and is a form of protein with a long molecular chain. The keratin molecule has important side linkages involving sulfhydryl and disulfide radicals, both of which contain sulfur atoms. A lesser amount of sulfur in keratin is associated with the soft keratin of skin, whereas a greater amount of sulfur is associated with the hard keratin of nails and hair. Keratin is the chemical basis of the dry, dead surface topping on the epidermis. The surface is constantly flaking off, a process known as desquamation. The process of keratinization is a cyclic activity and is counterbalanced by desquamation.

At this time the student is cautioned against using the above description of epithelial strata to categorize all types of skin. The above holds only for the epidermis of thick skin. It is customary to include under thick skin only those integumentary areas that are covered by all of the above 5 epithelial strata. In actuality, the volar surface of the palm and the plantar surface of the foot are perhaps the only sites of thick skin. Elsewhere on the body's surface there are 4, 3 or 2 epithelial layers; such regions are classified as thin skin. If 1 layer is absent, it is generally the stratum lucidum. When 2 epithelial strata are missing, they are the strata granulosum and lucidum; and when 3 layers are missing, the stratum spinosum is also not present. All skin surfaces, no matter how thin, contain a stratum basalis and usually a stratum corneum.

C. DERMIS

(Figs. 16-1 to 16-6)

The dermis is a layer of connective tissue that contains many of the accessory integumentary structures. It exhibits great variations in thickness, yet this feature is not considered in classifying a skin as thick or thin. The dermis serves as an attachment for the epidermis and also as the means for conveying blood vessels, lymphatics and nerves to areas adjacent to the epidermis and to the accessory structures of the dermis. The organization of vascularity in the dermis is a regular one. Blood vessels of different sizes are arranged in parallel networks at various depths and, by means of intercommunicating channels, effectively supply and drain integumentary epithelial structures, including epidermis, hair follicles, sweat glands and sebaceous glands. The dermis consists of 2 layers of connective tissue which tend to blend into each other. These are the papillary and the reticular layers.

PLATE 131—Accessory Integumentary Structures

FIG. 16-14. Accessory integumentary structures embedded in the dermal connective tissue (dct). Shown is a hair follicle (hf), a sebaceous gland (sg) and sweat glands (g). H & E stain. Low power.

FIG. 16-15. Intermediate-power view of sebaceous glands shown in Figure 16-14. Note that the duct of the gland (d) is sectioned through its wall so that its lumen is not seen. The size of the cells increases as they approach the middle portion. The duct communicates with the lumen (l) of the hair follicle (hf).

FIG. 16-16. Sweat glands. H & E stain. High power. (d, ducts; st, secretory tubules; b, basement membrane; ct, connective tissue)

FIG. 16-17. Thick section of fetal nail. H & E stain. Low power. (d, dermis of nail bed; np, nail plate; M, malpighian layer of nail bed; nr, nail root; nf, nail fold)

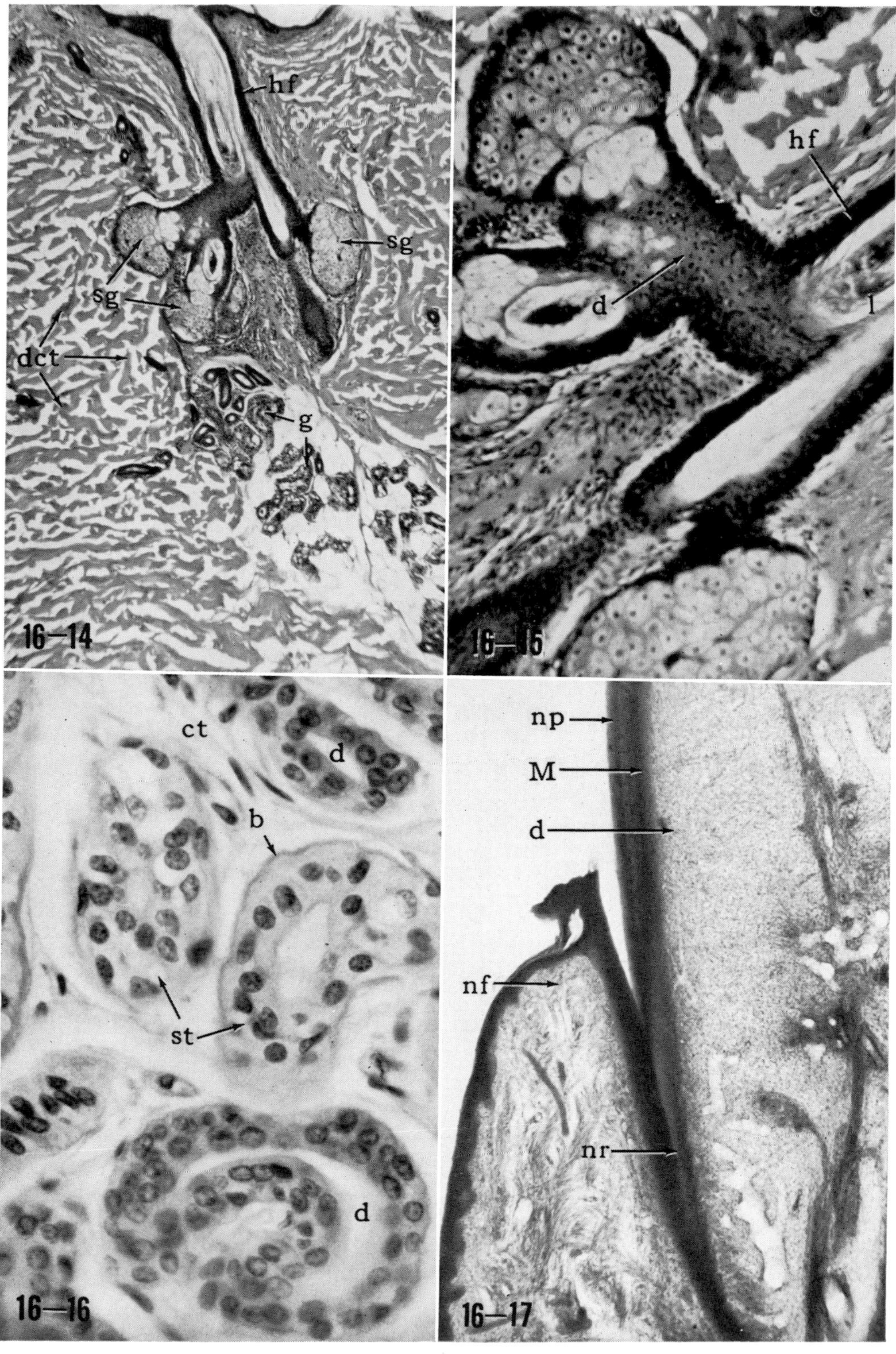
hf
sg
sg
dct
g
16—14
hf
d
l
16—15
ct
d
b
st
d
16—16
np
M
d
nf
nr
16—17

1. Papillary Layer

The connective tissue of this zone lies immediately beneath the epidermis. It consists of an areolar type of connective tissue in which cells are relatively abundant. The fibers present are almost entirely thin collagen and elastic elements. This connective tissue seems to push itself upward into the undersurface of the epidermis, creating projections of the dermis, called **papillae**, into the epithelium. As mentioned earlier, the dermal papillae interdigitate with downward projections of epithelial cells known as rete pegs, and this total configuration more firmly attaches the epidermis to the dermis. The height and the width of dermal papillae are quite variable. The tips of the papillary projections of connective tissue extend closer to the free skin surface than any other of the dermal elements, and capillaries and nervous elements utilize the papillae to bring nourishment and sensory innervation closer to the epidermis. Such papillae are referred to as **vascular** and **tactile papillae**, respectively.

2. Reticular Layer

This constitutes the deeper and thicker remaining portion of the dermis. It consists of a connective tissue made up of dense, irregularly arranged coarse fibers that are mainly collagenous in nature. Elastic fibers are also present, mixed with the collagen bundles. Connective tissue cells are present in small numbers. The reticular layer contains a majority of the hair follicles, sebaceous and sweat glands, and also certain of the deeper cutaneous sensory nerve endings (e.g., **pacinian corpuscles**) that respond to stimuli of high levels of intensity.

The dermis as a layer gradually blends into the nondermal subcutaneous connective tissue layer (superficial fascia, hypodermis). This is usually an areolar type of connective tissue, rich in fat, that binds the skin to deeper structures. In regions where this layer is overly laden with fat, it is called a panniculus adiposus. Some of the accessory skin structures may also be found extending through the dermis into this layer.

D. ACCESSORY STRUCTURES OF THE INTEGUMENT

These include all of the structures which are embryologically derived solely from the integument. In this category one would place the nails and the pilosebaceous apparatus (hairs, hair follicles and sebaceous glands) as well as the sweat glands. The other (vascular and nervous) structures found in the integument are not strictly skin derivatives.

1. Hairs and Hair Follicles (Piliary System) (Figs. 16-7 to 16-13)

Early in the development of the epidermis the hair primordia can be recognized as local downgrowths from the germinative portions of the surface epithelium. These push into the dermis and undergo differentiation into tubelike structures, the **hair follicles**. At the bottom of each follicle a thickened or swollen portion, the **hair bulb**, develops, and the cells of this mass, known as the **hair matrix**, become mostly responsible for hair production. A **hair** is produced from the cells of the hair bulb and the surrounding portion of the hair follicle and grows up through the lumen of the follicle until it projects above the surface of the skin. That part of the hair projecting above the skin and also the deeper part that is easily moved in the follicle constitute the **hair shaft**. The deepest part of the hair is continuous with the hair bulb and the base of the follicle and is known as the **hair root**.

Histologically, much of each hair shaft is composed of a thick cortical portion made up of stratified epithelium in which the cells are squamous and are converted into hard keratin. The hair may also contain a narrower medullary portion which runs up the central core; the medulla is composed of irregularly arranged cuboidal cells that contain soft keratin in their cytoplasm. Outside the hair shaft is a cellular **hair cuticle** which, for part of its length along the hair, is in contact with a similar cuticle that lines the inner surface of the hair follicle (**cuticle of the follicle**). Where the two cuticles approximate each other, scalelike squamous cells from each overlap one another and produce the same effect as shingles on a roof. Although the hair fits loosely in the hair follicle, the cells of the cuticles are overlapped so as to prevent the hair from being pulled from its follicle.

The hair follicle itself consists of two major sheaths, an inner epidermal portion composed of a stratified squamous epithelium that extends the full length of the hair, and a more limited, outer dermal portion that is analogous to a modified connective tissue capsule.

Many further histologic subdivisions of the hair and the hair follicle exist, but they are of limited value to the medical student unless he is especially interested in this subject. Additional ramifications include changes in hair coloration, alopecia, hair typing and other areas which extend into the commercial realm.

2. Sebaceous Glands (Figs. 16-7, 16-8, 16-14 and 16-15)

These are simple or compound alveolar glands that have a wide distribution and secrete an oily substance, **sebum**. Sebaceous glands usually, but not always, occur in association with hair follicles; in such a location, ducts and secretory end-pieces are both derived from the hair follicle wall. In this situation, single or multiple glands almost completely surround the circumference of the hair follicle at a level of the follicle that is about one third of the distance down from the free surface. The glands usually fit into an acute angle created at this depth by the inserting smooth muscle fibers of the arrectores pilorum muscle of the hair and the hair follicle itself. In an alveolus of a gland, the polyhedral cells are smaller toward the periphery and larger toward the center. The mode of secretion is holocrine, and entire cells and their contents are discharged through the stratified squamous epithelium-lined duct into the space present between the hair shaft and the follicle wall. Free sebaceous glands, that is, glands not found in connection with hair, communicate directly with the free skin surface and are found in the axilla, the nipple, the lips, the glans penis and the labia minora.

3. Sweat Glands (Sudoriporous Glands) (Figs. 16-9, 16-14 and 16-16)

These are simple coiled tubular glands that have a wide distribution, usually independent of hair follicles. They arise as solid downgrowths from the epidermis of skin and secondarily become a hollow tubular system. Each gland begins as a long excretory duct that passes through the epidermis and the papillary layer of the dermis into the deepest part of the reticular layer of the dermis. In the latter location the duct begins to coil and twist up into a ball, and soon the excretory portion widens into the secretory part of the gland.

Histologic examination of a section through the coiled portion discloses that the secretory elements generally have a larger diameter and stain less intensely than the conducting elements. The secretory portion of the tubule is lined by two types of cells. The first is the **myoepithelial cell** which rests against the basement membrane and can be recognized by its long spindle shape and the dense stain taken by its nucleus. This is a nonsecretory cell which is assumed to be a special type of muscle cell that aids in expressing the sweat from these glands. The second cell type is a **secretory cell** which faces the lumen and has a cuboidal or pyramidal shape and a centrally placed round nucleus. The excretory duct is lined by a double-layered cuboidal (stratified cuboidal) epithelium that contains prominent oval nuclei. The free surface of the inner layer of cells is provided with a cuticular border. In passing through the epidermis, the cells of the excretory duct wall become indistinguishable from those of the epidermis. In this location the excretory lumen or sweat duct becomes a sharply spiraled channel which opens onto the free surface via the **sweat pore.**

In the dermis and subcutaneous areas of certain locations such as the axilla and the circumanal region, sweat glands with extremely large lumina are present. These unusually large secretory end-pieces differ in that they secrete by the apocrine rather than the merocrine method utilized by most of the smaller sweat glands.

4. Nails (Fig. 16-17)

Many features about the nail complex can be realized from visual observation. (1) The flat, squarish **nail plate** is composed of nonflaking (nondesquamating) hard keratin (stratum corneum) and is subdivided into a **free edge**, an attached **body** and a hidden **root**. (2) The nail plate is inserted via a **nail groove** into a **nail wall** which is molded around the attached edge of the plate. (3) Soft keratin (stratum corneum) extends forward from the upper surface of the embedded root of the nail and covers the exposed surface of the nail plate for a varying distance. This material is the **eponychium** or **cuticle**. (4) Under the eponychium, where the body and the root of the nail plate are contiguous, is an arc-shaped whitish area, the **lunule.** (5) Soft keratin accumulates under the free edge of the nail and represents the stratum corneum of the epidermis of the finger tip. This material is known as the **hyponychium** and, in association with trapped dirt and skin secretions, is the material removed under the free nail edge with a nail file.

The nail plate is firmly attached on its undersurface to the nail bed, which consists of the stratum spinosum and the stratum basalis layers of the skin epidermis. Growth of the nail does not take place at this interface but in the region of the nail root. As a result, the nail plate appears to be forced slowly along the surface of the nail bed.

E. SOME SPECIAL ASPECTS OF INTEGUMENT

1. Langer's Lines

These are lines of tension of the skin, a knowledge of which is essential for the surgeon.

2. Regeneration and Transplantation of Skin

Both the epidermis and the dermis have a high regenerative capacity in small wounds. In large wounds most repair is by white fiber (scar) formation, producing a less aesthetic result. Transplantation of skin from an intact part of the body to the area at fault can greatly improve the cosmetic results.

3. Dactylography

The study of fingerprints depends on the unique patterns assumed by surface epidermal ridges and furrows on the hands and the feet. This is explained by the fact that the skin surface tends to parallel the deeper pattern taken by the dermal papillae.

17 · Mammary Gland

A. Introduction *B. Histology of Mammary Gland*

A. INTRODUCTION

Most considerations of the mammary gland in medicine are oriented toward the female structure. The male structure offers few complexities and, in adults, normally undergoes little development and is very seldom the site of pathology. The female gland, on the other hand, is of great importance medically because:

1. Its structure is constantly influenced by circulating hormones.
2. Maintenance of a normal histology is essential for performing its primary function of lactation.
3. It is not uncommonly a site of far-reaching pathologic changes.

This consideration, therefore, is based on the female gland only.

PLATE 132—Mammary Gland

FIG. 17-1. Oblique section through the edge of the nipple region of the mammary gland. The predominant elements are coarse fibers and bundles of smooth muscle cells cut mainly in cross section. Stratified squamous epithelium (e) of the free surface and a lactiferous (mammary) duct (ld) can be seen. H & E stain. Low power.

FIG. 17-2. Mammary gland in the region of the nipple, showing the tissue just subjacent to that depicted in Figure 17-1. Note that two of the lactiferous ducts (ld), sectioned obliquely, pass toward the nipple surfacc. Smooth muscle bundles and dense connective tissue preponderate. H & E stain. Low power.

FIG. 17-3. Mammary areola showing free sebaceous glands (sg), tall connective tissue papillae (p) and stratified squamous epithelium (e). Note the predominance of dense irregular connective tissue deep to the epithelium. H & E stain. Low power.

FIG. 17-4. Deeper section through the mammary gland to show the contrast between parenchymal and stromal tissue. Several lobules (l), separated by dense interlobular connective tissue (bct), are shown. Intralobular connective tissue (wct) can be seen to be cellular even at this low magnification. The large duct (d) at the bottom center is referred to as an intralobular duct while within the lobule and as an interlobular duct after having emerged. A lactiferous duct (ld) appears at the top left. H & E stain. Low power.

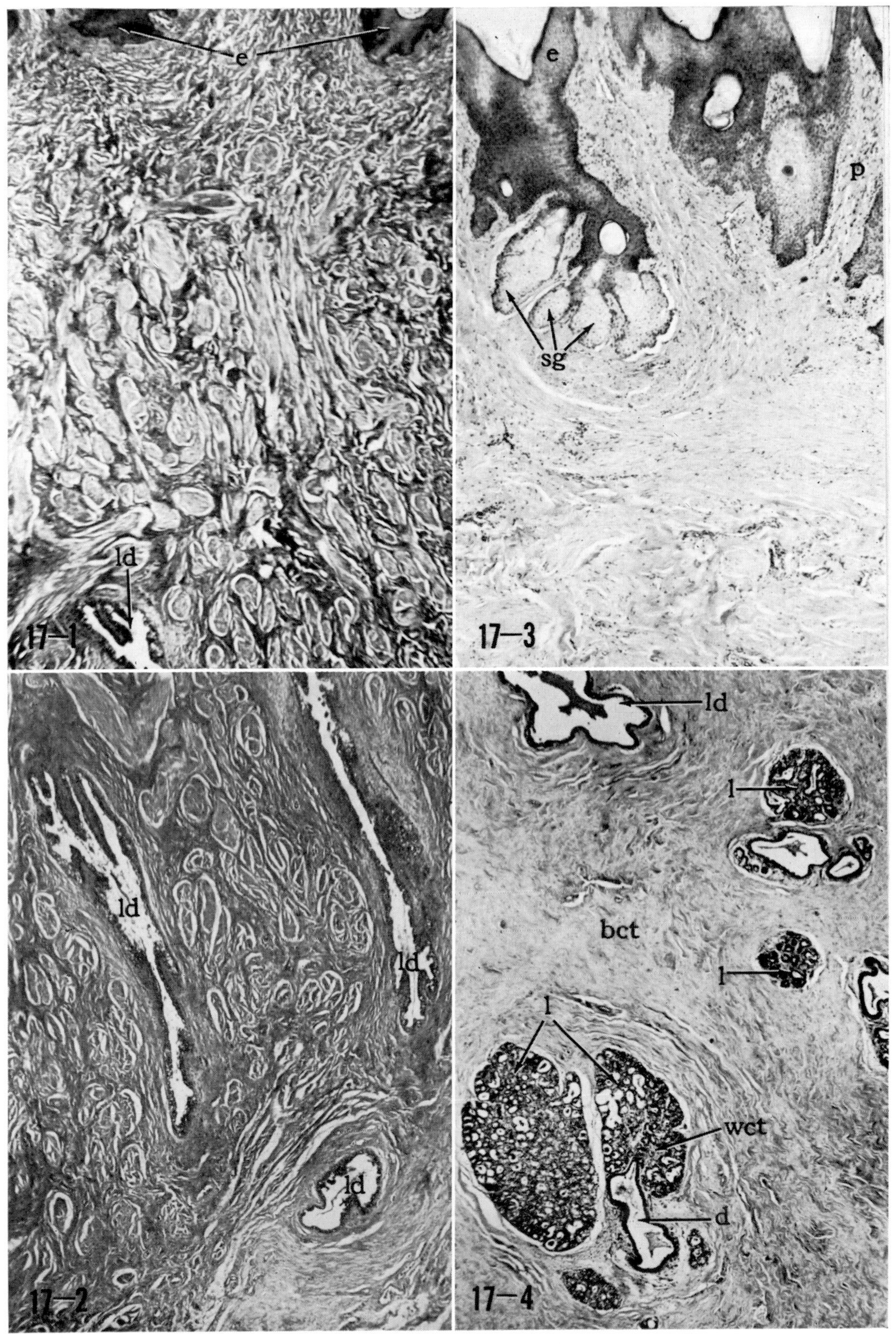
e
ld
17–1
e
p
sg
17–3
ld
ld
ld
17–2
ld
l
bct
l
l
wct
d
17–4

Because of the cyclic alterations that take place in its histology, it is difficult to classify the mammary gland into any single category of gland type. Nevertheless, most authors consider the female mammary gland to be a compound alveolar gland, without giving a satisfactory explanation for such a classification. There are two reasons for classifying the gland in this way. In the first place, when secretory end-pieces are created during the development of the mammary gland, they bud off as alveolar structures from terminal elements. The second reason, which is related solely to the secretory end-pieces, is based on the overwhelmingly alveolar appearance of the end-pieces of the gland at the height of lactation.

In fact, at maturity each mammary gland consists of 15 to 25 compound alveolar glands, and each of these, in turn, contains its own branching duct system. These 15 to 25 individual glands or lobes are separated from each other by connective tissue, and each lobe opens onto the surface of the nipple or mammary papilla by its own major excretory channel, the lactiferous duct.

The medical student may find himself somewhat confused when studying the stages of activity of this gland and may wonder why more satisfactory slide preparations are not available. In this connection, the student is asked to consider seriously 3 inherent problems that are associated with obtaining normal mammary gland slides for the medical histology collection. First, biopsy material of this particular gland obtained from the operating room is usually either frank of borderline pathologic. Second, relatively few female cadavers are available for dissection in the gross anatomy laboratory, and these are almost invariably too old to supply material related to the developing or the functionally active stages of the gland. Third, so much variability in the amount of adipose tissue exists in individual mammary glands of the same age and stage of activity that the commonly used method of classifying stage of mammary activity by the amount of fat present is rendered suspect.

A final problem that the student is warned about concerns the semantics employed. The terms used to classify certain of the stages of development of the mammary gland are frequently ambiguous and overlapping. The following listing will enlarge on this problem:

1. Terms applied to the appearance of the mammary gland before puberty: immature, prepuberal, young, early, resting, developing, inactive
2. Terms applied to the mammary gland from time of puberty up to onset of pregnancy: immature, puberal, developing, inactive, resting
3. Terms applied to mammary gland during pregnancy: gravid, active, developing, mammary gland of pregnancy
4. Terms applied to mammary gland during active secretion of milk: active, lactation, secretory phase

PLATE 133—Mammary Gland

FIG. 17-5. Young mammary gland showing the preponderance of dense irregular connective tissue (bct). Scattered in this connective tissue are a few primordia of future gland lobules (gl). H & E stain. Low power. (f, adipose tissue)

FIG. 17-6. Another region of young mammary gland to show primordia of lobules (gl) and duct (d) surrounded by dense connective tissue (bct). H & E stain. Intermediate power.

FIG. 17-7. Young mammary gland to show the irregular arrangement of dense connective tissue (bct) surrounding immature parenchymal elements (gl). H & E stain. Intermediate power.

FIG. 17-8. Parenchymal elements (gl) of young mammary gland. Intense staining reaction of cells in these primordia is indicative of great activity. H & E stain. High power. (bct, dense connective tissue)

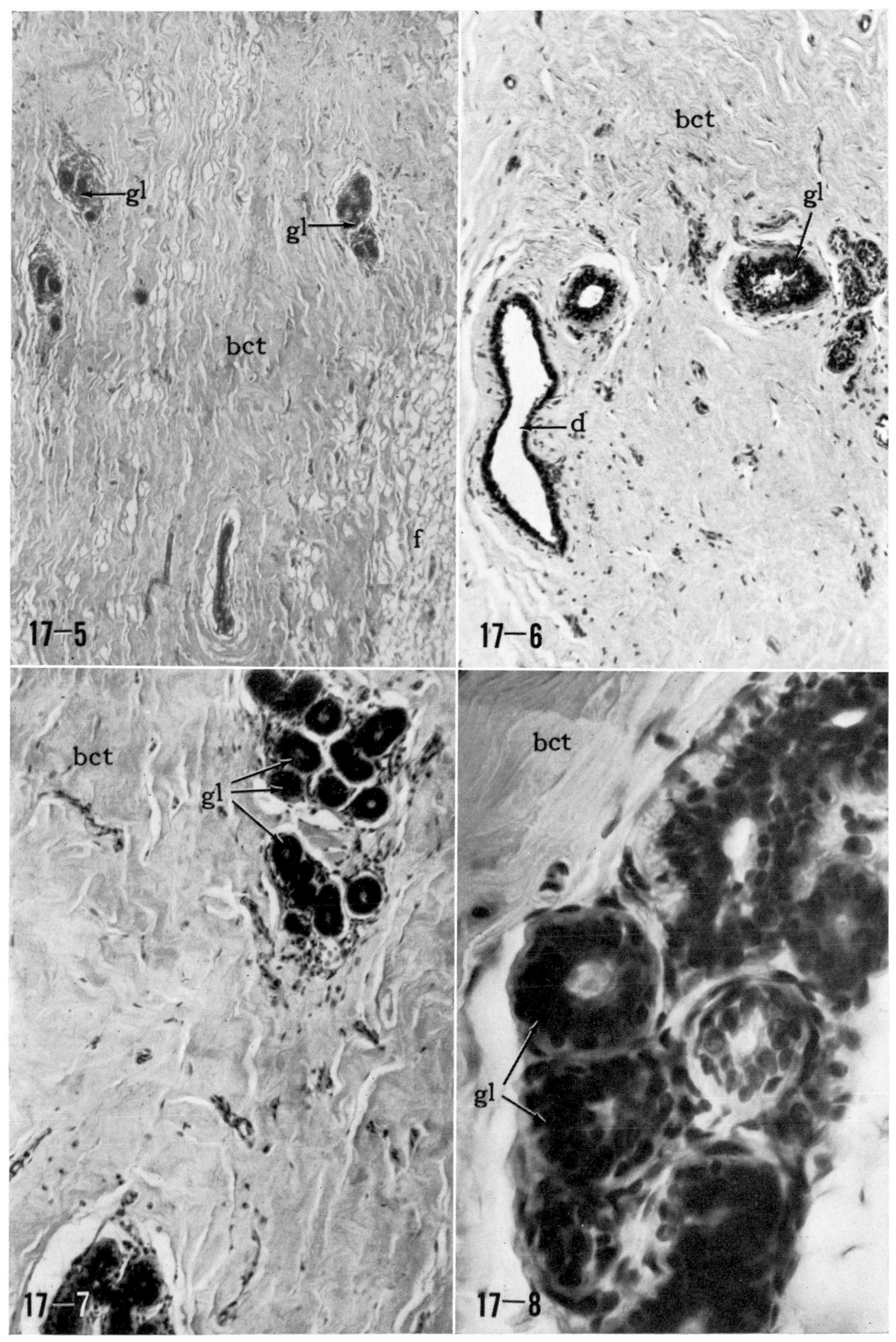
gl
gl
bct
f
17–5
bct
gl
d
17–6
bct
gl
17–7
bct
gl
17–8

5. Terms applied to mammary gland between pregnancies: resting, interphase, regression, regression after lactation.

6. Terms applied to mammary gland following menopause: involution, postmenopause, regression

Until such time that the overlapping terms are eliminated in the literature or spelled out (e.g., resting condition—appearance of the sexually mature, nonpregnant female breast), the student is cautioned not to use them without proper qualification.

B. HISTOLOGY OF MAMMARY GLAND

Before considering each of the stages of development of the breast, it is important to emphasize certain basic features of this gland. As with all exocrine glands, the mammary gland consists of an epithelial portion (the parenchyma) supported in a connective tissue portion (the stroma). The epithelial portion develops from the germinative layer of epidermis covering the pectoral region and invaginates into the subcutaneous region, which here becomes unusually thick and rich in fat and dense connective tissue. As the epithelial elements push their way into the underlying subcutaneous tissue, they push or carry along with them areolar elements of the papillary layer of the dermis. Because of this, the parenchymal elements within the lobular units of the mammary gland are surrounded by loose rather than dense connective tissue. This loose, cellular stroma within the lobular units is termed the intralobular connective tissue.

1. Histology Up To the Time of Puberty (Plates 132 and 133)

During childhood, each of the 15 to 25 epithelial downgrowths from the two embryonic milk lines develops a modest system of ducts. Except for portions of the duct system close to the nipple, these are closed cordlike structures. The over-all histologic impression during this stage is one of an overwhelming abundance of dense irregularly arranged connective tissue. Small knots of heavily basophilic epithelial cords are present in such small numbers that they may not be seen in any one section of the gland at this time.

2. Changes During Puberty

Under the influence of estrogen, the number of branches in each duct system increases. Each small group of ducts grows deeper into the underlying dense subcutaneous tissue of the pectoral region. Now these parenchymal elements and their enshrouding loose, cellular connective tissue

PLATE 134—Mammary Gland

FIG. 17-9. Appearance of the mammary gland during the first half of pregnancy. An increase in the parenchymal elements and a decrease in the stromal tissue is apparent. H & E stain. Low power. (l, lobules; bd, interlobular duct; bct, interlobular connective tissue)

FIG. 17-10. Two neighboring lobules of the mammary gland in the first half of pregnancy, separated by interlobular connective tissue (bct). Note that many new alveoli (na) appear to be budding off at this time. H & E stain. Intermediate power. (a, alveoli; wct, cellular intralobular connective tissue)

FIG. 17-11. Two adjacent lobules of the mammary gland in the first half of pregnancy, showing the marked difference in the nature of the interlobular connective tissue (bct) and the intralobular connective tissue (wct). Note that the lower lobule contains fewer alveoli (a) and larger numbers of dense-staining ducts or cords of cells (cc) that will give rise to additional alveoli and ducts. H & E stain. Intermediate power.

FIG. 17-12. Developing lobules (l) and a large interlobular duct (bd) in the mammary gland during the first half of pregnancy. H & E stain. Intermediate power.

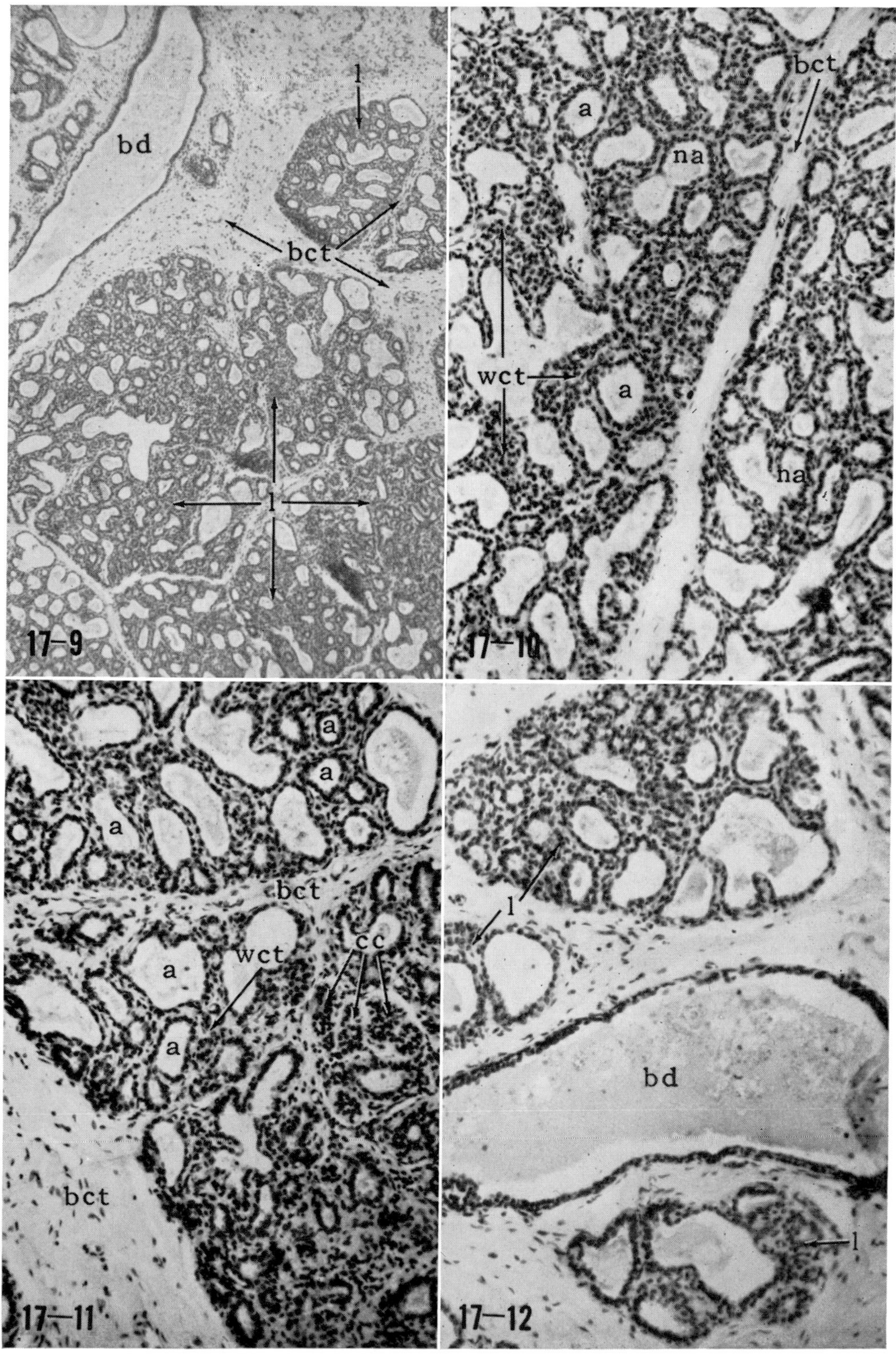
l
bd
bct
l
17-9
bct
a
na
wct
a
na
17-10
a
a
a
bct
a
wct
cc
a
bct
17-11
l
bd
l
17-12

may be termed lobules. With the beginning of puberty, large quantities of adipose tissue are deposited in the dense tissue of the pectoral region at sites between the 15 to 25 developing duct systems (interlobar connective tissue) and also between the lobules within any individual duct system (interlobular connective tissue). The over-all impression that one obtains from a section through the mammary gland during this stage is still overwhelmingly in favor of dense connective tissue, now infiltrated with fat. This is the appearance of the breast during puberty, and it is retained in the female for a varying number of years or until such time that pregnancy occurs. If pregnancy does not occur, the breast maintains this histology and undergoes involution at the female climacteric.

3. Mammary Gland During Pregnancy (Plates 134 and 135)

With the beginning of pregnancy, an alteration of hormonal titers occurs, and the mammary gland undergoes rapid growth. During the first half of pregnancy a dramatic increase in the number of glandular conducting elements and secretory end-pieces takes place. As repeated side branches come off the few ducts that existed before pregnancy, each branch appears to carry along with it a surrounding cover of loose connective tissue. As a result, great numbers of new lobules are created. The newly created parenchymal elements everywhere expand into regions that earlier were occupied predominantly by a fat-infiltrated dense connective tissue. In connection with this highly accelerated growth of glandular elements, the interlobar and the interlobular connective tissue is now altered. Adipose tissue seems to melt away, and the dense irregularly arranged connective tissue is reduced to rather narrow partitions that separate individual lobules. By the end of the 5th month of pregnancy, each lobule contains most of the secretory end-pieces that will show signs of secretory activity in the second half of gestation. Each lobule contains a mixture of alveolar and tubular end-pieces which have budded off the terminal portion of the duct system. Such a terminal conducting element is present within each of the lobules and is known as an alveolar duct. In many cases the secretory end-pieces are still solid knots of cells which as yet have not become hollowed out. When finally mature, each end-piece is lined by a simple epithelium, usually cuboidal or low columnar in nature, and has a large central space or lumen. The end-pieces rest on basement membranes, and peculiar myoepithelial elements gradually develop and wrap themselves around the secretory units. It is the presence of myoepithelial cells, also present about sweat glands, which gives rise to the belief in certain quar-

PLATE 135—Mammary Gland

FIG. 17-13. Formation of new alveoli (a) within a lobule of the mammary gland during the first half of pregnancy. H & E stain. High power. (wct, intralobular connective tissue)

FIG. 17-14. Alveoli (a) within a lobule of the mammary gland during the first half of pregnancy. Note that the cells lining the walls of the alveoli are simple cuboidal and possess large round nuclei which contrast with the nuclei of stromal cells within the intralobular connective tissue (wct). H & E stain. High power.

FIG. 17-15. Appearance of a group of lobules (l) of the mammary gland in late gestation. Compare with Figure 17-9 and note that the formation of alveoli has been almost completed. Mallory stain. Low power.

FIG. 17-16. A region of the mammary gland of late gestation just adjacent to that shown in Figure 17-15 and very slightly magnified. Note the contrast between the interlobular (bct) and the intralobular (wct) connective tissue and that alveoli (a) are very numerous. A large interlobular duct (bd) is also present.

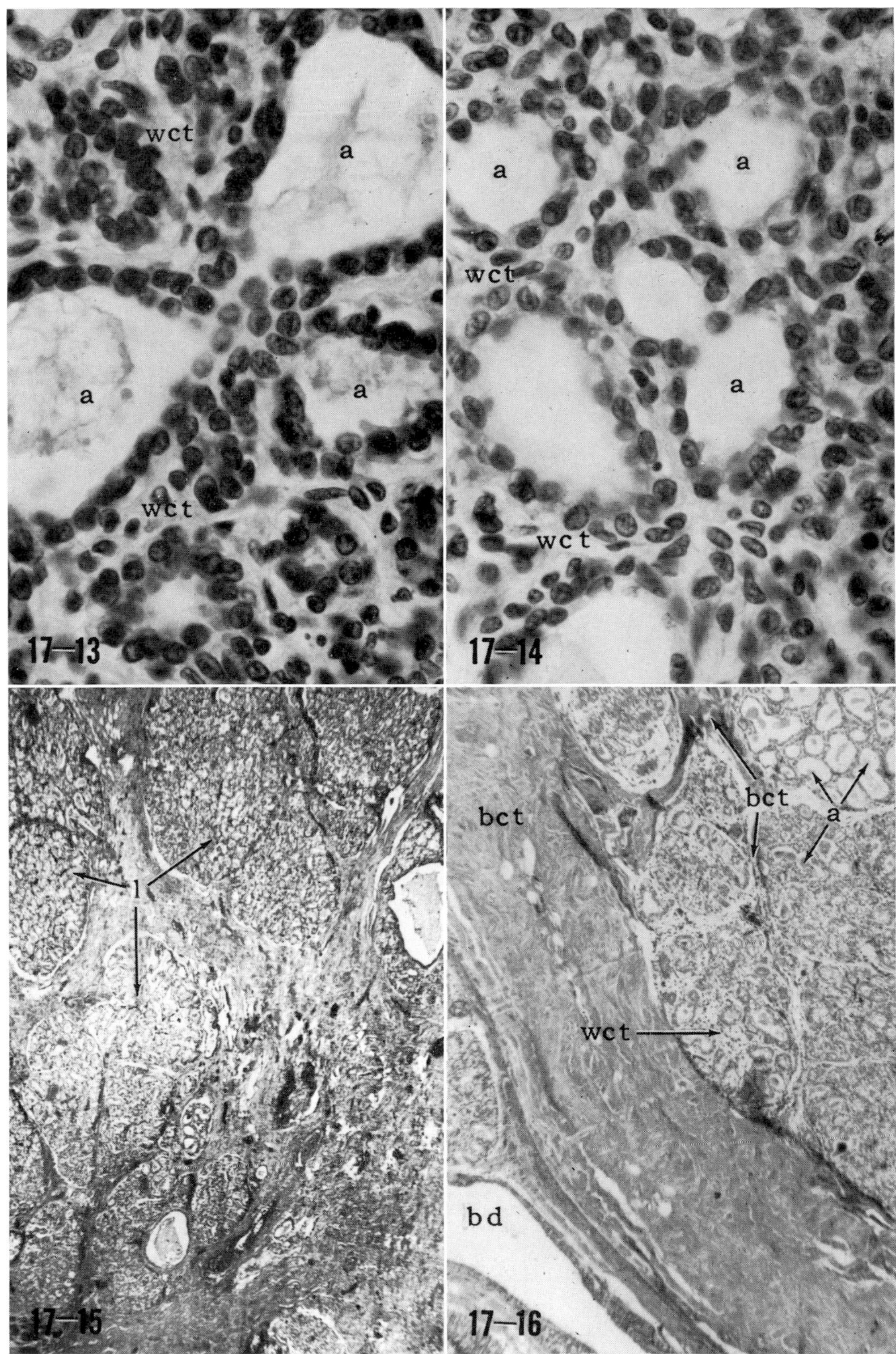
wct
a
a
a
wct
17–13
a
a
wct
a
wct
17–14
l
17–15
bct
bct
a
wct
bd
17–16

ters that the mammary gland is a highly modified sweat gland. With the increase in number of glandular end-pieces, each lobule increases in size. Such expansion of parenchymal elements can occur within lobules because of the presence of loose connective tissue around each of the glandular structures. With this expansion, the loose connective tissue seems to become reduced in amount.

During the second half of pregnancy, there is only a slight increase in the number of terminal end-pieces that bud off the alveolar ducts. The lobules become hypertrophied and compress the adjacent interlobular connective tissue into still thinner septa. This enlargement of the lobules is brought about primarily by the maturation of glandular cells and is associated with the appearance of secretory activity. Cells that are preparing to secrete are taller than they were earlier in pregnancy. Droplets of fat soon become formed and accumulate in greatly increasing numbers in the cytoplasm of cells, and a fluid is finally secreted into the duct system in the later stages of gestation. Heightened secretory activity and filling of the duct system are the underlying causes for further gross enlargement of the mammary gland during the final weeks. The material secreted at this time is not milk but a more watery fluid, colostrum, that is much richer in proteins than is milk and also lower in fat. In addition, whole cells and parts of cells may be found in colostrum. These include debris from depleted secretory cells of the alveolar walls and also blood and connective tissue. Certain of the latter, known as colostrum cells, apparently have macrophagic properties and become greatly distended with phagocytosed material.

4. Lactating Phase of Mammary Gland (Plate 136)

Colostrum is secreted by the mammary gland for the first few days following parturition. It is both more nutritive and more easily digested than milk and therefore is of greater value to the newborn infant during the first critical days of life. Although the structure of the parenchymal elements in the lactating gland does not actually undergo much change, the histologic picture appears to differ markedly from that of the gland during gestation. This marked difference resides in the fact that the secretory cells and the ducts are so distended with fatty material that cell and even alveolar outlines are difficult to make out. The internal pressure created by milk stored in the duct system appears to swell the alveoli to such an extent that intralobular connective tissue seems

PLATE 136—Mammary Gland

FIG. 17-17. Lactating mammary gland showing a group of lobules (l) in various phases of secretion. Note the presence of adipose tissue (f) and an interlobular duct (bd). H & E stain. Low power.

FIG. 17-18. Active lobules of a lactating mammary gland. Alveolar ducts (ad) can be seen leaving the lobules (l) as well as numerous interlobular ducts (bd) filled with debris, present within the interlobular connective tissue (bct). H & E stain. Low power.

FIG. 17-19. A lobule from the mammary gland during lactation. Note that the numerous alveoli (a) are lined by simple cuboidal cells, many of which contain large droplets of fat (empty white spaces) in the cytoplasm of these cells. The presence of fat cells (f) in the rim of interlobular connective tissue (bct) is an inconstant feature. H & E stain. Intermediate power.

FIG. 17-20. Mammary gland during lactation, showing fat droplets (fd) in the alveoli. Note the reduced intralobular connective tissue (wct). H & E stain. High power. (lu, lumen of alveolus)

FIG. 17-21. Mammary gland during lactation, showing interlobular ducts (bd) in the interlobular connective tissue (bct). H & E stain. High power.

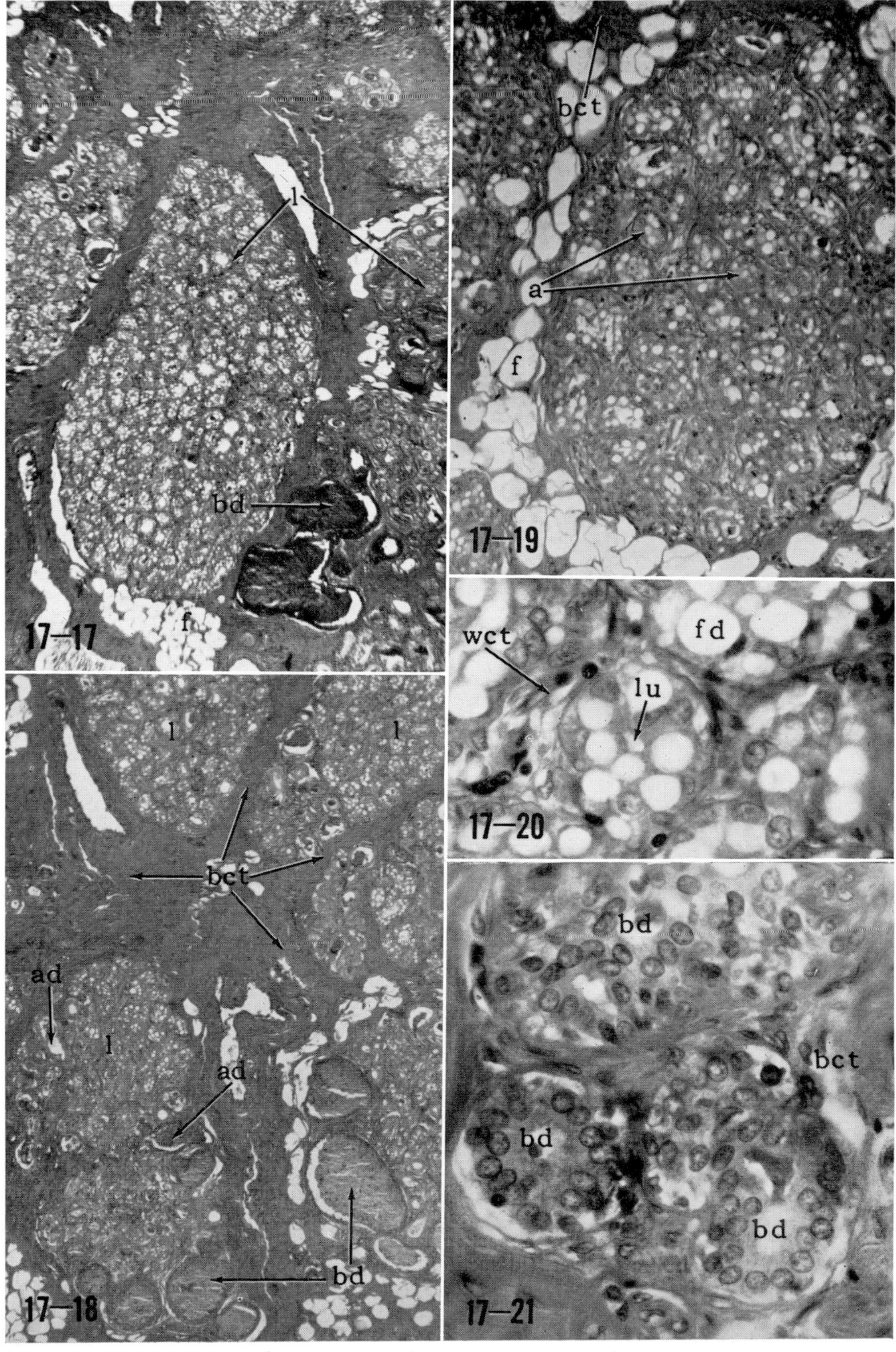
l
bd
f
17—17
bct
a
f
17—19
wct
fd
lu
17—20
l
l
bct
ad
l
ad
bd
17—18
bd
bct
bd
bd
17—21

to be absent and interlobular connective tissue appears further thinned. Routine histologic methods utilize fat solvents so that the regions occupied by fat droplets both within cell cytoplasm and in the milk appear as clear spaces. Normally, milk secretion does not occur in all of the lobules of the mammary gland at the same time and, therefore, alveoli can be found in all states of secretory activity. The alveolar cells are considered to secrete by the apocrine method, and frequently it is possible to see adjacent cells in an alveolus in which the apical surfaces appear broken and jagged.

5. Mammary Gland After Lactation (Plate 137)

As soon as suckling ceases, the breasts begin to undergo a form of regression. Secretory activity is gradually reduced, and the influence of lactogenic hormone no longer appears to affect the parenchymal elements of the gland. During this period, which may be very prolonged, milk remains trapped in the duct system and can be recognized histologically as a granular, vacuolated mass. Alveolar cells gradually return to the cuboidal appearance they had before pregnancy and in early pregnancy. Many of these cells actually undergo complete degradation and are cast off into the ducts. The loss of a considerable number of cells from the walls of many alveoli results in enlargement of lumina and the creation of distinctly tubular and irregularly shaped end-pieces. Not uncommonly, the walls between adjacent alveoli break down, resulting in the formation of a common lumen between them. As a result of this blending of adjacent end-pieces, the number of alveoli in the mammary gland appears to decrease. With this gradual reduction of parenchyma within each lobule, the loose intralobular connective tissue commences to be seen once again, and the dense interlobular connective tissue also appears more extensive. Finally, with the resorption of most of the alveoli, the histology of the mammary gland reverts to a condition essentially the same as before pregnancy. This appearance is maintained until another pregnancy ensues or until the menopause.

6. Menopausal Changes in the Mammary Gland

With the gradual lowering of blood estrogen titers that takes place toward the female climacteric, the mammary gland begins to undergo atrophy of both parenchymal and stromal elements. Few parenchymal structures remain other than parts of the duct system. A histologic preparation of the gland at this stage could easily be confused with one of the gland before puberty or even during early puberty. However, certain features

Plate 137—Mammary Gland

FIG. 17-22. Appearance of the mammary gland during regression. The absence of fat droplets in the alveoli of the lobules (l) is apparent. Alveoli seem fewer in number, and interlobular connective tissue is abundant. H & E stain. Low power. (f, adipose tissue)

FIG. 17-23. Superficial area near the nipple in a regressing mammary gland. Masson stain. Low power. (ld, lactiferous duct; sg, free sebaceous gland; ep, epidermis)

FIG. 17-24. Mammary gland during regression. A large interlobular duct (bd) filled with cellular debris is seen within the thickened interlobular connective tissue (bct). Adjacent lobules (l) contain degenerating alveoli. H & E stain. Intermediate power.

FIG. 17-25. Degenerating alveoli (a) within a lobule of a regressing mammary gland. The two alveoli in the center appear to have fused by the breakdown of adjacent walls. Note the increase in amount and cellularity of the intralobular connective tissue (wct) over the lactating condition. Compare with Figure 17-19. H & E stain. High power.

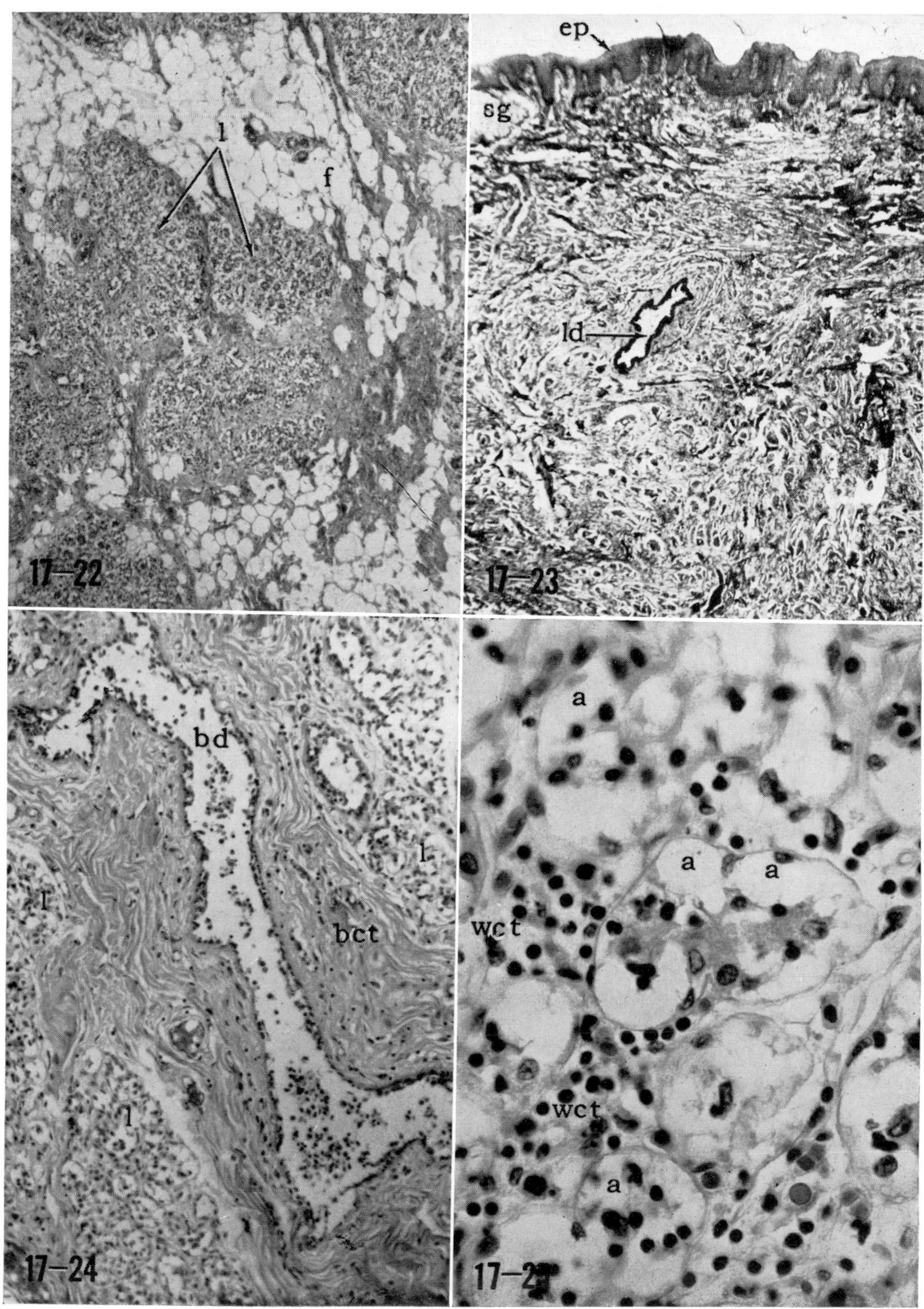
l
f
17–22
ep
sg
ld
17–23
bd
l
l
bct
l
17–24
a
a
a
wct
wct
a

may be found that make this similarity a little less apparent. First, with increasing age, the interlobular and the interlobar connective tissue matrix tends to undergo hyalinization and becomes a glassy amorphous mass that is usually more refractive to acid stains. Second, it is not unusual to find gland ducts that have become cystic and filled with a granular secretion. This feature is not present in all glands. Finally, there is a tendency for elastic fibers to be present in increasing amounts. The over-all appearance of the postmenopausal mammary gland again is one of dense connective tissue in which individual fibers are more difficult to make out than they were earlier in life.

18 · The Female Reproductive System

A. INTRODUCTION

The female reproductive system is situated within the pelvis and is composed of the ovaries, the fallopian tubes (oviducts), the uterus with its cervix and the vagina. In addition to its major function of reproduction, this system plays an important physiologic role in supporting the tangible and the intangible characteristics of the female sex. These functions are made possible by the following processes:

1. Production and maintenance of the female secondary sex characteristics
2. Production and development of ova by the ovaries
3. Provision of proper structural and physiologic conditions for both ovulation and the passage of ova into the fallopian tubes

PLATE 138—Ovary

FIG. 18-1. Section through the ovary (4-month-old infant) at the end opposite the mesovarium. Note that the follicles (pf) are of the primary type. Strands of smooth muscle fibers (m) extending from the mesovarium are present in the stromal connective tissue (ct). Masson stain. Low power. (v, blood vessels)

FIG. 18-2. Surface region of the ovary (cat) showing the primary follicles (pf), developing follicles (df) and part of a corpus luteum (cl). Mallory-Azan stain. Intermediate power. (ge, germinal epithelium)

FIG. 18-3. Young ovary, showing the cortex with its germinal epithelium (ge) and primary follicles (pf) in the stromal connective tissue (ct). H & E stain. Intermediate power. (ta, tunica albuginea)

FIG. 18-4. Young ovary, showing the presence of primary follicles (pf) and developing follicles (df). H & E stain. Intermediate power.

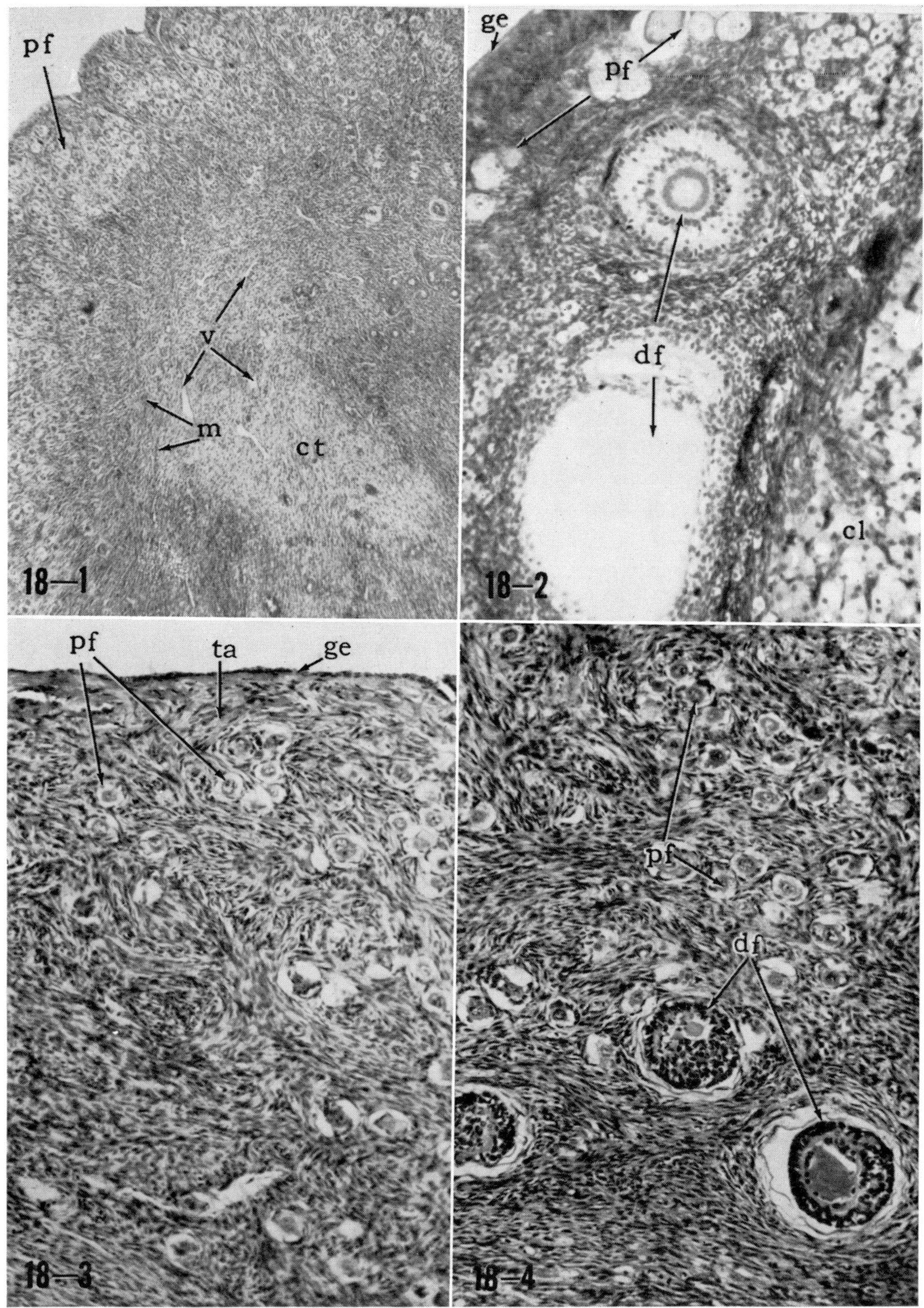
pf
v
m
ct
18—1
ge
pf
df
cl
18—2
pf
ta
ge
18—3
pf
df
18—4

4. Movement of the ovum, especially if fertilization has occurred, from the fallopian tube into the uterus

5. Preparation of the uterine wall for implantation of the developing fertilized egg

6. Creation of a favorable intra-uterine environment for the development and the maintenance of the fetus during pregnancy

7. Development of a mechanism for expelling the fetus and the placenta at the termination of pregnancy (parturition)

A knowledge of the structure and the functions of the female reproductive organs will reveal the system to be a remarkable example of a biologic clock that performs its normal tasks in a precise manner under the influence and the control of hormonal and nervous mechanisms.

B. OVARIES

(Plates 138 to 143)

The ovaries are two small, ovoid bodies that vary in size and weight according to their functional activity. Each ovary is attached at its hilus by the mesovarium to the back of the broad ligament. The suspensory ligament of the ovary attaches to the lateral wall of the lesser pelvis and further serves to hold this organ in place. Sections of the ovary reveal a thick outer layer, the **cortex**, which contains the functional elements (**follicles in various stages of development**) embedded in a connective tissue stroma, and a deeper, centrally located portion, the **medulla (zona vasculosa)**. The medulla is composed of loose connective tissue (reticular and fibroelastic fibers) rich in blood vessels, lymphatics and nerves. At the hilus, bundles of smooth muscle fibers are found. Covering the free surface of the ovary is the so-called **germinal epithelium**, a layer that formerly was believed to give rise to the ova during embryologic development. It is now thought that the primordial ova arise from coelomic epithelium of the hindgut and migrate into the developing ovary. Dense connective tissue, the **tunica albuginea**, forms a layer underneath the germinal epithelium. (See Figs. 18-1 to 18-7, 18-9 to 18-11, 18-17, 18-22.)

Studies have revealed that the total number of follicles found in the ovaries of newborn infants and young adults is approximately one half million. This number diminishes progressively with increasing age. The type of follicle that is most numerous in the infant, and also in the young adult, is the **primary follicle**. These are spheroid bodies that appear to be concentrated in the peripheral areas of the cortex. They measure about 30 to 50 μ in diameter, are lined by a layer of flattened follicular cells and contain a large, round, centrally placed ovum. The ovum has a large, eccentric nucleus with a dense nucleolus.

PLATE 139—Ovary

FIG. 18-5. Ovary (cat) showing a part of its surface epithelium (ge) and developing ova in the cortex. Numerous fibroblasts and smooth muscle cells can be seen in the stromal connective tissue. Mallory-Azan stain. High power. (nl, nucleolus; n, nucleus of ovum; fc, follicular cells)

FIG. 18-6. Survey of ovary (cat). Mallory-Azan stain. Low power. (G, graafian follicle; cl, corpus luteum; v, blood vessels)

FIG. 18-7. Ovary (cat), showing cells of the cumulus oöphorus with contained ovum (o) and zona pellucida (zp). Mallory-Azan stain. High power. (cr, cells of corona radiata)

FIG. 18-8. Portion of a degenerating corpus luteum from ovary (cat). Note the vacuolization (va). Mallory-Azan stain. Intermediate power. (gl, granulosa lutein cells)

FIG. 18-9. Ovary (cat), showing the granulosa cells of the developing follicle. Note that these follicular cells are polyhedral and arranged in several layers. Mallory-Azan stain. High power. (l, lumen of follicle; tc, theca cells)

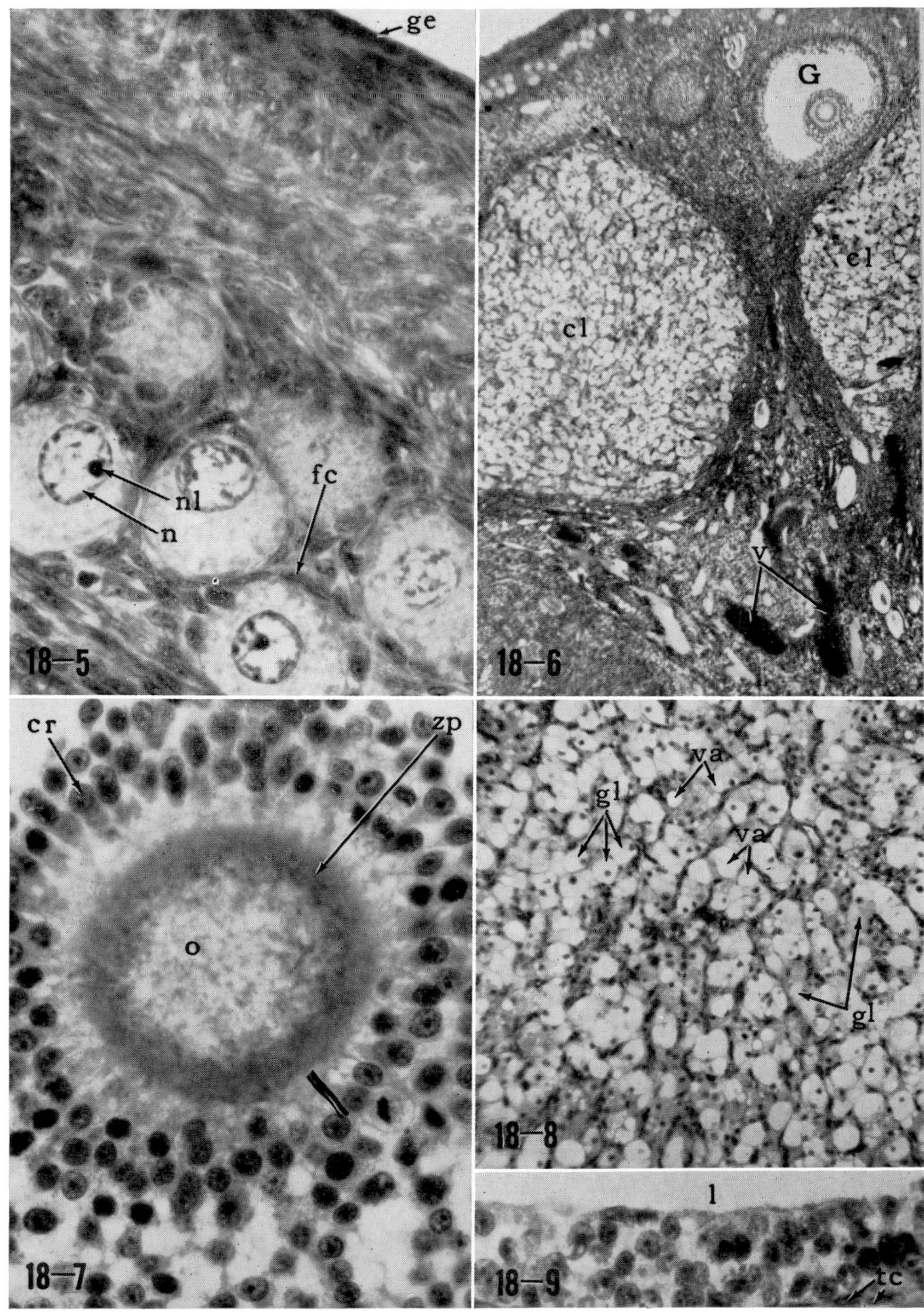
ge
nl
n
fc
18—5
G
cl
cl
v
18—6
cr
zp
o
18—7
va
gl
va
gl
18—8
l
tc
18—9

Progressive growth of the primary follicles begins with puberty and is characterized by a proliferation of follicular cells and an increase in the size of the ovum. Accompanying changes also occur in the surrounding connective tissue. The follicular cells first become columnar and then form a stratified epithelial layer around the ovum. Irregular, small, fluid-filled spaces make their appearance between the follicular cells. These spaces gradually increase in number and coalesce to form the **antrum** or **follicular cavity** which is filled with a clear serous fluid, the **liquor folliculi**. The lining of the follicular cavity is often called the **membrana granulosa**. The follicles become ovoid or vesicular in shape, and, as growth continues, the contained ovum becomes displaced to one side. In this eccentric location, the ovum is surrounded by a hillock-shaped accumulation of columnar follicular cells (the **cumulus oophorus** or **discus proligerus**) which protrudes into the follicular cavity. On the surface of a vesicular follicle, the connective tissue becomes modified into a follicular sheath, the **theca folliculi**. This sheath ultimately becomes differentiated into 2 layers, an inner one rich in blood capillaries that surrounds the basement membrane and is known as the **theca interna** and an outer one, the **theca externa**, which is dense and fibrous and contains concentrations of concentrically arranged fusiform cells.

The maturing vesicular follicle soon attains a diameter of 10 to 12 mm. or more and is designated a mature **graafian follicle**. Such a large follicle encroaches on the free surface of the ovary and produces a bulge, a feature that precedes the process of ovulation. Within the graafian follicle the ovum has a diameter of approximately 0.12 mm. and is separated from the follicle cells by a thick refractile membrane, the **oolemma** or **zona pellucida**. Adjoining the zona pellucida, the columnar cells of the cumulus oophorus become elongated and radially arranged as the **corona radiata**. The increase in amount of follicular fluid causes a build-up of pressure which is mainly expressed at the ovarian surface. At the same time, the tunica albuginea becomes thinned out. As the probable result of these alterations and immediately prior to ovulation, a spot appears on the surface of the ovary overlying the follicle. This spot is referred to as the **stigma**. If the mature follicle ruptures at ovulation, the follicular fluid oozes out into the peritoneal cavity, carrying with it the detached ovum and its adherent corona radiata. Ordinarily, the ovum then finds its way to the fallopian tube to await fertilization or degeneration. As a rule, during the reproductive period of a woman, the ovulatory cycle occurs at intervals averaging 28 days, and normally only one follicle fully matures and releases its ovum. Other follicles which have developed to a lesser degree during this period undergo a form of degeneration known as **atresia (involution)**. Primary follicles which undergo atresia completely disappear, whereas degenerate large follicles are converted into **scar** tissue within the ovarian stroma. The ruptured graafian follicle has a stellate-shaped cavity which may become filled with

PLATE 140—Ovary

FIG. 18-10. Young ovary, showing a degenerating graafian follicle and a few primary follicles near the surface. H & E stain. Low power. (fl, follicular liquid; mg, membrana granulosa; tf, theca folliculi; ct, stromal connective tissue)

FIG. 18-11. Section of ovary, revealing the dense nature of the stroma and its vascularity. H & E stain. Low power.

FIG. 18-12. Section of ovary, revealing its vascular nature and several corpora albicans (ca). H & E stain. Low power.

FIG. 18-13. Section of ovary showing a late stage of follicular atresia. Mallory-Azan stain. Low power. (ti, theca interna cells; gm, forming glassy membrane; ct, connective tissue scar; v, invading blood vessels)

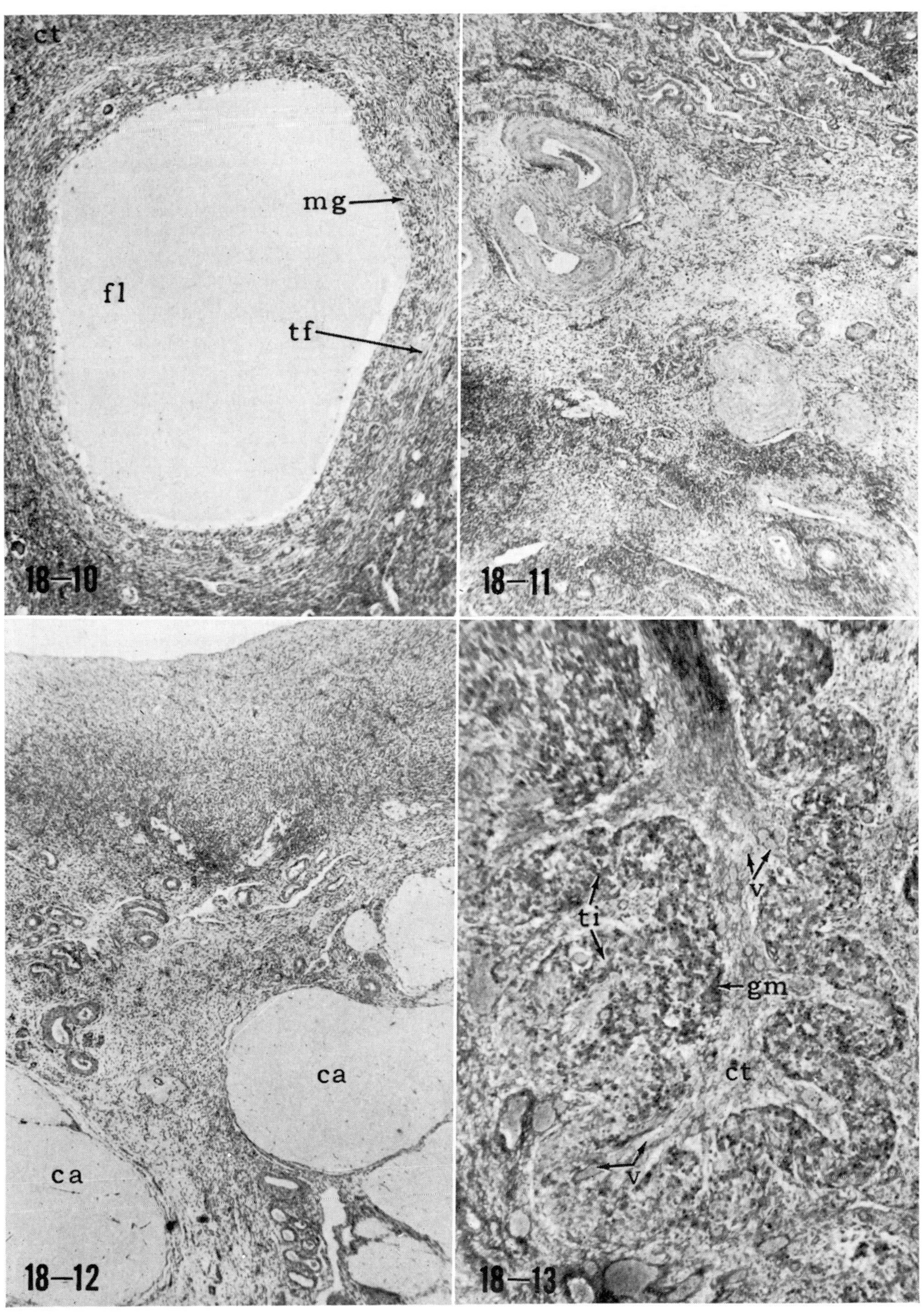
ct
mg
fl
tf
18–10
18–11
ca
ca
18–12
v
ti
gm
ct
v
18–13

blood (diapedesis of erythrocytes and hemorrhage from capillaries of the theca) and transiently is known as the **corpus hemorrhagicum**. Immediately following this change, a transformation of the follicle into a glandular body, the **corpus luteum**, commences. In this process, the wall of the follicle collapses, and the membrana granulosa becomes folded. The cells of the follicular epithelium become altered into large pale-staining elements that are arranged in cords. Lipochrome granules appear in these hypertrophied cells, giving rise to their designation as **granulosa lutein cells**. Likewise, the cells of the theca interna hypertrophy, and lipochrome granulation also appears in these cells, so that they are called **theca lutein cells**. These cells (somewhat smaller but more vacuolated than granulosa cells) penetrate the thickened layer of follicular cells. As they do so, they encroach on the clot, which is undergoing absorption, and carry with them the tiny capillary buds that provide the rich vascularity of the corpus luteum. (See Figs. 18-8, 18-13 to 18-16.)

If the ovum is not fertilized, the corpus luteum becomes the **corpus luteum of menstruation** and begins to involute about 2 weeks after ovulation. The lutein cells undergo fatty degeneration, fibrosis and hyalinization, and the yellow corpus luteum of menstruation becomes transformed to a whitish scar of microscopic dimensions, the **corpus albicans** (Figs. 18-12, 18-21). On the other hand, if the ovum is fertilized, the corpus luteum becomes the **corpus luteum of pregnancy**. This structure reaches its maximum development by about 3 months and does not begin to involute until about the 5th or the 6th month of gestation. Eventually, after parturition, the corpus luteum of pregnancy is also reduced to an ovarian scar (**corpus albicans**).

After more than 30 years of releasing ova and producing hormones, the ovary gradually ceases these functional activities and becomes quiescent. These changes, associated with menopause, mark the end of the reproductive period. Examination of sections of **old ovary** reveals that the cortex is thin, fibrotic and wrinkled and that few follicles, but many scars, are present in an abundant stroma (Figs. 18-18 to 18-21). As the probable result of these changes and of ovarian failure, hormonal disturbances occur. That the anterior pituitary is still functional is shown by the persistent secretion of follicle stimulating hormone (FSH).

Regarding the female sex hormones produced by the ovary, evidence indicates that most of the estrogen is elaborated by the theca interna. Beginning at puberty, the physiologic estrogen secretion is 17-beta estradiol; estrone and estriol are metabolites. Although direct control of estrogen secretion resides in the anterior pituitary, evidence points to the hypothalamus as a higher central nervous system control. As indicated in

PLATE 141—Ovary

FIG. 18-14. Survey of the ovary, showing the nature of a degenerating corpus luteum (cl). The cells are decreased in size and vacuolated. Mallory-Azan stain. Low power.

FIG. 18-15. Ovary, revealing a portion of the wall of a degenerating corpus luteum. Mallory-Azan stain. Intermediate power. (s, surrounding ovarian stroma tissue; tl, theca lutein cells; gl, granulosa lutein cells; va, vacuolization; v, blood vessels)

FIG. 18-16. Ovary, showing the granulosa lutein cells (gl) and theca lutein cells (tl) of a degenerating corpus luteum. Note the penetration of blood vessels (v). Mallory-Azan stain. High power.

FIG. 18-17. Ovary, revealing the cells of the wall of a large degenerating follicle. Mallory-Azan stain. High power. (p, precipitate from follicular liquid; mg, cells of the membrane granulosa; tc, theca cells; s, ovarian stroma)

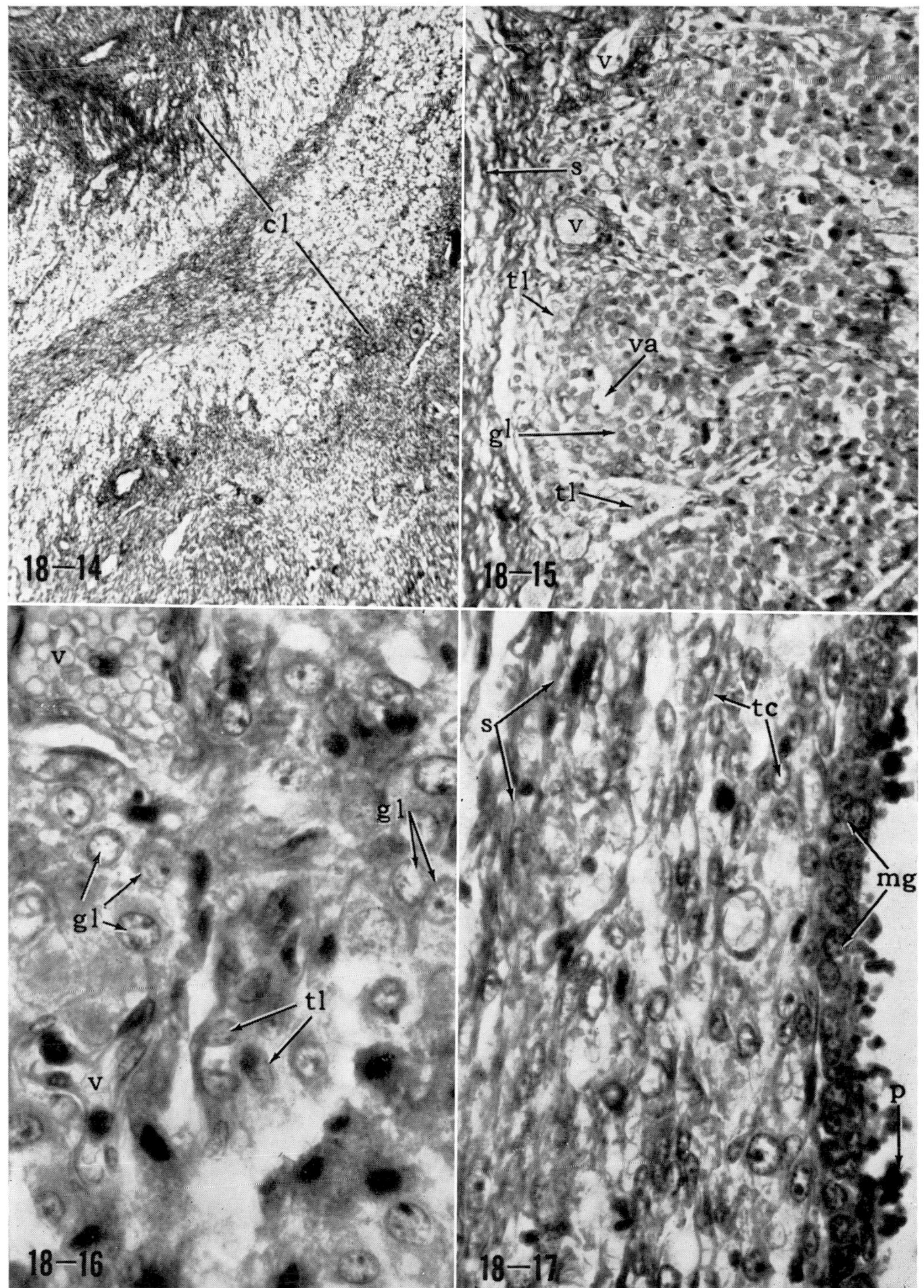
cl
v
s
v
tl
va
gl
tl
18—14
18—15
v
gl
gl
tl
v
s
tc
mg
p
18—16
18—17

the introduction, the primary endocrine function of the ovary is to maintain reproductive activity and to bring about the development and the maintenance of the secondary sex characteristics. At puberty and the onset of menstruation (**menarche**), the output of gonadotropin (largely FSH) increases. In this way pituitary FSH stimulates the growth and the maturation of immature follicles along with the production of estrogen. The production of the latter hormone decreases the output of FSH and stimulates the release of **luteinizing hormone** (LH). Luteinizing hormone acts synergistically with FSH, attaining the necessary concentrations, along with other factors, to cause ovulation of the mature follicle. The **luteotrophic hormone** (LTH, lactogenic hormone, prolactin) is concerned with the formation and the maintenance of the corpus luteum which secretes **progesterone**. This last-mentioned hormone is often referred to as the hormone of pregnancy in that it prepares the uterus for pregnancy. As was the case for estrogen, a feedback mechanism also exists for progesterone and its gonadotropin (LTH). Finally, it should be mentioned that luteotrophic hormone, along with other factors, is responsible for lactation in postpartum women.

C. FALLOPIAN TUBES (OVIDUCTS)

(Figs. 18-23 to 18-28)

Each of these muscular tubes is approximately 15 cm. long and 10 mm. in diameter and is suspended by a mesenteric peritoneal fold, the **mesosalpinx**. This fold represents the upper free margin and the adjacent portion of the broad ligament. The following regions of the fallopian tube can be recognized:

1. A proximal funnel-shaped portion, the **infundibulum**, containing a fimbriated opening which projects toward the ovary
2. An intermediate dilated portion, the **ampulla**
3. A narrower medial third, the **isthmus**, which passes through the uterine wall as the **interstitial** or **intramural** portion

The fallopian tube is organized into 3 layers, a **mucosa**, a **muscularis** and a thin external covering **serosa**. The mucosa is lined by a simple columnar epithelial surface in which occasional areas of pseudostratified cells are found. Beneath the epithelium, a lamina propria, rich in angular cells and a network of thin connective tissue fibers, is present. The muscularis consists of smooth muscle bundles arranged as two poorly delineated layers, a thick, inner circular one and a thin, outer longitudinal layer.

The mucosa of the fallopian tube presents variations according to the region. At the infundibular end, the mucosa is highly developed. It is covered by a ciliated columnar epithelium on which surface the cilia beat toward the uterus. Associated with the mucosa of the fimbriated opening is a ring of blood vessels which are separated by muscle fibers.

In the region of the ampulla, the mucosa is found to be highly convoluted or plicated

PLATE 142—Ovary

FIG. 18-18. Survey of central area of the ovary from an old woman. Note the lack of follicles, the abundance of vascularized connective tissue and the presence of a corpus albicans (ca). H & E stain. Low power.

FIG. 18-19. Cortical region of the ovary from an old woman, showing the germinal epithelium (ge), the absence of intact follicles and the nature of abundant connective tissue. H & E stain. Intermediate power. (ta, tunica albuginea)

FIG. 18-20. Ovary from an old woman, showing the vascularity of the stroma. H & E stain. Intermediate power.

FIG. 18-21. Ovary from an old woman, showing a few corpora albicans (ca). H & E stain. Intermediate power.

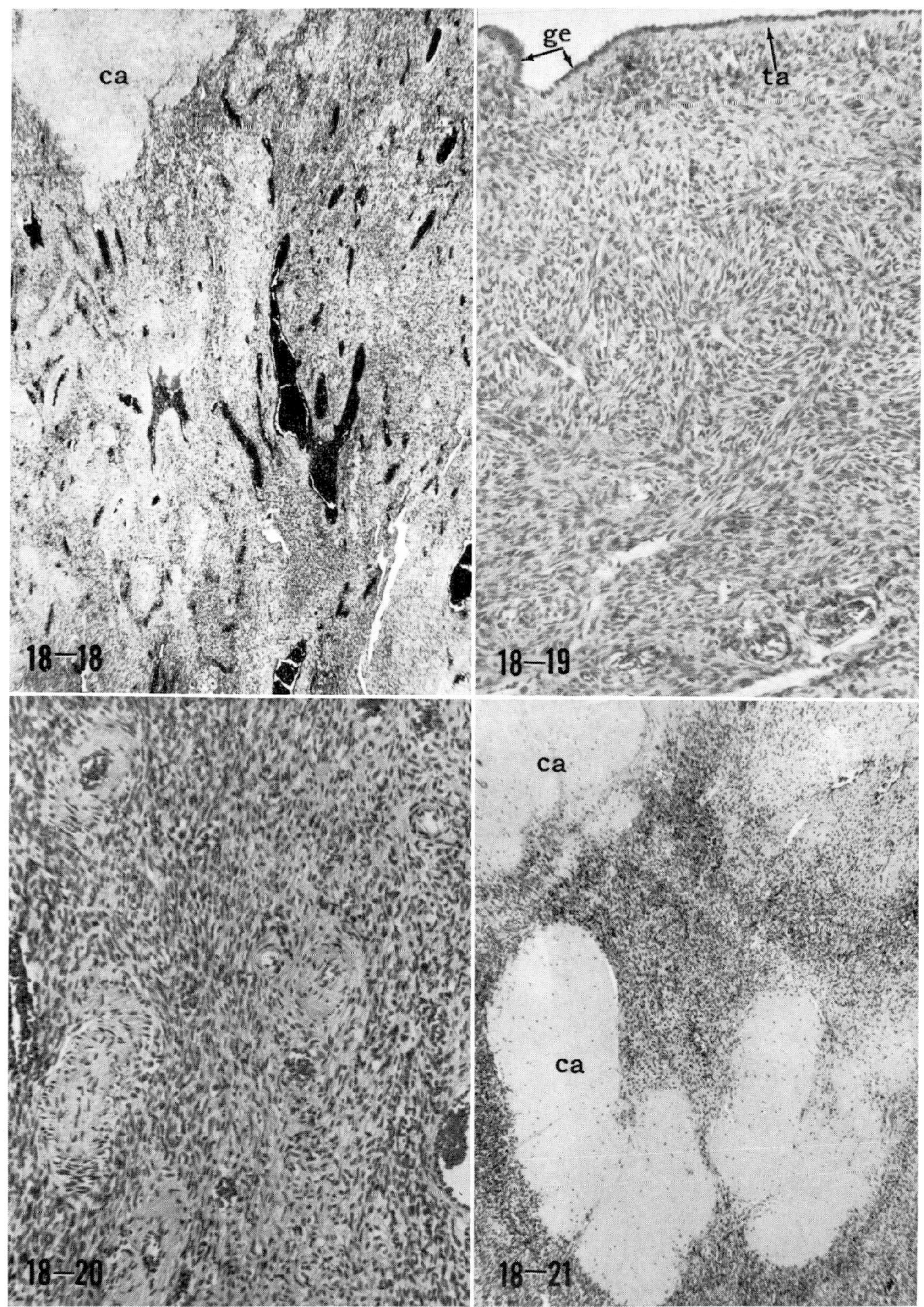
ca
18—18
ge
ta
18—19
18—20
ca
ca
18—21

and consists of numerous high branching longitudinal folds. These folds become less marked in the region of the isthmus and are further reduced in the intramural portion. The mucosal epithelium is highest in the ampulla and progressively diminishes in height toward the uterus. Two types of cells are present, ciliated and nonciliated cells. Ciliated columnar cells, already mentioned as being present in the infundibulum where they are most numerous, are also abundant in the ampulla. In conjunction with muscular contractions of the tubes, these epithelial cells aid in the transport of the fertilized ovum. The nonciliated columnar cells, which contain mucoid secretory granules, provide the ovum with a fluid vehicle for its passage down the tube to the uterus.

Within the fallopian tube, the height of the epithelium changes cyclically in response to the content of ovarian hormones present. Higher concentrations of estrogen result in increased height. Thus, at the time of ovulation, the epithelial cells are extremely tall, whereas at menstruation these cells are very short.

D. UTERUS

The uterus is a pear-shaped, hollow muscular organ located between the bladder and the rectum in the broad ligament. It is composed of an upper end, the body (**corpus uteri**) and its associated fundus (**fundus uteri**), a middle slightly constricted part, the **isthmus**, and a lower end, the **cervix**, with its **portio vaginalis** which opens into the anterior wall of the vagina. The body communicates directly with the fallopian tubes and is geared to receive and nurture a fertilized ovum until development is completed. Structurally, the wall of the uterus consists of an external serous coat, the **perimetrium** or **tunica serosa**, a thick middle muscular coat, the **myometrium** or **tunica muscularis** and an internal mucous coat, the **endometrium** or **tunica mucosa.**

1. Perimetrium

This is a typical, serosal coat and consists of an external mesothelial covering over a small amount of underlying loose connective tissue. The perimetrium is derived as a reflection of the pelvic peritoneum of the broad ligament and completely invests the uterus except at the attachment of the broad ligament and at the points of entrance of the fallopian tubes.

2. Myometrium

This massive muscular coat constitutes approximately three fourths of the thickness of the uterine wall. It is composed of interlacing bundles of smooth muscle fibers, reinforced and separated by loosely arranged connective tissue. Although a separation into distinct layers is difficult to recognize histologically, the myometrium is generally described as having its component muscle bundles disposed into 3 strata. These are (1) a thin outer layer located subjacent to the serosa, the **stratum supravasculare**, in which the fibers have primarily a longitudinal orientation, (2) an extremely thick and highly vascular middle layer, the **stratum vasculare**, made up of interlacing fibers that are predominantly circularly arranged, and (3) a thin innermost layer, the **stratum sub-**

PLATE 143—Ovary

FIG. 18-22. The follicle cells are somewhat cuboidal. The oocyte cytoplasm contains several mitochondrial rosettes, and paired membranes of rough endoplasmic reticulum are beginning to form. Note foot processes of ovarian stromal cells at top and lower left that apparently attach to the periphery of the follicle and become incorporated into its wall. Guinea pig. × 5,000. (n, nucleolus; ne, nuclear envelope; m, mitochondria; fcn, follicle cell nucleus). (Adams, E. C., and Hertig, A. T.: J. Cell Biol. *21*:405)

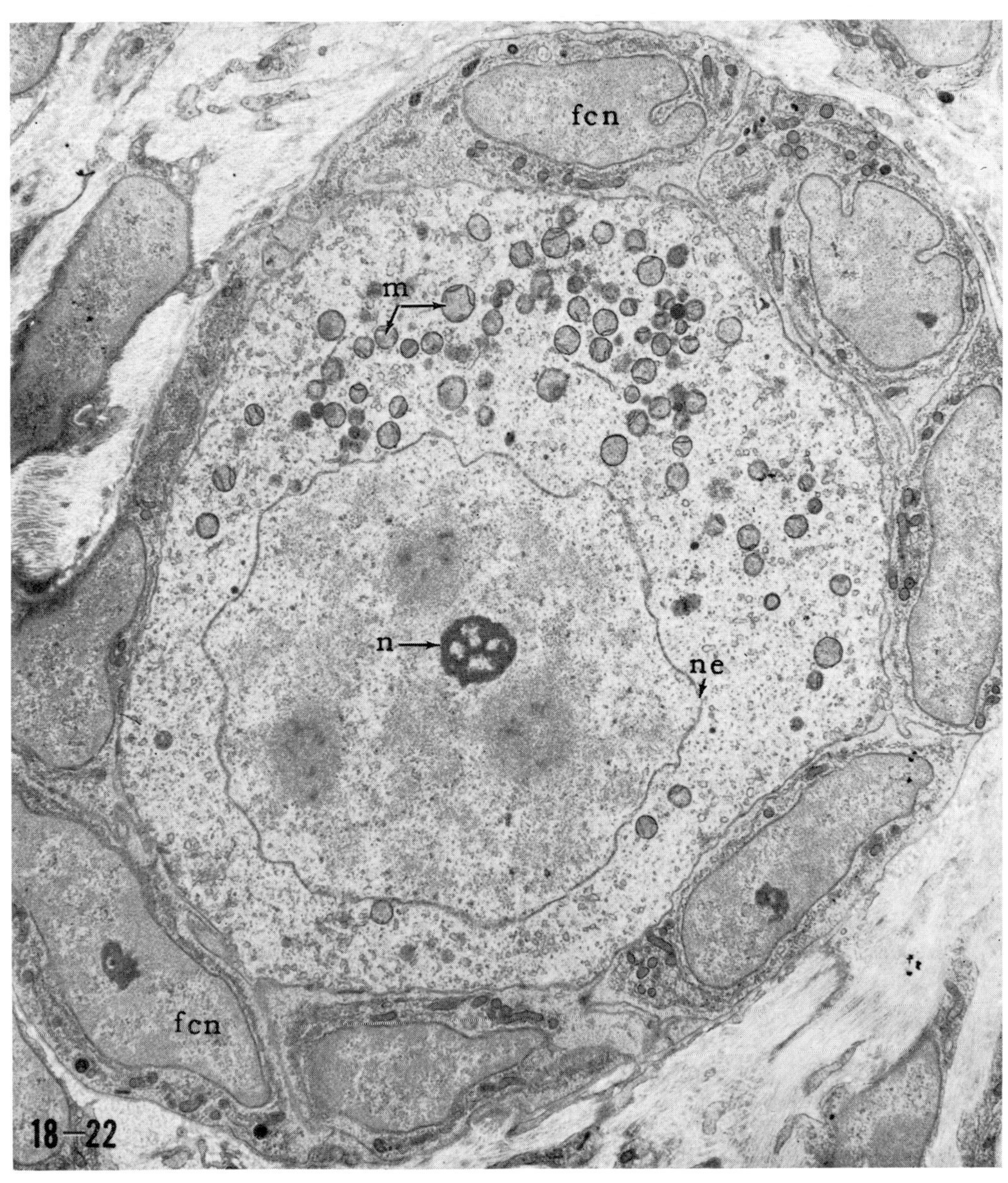
fcn
m
n
ne
fcn
18–22

mucosum or **subvasculare,** consisting primarily of longitudinal fibers and a smaller component of circularly and obliquely disposed fibers.

Regarding the thick middle layer, which makes up about two thirds of the myometrium, the presence of large blood vessels, especially veins, gives it a spongy appearance. A special feature of the thin inner layer is that it provides muscular rings around the intramural portions of the fallopian tubes.

The length of muscle fibers in the myometrium undergoes changes consistent with the functional phases of the uterus. In the nonpregnant condition, individual fibers generally range from 40 to 90 μ in length. However, during pregnancy, many of these muscle fibers may grow to a length of over 500 μ. In the process of growth, there is a concomitant increase in the muscle mass of the myometrium. In the puerperium, muscle fibers rapidly decrease in size and may exhibit fatty infiltration.

3. Endometrium (Within the Womb)

a. The uterine mucosa of both the corpus and the fundus is lined by a simple columnar epithelium. This epithelial surface consists primarily of nonciliated secretory cells, but occasional groups of ciliated cells may also be found scattered along the surface. Numerous **tubular glands** project into the underlying lamina propria. The glands are simple for the most part but may exhibit slight branching in the deeper part of the stroma. These glands are composed of columnar cells which elaborate mucoid or glycogen secretions, depending on the phase of activity of the uterus. Their secretions pass directly into the gland lumen without the intervention of a duct system. It should be emphasized that the primary function of the glands is epithelial regeneration rather than secretion. Such regeneration is required to replace the endometrial surface following menstruation. The stroma consists of embryonal type reticular connective tissue, richly supplied with cellular elements which are mainly small angular cells with large ovoid nuclei. In addition, macrophages, fibroblasts and leukocytes, especially of the lymphocytic variety, are found. The absence of both muscularis mucosae and submucosa cause the endometrial stroma to adhere closely to the underlying myometrium. From the myometrium, small arterioles with a coiled appearance and lymphatics enter the endometrium, course parallel with the glands and supply the **functionalis layer** of the endometrium. The functionalis layer is the thick superficial layer which undergoes marked cyclic changes in contrast with the narrow deep zone where practically no cyclic changes take place.

b. The **cervix** is lined with a simple columnar epithelium consisting of tall, pale-staining mucous-type cells. However, in the region of the external os uteri, this type of epithelium is replaced by the stratified squamous type. The glands are unlike those found in the corpus and the fundus in that

PLATE 144—Fallopian Tube

Fig. 18-23. Portion of the infundibulum of the fallopian tube showing the numerous mucosal folds, their epithelial lining (e) and stroma of the lamina propria (lp). H & E stain. Low power.

Fig. 18-24. Adjacent section of Figure 18-23, showing the mucosal folds (f) projecting into a wider portion of the lumen. Low power. (v, blood vessels; m, smooth muscle)

Fig. 18-25. Section showing the infundibular processes or fimbriae (f) of the mucosa projecting into the lumen. H & E stain. Intermediate power.

Fig. 18-26. High-power view of an infundibular process, showing its columnar cell lining consisting of nonciliated secretory cells (sc) and ciliated cells (cc). Mallory-Azan stain. (lp, core of lamina propria)

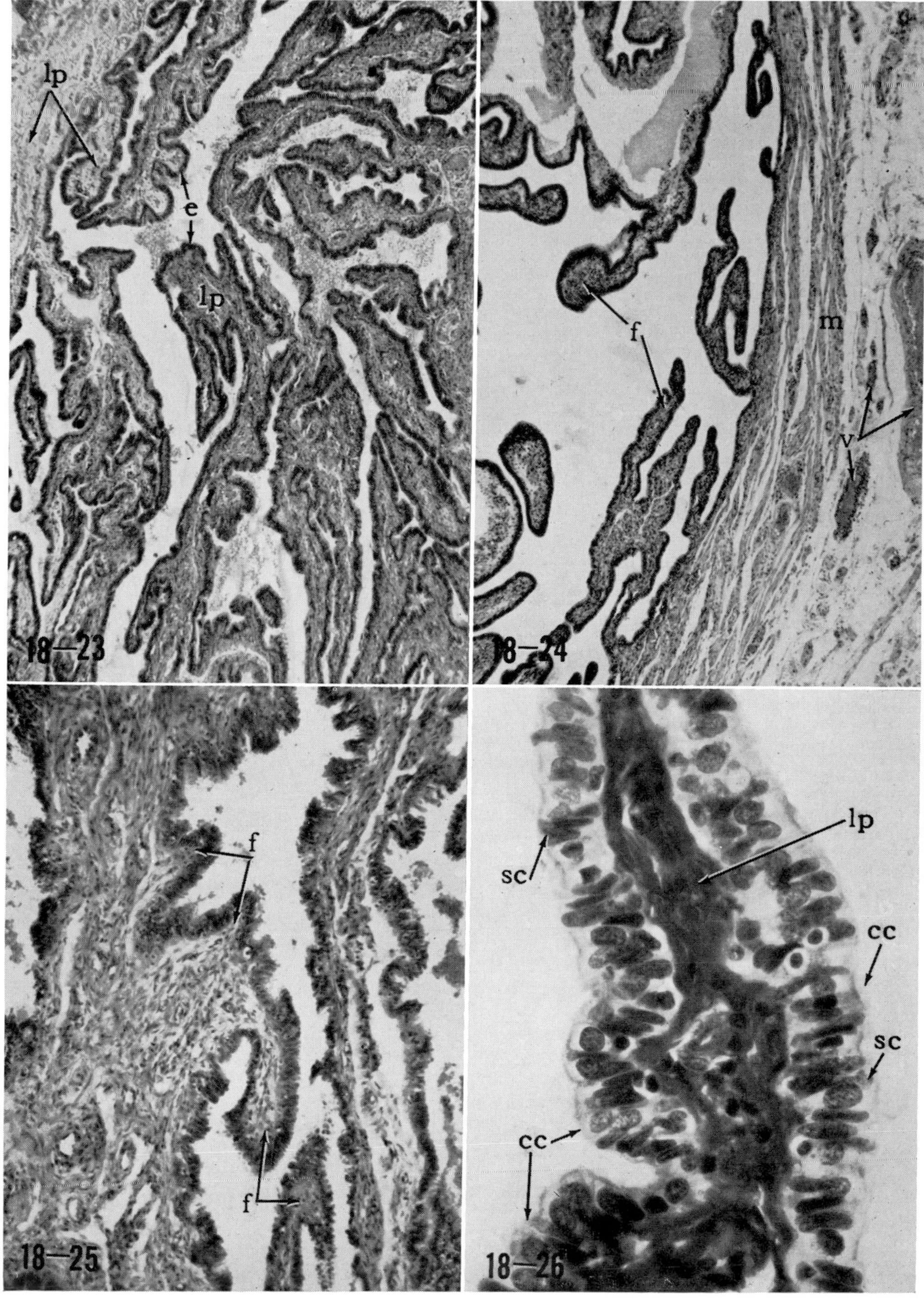
lp
e
lp
18–23
f
m
v
18–24
f
f
18–25
lp
sc
cc
sc
cc
18–26

they are large **branched** tubular structures. The appearance of these tall mucus-secreting cells does not change much during the menstrual cycle, although the nature of secretion does vary. On the other hand, during pregnancy the glands enlarge and secrete an abundance of mucus, forming a mucus plug which seals the cervical canal. It should be mentioned that some of the mucus-secreting cells frequently become occluded and dilated. Such mucus-filled cells result in a cystic condition and are referred to as nabothian follicles. (See Figs. 18-55 to 18-58.)

c. As was mentioned previously, most of the uterine mucosa is subject to extensive cyclic structural variations that are dependent on its functional state and related to the activities of the ovaries. It is therefore pertinent to recognize the various phases of the menstruating and the pregnant uterus. Beginning with puberty and ending with the menopause, the menstrual cycle represents a cyclical partial destruction and regeneration of the functionalis layer of the endometrium, which occurs approximately every 28 days (21-35). Four distinct stages are recognized.

1. Proliferative Stage (Follicular; Estrogenic)

This stage begins at the termination of the menstrual flow (usually day 3 to 5), is associated with the growth of the graafian follicle and the rising titer of estrogen, and continues until day 13 to 14 of the cycle (the onset of ovulation). A gradual regeneration and reconstitution of the endometrial lining from the glands of the basalis layer occur. An increase in the number and the length of the glandular elements and proliferation of the stroma with revascularization (capillaries and coiled arteries appear in the endometrium) are evident. The glands are at first long and straight with narrow lumina, but toward the end of this stage they start to become wavy, and the lumina become widened and filled with a thin mucoid, milky secretion. Glycogen, found to be present in the glandular cells, is not secreted at this time. By the end of this stage, the thickness of the endometrium has increased to approximately 2 mm. (Figs. 18-29 to 18-34).

2. Secretory Stage
(Luteal, Progravid or Progestational)

This stage begins on the 14th or the 15th day and continues until the 26th or the 27th day. It is associated with the development of the corpus luteum and the rising titer of progesterone. Characteristically, a marked hypertrophy in the endometrium to as much as 5 mm. occurs and is evidenced by a swelling of the glandular tissue, pronounced edema and increased vascularity. The glands, which copiously secrete a thick mucoid ma-

PLATE 145—Fallopian Tube and Uterus

FIG. 18-27. Ampulla of fallopian tube near the fimbriated extremity. Note the intricate foldings of the mucous membrane and the high degree of vascularity. Mallory-Azan stain. Low power.

FIG. 18-28. Uterine end of fallopian tube, revealing only slight folding of the mucous membrane (mm), an inner circular smooth muscle layer (cm) and its outer longitudinal smooth muscle layer (lm). H & E stain. Low power.

FIG. 18-29. Early follicular (proliferative) stage of the uterus, showing the endometrium (en) with the beginning of glandular development (gl) and the underlying myometrium (my) with numerous blood vessels in the interstitial tissue. H & E stain. Low power.

FIG. 18-30. Late follicular (proliferative) stage of the uterus, showing the endometrium (en) and the underlying myometrium (my). Note the thickened endometrium due to the development of numerous glands (gl) at this time. The glands appear as isolated elements because of the oblique plane of section through the uterine wall. (Compare with Fig. 18-29, photographed at the same magnification.) H & E stain. Low power.

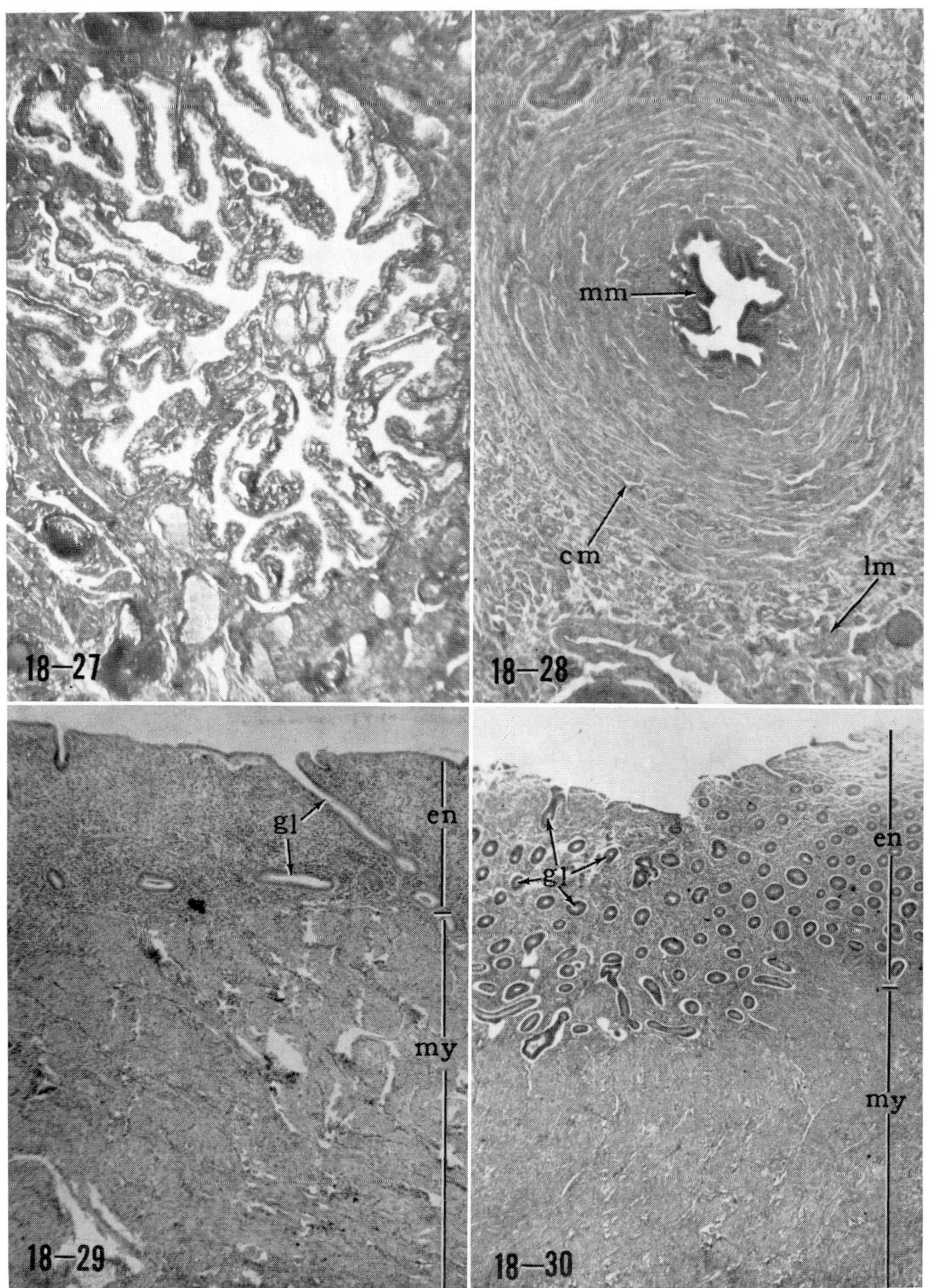
18–27
mm
cm
lm
18–28
gl
en
my
18–29
gl
en
my
18–30

terial rich in glycogen, become tortuous and saccular and exhibit many out-pocketings. Coiled arteries become maximally developed, tightly spiraled and extend to the surface. Close to the superficial surface of the endometrium (the compactum zone), the stroma becomes more compact and contains the necks of the glands, which are straight, and enlarged stromal cells (identical with the larger decidual cells of pregnancy). In the deeper spongy zone of the functionalis layer a reduced amount of stroma between the glands is present (Figs. 18-35, 18-36).

By the end of the secretory stage, the endometrium is structurally and functionally ready to receive a fertilized ovum. If fertilization and implantation occur, this stage becomes known as the **gravid** phase which results in the continued development and thickening of the endometrium for an additional 6 to 8 weeks.

3. Ischemic Stage (Premenstrual)

If pregnancy does not occur by the 26th or the 27th day, the increased concentrations of progesterone inhibits LH and LTH secretion, the corpus luteum undergoes involution, and the signal for endometrial breakdown is given. On day 27 or 28, the ischemic stage rapidly sets in. Intermittent constriction of the coiled arteries for periods up to several hours results in a decrease in the blood supply to the compact functionalis zone of the endometrium. This clamping-down process causes the functional layer to become blanched and shrunken with glandular collapse or fragmentation resulting in the loss of glandular secretion along with a loss of the interstitial tissue fluid. In addition, large numbers of lymphocytes are found to invade the stroma. The ischemic stage is a blood–holding-back phase so that as yet there is no evidence of blood loss.

4. Menstrual Stage

The low levels of hormones (progesterone and estrogen) mark the onset of the menstrual stage, which begins on day 1 and continues for 3 to 5 days. At this stage, the coiled arteries and capillaries become greatly engorged and finally rupture, resulting in blood oozing into the interstitial tissue and subsequently entering the uterine cavity. The epithelium and the stromal components of the functionalis layer are progressively destroyed, become necrotic and sloughed away. Thus, most of the uterine endometrium is essentially denuded, but the basalis layer, which maintains its blood supply, remains intact but somewhat shrunken and is ready to participate in the regeneration of the endometrium.

Regarding the postmenopausal uterus, the uterus undergoes marked atrophy, since it no longer is under the influence of estrogenic stimuli. (See ovary after menopause.) The

PLATE 146—Uterus

FIG. 18-31. Survey section of the endometrium in the late proliferative stage. Note that the glands (gl) are numerous, elongated and tortuous, and that the surrounding stroma (s) is becoming edematous. H & E stain. Low power.

FIG. 18-32. Late proliferative stage of the endometrium, showing the elongated and spiraling nature of the glands (gl) and the abundant stroma (s) which is beginning to become edematous. The 5 glandular segments (1 to 5) are probably parts of the same gland. H & E stain. Intermediate power.

FIG. 18-33. Late proliferative stage of the endometrium, showing the simple columnar nature of the surface epithelium (e) and connective tissue cells within the underlying edematous stromal connective tissue. H & E stain. High power.

FIG. 18-34. High-power view of an endometrial gland opening upon the surface in the late proliferative stage. Note the appearance of glycogenic mucoid material (gm) in the basal ends of the gland cells and in the lumen (l). H & E stain.

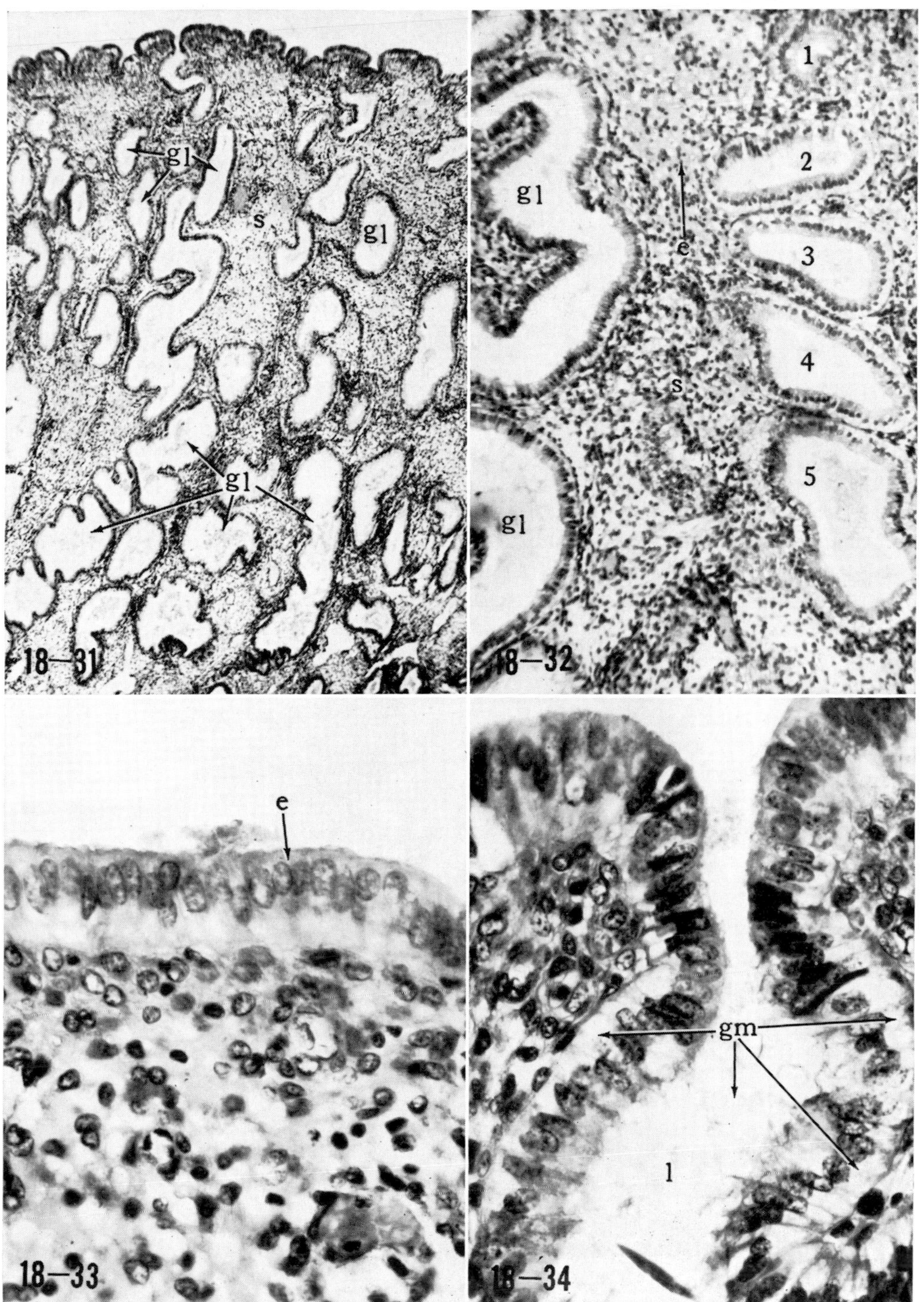
gl
s
gl
gl
18—31
1
2
gl
e
3
4
s
5
gl
18—32
e
18—33
gm
l
18—34

glands become few in number and shortened, with the stroma revealing a substantial increase in amount and also having the characteristic of invading the myometrium.

E. PLACENTA
(Plates 147 to 151)

The placenta is a transitory organ which develops as the result of interaction between the actively mitotic embryonic vesicle and the uterine wall against which it encroaches. This organ therefore comes to consist of two major portions, one fetal (a part of the chorion, see later) and one maternal (a segment of the endometrium). At term, the placenta has a flattened, cake-shaped appearance with a diameter of about 30 cm. and a thickness of about 3 cm. Throughout the entire period of gestation the placenta gradually increases in size, performing, as it does so, a dynamic role in supporting the development of the embryo. In this role it serves, at the same time, as a nutritive, an endocrine (it produces gonadotropin, estrogen and progesterone) and an excretory organ.

Slide material of the placenta is obtained at term and from stillbirths. It is extremely difficult to secure very early placentae.

During the course of gestation the placenta undergoes exuberant growth. This increase in mass is associated with histologic changes in the organ's most identifying feature, the placental villi. Such changes enable the student in histology to distinguish between early and late stages of placental development.

In order to fully understand the structure and the function of this vital organ, it is necessary for the student to recognize the placenta's dual origin and its relationship to the developing fetal membranes and the expanding uterus.

By the time implantation has occurred, the fertilized germinal mass has become transformed into a hollow sphere, the **blastocyst**. The wall of this vesicle, exclusive of the **inner cell mass**, is composed of a simple epithelium of ectodermal cells, the **trophoblast** or **trophectoderm**. The trophoblast has an extremely vigorous growth and invasive potential. At numerous sites along its surface, cells of the trophoblast rapidly divide and bud off as irregular cords into the adjacent endometrium. Since these buds are entirely epithelial in nature and since their appearance is that of rudimentary villuslike structures, they are commonly referred to as **primitive** or **primary villi**.

By the end of the 2nd week following implantation, a second layer of cells appears beneath the trophectodermal layer. This layer, representing the mesodermal contribution, soon differentiates into mesenchymal connective tissue that is rich in tiny blood spaces. Almost immediately, this second layer of connective tissue begins to push its way into the existing primitive villi, providing them with a core of vascular connective

PLATE 147—Progravid Uterus and Placenta

FIG. 18-35. Uterine endometrium during the progravid phase. Note the increase in thickness of the endometrium over that shown in Figures 18-29 and 18-30. Glands (gl) are becoming tortuous and exhibit sacculations (gs). H & E stain. Low power. (s, stroma)

FIG. 18-36. Progravid condition of the endometrium. Note the tortuous nature and the sacculations of the glands (gl), the surface epithelium (ep) and the cellularity of the stromal connective tissue (s). H & E stain. Intermediate power.

FIG. 18-37. Placenta during the first trimester of pregnancy. Note the origin of the chorionic villi (cv) from the chorionic plate (cp) and erosion of the endometrium. H & E stain. Low power. (db, decidua basalis; cc, chorionic cavity)

FIG. 18-38. Placenta during the first trimester of pregnancy, showing the nature of the chorionic villi. H & E stain. Low power. (ct, connective tissue core; tr, trophoblastic cells)

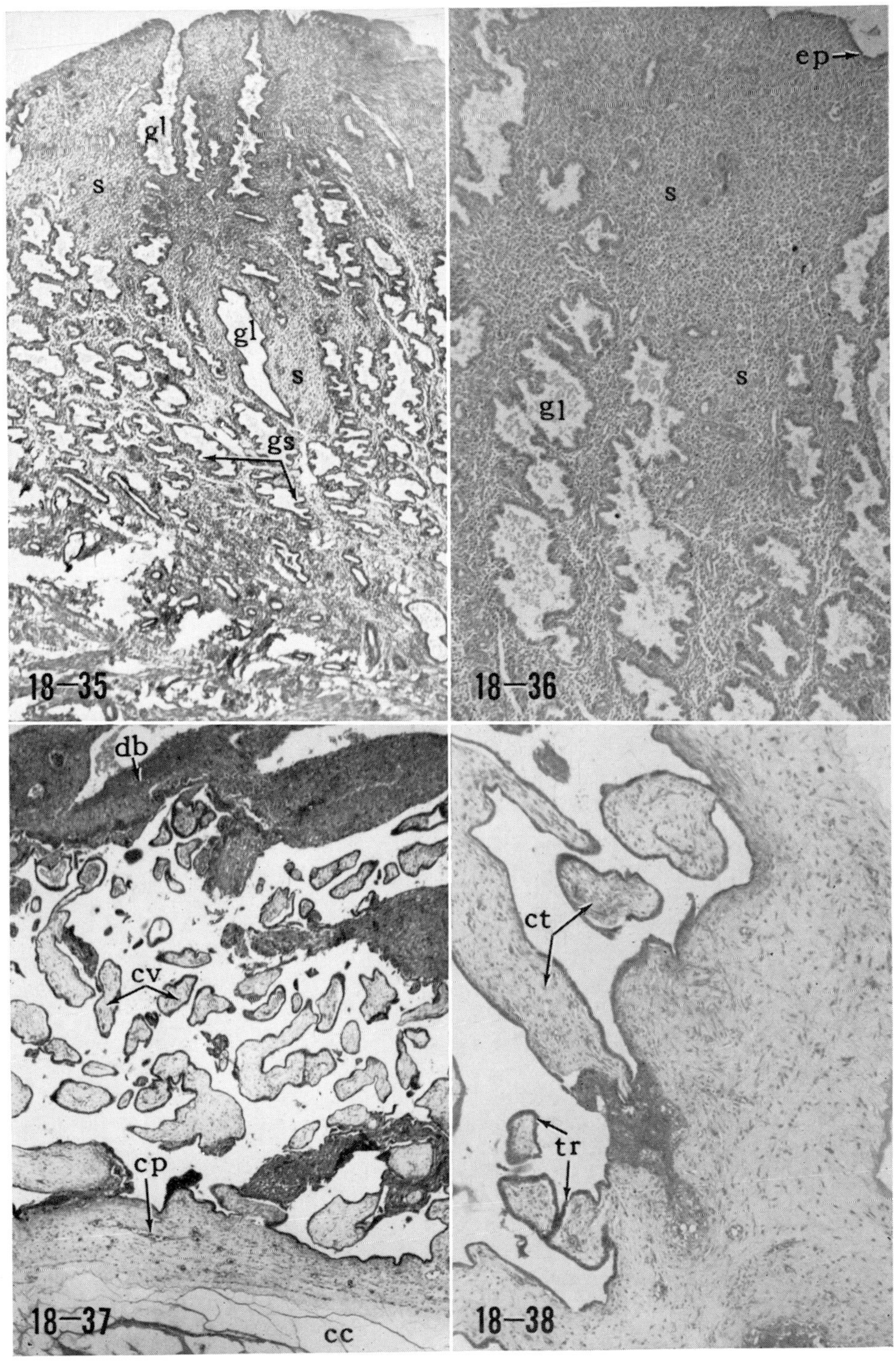
gl
s
gl
s
gs
18–35
ep
s
s
gl
18–36
db
cv
cp
18–37
cc
ct
tr
18–38

tissue. Villi consisting of a core of connective tissue covered by trophoblast cells are referred to as **secondary placental villi** and constitute the barriers across which the maternal fetal metabolic exchanges take place. The term **chorion** is applied to the combined connective tissue and trophectoderm layers, and at this time the blastocyst can be referred to as the **chorionic vesicle**. Similarly, the placental villi are usually referred to as **chorionic villi** to indicate their origin from an extra-embryonic, nonmaternal structure.

Marked differences in the chorionic villi are apparent, depending on what part of the endometrium the developing chorionic vesicle comes into relationship with. The villi which are most important for placental functions are those which push into the endometrium on the side away from the uterine cavity. Because of their rich branching and frondlike appearance, these villi and the chorion from which they take origin are collectively referred to as the **chorion frondosum**. **The chorion frondosum constitutes the fetal part of the developing placenta** and hence is often referred to as the **placenta fetalis**. The villi developing from the uterine cavity side of the chorionic vesicle are short, flattened and poorly branched. These do not contribute to placental function during most of gestation. Because of their flattened nature, these villi and the chorion from which they arise are collectively referred to as the **chorion laeve**.

In the early stages of placental development, the villi appear as islands of immature connective tissue of the dense type, covered by two layers of trophoblastic cells. The innermost cell layer, the **cytotrophoblast**, is a simple cuboidal layer (**Langhans' cells**), whereas the outer, the **syncytial trophoblast**, is a multinucleated syncytial layer. Although sections reveal the presence of blood inside and outside the villi, it is important to note that there is no direct communication between the maternal and the fetal blood channels. Abnormal exceptions to this may exist, as in the cases involving the Rh factor.

As gestation continues, especially during the late stages of pregnancy (last trimester), the cytotrophoblast seems to disappear, and the syncytial trophoblast exhibits bulges or clumps of nuclei referred to as **syncytial knots**. The disappearance of the cytotrophoblastic layer is more apparent than real, as shown by histochemical and electron microscope studies. That is, even up to term, the placenta reveals the persistence of cyto-

PLATE 148—Placenta

FIG. 18-39. Appearance of chorionic villi (cv) of placenta during the first trimester of pregnancy. The spaces between the villi (bs) represent a reservoir for maternal blood. Note the connective tissue cores of the villi. Mallory-Azan stain. Low power.

FIG. 18-40. A small group of chorionic villi from the placenta during the first trimester of pregnancy. At this magnification, nuclei within the trophoblastic layer (tl) covering each villus can just be made out. In addition, note the mesenchymal nature of the connective tissue (ct) forming the core of each villus. Mallory-Azan stain. Intermediate power.

FIG. 18-41. Oblique and longitudinal sections through two adjacent chorionic villi in a region adjacent to that shown in Figure 18-40. The trophoblastic cells consist of a deeper cellular layer (cytotrophoblast, cyt) and a surface syncytial portion (syncytial trophoblast, st). Mallory-Azan stain. High power. (bb, brush border on syncytial trophoblast; is, intervillous space; ct, connective tissue core of villus; v, vessels in villi)

FIG. 18-42. Another chorionic villus from the placenta during the first trimester of pregnancy. Note that the cytotrophoblastic layer (cyt) is almost continuous around the villus and that the 3 vessels (v) seen within the connective tissue contain young nucleated red blood cells. Mallory-Azan stain. High power. (e, primitive endothelial cells)

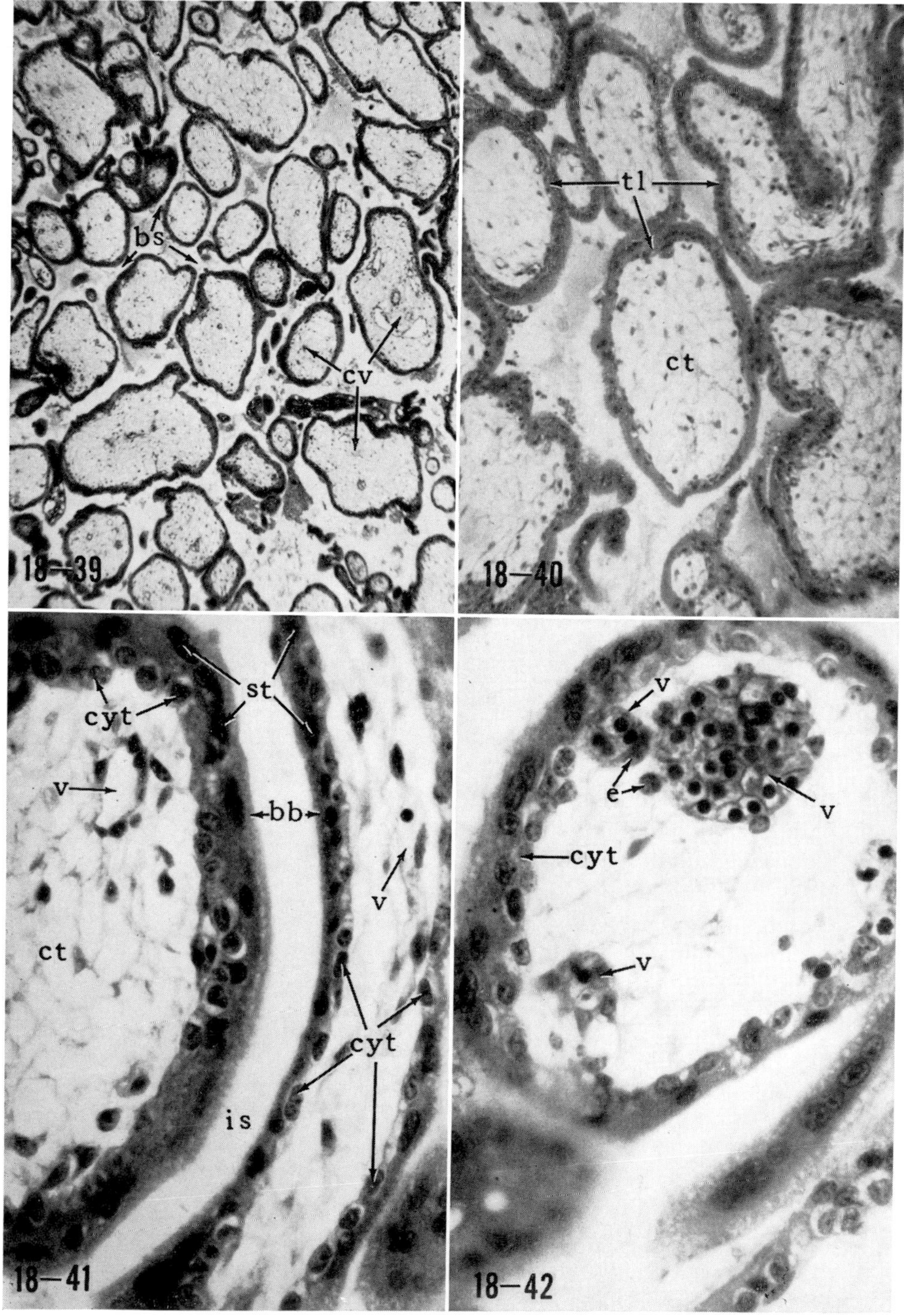
bs
cv
18–39
tl
ct
18–40
st
cyt
v
bb
v
ct
cyt
is
18–41
v
e
v
cyt
v
18–42

trophoblastic material which is capable of the continued elaboration of chorionic gonadotropins. In term placentae, the intervillous spaces (maternal blood lakes) show the presence of fibrin deposits.

Present at the implantation site, as a lining of the uterus and also as a covering over the chorionic surfaces of the embryonic membranes, are the **decidua**, maternal structures that are sloughed as the afterbirth following parturition. The decidua consists of 3 regions of modified endometrial tissue, the **decidua capsularis**, the **decidua basalis** and the **decidua parietalis (vera)**. The decidua capsularis constitutes the thin layer of endometrium adjacent to the uterine cavity and overlying the developing fetus. The decidua basalis is the congested portion of endometrium lying immediately adjacent and deep to the developing fetus and its membrane; it is this portion that becomes the maternal side of the placenta. The decidua parietalis includes all the remaining endometrial tissue in the gravid uterus. Especially during the first 8 weeks of pregnancy, the decidua parietalis reveals a continuous thickening. An obvious feature of the decidua is the appearance of the **decidual cells** which in reality are rounded, enlarged superficial stromal cells. That these large nucleated cells possess secretory ability is indicated by the presence of a granular cytoplasm.

All of the decidua are eliminated as the afterbirth except for a narrow, basal zone.

F. VAGINA

(Figs. 18-59 to 18-64)

This fibromuscular, tubular organ connects the uterus with the exterior and serves as a cavity for the reception of semen at coitus and as a birth canal at the time of parturition. The wall of the vagina consists of an inner mucosa, a muscularis and an outer adventitia (fibrosa).

The mucous membrane is thrown into numerous, irregular, broad transverse folds or rugae. The epithelial lining is of the stratified squamous type. In the adult, the epithelium is organized into 3 zones of cells. The deepest zone (basal) is composed of several rows of deeply staining cells. Above this, the intermediate zone consists of round cells of a transitional type. A superficial zone of flattened, squamous cells, in varying stages of cornification, is often referred to as the functional layer. That is, during the normal menstrual cycle, it is here that desquamation occurs.

Depending on the amount of circulating estrogenic hormone, the epithelium exhibits variations in thickness and contains variable amounts of glycogen. Thus, in the newborn, the vaginal epithelium is quite thick in the early postnatal period, the result of the influence of maternal estrogen. Once this maternal hormonal influence has disappeared, the epithelium becomes thinner and remains so until puberty. At puberty and during the active reproductive period, the epithelium

PLATE 149—Placenta

FIG. 18-43. Appearance of chorionic villi from the placenta at mid-pregnancy. Note that the terminal branches of the villi are more numerous than during the first trimester. The large villus vertically oriented in the upper right corner appears to be a main stem villus (sv) from which side branches (sb) and their subdivisions take origin. Also note the major branch of the umbilical vessel (uv), longitudinally sectioned, within the stem villus. H & E stain. Low power.

FIG. 18-44. Chorionic villi at mid-pregnancy, showing points of attachment (pa) to the underlying wall of the endometrium. H & E stain. Low power.

FIG. 18-45. Chorionic villi (cv) of placenta at mid-pregnancy. The tendency of the nuclei of the syncytial trophoblastic layer to accumulate as syncytial knots (sk) can be made out. H & E stain. Intermediate power.

FIG. 18-46. Chorionic villi of placenta at mid-pregnancy. Dark-staining areas are syncytial knots (sk). H & E stain. High power.

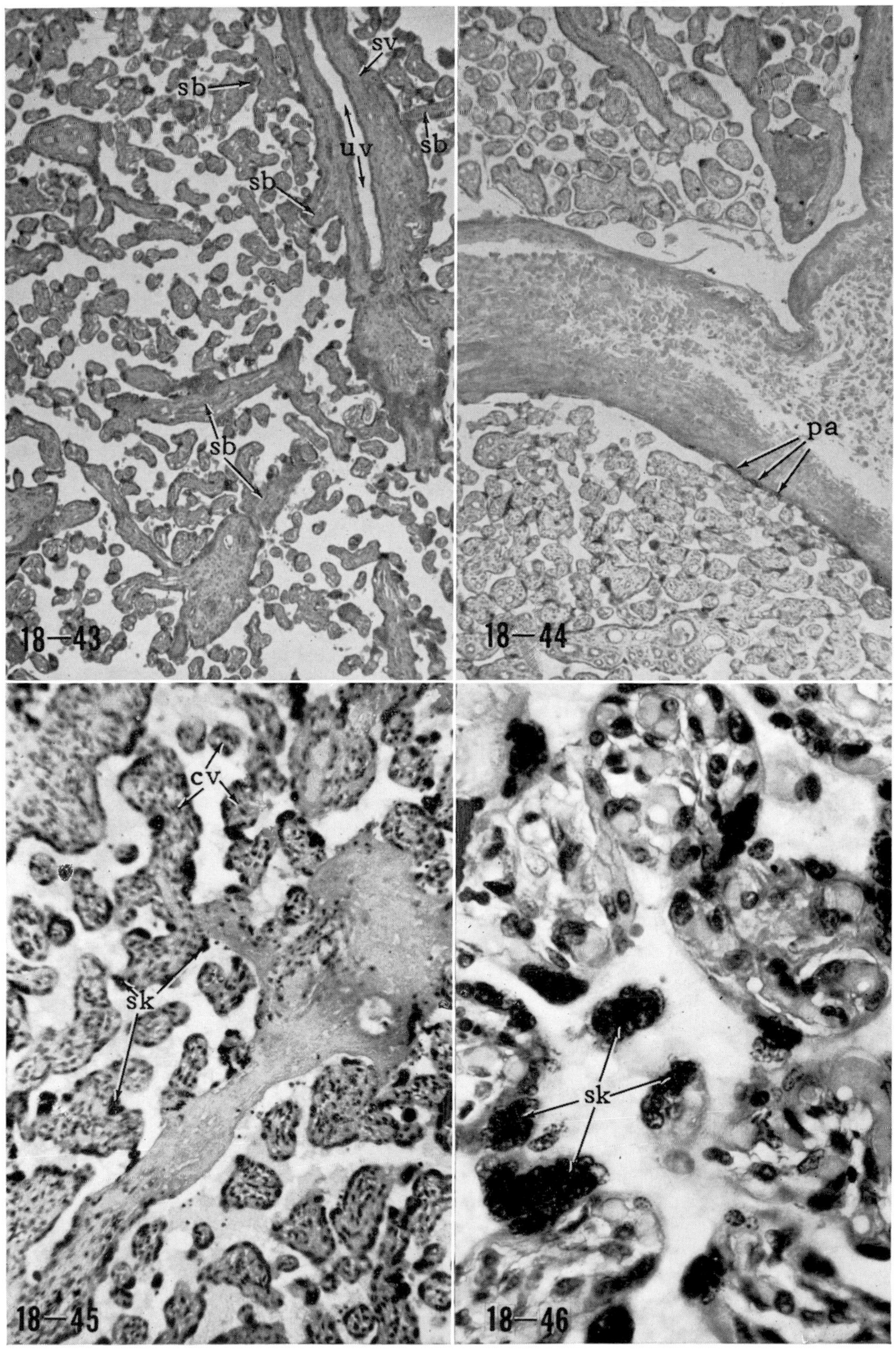
sv
sb
uv
sb
sb
sb
18—43
pa
18—44
cv
sk
18—45
sk
18—46

once again thickens and varies cyclically, depending on ovarian activity. It should be mentioned that changes in the vaginal epithelium are less defined than those that occur in the uterine endometrium. As would be expected, with waning estrogenic levels, following the menopause, the vaginal epithelium becomes thinned.

The epithelium rests on a lamina propria composed of a dense type of connective tissue that is rich in elastic fibers. In addition, this connective tissue contains an abundance of lymphocytes. In the deeper portion of the lamina propria the connective tissue becomes looser and even more vascular, containing dense plexuses of small veins. Especially in the posterior wall, the lamina propria forms numerous high papillae that jut into the covering epithelium. Except for a few isolated cervical-type glands in the region of the fornix (uppermost) of the vagina, no glands are present. Therefore, the mucosa is lubricated by secretions derived from glands of the cervix (Plate 152).

The tunica muscularis consists of interlacing bundles of smooth muscle fibers irregularly arranged into indefinite inner circular and outer thicker longitudinal layers. An abundance of fibrous connective tissue rich in elastic fibers is found interspersed between the muscle bundles. In addition, the presence of vascular spaces between the muscle bundles often gives this tunic the appearance of erectile tissue. Guarding the external orifice of the vagina (the introitus) is a circular sphincter of striated muscle fibers.

The thin fibrous coat of dense connective tissue rich in elastic fibers merges with the looser adjoining connective tissue that attaches the vagina to adjacent structures. A large venous plexus, lymphatics and nerve bundles are found in this connective tissue layer.

At the lower end of the vagina is a transverse, semicircular fold of the mucous membrane, the **hymen**. Histologically, it is characterized by a thin connective tissue core and stratified squamous epithelium on both surfaces.

G. EXTERNAL GENITALIA

The external genitalia include the **clitoris**, the **labia majora** and **minora** and the **glands of Bartholin** which open into the vestibule of the vagina.

1. Clitoris

The clitoris consists of two small, erectile cavernous bodies covered by the mucous membrane of the vestibulum vaginae which is lined by stratified squamous epithelium.

PLATE 150—Placenta

Fig. 18-47. Placenta at term showing dense packing of chorionic villi (cv). H & E stain. Low power.

Fig. 18-48. Placenta at term, showing larger villi among numerous smaller villi. Note the large blood vessels (v) in the connective tissue cores of the larger villi. H & E stain. Low power.

Fig. 18-49. Placental villi at term. Note that large numbers of syncytial knots (sk) are present as small dark areas scattered throughout the field. H & E stain. Low power.

Fig. 18-50. Placental villi at term. Note that the connective tissue cores of the villi contain large numbers of blood vessels. H & E stain. Low power.

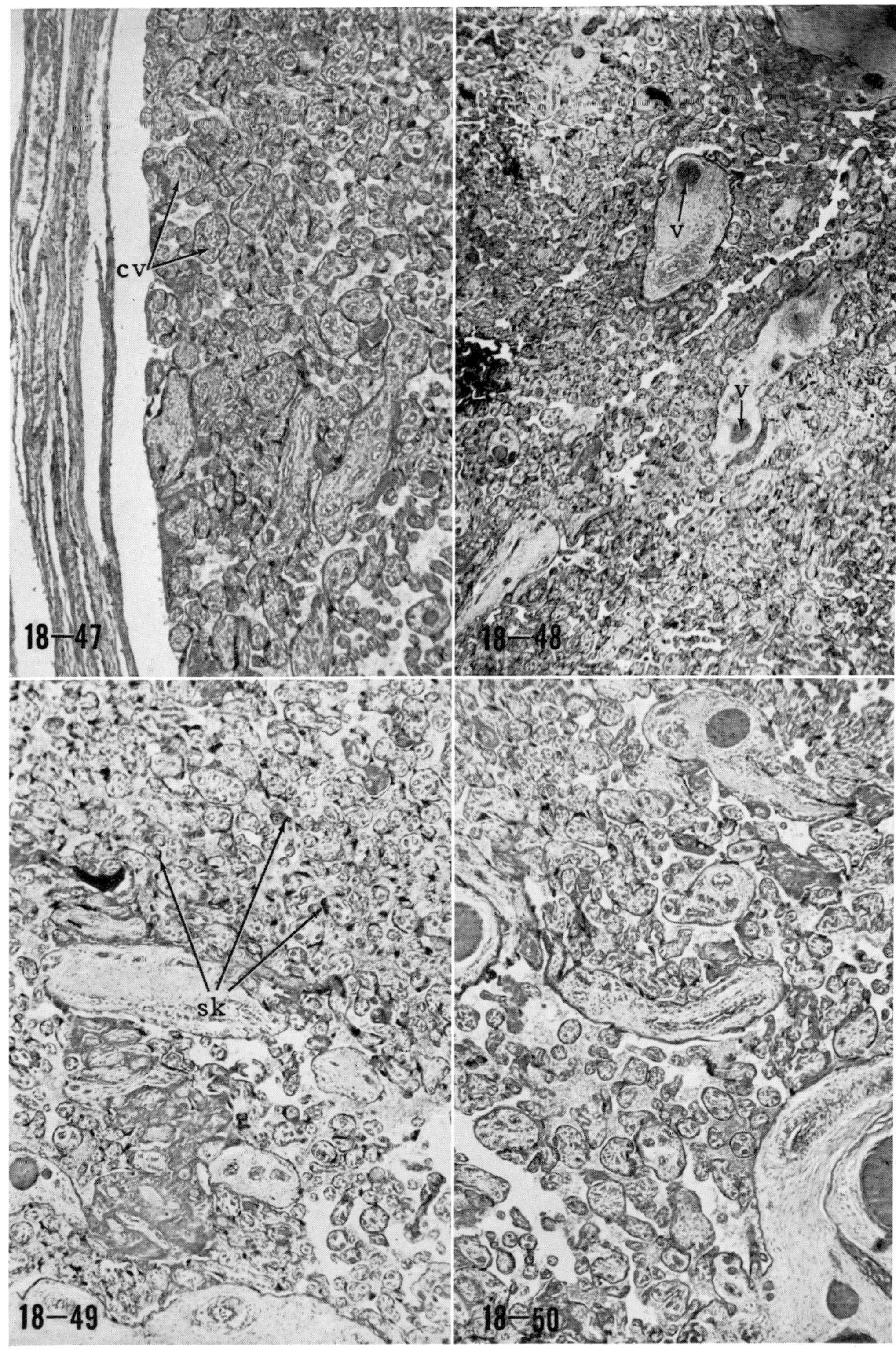
cv
18—47
v
v
18—48
sk
18—49
18—50

2. Labia Majora

The labia majora are folds of skin containing a large amount of adipose tissue and a thin layer of smooth muscle. Hair covers only the outer surface, but numerous sebaceous and sweat glands are found on both surfaces.

3. Labia Minora (Figs. 18-65, 18-66)

Each of the labia minora consists of a core of spongy connective tissue that is rich in blood vessels and elastic fibers and is covered by stratified squamous epithelium. Both surfaces contain numerous large sebaceous glands and are hairless.

4. Glands of Bartholin

Two tubulo-alveolar glands, the glands of Bartholin, secrete a lubricating mucus onto the inner surface of the labia minora.

Sensory nerve endings are found associated with the external genitalia.

PLATE 151—Decidua

FIG. 18-51. Gravid uterine endometrium at early pregnancy. The site of this section is adjacent to the developing embryo. Note that the uterine glands either appear very much sacculated (sg) or appear to have been broken down (bg). Also note the vascular engorgement (ve) and the appearance of the stromal connective tissue (ct). H & E stain. Low power.

FIG. 18-52. Decidua in early pregnancy, showing massive erosion of the endometrial tissue. H & E stain. Low power.

FIG. 18-53. Intermediate-power view of an adjacent portion of Figure 18-52, showing the masses of decidual cells (dc) in the stroma.

FIG. 18-54. Decidual cells (dc) under the epithelium (ep) lining the free surface of a gravid uterus. Mallory-Azan stain. High power.

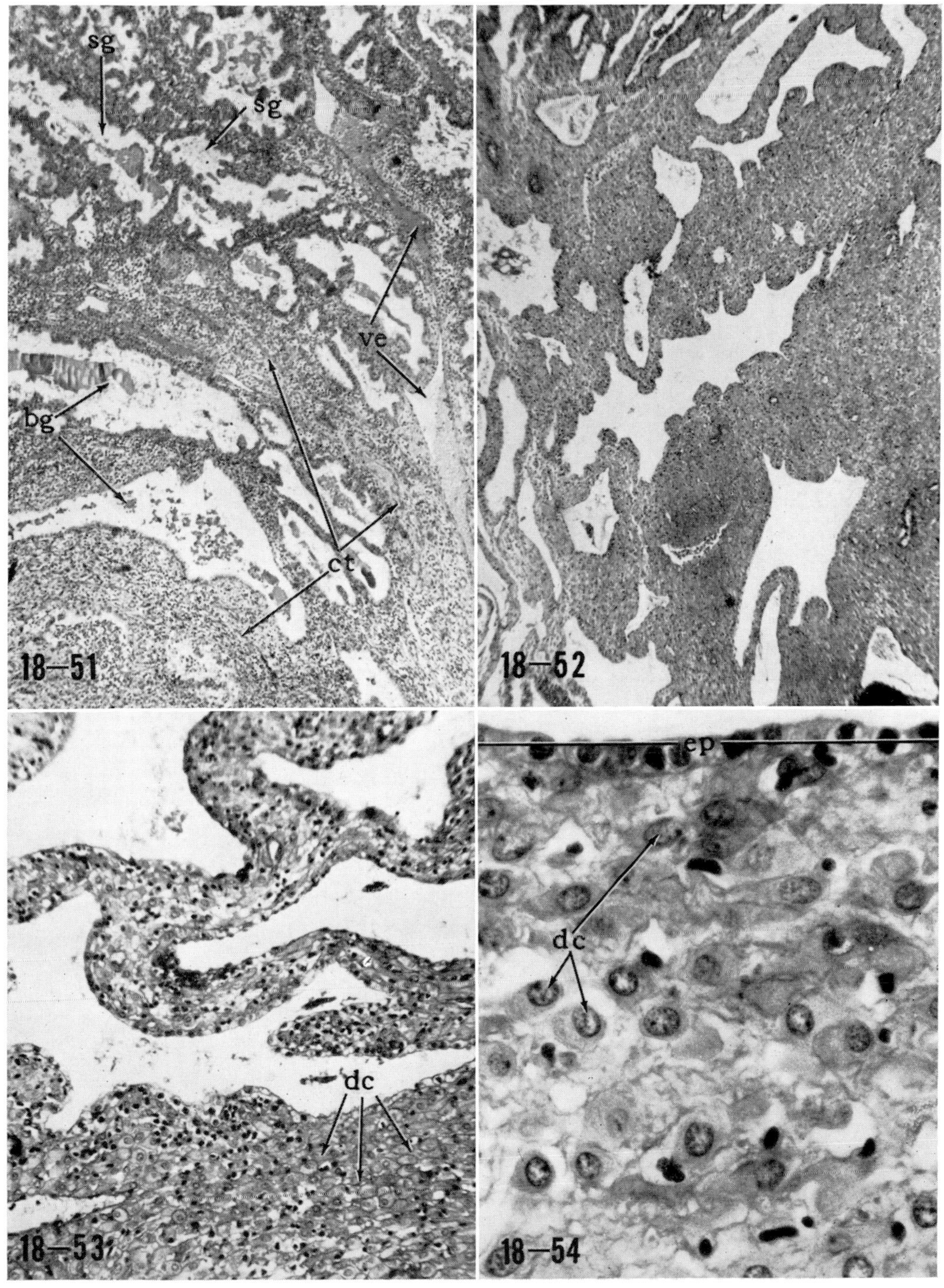
sg
sg
ve
bg
ct
18–51
18–52
dc
18–53
ep
dc
18–54

PLATE 152—Cervix

FIG. 18-55. Survey section of the cervix, showing several cervical glands (g) lying in the lamina propria with some of them opening directly into the uterine lumen. H & E stain. Low power. (e, simple columnar epithelium lining)

FIG. 18-56. Section showing the abrupt beginning of stratified squamous epithelium (ss) at the junction of the cervical canal and the portio vaginalis. Note the presence of the cervical glands (g) in the lamina propria and also note the muscular layer (m). H & E stain. Low power.

FIG. 18-57. Cervical glands in the lamina propria of the cervical-vaginal junction area, showing their tall columnar epithelial nature. H & E stain. Intermediate power.

FIG. 18-58. High-power view of the cervical glands in the lamina propria (lp) of the mucosa. H & E stain. (v, blood vessels)

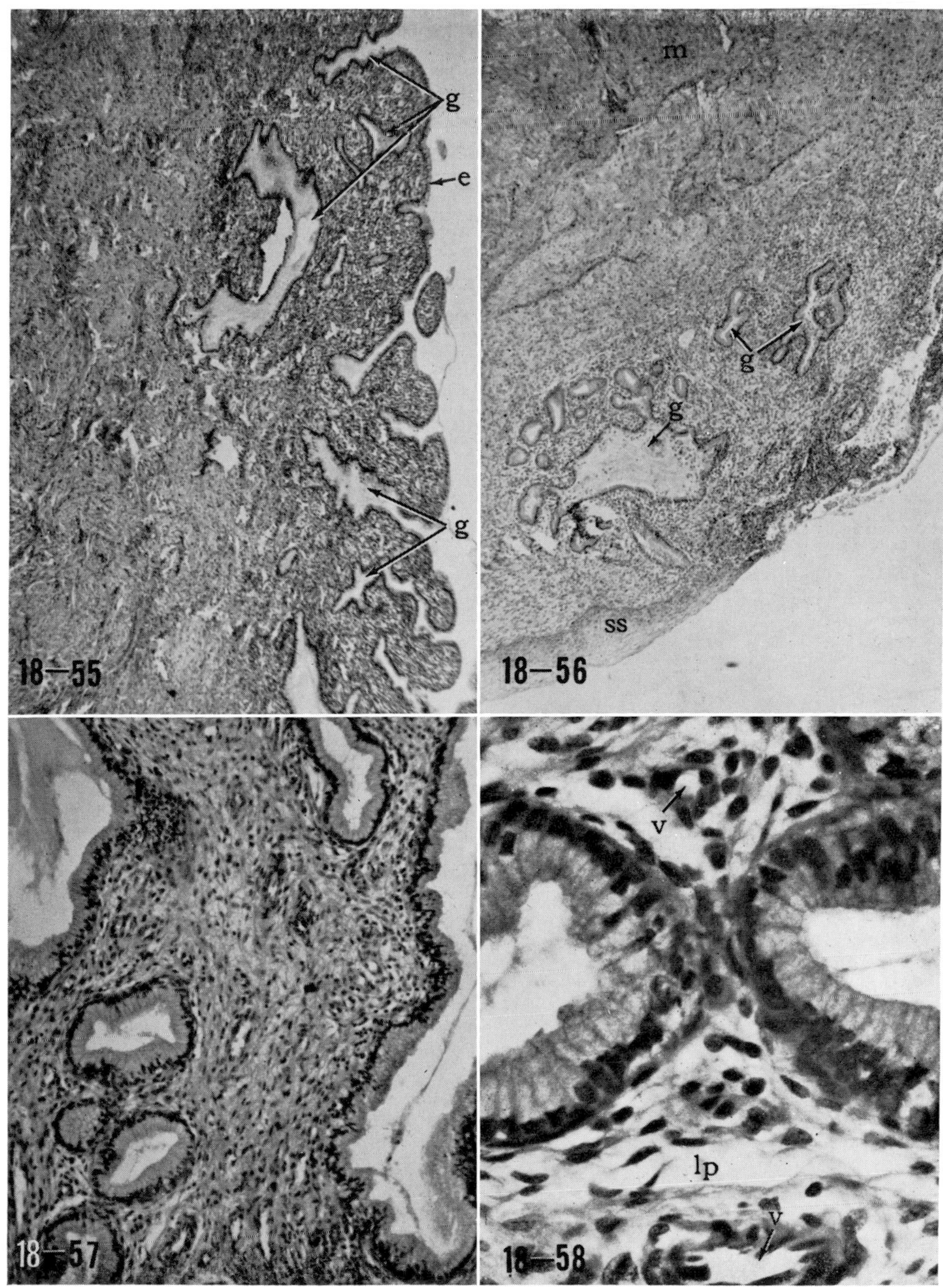
g
e
g
18—55
m
g
g
g
ss
18—56
18—57
v
lp
v
18—58

PLATE 153—Vagina

FIG. 18-59. Section of the mucosa of the portio vaginalis showing the presence of cervical glands (g) and blood vessels (v). H & E stain. Low power. (ss, stratified squamous epithelium)

FIG. 18-60. Survey section through the wall of the vagina. H & E stain. Low power. (ss, stratified squamous epithelium; p, papillae; v, blood vessels; lp, lamina propria; lm, longitudinal smooth muscle layer)

FIG. 18-61. Survey section of the vagina, revealing arterial blood vessels (v) in the longitudinal smooth muscle layer (lm). H & E stain. Low power. (ss, stratified squamous epithelium; lp, lamina propria)

FIG. 18-62. Section of the deeper portion of the lamina propria of the vagina, revealing the presence of a large plexus of venous and lymph channels. H & E stain. Intermediate power.

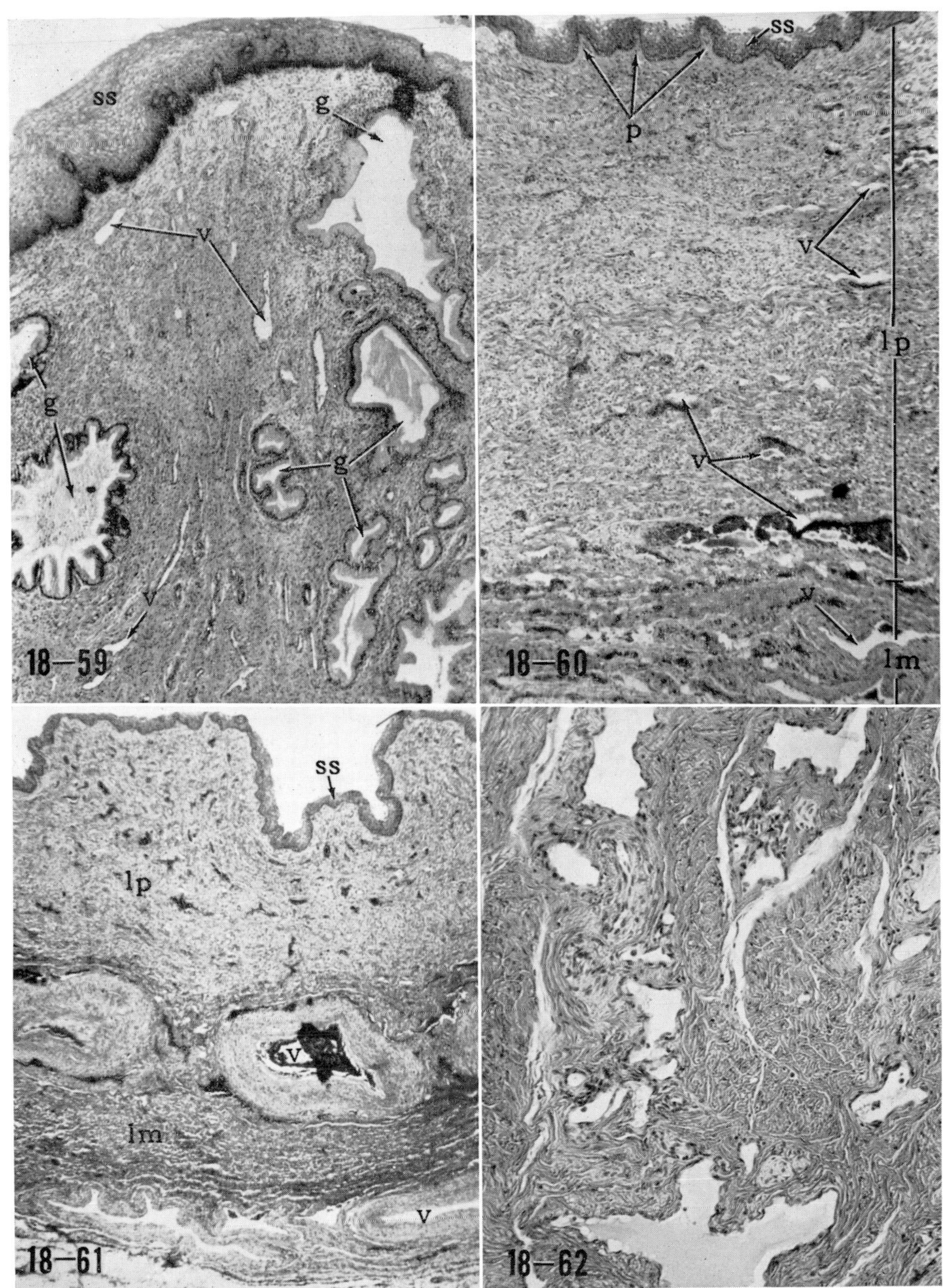
ss
g
v
g
g
v
18-59
ss
p
v
lp
v
v
lm
18-60
ss
lp
v
lm
v
18-61
18-62

PLATE 154—Vagina and Labia Minora

FIG. 18-63. Mucosa of the vagina, emphasizing the nature of its lamina propria and epithelium. Note the dense interlacing arrangement of the connective tissue with the presence of diffuse lymphocytic material and vessels. H & E stain. Intermediate power. (ss, stratified squamous epithelium; p, connective tissue papillae)

FIG. 18-64. High-power view showing the stratified squamous epithelium and the underlying lamina propria (lp) of the vagina. H & E stain.

FIG. 18-65. Survey section of the labia minora. Note the spongy nature of the connective tissue due to the large numbers of blood vessels (v). H & E stain. Low power. (ss, stratified squamous epithelium; sg, sebaceous glands)

FIG. 18-66. Intermediate-power view of a portion of Figure 18-65, showing the stratified squamous (ss) nature of the epithelium with underlying connective tissue containing many vessels (v) and large sebaceous glands (sg).

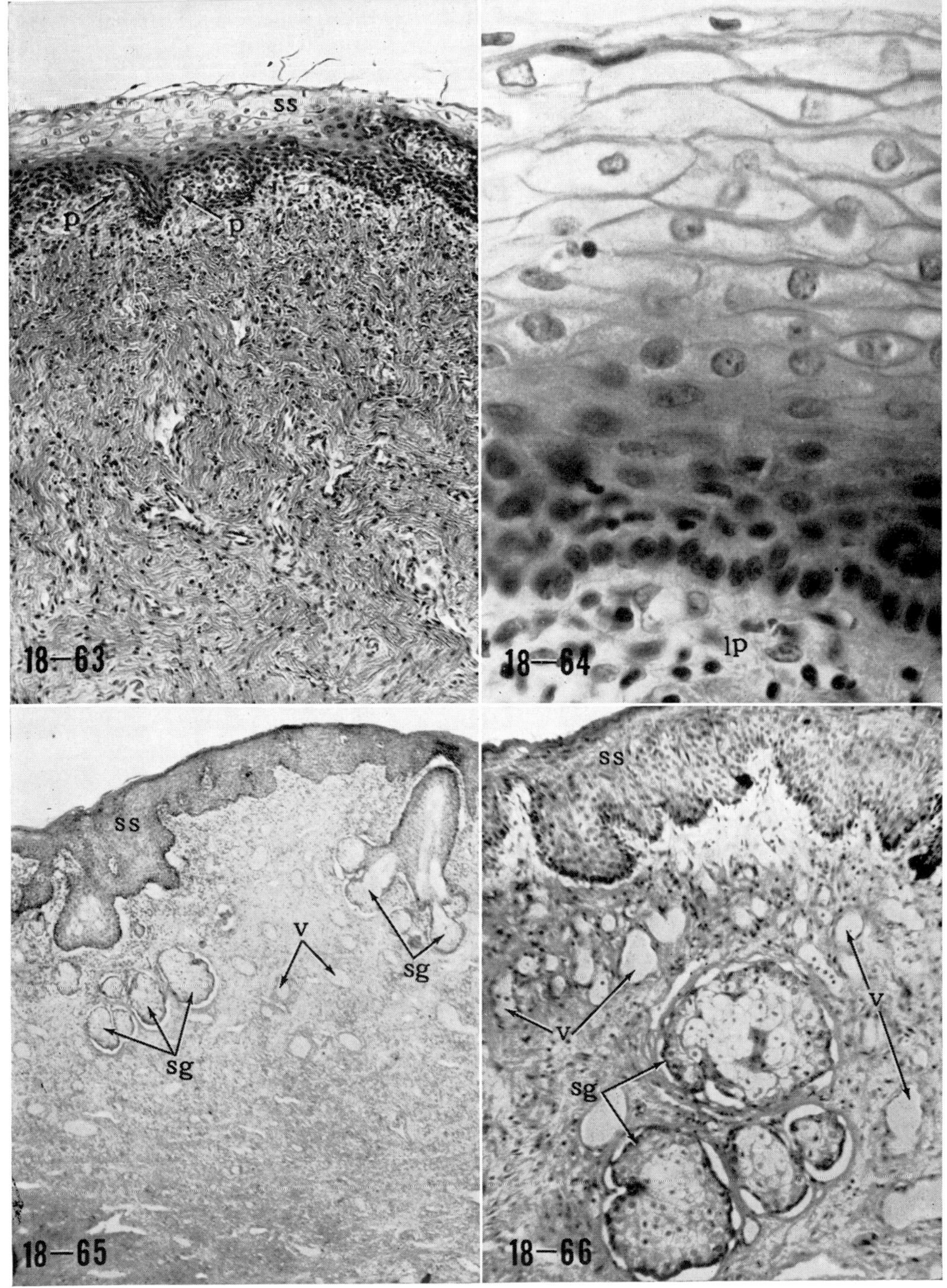
ss
p
p
18–63
lp
18–64
ss
v
sg
sg
18–65
ss
v
v
sg
18–66

19 · The Male Reproductive System

The male reproductive system consists of the testes, organs that produce the male sex cells and hormone, a system of excretory ducts for transmitting and storing the sperm, accessory glands and the penis.

A. TESTIS

(Plates 155 and 156)

This organ is a compound tubular gland invested by a thick outer capsule of dense collagenous tissue, the **tunica albuginea**, and an inner vascular layer of loose connective tissue, the **tunica vasculosa**. Trabeculae extend into and through the gland to a mass of connective tissue, the **mediastinum testis**, which contains the proximal portion of the excretory duct system. The parenchyma consists mainly of convoluted and coiled **seminiferous tubules**. These structural and functional units of the testis are organized into lobules, the **lobuli testis**, by connective tis-

PLATE 155—Testis

FIG. 19-1. Over-all view of a 7-month-old fetal testis, showing the arrangement of the seminiferous tubules (st) in each of the conical lobules (l), and part of the excretory duct system. Note the portion of the tunica albuginea (ta) with its septuli testis (s) forming thin partitions which divide the testis into lobules. H & E stain. Low power. (tr, area of tubuli recti; rt, rete testis)

FIG. 19-2. A slightly higher magnification of a portion of Figure 19-1, showing the arrangement of the seminiferous tubules (st) into compartments. Low power. (s, septuli testis)

FIG. 19-3. Section through the adult testis, showing a portion of the capsule or tunica albuginea (ta) overlying the convoluted seminiferous tubules. H & E stain. Low power.

FIG. 19-4. A slightly higher magnification of an adjacent portion of Figure 19-3, showing the stratified epithelial nature of the convoluted seminiferous tubules. H & E stain. Low power.

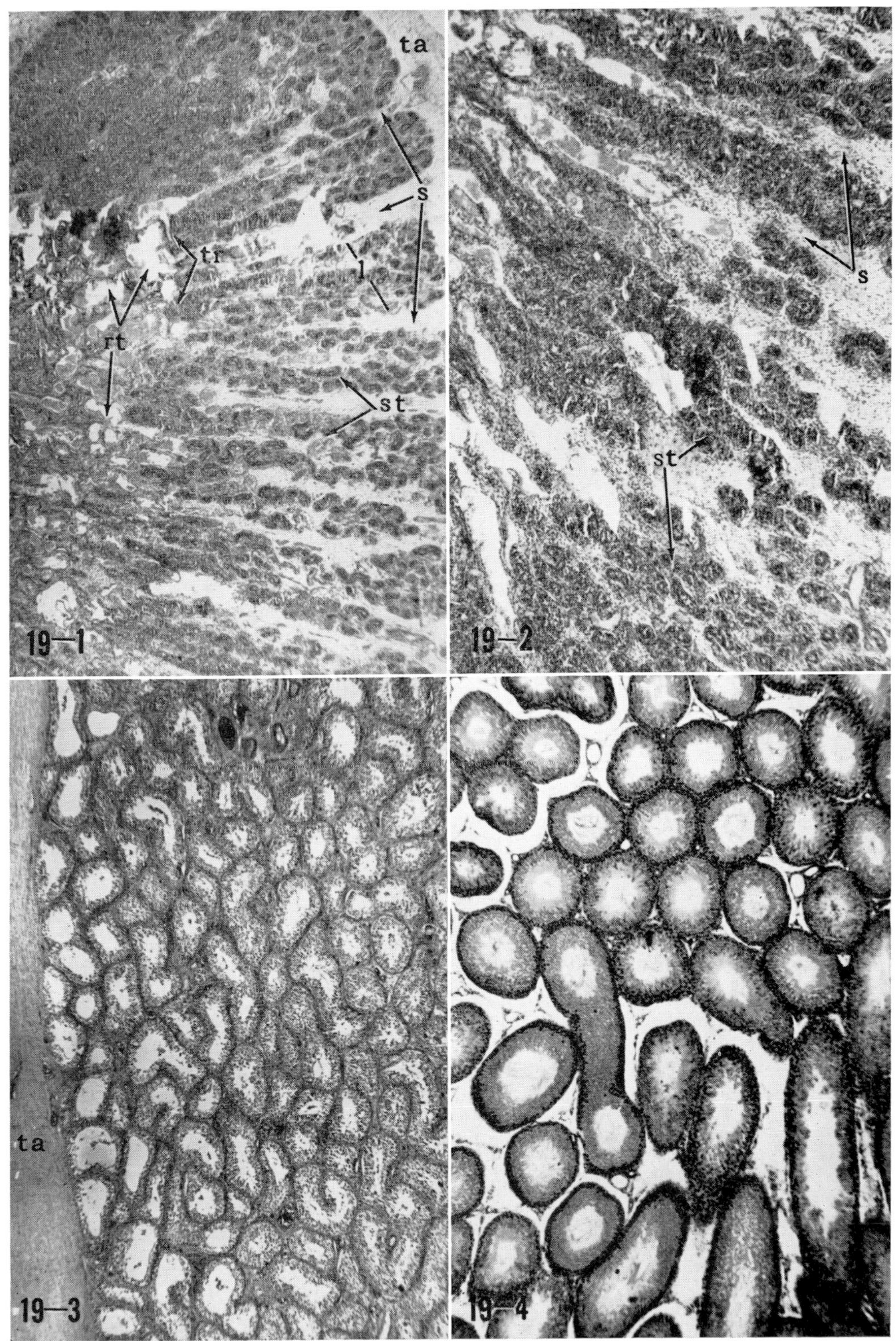
ta
s
tr
l
rt
st
19—1
s
st
19—2
ta
19—3
19—4

sue septa, the **septula testis**, which radiate from the mediastinum to the tunica albuginea. The seminiferous tubules are embedded in a vascularized, loose connective tissue and are lined by a complex stratified epithelium consisting mainly of **spermatogenic cells** and a small number of **sustentacular cells of Sertoli**. (See Figs. 19-1 to 19-6.) The **spermatogenic** or **germinal cells** vary in size and are round to polyhedral in shape. These cells are usually grouped into 4 to 6 layers depending on the activity of the tubule at any given time. During spermatogenesis, each layer contains different proliferative and developmental stages related to the maturation of spermatozoa. Within the seminiferous tubule, this process takes place from without inward so that the most immature cells, the **spermatogonia**, are close to the basement membrane. These cells are round or cuboidal, with characteristic rounded nuclei rich in chromatin material. The next layer of cells occupies the middle epithelial zone of the seminiferous tubule and is the result of mitotic division of the spermatogonia. These daughter cells, the **primary spermatocytes**, are somewhat larger spherical elements with conspicuous large nuclei. Characteristically, the nuclei contain dense and clumped chromatin which is associated with a high frequency of mitosis. Adjacent to and arising from the primary spermatocytes are found the **secondary spermatocytes**. These cells have the same general characteristics as their parent cells but are somewhat smaller. Next to the spermatocytes are found the **spermatids**. These are still smaller cells that have elongate vesicular nuclei. Finally, the spermatids undergo a series of morphological transformations into **spermatozoa** which border on the lumina of the tubules. Each spermatozoon consists of a flattened, almond-shaped head and an attenuated tail. The tail is composed of (1) a middle piece containing the axial filament surrounded by a spiral mitochondrial sheath; (2) a principal piece containing the axial filament enclosed by a fibrous sheath; and (3) an end-piece containing the axial filament enclosed only by the plasma membrane that invests the entire sperm. (See Plate 157.)

It should be mentioned that spermatogenesis is under the control of follicle-stimulating hormone (FSH) in most mammalian forms.

The **Sertoli cells** (Fig. 19-7) are slender elongated elements that extend full length across the wall of the seminiferous tubules from basement membrane to lumen. They are interspersed among but are poorly delineated from adjacent spermatogenic cells.

PLATE 156—Testis

FIG. 19-5. Adult testis showing seminiferous tubules cut obliquely. Note the vascularized interstitial connective tissue (ict) between the tubules. The stratified arrangement of the epithelial cells of the tubules is evident. H & E stain. Intermediate power. (sp, spermatozoa in lumen)

FIG. 19-6. Adult testis, showing seminiferous tubules cut transversely. H & E stain. Intermediate power. (ict, vascularized interstitial connective tissue; sc, stratified epithelium of tubules; sp, spermatozoa in lumen)

FIG. 19-7. Adult testis, revealing a portion of a seminiferous tubule to demonstrate the large numbers of spermatogenic cells in various stages of spermatogenesis and a few sustentacular cells of Sertoli (S). H & E stain. High power. (b, basement membrane; l, lumen; sg, spermatogonia; ps, primary spermatocytes; sd, spermatids; s, maturing sperm)

FIG. 19-8. Adult testis, revealing portions of 3 contiguous seminiferous tubules with a group of interstitial cells of Leydig (L) within the vascularized interstitial connective tissue. H & E stain. High power. (b, basement membrane; sg, spermatogonia; m, spermatogonium in mitosis; ps, primary spermatocytes; ss, secondary spermatocytes; sd, spermatids; s, maturing sperm; S, Sertoli cell)

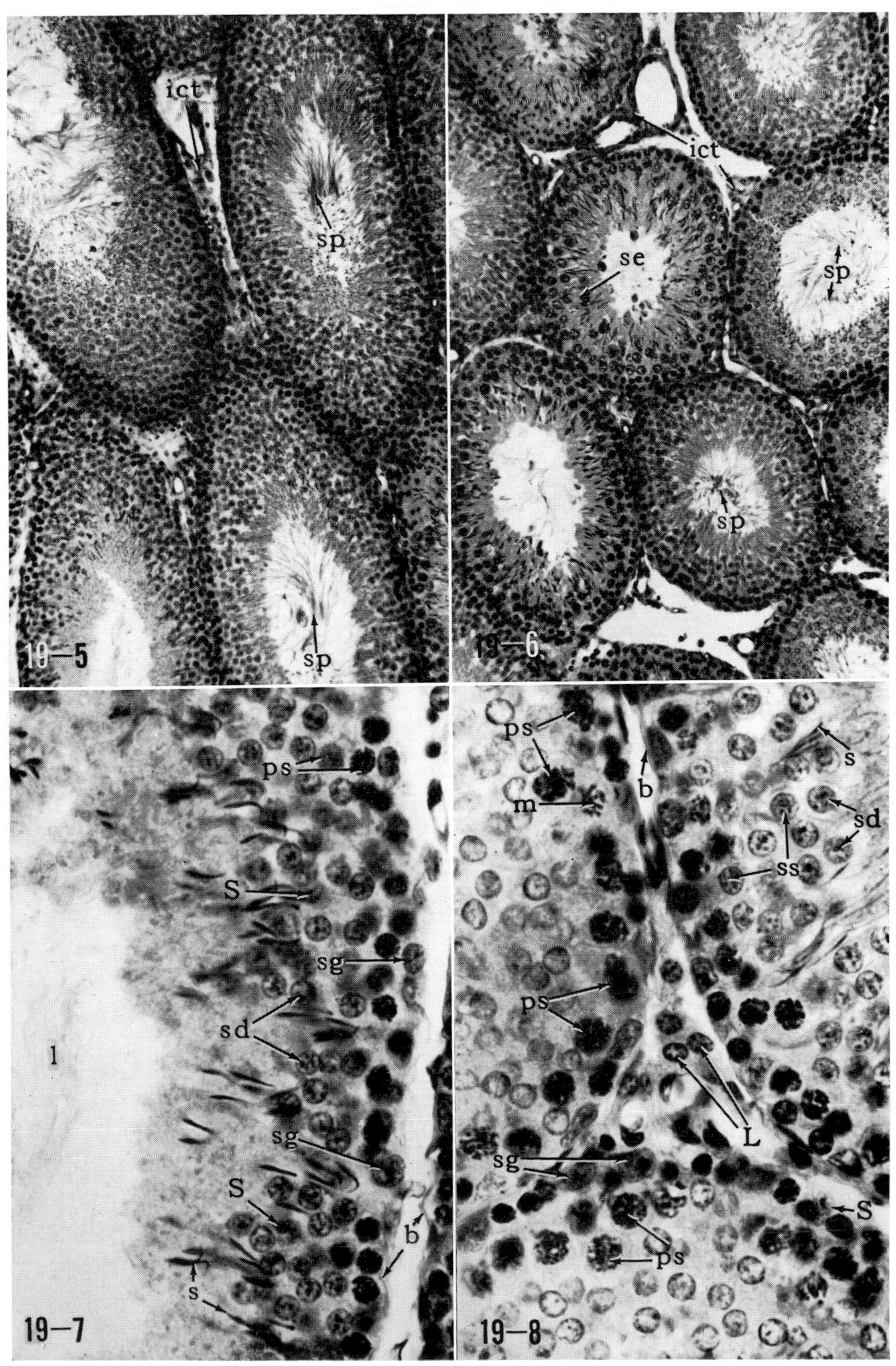
ict
sp
sp
19—5
ict
se
sp
sp
19—6
ps
S
sg
sd
1
sg
S
b
s
19—7
ps
b
m
s
sd
ss
ps
L
sg
S
ps
19—8

Characteristically, the Sertoli cell has a pale, loosely reticular cytoplasm and a vesicular, oval nucleus, that is oriented in the same direction as the cell. A large compound nucleolus is present. These cells have an indistinct outline, and in certain sections it often appears that maturing spermatozoa have their heads embedded in the apical ends of the cells. Electron micrographs reveal that the spermatozoa are not embedded but rather lie outside the plasma membrane of the Sertoli cell in deep surface recesses. Presumably, the Sertoli cells serve as a structural support for the spermatogenic cells and also serve to provide nutriment for the spermatids.

The **interstitial cells (of Leydig)** (Fig. 19-8) are located in the loose connective tissue spaces between the seminiferous tubules and usually occur as cell groups associated with capillaries. Characteristically, these cells are large, irregular and polyhedral and contain large spherical or ovoid nuclei with distinct nucleoli in an abundantly granular cytoplasm.

The site of production of testicular hormones is ascribed variously by different investigators to the interstitial cells, the seminiferous epithelium or to both of these elements. However, most data favor the interstitial cells as the hormone-producing elements. The male sex hormones produced by the testis are called androgens (testosterone and the principal partially metabolized excretory product, androsterone). However, androgenic substances may also be produced by the adrenal cortex and the ovaries (presumably secreted by the corpus luteum). With the onset of puberty, gonadotropin production (ICSH or LH) by the pituitary causes significant changes in the testes (maturity) with the elaboration of the steroid testosterone. This anabolic steroid induces the development and provides for the maintenance of the male accessory sexual organs and sex characteristics (beard development, deepening of voice and general metabolic effects such as growth and the associated increase in muscle mass during adolescence) and is responsible for the occurrence of sex drive.

B. TUBULI RECTI

Spermatozoa leave the seminiferous tubules and pass into the **tubuli recti** (Fig. 19-12), the first segment of the passageway of excretory ducts located adjacent to and extending into the mediastinum. The exact mode of passage of the germinal products into the short, straight tubules is still unsolved. The walls of the tubuli recti are lined by a columnar epithelium of the Sertoli cell type that are richly laden with fat droplets. The fibrous basement membrane, characteristic of the seminiferous tubules, is diminished in amount around the straight tubules. In addition, smooth muscle is absent around these tubules.

PLATE 157—Developing Sperm

FIG. 19-9. Young spermatid (human). Note the acrosome vacuole (a), the Golgi apparatus (G) and the mitochondria (m). × 17,500.

FIG. 19-10. Maturing spermatid (human). Note that the distribution of the cytoplasmic granules (g) is compact. Also observe the vacuole (v), the centriole complex (c), the tail sleeve (ts) and the remnant of lamellar bodies (lb). × 23,000.

FIG. 19-11. Anchoring of the sperm tail (human). Note the development of the nuclear membrane at the anchoring site. During the course of segmentation of the tail root (tr), a lateral projection (lp) consisting of multiple fibrils is seen grasping the tail root. Also observe the axial filament (af), the side filaments (sf) and the centriole material (c), × 40,000.

(Figs. 19-9 to 19-11 from Horstmann, E.: Z. Zellforsch. *54*:68)

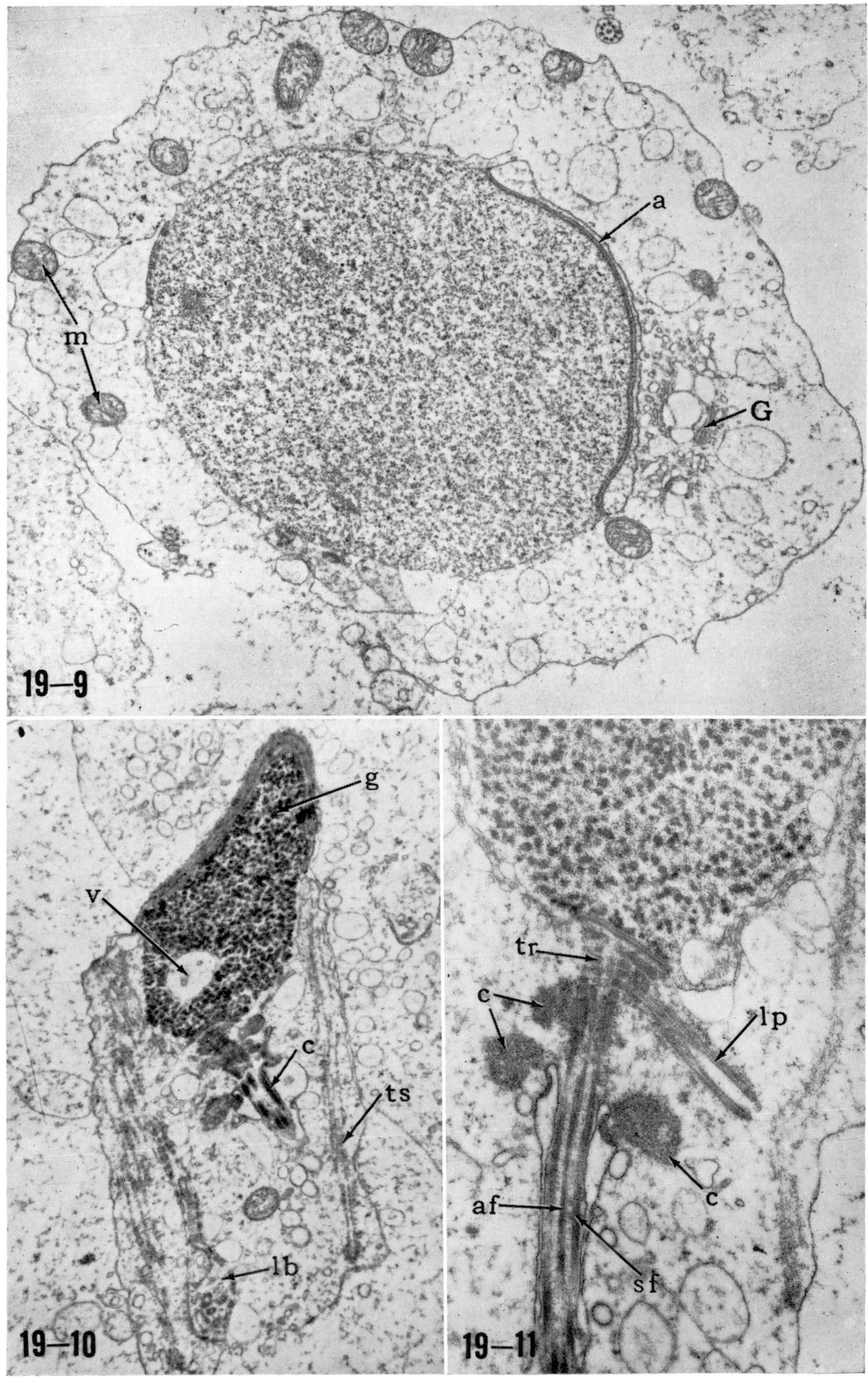
a
m
G
19—9
g
v
c
ts
lb
19—10
tr
c
lp
c
af
sf
19—11

C. RETE TESTIS

From the tubuli recti, spermatozoa move into the **rete testis** (Fig. 19-12). This segment of the excretory duct system, located in the mediastinum, is composed of a series of wide, irregular, anastomosing spaces lined by a simple cuboidal or squamous epithelium. Because of the delicate nature of the epithelial walls of the rete testis, the absence of a fibrous membrane and the absence of associated smooth muscle fibers, these passageways are frequently compressed during histologic preparation and appear as epithelial streaks.

D. DUCTULI EFFERENTES (Figs. 19-13 and 19-14)

Twelve to 20 **ductuli efferentes** arise from the rete testis in the upper posterior portion of the mediastinum. At first these ductules are straight; then they become highly coiled and convoluted, forming a series of conical bodies, the **coni vasculosi**, which are held together by connective tissue and constitute the head of the epididymis. The epithelium of the ductuli efferentes rests on a thin basement membrane and consists of groups of simple high columnar ciliated cells which alternate with a type of nonciliated cuboidal cells referred to as **intraepithelial glands**. Both types of epithelia have a granular cytoplasm and appear to be secretory in function. Unlike the tubuli recti and the rete testis, the ductuli efferentes are all surrounded by a layer of circularly arranged smooth muscle. Contraction of this muscle propels the sperm to the next portion of the excretory duct system.

E. DUCTUS EPIDIDYMIS (Figs. 19-14 to 19-17)

Opposite the bases of the coni vasculosi, the ductuli efferentes open into a single convoluted tube, the **ductus epididymis**, which constitutes the body and the tail of the epididymis. Unlike the irregular contour found in association with the lumen of the ductuli efferentes, the ductus epididymis presents a smooth luminal surface which is wider and more circular. A pseudostratified secretory columnar epithelium possessing **stereocilia** lines the passageway. There is a well-developed basement membrane surrounded by a small amount of circularly disposed smooth muscle. The ductus epididymis serves as a temporary storehouse for spermatozoa that enables maturation to occur before they are pushed into the ductus deferens.

F. DUCTUS DEFERENS (Figs. 19-18 and 19-19)

That portion of the excretory duct that extends from the tail of the epididymis,

PLATE 158—Testis, Ductuli Efferentes and Ductus Epididymis

FIG. 19-12. Adult testis, showing a few tubuli recti (tr) and the irregular anastomosing spaces, the rete testis (rt), in dense connective tissue (ct). Mallory stain. Low power. (v, blood vessels)

FIG. 19-13. Ductuli efferentes (de) of adult testis. Note the wavy appearance of the inner surface of these tubules due to the varying height of the cells. The basement membranes (b) are surrounded by vascularized lamina propria (lp) and some circularly arranged smooth muscle cells (sm). Mallory stain. Low power. (s, sperm)

FIG. 19-14. Ductuli efferentes (de) and adjacent ductus epididymis (ep) embedded in connective tissue (ct). H & E stain. Low power.

FIG. 19-15. A slightly higher magnification of an adjacent portion of the ductus epididymis of Figure 19-14. Note the convoluted nature of this canal and the smooth inner surface of these tubules. The surrounding lamina propria is richly vascularized. H & E stain. Low power.

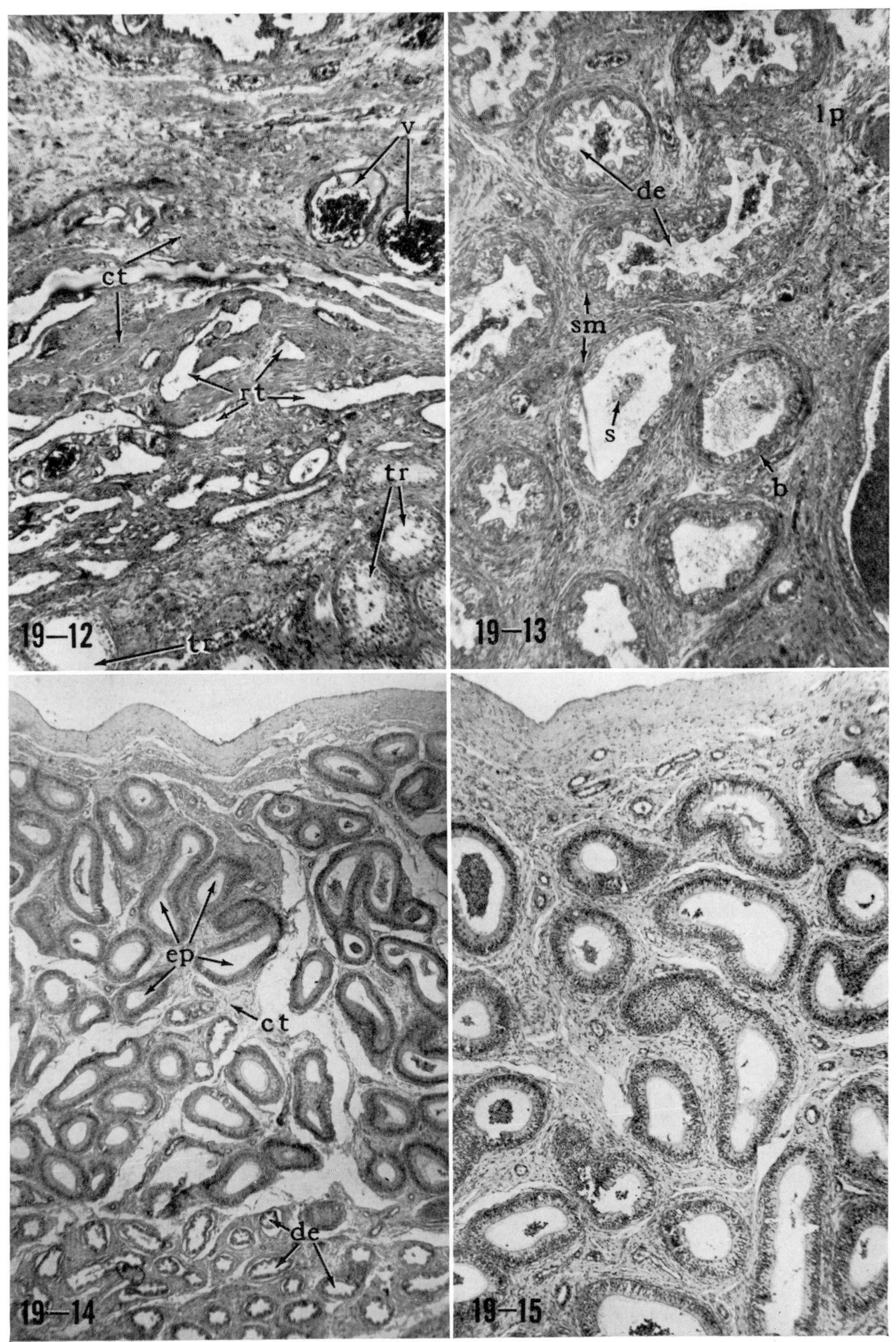
v
ct
rt
tr
tr
19—12
de
lp
sm
s
b
19—13
ep
ct
de
19—14
19—15

enters the spermatic cord and continues as far as the posterior surface of the prostate gland, is known as the **ductus deferens**. Its mucosa is not uniform in all parts. Near the beginning, the mucosa is thrown into longitudinal folds and is lined with an epithelium similar to but somewhat lower than that in the epididymis. Further along, most of the folded mucosa becomes lined with a nonciliated pseudostratified columnar epithelium. The tunica propria is distinct, being compact and richly laden with elastic fibers. The muscularis is well developed, constitutes the thickest coat of the wall, and is arranged as 3 layers of smooth muscle—an inner longitudinal, a thick intermediate circular, and an outer longitudinal. (The quick transmission of sperm that occurs with ejaculation is promoted by the strong musculature and also by the presence of large amounts of elastic fibers in the walls of the duct.) An external adventitial coat of a loose fibroelastic nature is present and contains numerous blood vessels (including the veins of the pampiniform plexus) and nerves.

The lumen of the ductus deferens remains narrow until, after crossing in front of the ureter, it reaches the medial border of the seminal vesicle. Here the lumen broadens into a spindle-shaped enlargement, the **ampulla**. Other histologic differences between the region of the ampulla and the rest of the ductus deferens are the presence of numerous, thin, complicated folds of mucosa and the existence of a thinner muscular coat.

Just before joining the excretory duct of the seminal vesicle, the ductus deferens becomes the short, straight **ejaculatory duct**. As the ejaculatory duct, it pierces the body of the prostate and opens into the prostatic portion of the urethra. The mucosa of the ejaculatory duct is thrown into many fine folds that form recesses. The epithelium lining these folds is of the pseudostratified columnar type; it becomes transitional near the urethral opening. These epithelial cells contain large quantities of yellow pigment granules, a feature that is indicative of a glandular function. The remainder of the wall is composed of a surrounding stroma of connective tissue that is rich in elastic fibers. There is no muscular layer as such, except for the presence of the fibromuscular tissue of the prostate gland.

G. SEMINAL VESICLES
(Plate 160)

The **seminal vesicles** are elongated branched saccular evaginations of the ampulla of the ductus deferens, whose lower portions join with the ductus deferens to form the ejaculatory duct. The most striking feature of these glandular organs is the fold-

PLATE 159—Epididymis and Ductus Deferens

FIG. 19-16. Intermediate-power view of the ductus epididymis, showing the smooth inner surface of the tubules with their lumina containing spermatozoa. Tubules are embedded in a vascularized lamina propria. Mallory stain.

FIG. 19-17. Ductus epididymis, showing the nature of the epithelium and the subjacent lamina propria (lp). Note the nonmotile stereocilia (sc) on the free surface of the columnar cells. Basal cells (bc) form a discontinuous layer on the inner surface of the basement membrane (b). H & E stain. High power. (s, sperm in lumen; v, blood vessels in connective tissue)

FIG. 19-18. Cross section through the ductus deferens, showing the tunica mucosa (m), muscularis (sm) and fibrosa (f) blending with the surrounding connective tissue. Masson stain. Low power. (v, blood vessels)

FIG. 19-19. Intermediate-power view of ductus deferens. Masson stain. (e, columnar epithelium with a suggestion of stereocilia; lp, lamina propria; ilm, inner longitudinal smooth muscle; mcm, middle circular smooth muscle; elm, external longitudinal smooth muscle; v, blood vessels)

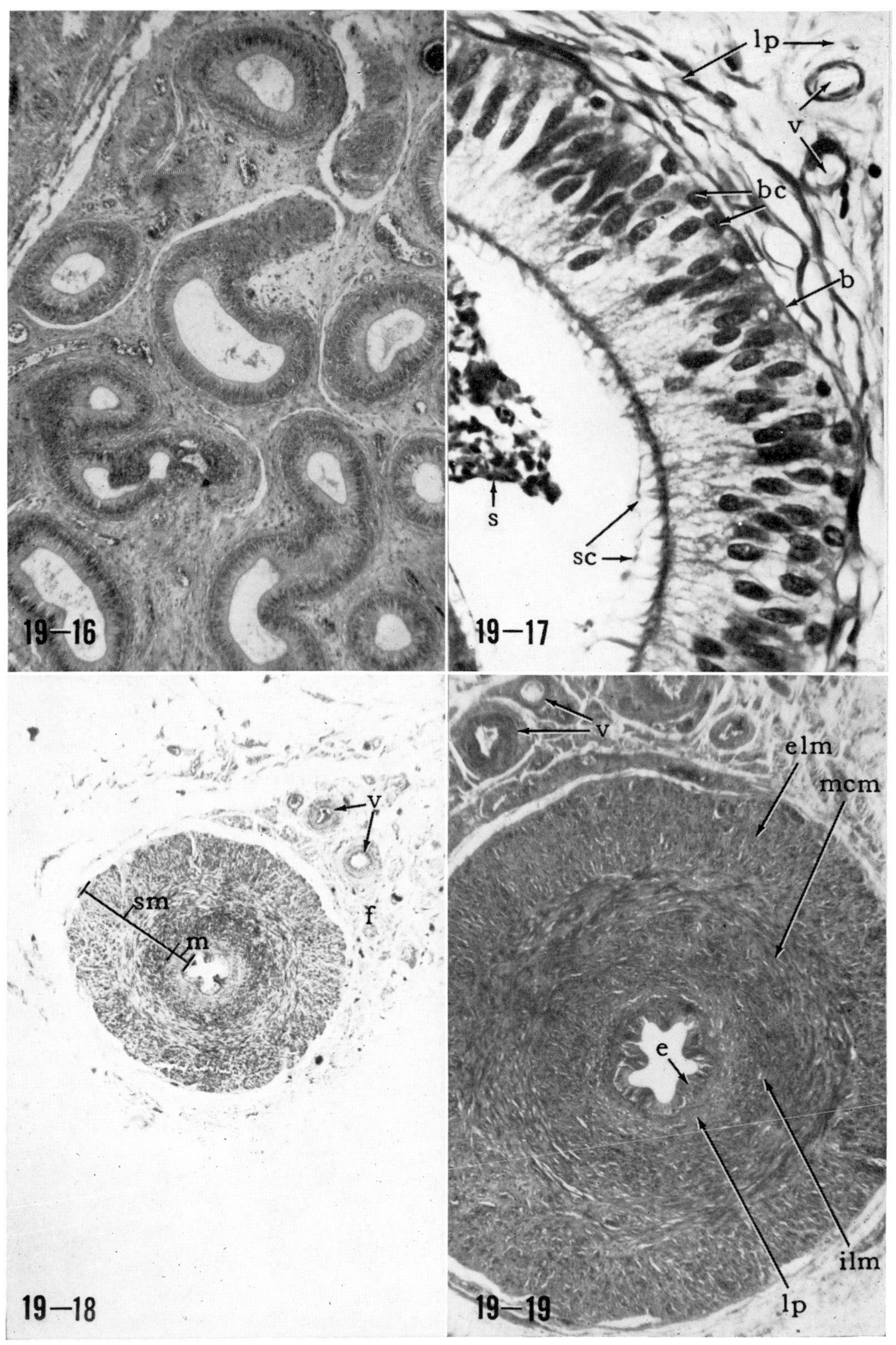
lp
v
bc
b
s
sc
19—16
19—17
v
sm
m
f
19—18
v
elm
mcm
e
ilm
lp
19—19

ing of the mucosa which forms numerous projections and irregular pockets or chambers about the lumen. The mucosa consists of fibroelastic connective tissue, usually lined by a pseudostratified columnar epithelium. The epithelial cells contain numerous secretory granules and a yellow lipochrome pigment. The secretion added to the seminal fluid by the seminal vesicle is a slightly alkaline, viscid liquid containing globulin; it serves as a vehicle for sperm. The muscular walls of the seminal vesicles are composed of an inner layer of interlacing circular strands and an outer longitudinally arranged layer of smooth muscle. A thin adventitia containing elastic fibers marks the external covering of the walls.

H. PROSTATE GLAND (Plate 161)

The **prostate** is an encapsulated, conical gland located below the internal urethral orifice at the neck of the bladder and perforated by the prostatic urethra and the ejaculatory ducts. The thin but firm capsule is composed of vascularized fibroelastic connective tissue intermingled with smooth muscle fibers. Septa arise from the capsule and extend inward to divide the gland into lobules. Septal projections penetrate the lobules further to form a support for some 30 to 50 **branched tubulo-alveolar glands**. These secretory follicular-appearing elements are of the apocrine type, have large irregular lumina and are lined by a simple cuboidal to columnar type of epithelium. In the adult, the follicles contain laminated prostatic concretions, the **corpora amylacea**. These concretions increase in number and size with age and may calcify, producing **calculi**. As many as 20 to 30 separate **wide excretory ducts** exist and drain the prostatic secretion (a protein, lipid material rich in acid phosphatase) into the prostatic urethra. The presence of scattered strands of smooth muscle fibers in the vascularized fibroelastic connective tissue surrounding each of the follicles is a distinctive histologic feature and aids in distinguishing the prostate from certain sections of the thyroid gland.

I. BULBO-URETHRAL GLANDS (COWPER'S)

The **bulbo-urethral glands** are small, round paired bodies located behind and on each side of the membranous portion of the urethra. Each gland is invested with a thin fibrous capsule containing elastic fibers and muscle strands that have migrated in from the surrounding urogenital diaphragm. Arising from the capsule, connective tissue septa containing skeletal and smooth muscle fibers penetrate and separate the glands into several lobules. Further, these septa penetrate the

PLATE 160—Seminal Vesicle

FIG. 19-20. Survey section of the seminal vesicle. Note that folds (f) of the mucosa form numerous crypts or chambers (c). Mallory-Azan stain. Low power. (w, convoluted wall of seminal vesicle showing part of the lamina propria and smooth muscle)

FIG. 19-21. Section of seminal vesicle, revealing a partition between adjacent sacs. Note the complex folding (f) of the tunica mucosa. Mallory-Azan stain. Low power. (l, lumen of sacs; c, crypts)

FIG. 19-22. Intermediate-power view of a portion of Figure 19-21. Note the crypts (c) and the origin of the folds (f). Mallory-Azan stain. (lp, lamina propria; m, smooth muscle coat)

FIG. 19-23. High-power view of a primary fold (pf) and a secondary fold (sf) of a seminal vesicle. Note that the folds consist of a columnar to a pseudostratified columnar type of epithelium and have a connective tissue stroma with some smooth muscle cells. Mallory-Azan stain.

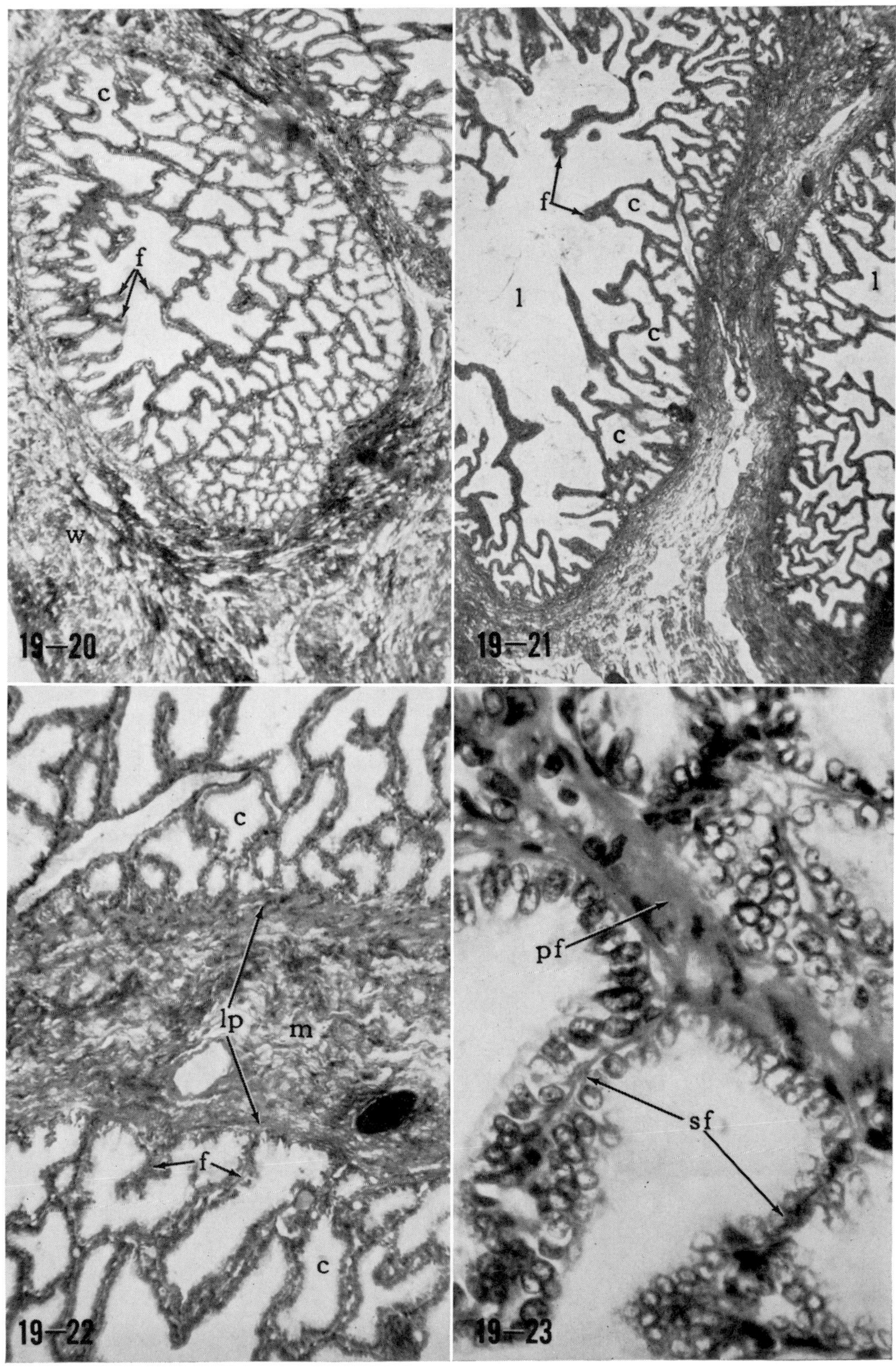
c
f
w
19–20
f
c
l
c
c
l
19–21
c
lp
m
f
c
19–22
pf
sf
19–23

parenchyma of each lobule to invest the individual secretory end-pieces and their associated ducts. The secretory portions consist of compound tubulo-alveolar end-pieces but are variable in size and form. These glandular elements are lined by epithelial cells varying in type from squamous to cuboidal to columnar. The cellular cytoplasm contains mucigen droplets, and, in addition, spindle-shaped inclusions may be demonstrated with acid stains. The ducts are also variable in size and form but for the most part are lined with a simple columnar epithelium which becomes pseudostratified columnar near the excretory duct. Each secretory unit opens into a duct, and all of the ducts ultimately join to form the two excretory ducts (one from each glandular body) which open onto the floor of the cavernous part of the urethra. The secretion elaborated by the bulbo-urethral glands is a clear, viscid mucoid substance which is a component of the seminal fluid.

J. PENIS

(Plates 162 and 163)

The male copulatory organ, the **penis**, is composed of 3 cylindrical masses of erectile tissue enclosed within a covering of stratified squamous epithelium. The erectile tissue consists of a pair of dorsolaterally placed structures, the **corpora cavernosa penis** and an unpaired ventromedially located element, the **corpus cavernosum urethrae (spongiosum)** which contains the penile urethra. The 3 cavernous bodies are bound together by thick layers of fibroelastic tissue, the **tunica albuginea**, arranged as inner circular and outer longitudinal layers. Medially, between the corpora cavernosa penis, the tunica albuginea forms a partition, the **septum penis**. The tunica albuginea of the corpus spongiosum is thinner and contains more elastic fibers than that around the corpora cavernosa penis. In addition, its inner layer contains circularly arranged smooth muscle fibers. The internal erectile tissue of the corpora consists of a network of irregular vascular spaces lined by endothelium. In the corpora cavernosa penis, the spaces are larger at the center than at the periphery. No essential difference in the size of the vascular spaces is seen in the corpus spongiosum. In erection of the penis, the centrally located vascular spaces become filled with blood under high pressure, while those at the periphery, the venous channels, are compressed and thus prevent efferent blood flow. Partitions are present between the vascular spaces that constitute the **erectile tissue** of the 3 cavernous bodies. These partitions are termed **trabeculae**, and they consist of dense collagenous tissue, some elastic networks,

PLATE 161—Prostate

FIG. 19-24. Prostate gland, including part of its wall. Masson stain. Low power. (a, tubulo-alveolar glands; c, concretions and secretory material; i, interstitial tissue consisting of connective tissue and smooth muscle fibers; w, wall consisting of vascularized connective tissue and bundles of smooth muscle fibers)

FIG. 19-25. Central portion of the prostate gland, revealing its lobular nature resulting from the penetration of septa (s) from its capsule. Note the large numbers of tubulo-alveolar glands embedded in the stroma. Masson stain. Low power. (c, a concretion body)

FIG. 19-26. Intermediate-power view of the prostate gland, showing the irregular branching nature of the tubulo-alveolar glands and the abundant stroma of connective tissue and smooth muscle fibers. Masson stain.

FIG. 19-27. High-power view showing the nature of the glandular epithelium and the interstitial tissue of the prostate gland. Note the variation in epithelium from a simple to a pseudostratified columnar type of arrangement in the same branching gland. Also observe the smooth muscle fibers in the interstitial tissue. Masson stain.

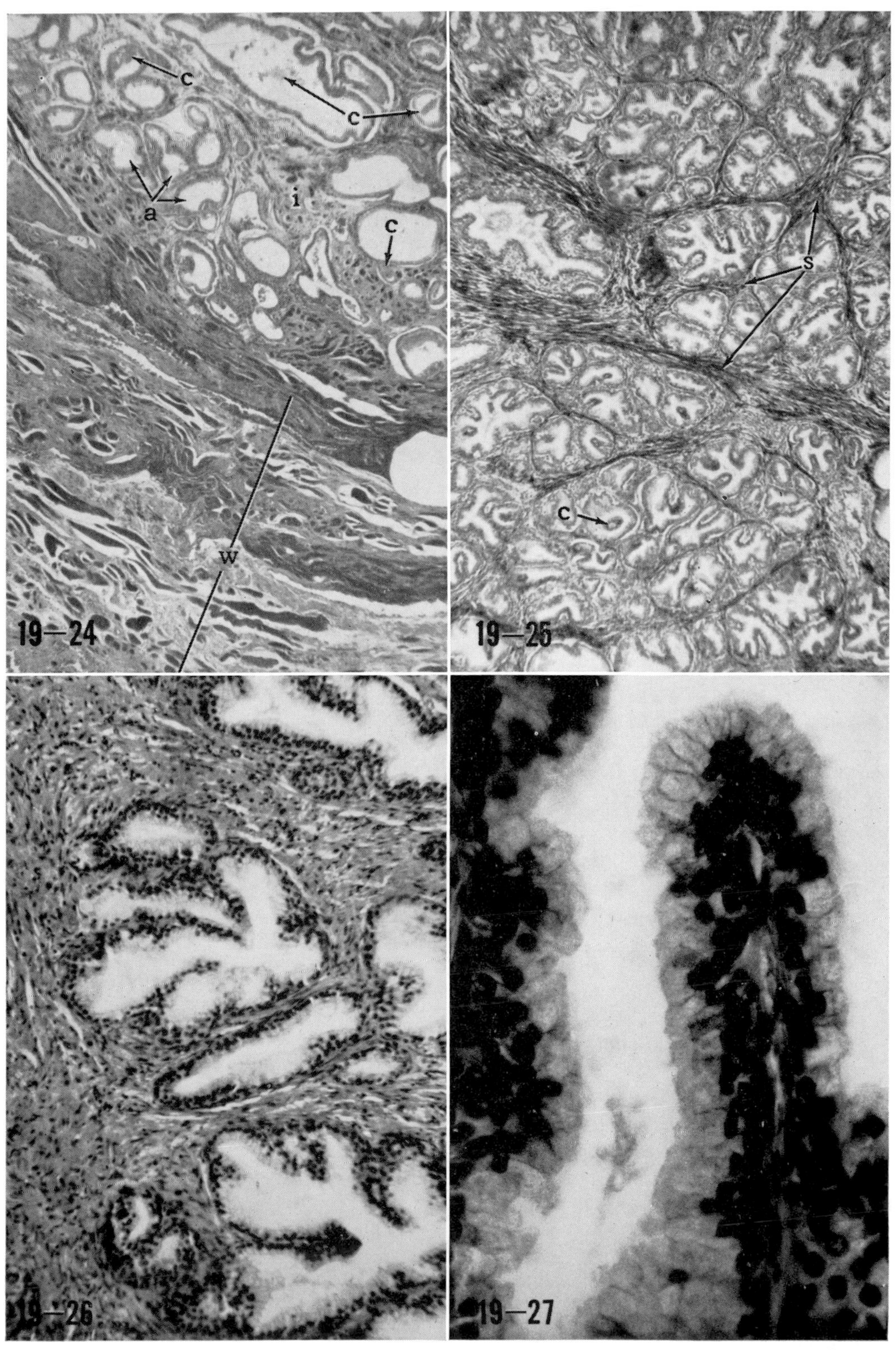
c
c
a
i
c
w
19—24
s
c
19—25
19—26
19—27

and strands of smooth muscle fibers. In addition, they contain numerous arteries and nerves.

The cap-shaped expansion of the anterior end of the corpus cavernosum urethrae, the **glans penis**, consists of dense connective tissue containing large anastomosing veins. The glans penis has no tunica albuginea but is surrounded by a fold of skin, the **prepuce** or **foreskin**. The skin covering the penis is thin and loosely attached to the underlying layer of connective tissue and smooth muscle. Fat is absent. Hairs and sebaceous glands are few in number and are limited to the proximal part of the penis. The prepuce is thin, translucent and devoid of hairs. On its inner surface, modified sebaceous glands, the **glands of Tyson** are found. The secretion from these glands, mixed with desquamated cells, is called **smegma**.

PLATE 162—Penis

FIG. 19-28. Cross section of penis (fetal) at the junction of the corpora cavernosa. Note the spongelike nature of the cavernous erectile tissue (et). Masson stain. Low power. (ta, tunica albuginea surrounding each of the corpora cavernosa; ms, median septum; u, urethra piercing the corpus cavernosum urethrae [corpus spongiosum]; ca, central artery)

FIG. 19-29. Intermediate-power view through the cavernous erectile tissuc of the penis (fetal) showing that it consists of irregular vascular spaces (s) in a trabecular network (t). Masson stain. (ta, tunica albuginea)

FIG. 19-30. High-power view through the cavernous erectile tissue of the penis (fetal) revealing the endothelial lining (e) of the vascular spaces (s) and the nature of the trabeculae (t) between them. Masson stain.

FIG. 19-31. Cross section of penis (fetal) through the corpus cavernosum urethrae at the level of the glans penis. Especially note that the albuginea is absent, being replaced by the dermis (d) of the skin. H & E stain. Low power. (ss, stratified squamous epithelium of prepuce; et, erectile tissue; u, urethra)

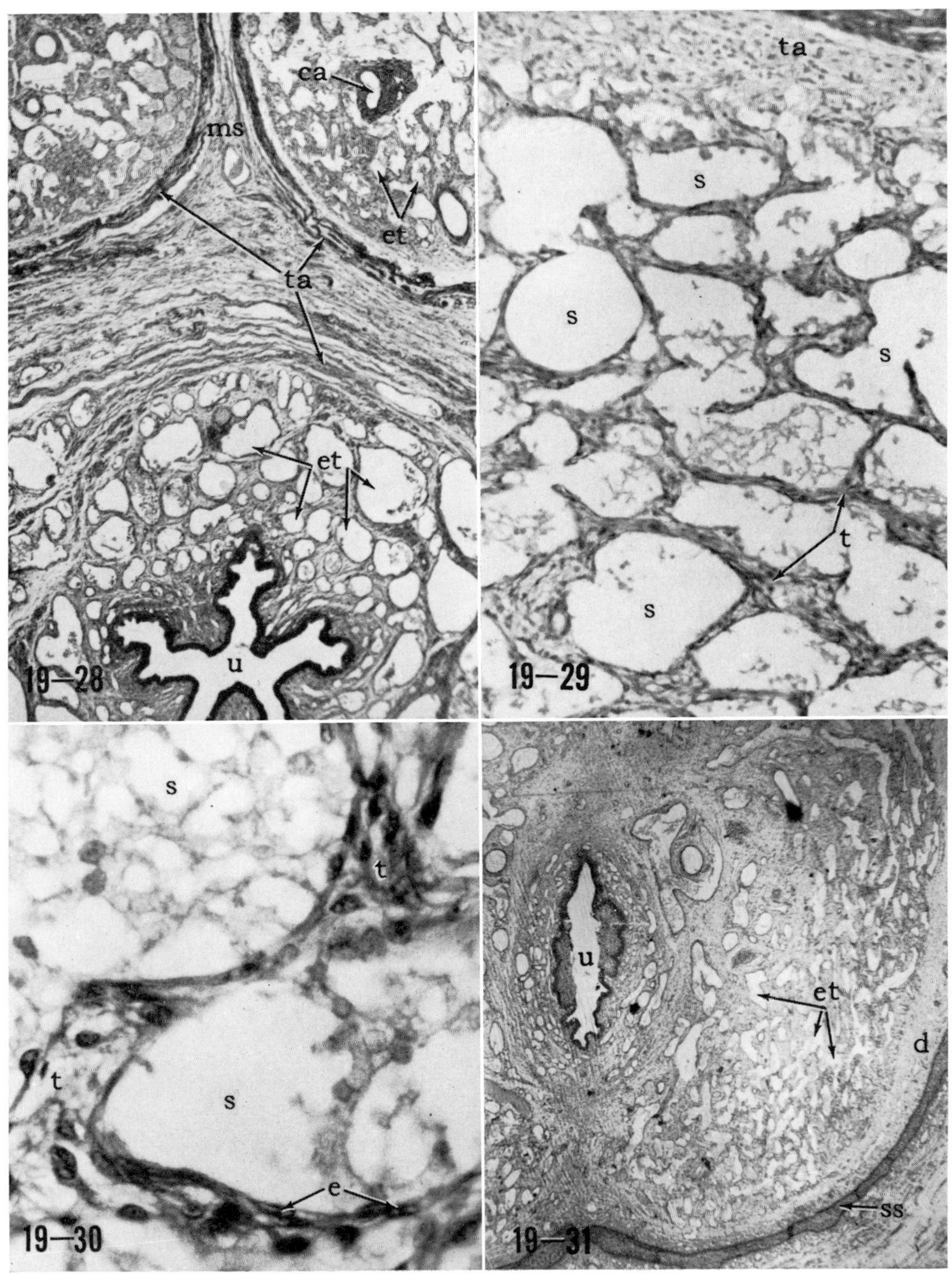
ca
ms
et
ta
et
u
19—28
ta
s
s
s
t
s
19—29
s
t
t
s
e
19—30
u
et
d
ss
19—31

PLATE 163—Penis

FIG. 19-32. Intermediate-power view of penis (fetal) through the corpus cavernosum urethrae at the level of the glans penis. Masson stain. (ss, stratified squamous epithelium of prepuce; et, erectile tissue; u, urethra)

FIG. 19-33. Portion of the glans penis (fetal) showing an outpocketing (o) of the surface of the mucous membrane of the urethra. Masson stain. Low power. (ss, stratified squamous epithelium of the prepuce; d, dermis of skin)

FIG. 19-34. Cross section through the peripheral portion of fetal glans penis (gl) and surrounding prepuce (pr). Note that the epithelial coverings of the glans penis and the prepuce are fused (fe). The stratum germinativum of both the glans (gg) and the prepuce (gp) are actually continuous with each other although not apparent in this section. The external surface of the prepuce (ep) is apparent and, although not shown, forms a continuity with its inner surface. Masson stain. Low power. (m, smooth muscle)

FIG. 19-35. Section of penis (child) at the prepuce end showing a few of the glands of Tyson (T). Note that the surface of the mucous membrane of the urethra (u) reveals the lacunae of Morgagni (M). H & E stain. Low power. (m, smooth muscle; et, erectile tissue)

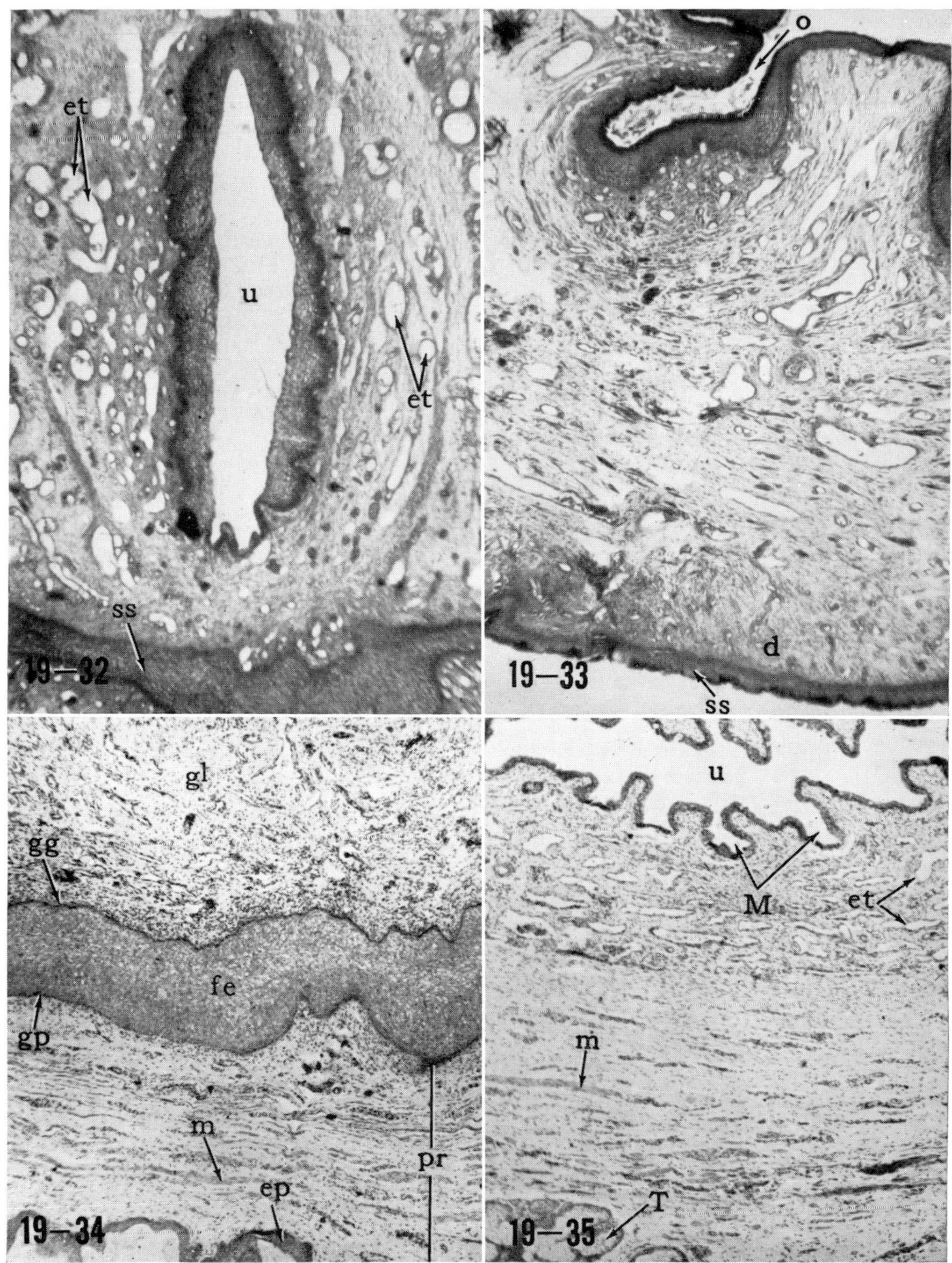
et
u
et
ss
19—32
o
d
19—33
ss
gl
gg
fe
gp
m
pr
ep
19—34
u
M
et
m
T
19—35

20 · The Urinary System

A. Kidneys
B. Excretory Passages
C. Male Urethra
D. Female Urethra

A. KIDNEYS

The kidneys are encapsulated, paired multilobated, bean-shaped organs located in the posterior portion of the abdominal cavity on either side of the vertebral column. The **capsule** invaginates along the medial indented border, the **hilus**, to form the **sinus**. Surrounding the hilus is the kidney parenchyma consisting of an **outer cortex** and an **inner medullary substance**. The sinus contains the upper expanded funnel portion of the ureter, the **renal pelvis**, and is filled with loose connective tissue (areolar and adipose) through which the renal vessels and nerves pass into the parenchyma and into which urine is drained from the kidney. Adjacent to the renal parenchyma, the renal pelvis is expanded into 3 outpocketings, the **major calyces**, which in turn divide into smaller outpocketings, the **minor calyces** (8 in all). The medullary substance consists of 8 to 18

PLATE 164—Kidney

FIG. 20-1. Survey section through a portion of the cortex of a kidney showing the structure of the medullary rays (mr) and adjacent cortical labyrinths. H & E stain. Low power. (g, glomeruli; Bs, Bowman's space; ct, convoluted tubules; cot, collecting tubules)

FIG. 20-2. Survey section through a portion of the medulla of an injected animal kidney showing the high degree of vascularity (v) between the closely packed tubules. Radially sectioned tubules in the lower left region are the collecting tubules (cot), whereas most of the transversely sectioned tubules are segments of Henle's loop (Hl). Low power.

FIG. 20-3. Intermediate-power view through a portion of the cortex of a kidney showing structures similar to those seen in Figure 20-1. Note the appearance of the medullary rays (mr) and the adjacent cortical labyrinths (cl). H & E stain. (g, glomerulus; Bs, Bowman's space; pct, proximal convoluted tubules; dct, distal convoluted tubules; cot, collecting tubules)

FIG. 20-4. Renal (malpighian) corpuscle, showing the afferent arteriole (aa) entering the glomerular tuft (gt). Mallory-Azan stain. High power. (ge, glomerular epithelium; rbc, red blood cells; pB, parietal layer of Bowman's capsule; Bs, Bowman's space; dct, distal convoluted tubule)

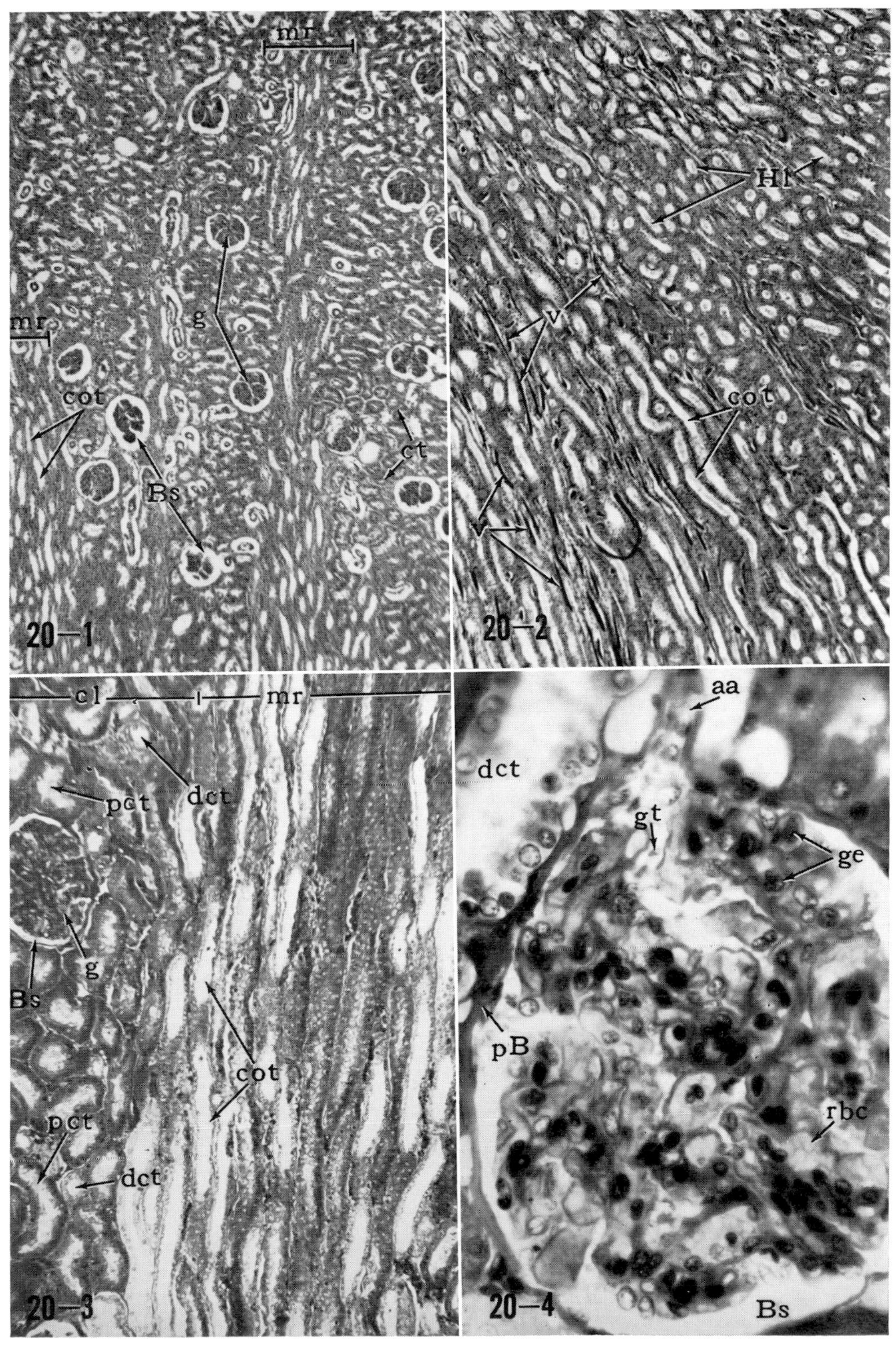
mr
mr
g
cot
ct
Bs
20—1
HI
v
cot
20—2
cl
mr
dct
pct
g
Bs
cot
pct
dct
20—3
aa
dct
gt
ge
pB
rbc
Bs
20—4

medullary pyramids. Each pyramid is a conical body placed with its base outward and its apex (**papilla**) projecting into the lumen of a minor calyx. Generally, the apices of 2 or 3 medullary pyramids unite to form a single papilla. Small pores (10-25 **foramina papillaria**) perforate the apex of each papilla to form a sievelike structure, the **area cribrosa**. Columns of straight tubules (**medullary rays** or **pars radiata**) radiate outward into the cortex from the substance of the medullary pyramids. The lateral surfaces of the pyramids are separated from each other by pluglike inward extensions of the cortex, the **renal columns of Bertini**. These cortical plugs or columns penetrate the medullary substance and extend inward toward the pelvis.

Together, each pyramid and the cortical material which surrounds it constitute a **kidney lobe**. The lobes (8-18) of the kidney are subdivided into **renal lobules** on the basis of the branching of the excretory ducts.

1. Microscopic Structure
(Plates 164 to 166)

a. The kidney is invested by a dense connective tissue capsule composed primarily of collagenous fibers and a few elastic fibers. The functional and structural unit (secretory portion) of the kidney consists of a long continuous tortuous tube known as the **nephron**. The nephron begins with a double-walled cup, the **capsule of Bowman** and terminates by joining a collecting duct (excretory portion). Bowman's capsule, located in the cortex, consists of an outer wall of parietal epithelium (flattened low cuboidal or simple squamous epithelium) and an inner layer of visceral epithelium (simple squamous epithelium) which encloses a knot of contractile capillaries, the **glomerulus**. Together, Bowman's capsule and the glomerulus make up the **renal corpuscle** (**malpighian corpuscle**). These corpuscles appear in large numbers (approximately one million/kidney) and act as filtration bodies. The glomerulus is supplied by an **afferent arteriole** (**intralobular branch of renal artery**). Near the entrance of the afferent arteriole at the vascular pole of the glomerulus, the smooth muscle cells of the vessel become large and pale-staining **myoepithelioid granular elements** (**juxtaglomerular cells**). Although these cells have been implicated in the production of a vasoconstrictor substance called **renin**, their fundamental functional nature still remains unclear.

PLATE 165—Kidney

FIG. 20-5. Portion of the malpighian corpuscle from the kidney showing the glomerulus with the double-walled capsule (Bowman's). Mallory-Azan stain. High power. (pB, cell of parietal layer of Bowman's capsule; vB, cell of visceral layer of Bowman's capsule; c, glomerular capillaries; gb, glomerular basement membrane; cb, capsular basement membrane; Bs, Bowman's space)

FIG. 20-6. Kidney, showing the afferent arteriole (aa) and associated juxtaglomerular apparatus. Mallory stain. High power. (jgc, cells of the juxtaglomerular apparatus)

FIG. 20-7. High-power view of a collecting tubule (cot) passing longitudinally between segments of the kidney nephridia. Observe the clear cytoplasm, the round nuclei and the distinct intercellular boundaries between adjacent cells. Mallory stain. High power.

FIG. 20-8. Section through the inner portion of the renal medulla. This field shows the appearance of a renal pyramid cut transversely. The larger tubules with pale cytoplasm and distinct nuclei are mainly collecting tubules. The smaller elements with dark cytoplasm and less obvious nuclei are mainly segments of Henle's loops. The space at the upper right is part of a minor calyx (c), the wall of which is lined by a transitional epithelium (te), separated from its normal position against the pyramid in this preparation. H & E stain. Low power.

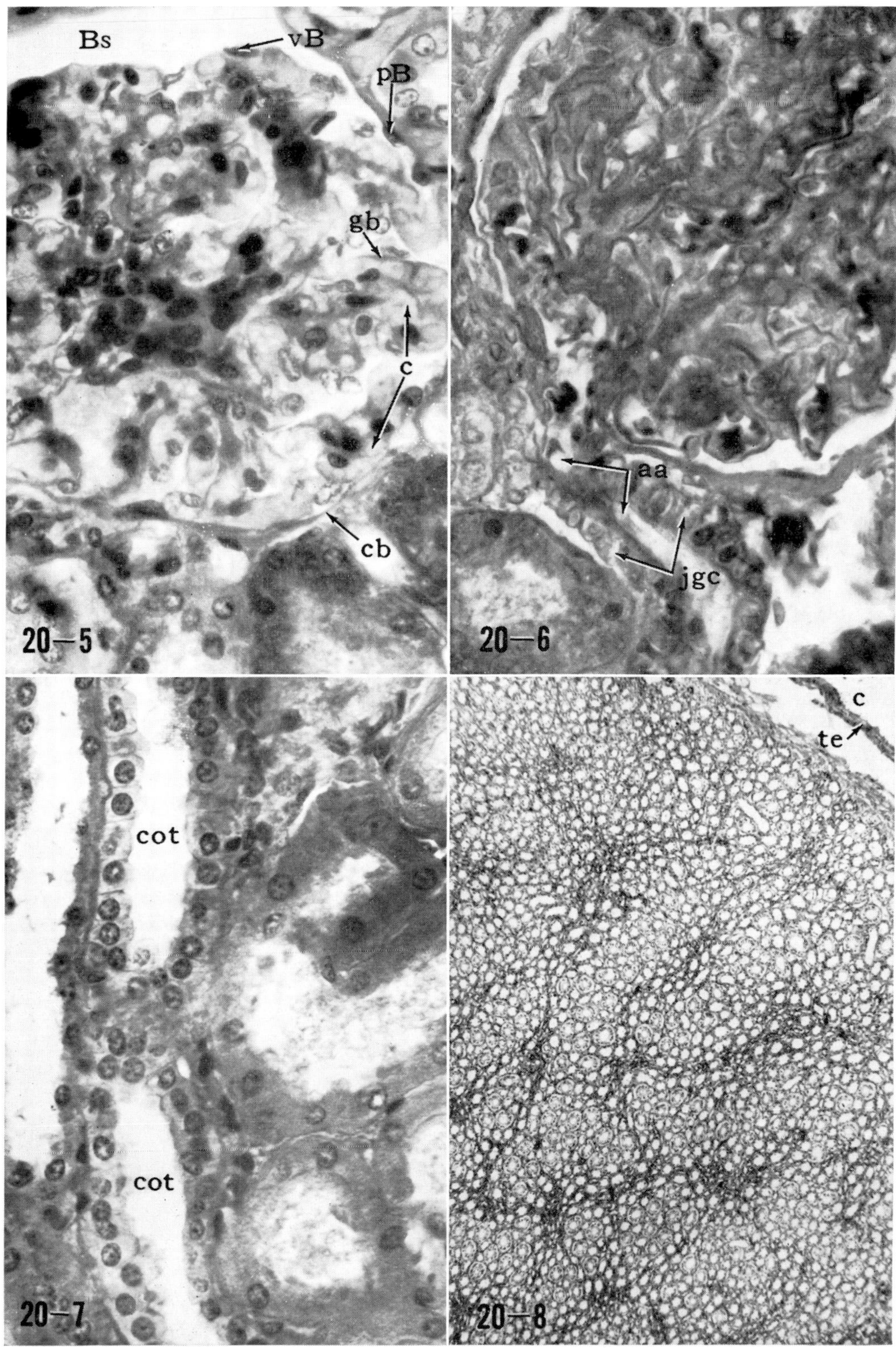
Bs
vB
pB
gb
c
cb
20—5
aa
jgc
20—6
cot
cot
20—7
c
te
20—8

Electron microscopic studies reveal that the glomerulus is invested with a basement membrane (**lamina densa**) which is continuous with the basement membrane of the outer capsular epithelium and the lamina propria of the afferent and the efferent arterioles. Regarding the afferent arteriole, on entering the renal corpuscle it divides into 2 to 5 primary branches (**trunks**), each of which in turn divides into secondary branches. All of these branches constitute a lobe of the glomerulus. From these secondary branches, approximately 50 tortuous capillary loops arise. Ultimately, the capillaries in each glomerular lobe form numerous anastomoses and lead into collecting trunks which empty into the **efferent arteriole**.

Electron microscopy also reveals that the epithelium of the visceral layer of Bowman's capsule consists of many cells (**podocytes**) with footlike processes (pedicels) that are in intimate contact with the basement membrane of the capillary endothelium (endenchyma). In addition, the capillary walls have been shown to be porous (**lamina fenestrata**). It seems likely that the electron microscopic findings, along with physiologic studies, will lead to better understanding of the filtration process that occurs in the glomerulus.

b. At the urinary pole of the renal corpuscle, the capsular space into which the blood filtrate passes becomes continuous with the lumen of the next portion of the nephron, namely, the **proximal convoluted tubule**. This portion, which has a tortuous course, is located for the most part in the renal cortex and is concerned with the reabsorption of various constituents of the glomerular filtrate. The proximal convoluted tubules are approximately 14 mm. long and 60 μ in diameter and are the broadest of the tubular segments. The epithelium consists of columnar cells which interdigitate freely and contain a deep eosin-staining granular cytoplasm and large pale nuclei. On the luminal surface, the cells are characterized by the presence of a brush border consisting of microvilli. Basal striations composed of mitochondria are also found.

c. The descending portions of the proximal convoluted tubules are straight and pass into the kidney medulla, giving rise to the **medullary loops of Henle**.

(1) The **descending part of the loop of Henle** is thin and straight, has a diameter of 14 to 22 μ and is characterized by a simple squamous epithelial cell lining. These cells have a pale cytoplasm and flattened nuclei which tend to bulge into the lumen. Terminal bars are found on the luminal surface.

(2) After a hairpin turn, the **ascending part of the loop** begins. It is thicker (30 μ in diameter) and runs parallel with the thin limb. Here, the epithelium is cuboidal and has a darkly staining cytoplasm.

d. The ascending loop enters the cortex, heading toward its renal corpuscle, before becoming the **distal convoluted tubule**. Of interest is the portion of the distal segment that is located in the area between the afferent and the efferent arterioles. Here, the lining cells are modified, appear more columnar and reveal a concentration of nuclei. This area is known as the **macula densa**; its

PLATE 166—Kidney

FIG. 20-9. Electron micrograph of a portion of the renal corpuscle (rat). Note that the capillary endothelium (end) of the glomerulus is invested with a basement membrane (bm). Also observe the cells of the visceral epithelium of the glomerular capsule, the podicytes (p) with their footlike processes, the pedicels (ped). PTA & Uranyl acetate stain. × 6,700. (tp, trabeculae of podocytes; crt, contact ridges of trabeculae; ss, subpodocytic spaces which are continuous with the subcapsular space of the glomerulus; rbc, red blood cells in the lumina of glomerular capillaries). (Latta, H.: J. Ultrastruct. Res. *5*:369)

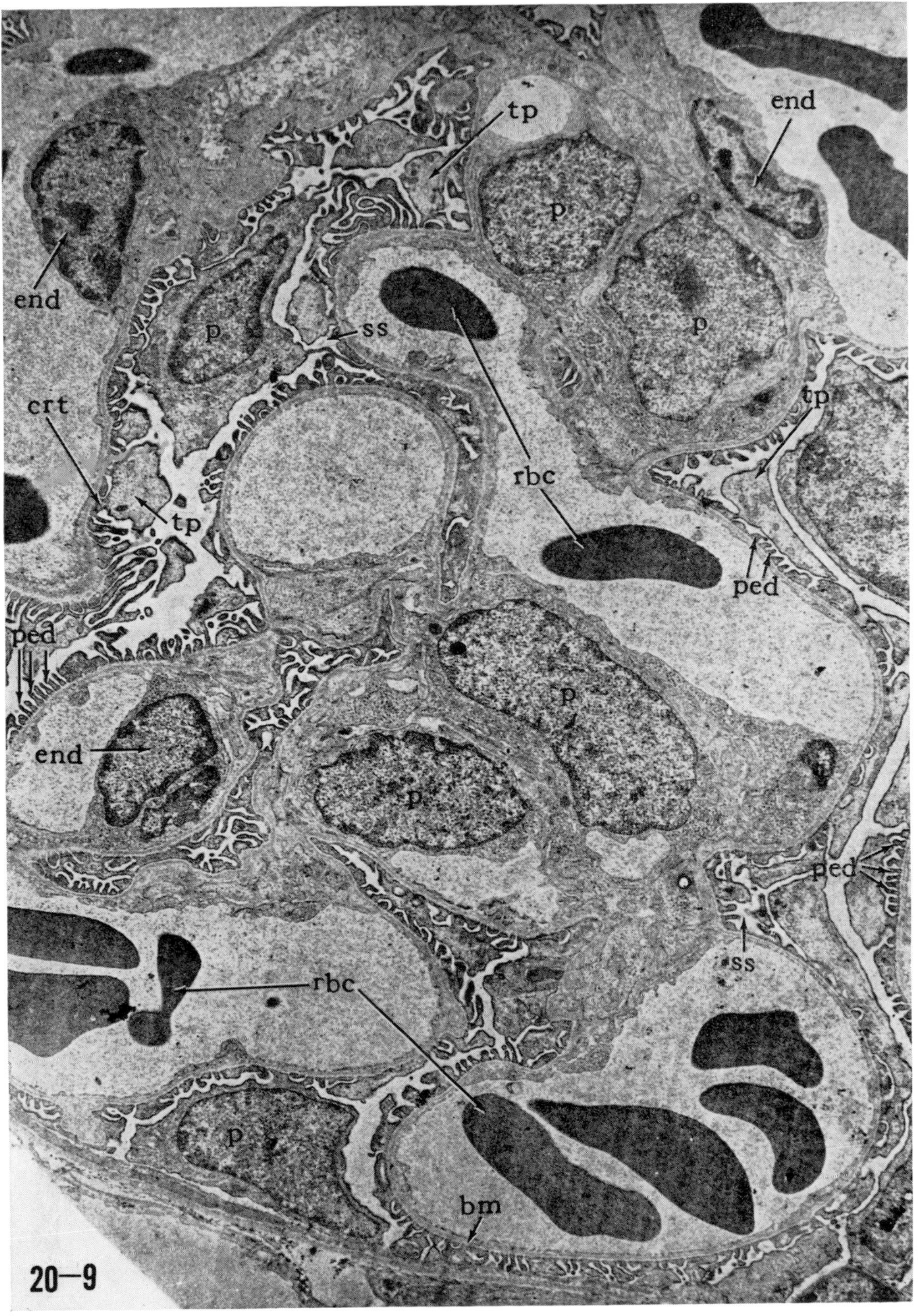

tp
end
p
end
p
ss
p
crt
tp
rbc
tp
ped
ped
p
end
p
ped
ss
rbc
p
bm
20–9

function, although not definitely established, may be important in the hemodynamics of the kidney. Beyond the macula densa, the distal segment now becomes convoluted (**distal convoluted tubule**) and constitutes the last segment of the nephron. It has shorter and fewer coils than the proximal convoluted segment. In addition, its diameter is smaller, the epithelial cells are shorter (cuboidal without brush borders), and the cytoplasm is less eosinophilic.

e. From the termination of the distal convoluted tubule, the excretory portion begins in the cortex with the **arched collecting tubules**. Subsequently, these tubules join the **straight collecting tubules** in the medulla which finally become the large **papillary ducts of Bellini**. The papillary ducts empty their contents at the pelvis of the kidney. Each collecting tubule, which serves 4 or more nephrons, is characterized by a cuboidal epithelium. These cells contain dark nuclei and a clear basophilic cytoplasm with distinct boundaries. The larger collecting ducts are structurally similar except that the cells become taller as the caliber of the ducts increases.

2. Blood Circulation (Figs. 20-10 and 20-11)

From the **abdominal aorta**, the right and the left hilar areas of the kidney receive the **right** and the **left renal arteries**, respectively. Each renal artery divides within the renal sinus into two sets of **renal end arteries**, a ventral set that supplies the anterior two thirds of the kidney and a dorsal one that supplies the posterior one third. As they pass through the loose connective tissue of the renal sinus, the renal end arteries divide into **interlobar arteries** (in the renal columns between the medullary pyramids). These branch into divisions which run parallel with the surface of the kidney, curving in the area of the juxtamedullary region (between the bases of the pyramids and the cortex) to form the **arciform** or **arcuate arteries**. Over the bases of the pyramids, the arciform arteries give off smaller branches, the **interlobular arteries** which run radially in the cortex between the medullary rays. These interlobular arteries in turn give rise: (1) to numerous **straight afferent arterioles** (interlobular) which supply the glomeruli, (2) to the **capillary plexus** around the convoluted tubules, and (3) to **capsular vessels**. Blood leaving the glomeruli is transported via the **efferent arterioles** which break up into a series of arterioles supplying the convoluted tubules of the cortex and the medulla. These are referred to as **arteriolae rectae**. In the medulla their course is straight, passing toward the renal pelvis. Frequently, these vessels are known as **arteriolae rectae**

PLATE 167—Kidney

FIG. 20-10. Section through the cortical region of the kidney, showing a dilated interlobular vessel (er) filled with blood. Note the longitudinal course of the interlobular vessel within a cortical labyrinth (cl) between adjacent medullary rays (mr). Observe a few of the intralobular branches (ra). Mallory-Azan stain. Low power.

FIG. 20-11. Section of the kidney in the juxtamedullary region, showing the origin from the interlobar vessel (il) of a dilated arcuate vessel (av) and two branches, the interlobular vessels (er). Mallory-Azan stain. Low power.

FIG. 20-12. Section of the kidney, showing the papillary region (p) of a medullary pyramid in relation to the minor calyx. Mallory-Azan stain. Low power. (l, lumen of minor calyx; mc, transitional epithelium lining of minor calyx)

FIG. 20-13. Intermediate-power view of a portion of Figure 20-12. Note the nature of the papillary ducts (pd). Smaller tubular elements between the papillary ducts represent capillaries and some of the thin segments of Henle's loops. (l, lumen of minor calyx; mc, transitional epithelium of minor calyx with underlying lamina propria)

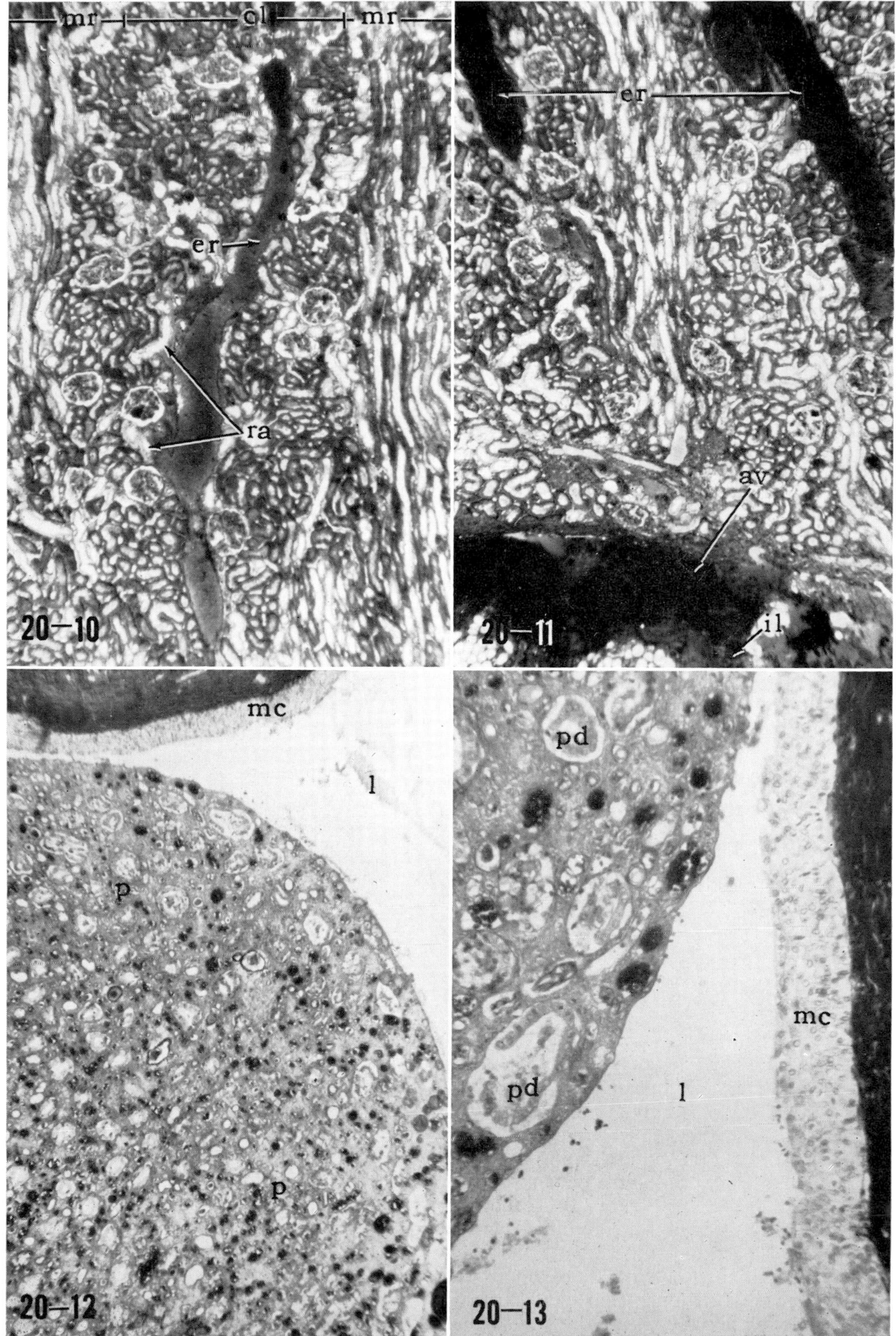
mr
cl
mr
er
ra
20—10
er
av
il
20—11
mc
l
p
p
20—12
pd
pd
mc
l
20—13

spuriae to distinguish them from vessels arising directly from arcuate or interlobular arteries not related to the glomeruli (**arteriolae rectae verae**).

From **capillary networks** near the kidney surface a number of star-shaped vessels are formed, the **stellate veins**. Subsequently, these join to form the **interlobular veins** which in turn fuse to form the **arciform veins**. **Intralobular veins** that drain the peritubular capillaries in the cortex join the interlobular veins. In the medulla, a series of straight vessels, the **venae rectae**, arise from the terminal plexuses around the tubules and directly join the **arciform veins** in the juxtamedullary region. Finally, the arciform veins fuse to form the **interlobar veins** that then drain into the **renal vein**.

3. Lymphatic Circulation

Networks of lymphatic capillaries do not enter the tubules but are found in the capsule, the renal sinus and around the larger blood vessels in most of the cortex and the renal columns. Lymphatics are lacking in the glomeruli and the medullary rays.

B. EXCRETORY PASSAGES FOR URINE (CALYCES, PELVIS, URETER, BLADDER, URETHRA) (Figs. 20-12 to 20-15)

The excretory passages differ markedly from the nephrons and the collecting tubules in that their epithelial linings are of a stratified type, consisting of layers of closely fitted cells, and their walls possess muscle, mainly for the propulsion of urine.

1. Main Excretory Portion of Kidney

Urine is pressed out of the pyramids by the **calyces**, collects in the **renal pelvis** and then is passed along by the rhythmic contractions of the **ureters**. The structures responsible for this activity constitute the main excretory portion of the kidney. Except for the increased thickness of their walls in the order cited, the calyces, the pelvis and the ureters have a similar structural organization. They are lined by mucous membranes consisting of transitional epithelium resting on a lamina propria of reticular and areolar connective tissue. Unlike the gastrointestinal tract, there is no muscularis mucosae. The mucous membranes are thrown into several longitudinal folds in the contracted (empty) condition. In addition, no true glands are present, but they are often simulated by small nests of epithelial cells. It is to be noted that the lumen of the ureter, in comparison with those of the calyces and the pelvis, is distinctly more stellate in cross section. The submucosa is not present as a separate and distinct layer but blends in with the lamina propria. The muscularis is of the smooth

PLATE 168—Ureter and Urinary Bladder

FIG. 20-14. Cross section of a contracted ureter (lower part). H & E stain. Low power. (t, transitional epithelium; lp, lamina propria; ilm, inner longitudinal smooth muscle; cm, circular smooth muscle; olm, outer longitudinal smooth muscle; a, adventitial connective tissue)

FIG. 20-15. Intermediate-power view of a portion of Figure 20-14 showing the mucosa lined by transitional epithelium (t) overlying the richly cellular lamina propria (lp). Note that the muscularis consists of inner (ilm) and outer (olm) longitudinally arranged layers with a middle circular layer (cm) of smooth muscle.

FIG. 20-16. Low-power view of a section through the wall of a contracted urinary bladder. H & E stain. (e, epithelium; lp, lamina propria; sm, submucosa with numerous large blood vessels [v]; m, muscularis)

FIG. 20-17. Slightly higher magnification of a section of the wall of a contracted urinary bladder adjacent to that shown in Figure 20-16. Low power. Note the numerous blood vessels (v) in the submucosa (sm). (t, transitional epithelium; lp, cellular connective tissue of the lamina propria; ilm, inner longitudinal smooth muscle layer of the muscularis)

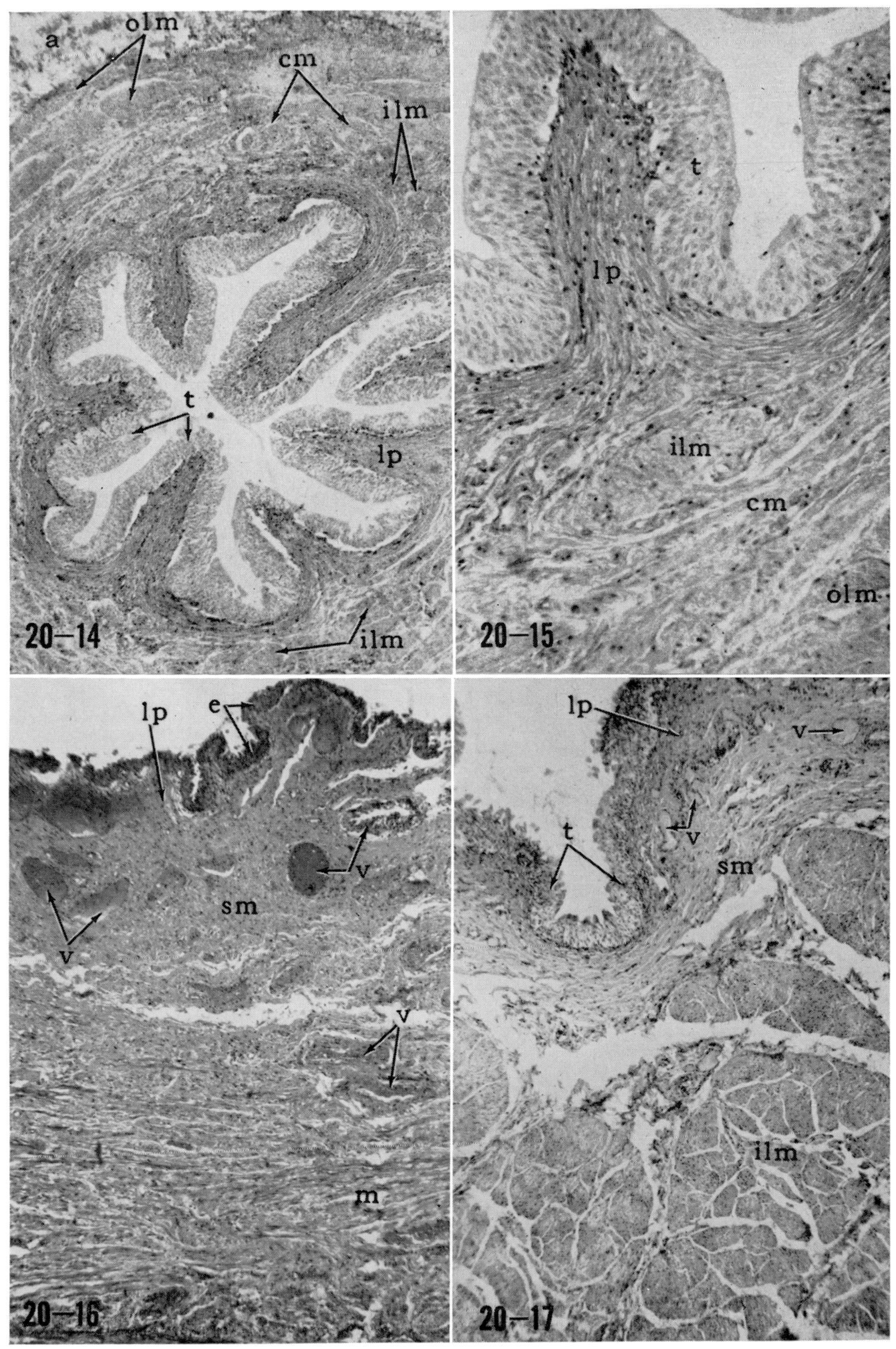
a
olm
cm
ilm
t
lp
ilm
20–14
t
lp
ilm
cm
olm
20–15
lp
e
v
sm
v
v
m
20–16
lp
v
t
v
sm
ilm
20–17

variety and, unlike that of the digestive system, is arranged so that there is an inner longitudinal and an outer circular layer. These layers are arranged in loose, anastomosing strands separated by an abundance of areolar connective tissue. These layers become progressively thicker as one passes from the calyces to the ureter. Close to the bladder, the lower portion of the ureter has the addition of a third layer of longitudinally disposed muscle. A strong adventitia of loose connective tissue binds the ureter to adjacent tissues.

2. Urinary Bladder (Figs. 20-16 and 20-17)

The urinary bladder is a reservoir whose walls are quite similar to those described for the ureter. In the contracted state, the mucous membrane is thrown into many folds with the transitional epithelium being usually 5 cells thick and characterized by ovoid, polygonal and cubical types of cells. On the other hand, in the distended state, the mucous membrane smoothes out and is usually made up of 2 to 3 cell layers consisting of uniform balloon-shaped cells. Although rarely observed, mucus-secreting cells similar to the glands of Littré found in the urethra have been described. The lamina propria of the bladder is similar to that of the ureter except for its greater thickness and the presence in it of diffuse lymphoid tissue. Likewise, except for the increased thickness of its muscular layers and a more irregular arrangement, the muscularis of the bladder is similar to that found in the lower portion of the ureter. In the area of the trigone, thin dense bundles of smooth muscle form a circular mass around the internal opening of the urethra, giving rise to the internal sphincter of the bladder. A serosa is found on the superior and the upper parts of the lateral surfaces of the bladder, whereas the rest of the bladder is covered by an adventitia.

C. MALE URETHRA (Figs. 20-18 and 20-19)

This tube extends from the bladder to the external orifice and serves for the evacuation of urine and sperm. It is divided into the following 3 parts: (1) a short proximal **prostatic portion**, (2) a very short **membranous portion**, and (3) a relatively long, distal **cavernous portion.**

a. *Pars prostatica* (Fig. 20-18). This tube is surrounded by the prostate gland from which it receives secretions. The epithelium that lines the pars prostatica urethra is of the same type as that of the bladder (transitional). The lamina propria is composed of a loose fibroelastic connective tissue containing a rich venous plexus. Scattered, longitudinally disposed smooth muscle fibers are also found in the connective tissue. No discernible submucosa is found. The outer

PLATE 169—Urethra

FIG. 20-18. Cross section of the colliculus seminalis (cs) showing the pars prostatica urethrae (ppu). The orientation of the convex surface of the colliculus seminalis is normally uppermost, but in this figure it is oriented to the left. H & E stain. Low power. (e, transitional epithelium)

FIG. 20-19. Cross section of a part of the cavernous portion of the urethra (cu) surrounded by erectile tissue (et). H & E stain. Low power. (e, epithelium of urethra)

FIG. 20-20. Female urethra. H & E stain. Low power. (l, lumen; e, stratified epithelium showing invaginations; gl, glandlike lacuna; v, thin-walled veins in the stromal tissue; m, smooth muscle)

FIG. 20-21. Section of female urethra, especially to demonstrate the plexus of numerous veins (v) present in the stromal tissue. H & E stain. Low power. (l, lumen; e, stratified epithelium; gl, glandlike lacunae; m, smooth muscle)

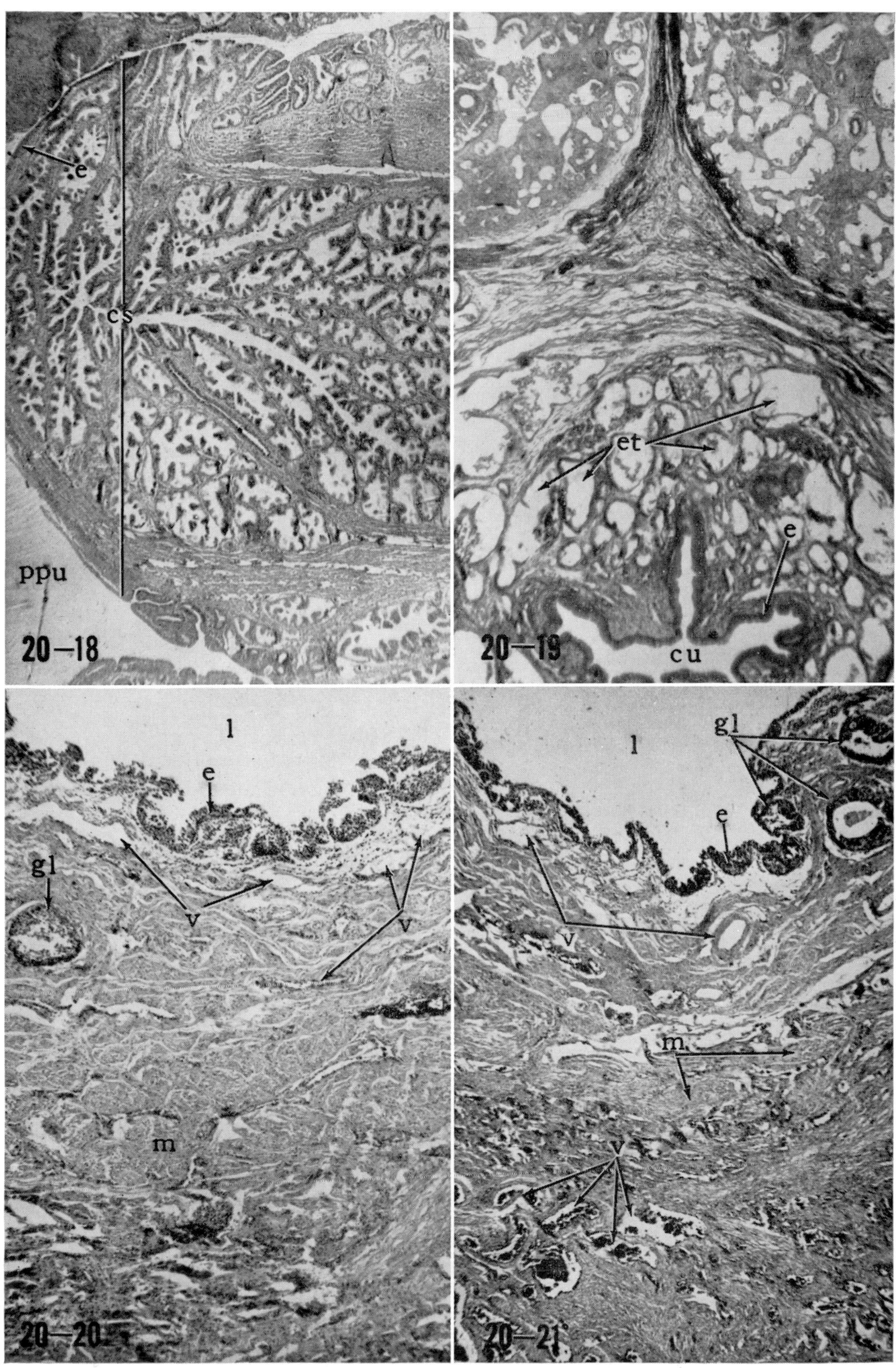
e
cs
ppu
20—18
et
e
cu
20—19
l
e
gl
v
v
m
20—20
l
gl
e
v
m
v
20—21

tunic is made up of inner longitudinal and outer circular smooth muscle fibers. This tunic is highly developed at the internal urethral orifice.

The surface of the mucous membrane shows deep folds forming the **lacunae of Morgagni** which lead into branched tubular urethral glands (the **glands of Littré**) located deep in the mucosa. **Intraepithelial glands**, clear mucus-secreting cells, are also found in connection with the lacunae of Morgagni.

b. *Pars membranacea.* This, the narrowest and shortest portion of the urethra, passes through the urogenital diaphragm. Here the lining cells are of the stratified or the pseudostratified columnar epithelial type. The lamina propria is essentially the same as described for the pars prostatica. The pars membranacea urethra is surrounded by striated muscle fibers (part of the urogenital diaphragm) which make up the sphincter muscle of the urethra. The **bulbo-urethral glands of Cowper** (tubulo-alveolar mucous glands) are located on the undersurface of the pars membranacea. Their ducts run distally to enter the first portion of the cavernous urethra.

c. *Pars cavernosa* (Fig. 20-19). This so-called spongy part is the longest portion of the urethra and extends through the remainder of the penis to open on the end of the glans penis. The epithelium varies from a stratified or pseudostratified columnar type proximally to a stratified squamous variety in the region of the fossa navicularis. The lamina propria in the distal portion (**fossa navicularis**) is papillated, contains more glands of Littré and is even more extensive in its vascularity (this accounts for its spongy appearance) than elsewhere. The characteristic muscle tunic of the urethra is replaced by scattered groups of smooth muscle fibers.

D. FEMALE URETHRA

(Figs. 20-20 and 20-21)

The female urethra extends from the bladder to the external orifice and serves exclusively for the evacuation of urine. As in the case of the male urethra, the epithelium of this tube varies, being transitional in the proximal part near the bladder, then, for most of the tube, stratified or pseudostratified columnar in type and, finally, at the distal end, stratified squamous. The lamina propria consists of a thick loose connective tissue with an abundance of elastic fibers. It contains a rich venous plexus resembling that seen in the pars cavernosa portion of the male urethra but is not as extensive as that. The thick muscle wall consists of inner longitudinally and outer circularly disposed smooth muscle fibers. Distally, at the external orifice, the smooth muscle is reinforced by striated muscle to form an external sphincter.

Comparable to the male urethra, the surface of the mucous membrane shows outpocketings of epithelium forming glandlike structures containing mucous cells.

21 · Special Sense Organs

I. EYE

A. Introduction

The eye is a nearly spherical organ consisting of a larger, nonexposed posterior or orbital portion and a smaller, exposed anterior part that permits the entrance of light. The organ can be considered as an enclosed system of fluids and masses with a covering made up of 3 layers. The contents of the optic vesicle serve mainly to refract and transmit light, while the covering layers protect and nourish the eye as a whole and also contain the photoreceptors that transmit nervous impulses in response to stimulation by light.

The manifold functions of the various coats and internal media of the eye include the following:

1. Protection of the delicate end organ
2. Attachment of extrinsic eye muscles
3. Provision of an intricate and precise

PLATE 170—Eye

FIG. 21-1. Survey section of the eye through a portion of the sclera (s), the choroid (c) and the retina (r). Note the numerous large vessels (v) associated with the sclera. Mallory-Azan stain. Low power. (m, extrinsic ocular muscle)

FIG. 21-2. Survey section of the eye through a portion of the sclera (s), the choroid (c) and the retina (r). Especially note the dense fibrous nature of the sclera. Mallory-Azan stain. Low power.

FIG. 21-3. Intermediate-power view of a portion of Figure 21-2. (s, sclera; c, choroid; r, retina; cc, choriocapillary layer of choroid; vl, vessel layer of choroid; pr, pigmented epithelium of the retina)

FIG. 21-4. Portion of a meridional section of the eye, showing part of the cornea (c) near its junction with the sclera (s), and the ciliary body. H & E stain. Low power. (ce, corneal epithelium; cme, corneal mesenchymal epithelium; cm, ciliary muscle; cp, ciliary processes; pre, pigmented retinal epithelium; dp, dilator pupillae muscle of the iris; pe, pigment epithelium of the iris; ac, anterior chamber; pc, posterior chamber)

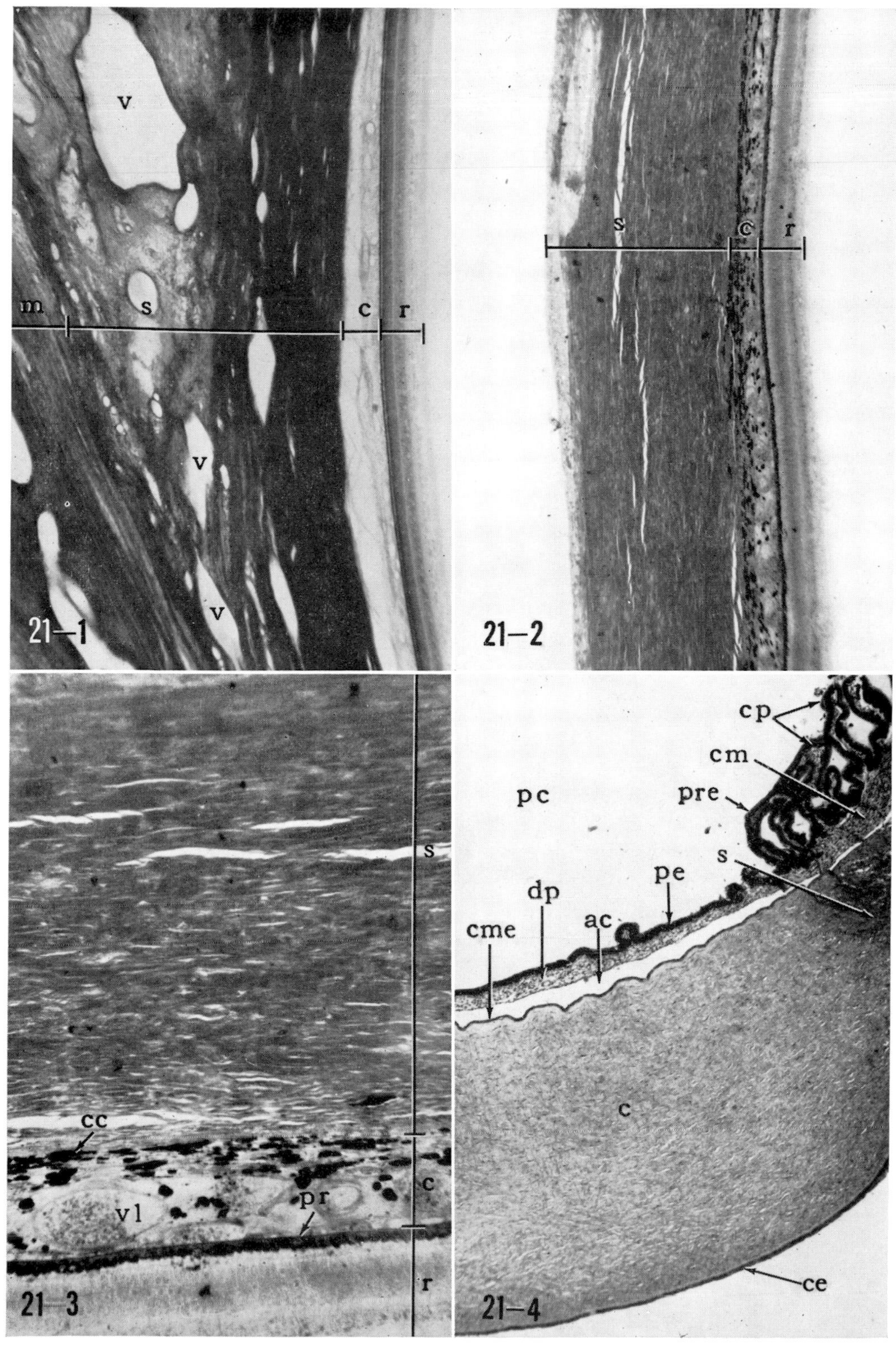
v
m
s
c
r
v
v
21–1
s
c
r
21–2
s
cc
c
vl
pr
r
21–3
cp
cm
pc
pre
s
pe
dp
ac
cme
c
ce
21–4

vascularization of the various subdivisions of the eye

4. Regulation of the amount of entering light

5. Focusing of light rays on a photosensitive surface

6. Prevention of light scattering

7. Transmission of nerve impulses in response to stimulation by light

8. Regulation of near and far vision by alterations in focal length and by convergence and divergence of the pupils

The interested student should refer to one of the many textbooks of ophthalmology for a fuller understanding of these functions. From the standpoint of histology, these topics are related to the following structures: sclera, cornea, iris, iris angle, retina, lens, aqueous humor, vitreous body, eyelid and conjunctiva. Each of these components of the eye will now be discussed.

B. Tunica Fibrosa

The outermost coat, known as the **tunica fibrosa**, is continuous around the eyeball, being pierced only posteriorly at a region (**lamina cribrosa**) where the trunk of the optic nerve takes origin. The posterior five sixths of the tunica fibrosa is opaque to light and is recognizable in the anterior exposed portion as the white of the eye. This opaque portion is called the **sclera**. The remaining sixth of the fibrous layer, representing the anterior continuation of the sclera, is transparent. This portion is called the **cornea**, and through it can be seen a pigmented centrally perforated, disk-shaped structure. The central opening is the **pupil**; the pigmented region surrounding it is the **iris**.

1. *Sclera* (Figs. 21-1 to 21-3). The thick scleral portion of the fibrosa is usually subdivided into 3 apposed layers. These are an external region of **episcleral** tissue, an intermediate zone, the **sclera proper**, and an internal layer, the **lamina fusca**. The **episcleral tissue** is made up primarily of an admixture of loosely arranged collagen and elastic fibers and is quite vascular. Anteriorly, this layer attaches the lining of the inner surface (**conjunctiva**) of the eyelids to the sclera. The **sclera proper** is a dense connective tissue coat made up mainly of interlacing collagen fibers, with fewer delicate elastic fibers. Because of its strength, it serves as a structure for the attachment of the tendons of the extrinsic muscles of the eye. The **lamina fusca**, or internal layer, differs from the rest of the sclera in that it contains pigment cells and many more elastic fibers. This layer can be regarded as transitional with the underlying choroid.

2. *Cornea* (Figs. 21-4 to 21-12). Vertical sections through the cornea reveal that it is composed of the following 5 layers from without inward: (a) the corneal epithelium, (b) Bowman's membrane, (c) the corneal

PLATE 171—Eye

FIG. 21-5. Posterior corneal surface and a portion of the iris of the eye. H & E stain. Intermediate power. (cme, corneal mesenchymal epithelium; Dm, Descemet's membrane; sp, substantia propria; en, endothelium of anterior surface of the iris; ab, anterior border layer and stroma of the iris; dp, dilator pupillae muscle of iris; pe, pigment epithelium of iris; ac, anterior chamber)

FIG. 21-6. High-power view of a portion of Figure 21-5. (cme, corneal mesenchymal epithelium, Dm, Descemet's membrane; sp, substantia propria; en, endothelium of anterior surface of the iris; s, stroma of iris with the anterior border layer [ab]; dp, dilator pupillae muscle of iris; pe, pigment epithelium of iris; ac, anterior chamber)

FIG. 21-7. Anterior corneal surface of the eye. H & E stain. Intermediate power. (ce, corneal epithelium; Bm, Bowman's membrane; sp, substantia propria)

FIG. 21-8. High-power view of a portion of Figure 21-7. (ce, corneal epithelium; Bm, Bowman's membrane; sp, substantia propria)

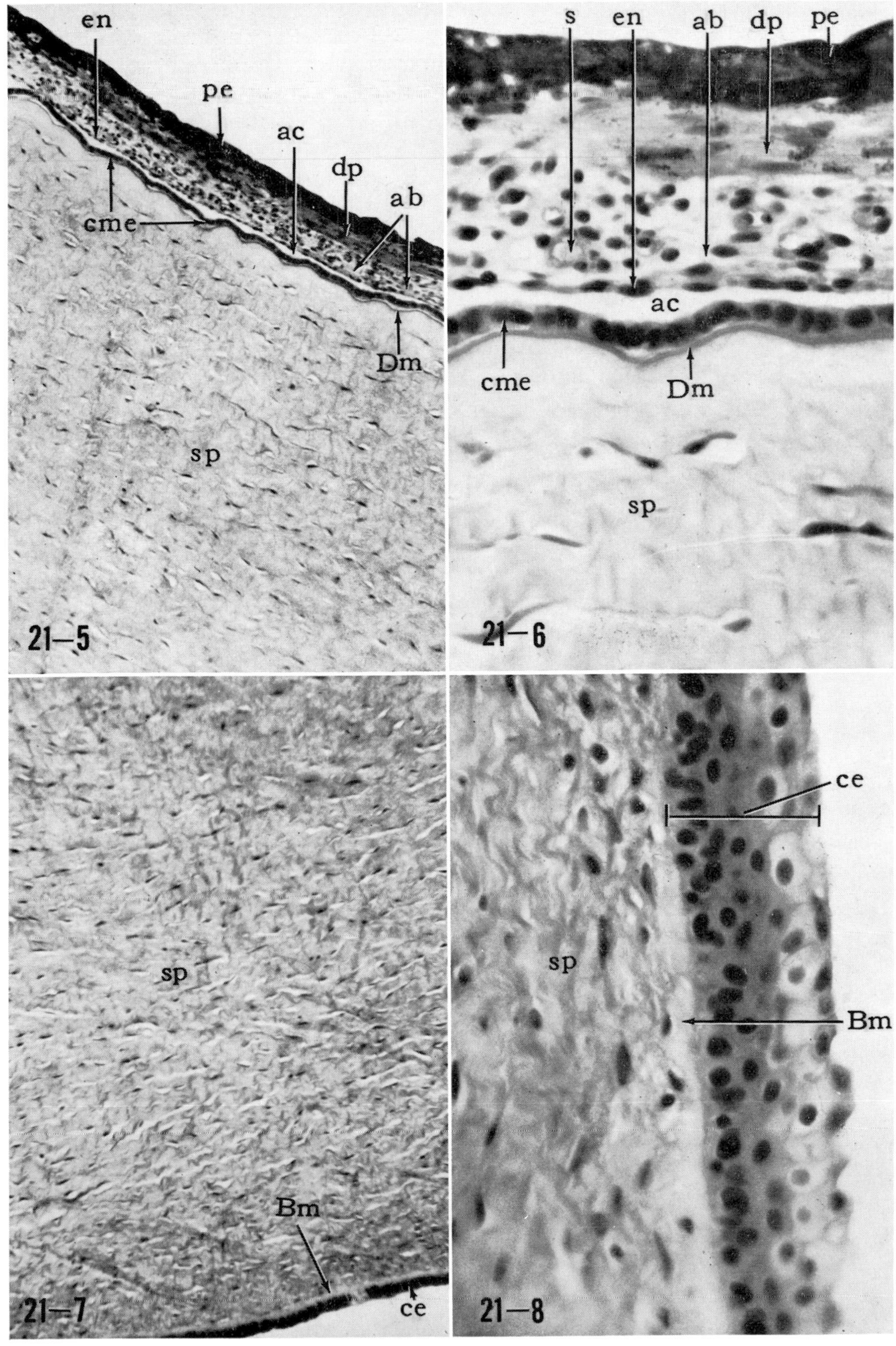
en
pe
ac
dp
ab
cme
Dm
sp
21—5
s
en
ab
dp
pe
ac
cme
Dm
sp
21—6
sp
Bm
ce
21—7
ce
sp
Bm
21—8

stroma or substantia propria, (d) Descemet's membrane and (e) the corneal mesenchymal epithelium.

a. *Corneal Epithelium.* This layer is composed of stratified squamous epithelium, usually arranged as 5 rows of cells. Numerous free nerve endings are contained within this sensitive epithelium.

b. *Bowman's Membrane.* This is an indistinctly fibrillated membrane on which the corneal epithelium rests. Electron microscopic studies reveal that the membrane consists of a network of collagenous fibrils which are randomly arranged. No elastic fibers are observed in the membrane, nor has elastin been isolated.

c. *Corneal Stroma.* Approximately 90 per cent of the cornea is formed by the corneal stroma. This layer is composed of transparent, regularly arranged connective tissue that consists mainly of collagenous fibers arranged in thin lamellae. The direction of the lamellae and their contained fibers is always parallel with the surface, but the individual fibers in adjacent lamellae are oriented in different planes. Fine elastic networks and lymphoid wandering cells are found in the corneal stroma.

d. *Descemet's Membrane.* This posterior membrane is elastic and probably constitutes a basement membrane secreted by the corneal mesenchymal epithelium. When studied with the light microscope, this membrane appears to be homogeneous, but when cross sections are studied by electron microscopy the membrane exhibits cross striations of granular bands connected by filaments.

e. *Corneal Mesenchymal Epithelium.* This is a layer of large squamous cells covering the inner surface of Descemet's membrane.

C. Tunica Vasculosa (Uvea)

The **tunica vasculosa** is an ensheathment of the posterior five sixths of the eyeball and includes the **choroid**, the **ciliary body** and the **iris**. It provides a lining anteriorly between the iris and the scleral spur and reaches as far forward as the ora serrata of the retina. (See Figs. 21-13 and 21-14.)

1. *Choroid.* The **choroid** is located between the inner surface of the sclera and the pigmented epithelial layer of the retina. The choroid layer extends as far forward as the ora serrata of the retina. The following 4 layers can be recognized from outside inward, namely: (a) suprachoroid or lamina suprachoroidea, (b) vessel layer or lamina vasculosa, (c) capillary layer or lamina choriocapillaris and (d) glassy (Bruch's) membrane or lamina vitrea (Fig. 21-7).

PLATE 172—Cornea

FIG. 21-9. Electron micrograph of a section of the human cornea, showing Bowman's layer of the stroma (Bl), epithelium (e) resting on a basement membrane (bm) and the beginning of organized stroma (os). Buffered osmic acid fixation. × 18,000.

FIG. 21-10. Electron micrograph of Descemet's membrane from beef cornea in cross section. Notice the striate appearance of the granular bands, about 1,070 Å apart, connected by filaments less than 100 Å in width and about 270 Å apart. × 37,000.

FIG. 21-11. Electron micrograph of Descemet's membrane from beef cornea in tangential section. Notice the hexagonal arrangement of the 2-dimensional array of nodes, about 1,070 Å apart and connected by filaments. × 24,000.

FIG. 21-12. Diagram of structure of Descemet's membrane, based on electron micrographs. The diagram shows the relationship between the structures seen in the two planes. Based on histochemical data, chemical analyses and x-ray diffraction, it is concluded that the membrane belongs to the collagen class of fibrous proteins.

(Figs. 21-9 to 21-12 from Jakus, M.: J. Biophys. Biochem. Cytol. *2*:243)

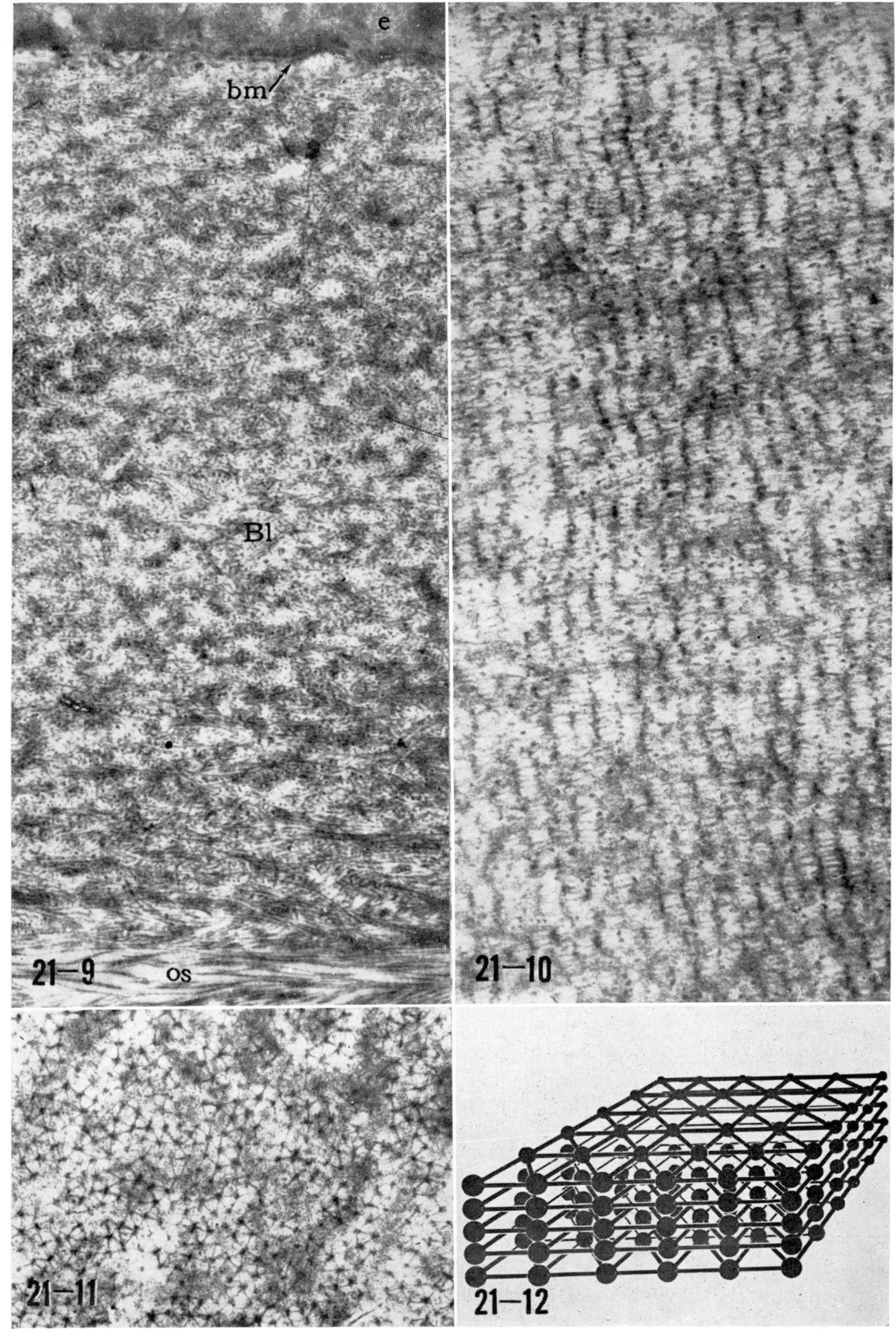
e
bm
Bl
21–9
os
21–10
21–11
21–12

a. *Suprachoroid.* This is a transparent layer consisting of loose connective tissue arranged in a series of thin slanting lamellae. Each lamella is composed of a membrane which contains large melanoblasts, occasional fibroblasts and a rich supply of elastic fibers. The thin lamellae traverse the perichoroidal space, a potential cleft between the sclera and the choroid. Smooth muscle fibers are seen in the equatorial region and in front of it. No blood vessels are found in the suprachoroidal layer.

b. *Vessel Layer.* This layer consists of many large and medium-sized blood vessels (arteries and veins). Between the vessels is found a loose connective tissue arrangement similar to that of the suprachoroidal layer but with an additional contribution of some collagenous fibers and a rich supply of stellate pigment cells.

c. *Capillary Layer.* The choriocapillary layer consists of wide-bored capillary networks arranged in one plane. It supplies nutriment and oxygen to the outer layers of the retina by diffusion out through the glassy membrane. Filling in the net is a stroma of collagenous and elastic fibrillae. The stroma is devoid of pigment cells, but some fibroblasts are present.

d. *Glassy Membrane.* This brilliant noncellular basal membrane (1 to 2 μ thick) located between the choroid and the pigment epithelium of the retina is composed of 2 lamellae. The outer thin lamella, next to the capillary layer, is composed of a dense sheet of elastic fibrillae. The inner homogeneous lamella is thicker and cuticular. This lamella is considered to be a product of the pigment epithelium of the retina.

2. *Ciliary Body.* This, the thickest portion of the tunica vasculosa, is a specialized fibromuscular band that is interposed between the choroid and the root of the iris and surrounds the lens. The ciliary body extends forward from the choroid (at the ora serrata) to a point just behind the sclerocorneal junction (to the scleral spur). The inner surface of the ciliary body is thrown into 70 to 80 ridges or meridionally radiating folds known as the **ciliary processes**. Thus, a ciliary crown or ringlike arrangement is formed which attaches to and anchors the fibers of the suspensory ligament of the lens. Histologically, the ciliary body contains the same elements as the choroid except that the capillary layer is absent and the smooth muscle within the suprachoroid layer is prominent and is referred to as the **ciliary muscle**. Lining the inner surface of the ciliary body is the **pars ciliaris retinae**.

PLATE 173—Eye

FIG. 21-13. Portion of the cornea (c), the iris (i) with iris angle (ia), the ciliary processes (cp) of the ciliary body and the lens (l) of the eye. H & E stain. Low power. (lc, lens capsule with underlying simple cuboidal epithelium; lf, lens fibers; pre, pigmented retinal epithelium; pe, pigment epithelium of the iris; ac, anterior chamber; pc, posterior chamber; s, sclera near its junction with the cornea; ce, corneal epithelium)

FIG. 21-14. Portion of the cornea (c), the iris (i) with iris angle, the ciliary body and the lens (l) of the eye. Mallory-Azan stain. Low power. (cp, ciliary processes of the ciliary body; mia, meshwork of the iris angle; s, sclera near its junction with the cornea; sm, scleral meshwork; S, canal of Schlemm)

FIG. 21-15. Section through the retina. Mallory stain. High power. (pc, pigment cells; c, cones; r, rods; olm, outer limiting membrane; cn, nuclei of cones of outer nuclear layer; rn, nuclei of rods of outer nuclear layer; op, outer plexiform layer; in, inner nuclear layer; ip, inner plexiform layer; gc, outer border of ganglion cell layer)

FIG. 21-16. Horizontal meridional section of the place of emergence of the optic nerve (on). Mallory-Azan stain. Low power. (lc, area of lamina cribrosa; nl, optic nerve fiber layer over retina [r]; c, choroid; s, sclera; pa, pia-arachnoid sheaths; d, dural sheath; cv, central vein)

i
c
ce
pc
ac
pe
lf
s
cp
ia
pre
l
lc
21–13
i
c
cp
mia
l
s
sm
S
21–14
pc
c
r
olm
cn
rn
op
in
ip
gc
21–15
on
d
pa
cv
s
lc
nl
r
c
21–16

The surface adjacent to the stroma of the ciliary body is composed of a single layer of columnar cells, heavily laden with pigment, derived from the pigment layer of the retina, while those cells on the inner surface known as the ciliary epithelium are less pigmented. Electron microscope studies reveal that the cells of the ciliary epithelium possess characteristics commonly found in secretory cells. A thin glassy structureless membrane, the **internal limiting membrane**, is found on the inner side of the ciliary epithelium.

The **ciliary muscle** consists of outer meridional (longitudinal or Brücke's muscle), middle radial and inner circular fibers (Müller's muscle). Between the muscular bundles, a small amount of connective tissue rich in elastic fibers and melanocytes is found. Contraction of the ciliary muscle pulls the ciliary body toward the lens. This results in a relaxation of the **zonula**, a structure that suspends the lens. Thus, a contraction of the ciliary muscle reduces the tension of the suspensory ligament of the lens and enables the latter to assume a more convex form, thus enabling the eye to accommodate for near vision. That is, the more divergent rays entering the eye from a near object are brought to a proper focus on the retina when the lens is rounded (accommodated). If accommodation were not possible, the rays would not be focused on the retina, and the resulting image would be blurred.

3. *Iris* (Fig. 21-14). The **iris** is the thin membranous structure which is a continuation of the ciliary body. Its posterior surface rests on the anterior surface of the lens and separates the **anterior chamber** of the eyeball from the narrow circular **posterior chamber.** The anterior chamber is bordered by the ciliary portion of the anterior surface of the lens. Bounding the posterior chamber are the iris, the lens, the ciliary body and the vitreous body. **Aqueous humor,** intraocular lymphlike fluid, fills these chambers. The **ciliary margin** of the iris is its peripheral part or root, and thus is connected with the ciliary body. The inner margin, surrounding the pupil, is called the **pupillary margin** of the iris. The anterior surface of the iris is separated into a pupillary and a ciliary zone.

The bulk of the iris consists of a loose, pigmented, highly vascular connective tissue and also smooth muscle fibers. The **anterior surface of the stroma** is covered by a layer of mesenchymal epithelium which continues from the posterior surface of the cornea. Beneath this epithelium is the **anterior stromal sheet** which contains a few collage-

PLATE 174—Optic Nerve, Lens and Eyelid

FIG. 21-17. Intermediate-power view of half of a portion of the optic nerve shown in Figure 21-16. It should be noted that the place of formation and emergence of the optic nerve constitutes a blind spot, since the retina terminates adjacent to it, and this region therefore contains only nerve fibers and vessels. Mallory-Azan stain. (lc, area of lamina cribrosa; nl, optic nerve fiber layer of retina [r]; c, choroid; s, sclera; v, blood vessels)

FIG. 21-18. Intermediate-power view of a portion of the lens of the eye shown in Figure 21-13. (lc, lens capsule; ae, anterior epithelium consisting of simple cuboidal cells; lf, lens fibers arranged meridionally in layers)

FIG. 21-19. Vertical section through a portion of the upper and the lower eyelids and the cornea (c). Mallory-Azan stain. Low power. (co, conjunctiva; M, meibomian glands in the tarsal plate; o, opening of meibomian gland; om, orbicularis oculi muscle; ts, tela subcutanea; v, blood vessels)

FIG. 21-20. Vertical section through a portion of the eyelid. Mallory stain. Low power. (co, conjunctiva on the posterior surface; tp, tarsal plate; M, meibomian glands; om, orbicularis oculi muscle; Z, sebaceous glands of Zeis; e, epidermis of skin; v, blood vessels)

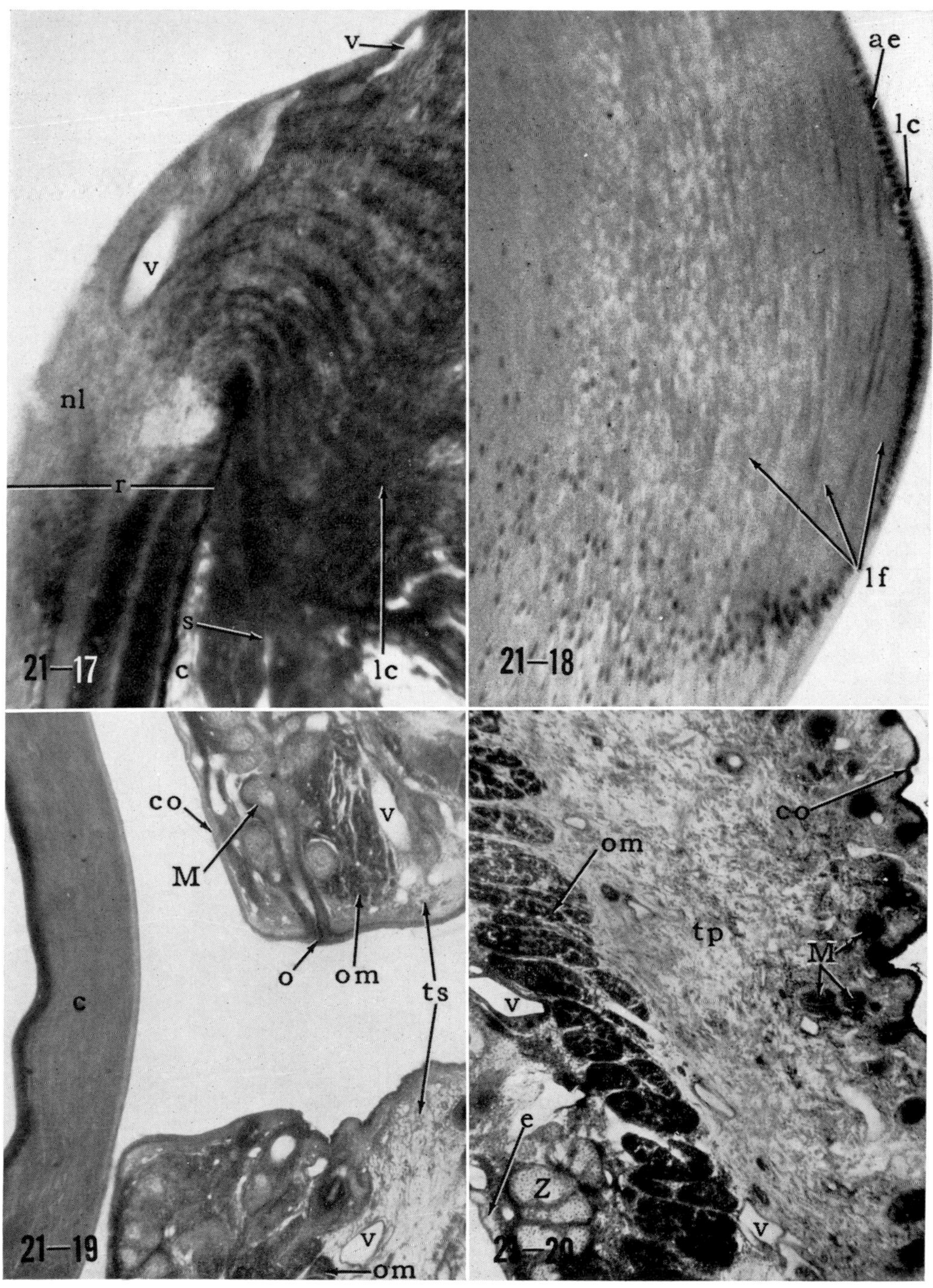
v
v
nl
r
s
c
lc
21—17
ae
lc
lf
21—18
co
M
v
o
om
ts
c
v
om
21—19
co
om
tp
M
v
e
Z
v
21—20

nous fibers and many fibroblasts and chromatophores. This lamella is devoid of blood vessels.

Iris color is dependent on the quantity and the arrangement of pigment and on the thickness of the sheet. Beneath the anterior stromal sheet is the **vessel layer** containing numerous blood vessels embedded in a loose connective tissue. Some branched chromatophores are also found here. The **posterior surface of the iris** consists of a double layer of pigmented columnar epithelium. The outer, less pigmented layer differentiates into two groupings of smooth muscle with different spatial orientations. One of these groups consists of circularly arranged bundles (the **sphincter pupillae muscle**) surrounding the margin of the pupil. The other smooth muscle elements (myoepithelium) are radially arranged (**dilator pupillae muscles**). Contraction of the sphincter pupillae muscle causes a reduction in the size of the pupil, whereas contraction of the dilator pupillae muscle results in a widening of the pupil. The iris exerts its principal effect in producing clear images.

4. *Iris Angle.* The filtration angle of the iris is located at the periphery of the anterior chamber of the eyeball (iridocorneal junction) and subtends a circular recess. At the corneoscleral junction a circular scleral venous sinus, the **canal of Schlemm**, is present. This canal is lined by endothelium and is surrounded by loose connective tissue. In addition, it is separated from the anterior chamber by connective tissue lined by mesenchymal epithelium. Actually, the iris angle constitutes the loose connective tissue meshwork which extends from the edge of Descemet's membrane to the scleral roll and the root of the iris. Just behind the limbus and encircling the eyeball is a ridge, the **scleral spur**. In front of the scleral spur, the meshes of the iris angle form the **spaces of Fontana** which communicate directly with the anterior chamber and indirectly with the canal of Schlemm. Aqueous humor is present in the spaces of Fontana. The fluid passes into the canal of Schlemm and finally out into the venous circulation.

D. Tunica Interna (Retina)

The innermost tunic of the eyeball is derived from the optic vesicle of the embryonic brain. In the adult, it consists of an outer, pigmented layer of simple columnar

PLATE 175—Cochlea

FIG. 21-21. Axial section of a portion of the cochlea (guinea pig). Masson stain. Low power. (sv, scala vestibuli; cd, cochlear duct; st, scala tympani; vm, vestibular membrane; tm, tectorial membrane; sl, spiral ligament; sg, spiral ganglion; osl, osseous spiral lamina; cn, cochlear nerve; bm, basilar membrane; C, organ of Corti; lw, lateral wall of cochlea)

FIG. 21-22. Axial section of a portion of one turn of cochlea. H & E stain. Intermediate power. (lw, lateral wall of cochlea; sl, spiral ligament; cd, cochlear duct; sv, scala vestibuli; st, scala tympani; C, organ of Corti; tm, tectorial membrane; vm, vestibular membrane; osl, osseous spiral lamina; sp, spiral prominence; vs, stria vascularis)

FIG. 21-23. Section of cochlea revealing the structure of the organ of Corti. H & E stain. High power. (cd, cochlear duct; st, scala tympani; tm, tectorial membrane; bm, basilar membrane; tl, tympanic lip; H, cells of Hensen; ot, outer tunnel; oph, outer phalangeal cells; oh, outer hair cells; op, outer pillar; it, inner tunnel; ip, inner pillar; bc, border cells; ist, inner spiral tunnel)

FIG. 21-24. Section of a portion of the cochlea to demonstrate especially the nature of the spiral ligament (sl). Masson stain. High power. (bw, portion of bony wall of cochlea; cd, cochlear duct; st, scala tympani; ess, external spiral sulcus; sp, spiral prominence; vp, vas prominens; cb, crista basilaris; bm, basilar membrane [the separation of the membrane from the adjacent cellular elements is a fixation artifact]; C, part of the organ of Corti)

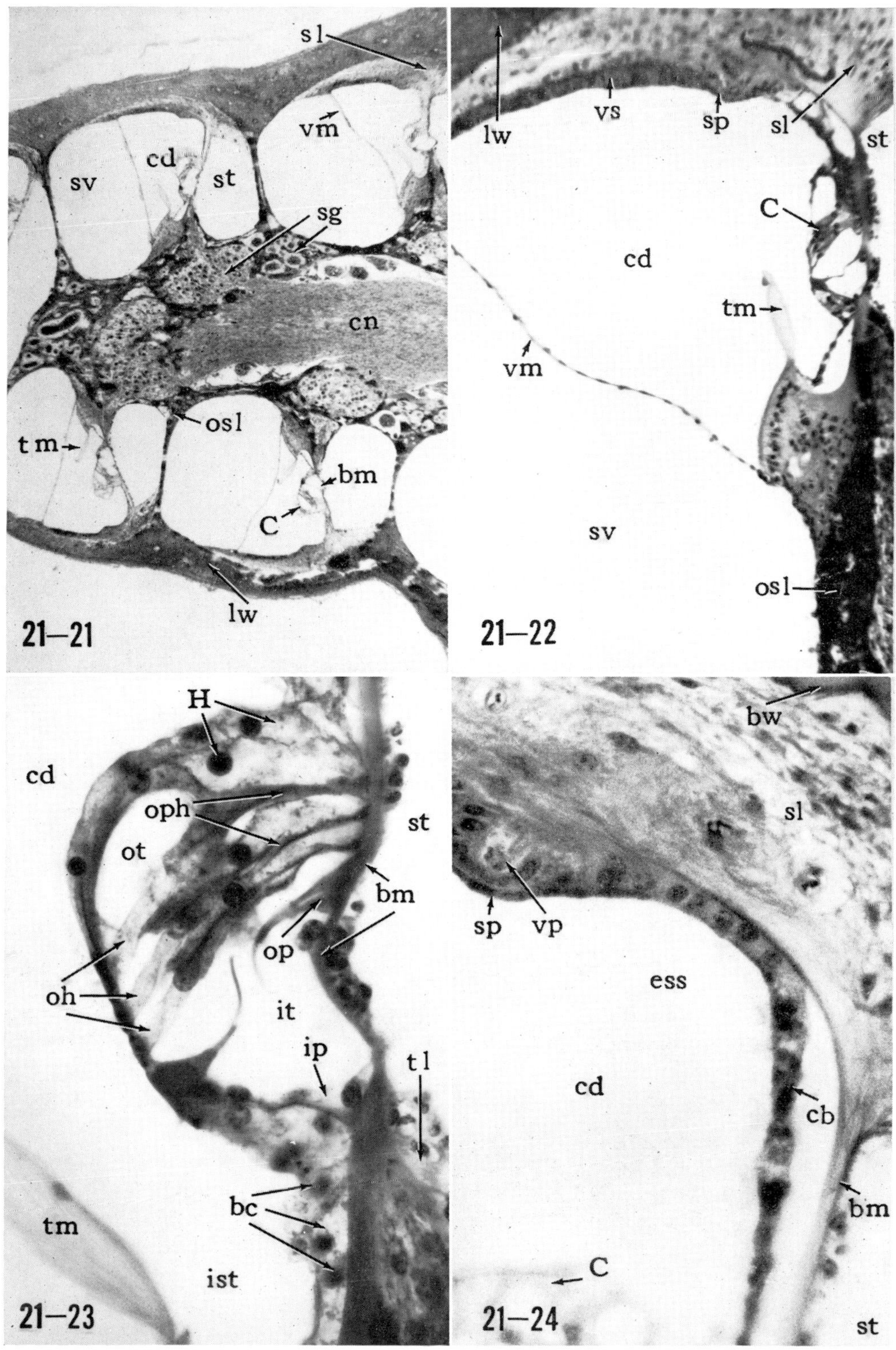
sl
vm
sv
cd
st
sg
cn
tm
osl
bm
C
lw
21—21
lw
vs
sp
sl
st
C
cd
tm
vm
sv
osl
21—22
H
cd
oph
st
ot
bm
op
oh
it
ip
tl
bc
tm
ist
21—23
bw
sl
sp
vp
ess
cd
cb
bm
C
st
21—24

epithelium subjacent to the choroid which absorbs light, and an inner thin sheet of photosensitive nervous tissue, the **retina proper**. The retina proper is composed of neurons and neuroglia isolated from fibrous connective tissue and blood vessels by two astrocytic membranes, the **external** and the **internal limiting membranes**. The internal limiting membrane forms the retinal surface bordering the vitreous body. (See Figs. 21-5, 21-6, 21-7, 21-15.)

The retina proper consists of 10 layers except at the fovea centralis and the serrated margin. From outside inward, they are arranged in the following parallel layers:

1. The pigment epithelium
2. The layer of rods and cones
3. The external limiting membrane
4. The outer nuclear layer
5. The outer plexiform layer
6. The inner nuclear layer
7. The inner plexiform layer
8. The ganglion cell layer
9. The optic nerve fiber layer
10. The internal limiting membrane

1. *The Pigment Epithelium.* This is a single layer of cuboidal cells appearing as hexagons in surface view and bound to the choroid. The inner segments of the cells are filled with dark pigment granules (fuscin) which also occupy the fine protoplasmic processes of these cells. The processes extend down between the rods and the cones, separating them. The outer portion of the cells (next to the choroid) contain oval nuclei and are relatively free of pigment granules. In certain animals, it has been demonstrated that variations in illumination alter the position of the pigment granules. Thus, at low light intensities, the pigment granules are found massed in the cell body, whereas in bright light the pigment granules move inwardly into the cell processes so as to form a protective sheath around each rod and cone.

2. *The Layer of Rods and Cones.* The rods and the cones constitute the outermost portion of the light-sensitive photoreceptor cells. They are arranged vertically and in parallel fashion perpendicular to the surface of the retina.

a. *Rod Cells.* These neuroepithelial elements are slender cylinders (60 μ long and 2 μ in diameter) and consist of outer and inner segments. The outer segment exhibits a rounded outer end, is highly refractile and contains visual purple (rhodopsin). The inner segment is slightly stouter, finely granular and possesses at its outer end a longitudinal arrangement of fibrils (the dark-staining fiber apparatus). The rod fiber (a slender protoplasmic filament) and the rod body containing the nucleus extend from the inner end of the rod proper to the outer nuclear layer, with the rod fiber continuing into the plexiform layer and terminating in a small, round swelling, the rod spherule or end bulb. The rods, which number approximately 130 million, with their contained visual purple are primary concerned with vision in dim light. Exposure of the retina to bright light causes rhodopsin to disintegrate, but it undergoes constant regeneration so long as the connection of the rods with the pigment epithelium is maintained.

b. *Cone Cells.* These neuroepithelial elements appear as long-necked flasks (varying in different regions from 75 to 30 μ in length and from 7 to 1 μ in diameter) consisting of outer and inner segments. The outer segment contains a visual pigment (iodopsin) and appears to be highly refractive; it is conical in shape. The inner segment is bulblike in shape, finely granular and possesses a dark-staining fiber apparatus. Merging with its body the inner segment passes through the external limiting membrane. A thick inner fiber from the body extends to the outer plexiform layer and terminates in a club-shaped swelling, the cone pedicle, with numerous filamentous lateral outgrowths, referred to as the cone foot. The cones, which number approximately 7 million, with their contained iodopsin are primarily concerned with vision in bright light and consequently also with color vision.

3. *External Limiting Membrane.* This is a thin sievelike membrane composed of radial supporting fibers of the retina (Müller's fibers). The dendritic processes of the rods and the cones pass through the numerous perforations in the membrane.

4. *Outer Nuclear Layer.* This layer contains the nuclei of the photoreceptor cells. The cone nuclei are situated in a single row next to the external limiting membrane and appear as oval, pale-staining bodies. Deep to these are many closely packed nuclei, smaller, rounder and darker staining than cone nuclei. These represent the nuclei of the rod photoreceptors.

5. *Outer Plexiform Layer.* As previously mentioned, the axons of the rods and the cones terminate within this layer to synapse with the dendritic processes of the bipolar cells, which are arranged as plexuses or networks. The spherules (ends of rod axons) of several rods may synapse with the dendritic endings of a single bipolar cell. The cone axons (filament axon pedicles) enter into a single synaptic relationship with the dendritic arborization of a bipolar cell.

6. *Inner Nuclear Layer.* This layer contains the cell bodies of association neurons (amacrine cells, bipolar cells, horizontal cells) as well as the neuroglial supporting fibers of Müller. The cell bodies of the horizontal cells and those of Müller's fibers are generally found in the region of this layer, those of the bipolar cells in a middle region and those of the amacrine cells in a more internal part of this layer. The horizontal cells and the amacrine cells relay impulses to adjacent areas of the retina. The bipolar cells, on the other hand, transfer impulses to the next order of neurons in the discriminative pathway to the brain.

7. *Inner Plexiform Layer.* This layer represents a synaptic region between the axons of the bipolar cells and the profusely arborized dendritic plexuses of the ganglion cells. Axonic processes of amacrine cells are also present within this layer.

8. *Ganglion Cell Layer.* This layer is comprised of the multipolar cell bodies of ganglion cells and their contained nuclei. Scattered neuroglial elements are also present.

9. *Nerve Fiber Layer.* This layer is composed of the nonmedullated axons of the ganglion cells which course parallel with the inner surface of the retina. These axons converge at the optic disk (blind spot) where they acquire a myelin sheath and form the optic nerve. Neuroglial cells (spider cells), the inner branches of Müller's fibers and retinal blood vessels are also present in this layer.

10. *Internal Limiting Membrane.* The expanded ends of the radial fibers of Müller form this thin homogeneous membrane.

E. Macula Lutea and Fovea Centralis

Near the center of the retina and very close to the posterior pole of the visual axis, a central depression, the **fovea centralis**, is present. Surrounding this little depression is the **macula lutea**, a small area (2 mm. in diameter) of the retina that is yellower than the rest of the retina. In the fovea, the only photoreceptor elements present are closely packed cone cells which here are long and slender. Therefore, light rays pass directly to these photoreceptor cells without having to traverse all the other layers of the retina and blood vessels, all of which are absent. Thus, this area is specialized for greater visual acuity.

F. Optic Nerve (Figs. 21-16 and 21-17)

Converging at the light-insensitive **optic papilla (disk)**, commonly known as the **blind spot** of the retina, and turning outward to pass through the lamina cribrosa are the retinal nerve fibers which form the **optic nerve**. The optic nerve is actually a fiber tract that connects the retina with the brain rather than a true peripheral nerve like other cranial nerves. It consists of bundles of myelinated fibers without neurilemma and is ensheathed by the meningeal coverings of the brain which fuse with the sclera at the bulb. Glial cells are present between the individual nerve fibers. The middle portion of the optic nerve is occupied by the central artery and vein which are carried in an investing sheath of supporting tissue. Branches of these vessels reach the eyeball to feed into the retinal nerve fiber layer and the inner nuclear layer of the choroid.

G. Lens
(Figs. 21-13, 21-14, 21-18)

The biconvex crystalline **lens**, located between the iris and the vitreous body, is a specialized body of great plasticity enclosed in a transparent, homogeneous, highly refractive, elastic membrane called the **lens capsule**. Beneath the capsule, a single layer of cuboidal epithelium (sometimes squamous) makes up the anterior wall of the lens. Toward the equator, they become elongated meridional cells which become transformed into new lens fibers at the equator. The posterior wall of the lens has no epithelium, being composed of tall concentrically arranged fibers. Making up the center of the lens (lens substance), and arranged as concentric lamellae, are long, prismatic, meridionally arranged lens fibers united by an amorphous cement substance. These lens fibers are formed from epithelial cells on the posterior surface of the embryonic lens vesicle. As mentioned in the section on the ciliary body, the lens is held in position by the fibers that constitute the ciliary zonula. Finally, where the vitreous touches the lens capsule, the zonular fibers form the **hyaloideocapsular ligament**.

H. Vitreous Body

Filling the posterior portion of the potential eye cavity between the lens and the retina is the **vitreous body**. In the fresh condition, the vitreous body is a viscous, transparent, jellylike intercellular substance composed of approximately 99 per cent water and in which are dissolved hyaluronic acid and the protein vitrein. After fixation, the vitreous body appears as a fibrillar network with a clear liquid in its meshes. A remnant of the embryonic hyaloid artery, the **hyaloid canal of Cloquet**, runs through the axis of the vitreous body, extending from the optic papilla to the posterior surface of the lens. Functionally, in addition to transmitting light rays, the vitreous body (along with the aqueous humor) aids in the maintenance of the proper pressure within the eyeball cavity so as to prevent the eyeball from collapsing. Thus, the vitreous body, anteriorly, helps to hold the lens in place and, posteriorly, keeps the inner coat of the retina from separating from the outer pigmented coat.

I. Eyelids

Protecting the eye from foreign bodies and excessive light are movable folds of skin, the **eyelids** (Figs. 21-19, 21-20). The **skin** constitutes the outermost layer and is characteristically very thin, with many small, downy hairs with which are associated sebaceous and small sweat glands. The **dermis**, containing numerous pigment cells, constitutes the subcutaneous layer and is composed of loose connective tissue that is rich in elastic fibers but devoid of fat. Toward the edge of the lid, the dermis becomes denser and has few but higher papillae.

Thin, pale, **skeletal muscle fibers** disposed in concentric bundles (the **orbicularis oculi**) form the next layer in front of the underlying tarsal plate. In addition, the tendinous fibers of the **superior levator palpebral** muscle fibers of the orbicularis oculi serves and insert on the lower anterior surface of the tarsal plate. Contraction of the palpebral muscle fibers of the orbicularis oculi serve to close the lids, whereas raising the upper lid is a function of the superior levator palpebral muscle.

The **tarsal plate**, which gives form to each eyelid, consists of dense fibrous connective tissue with some elastic fibers. Attached to the upper border of the plate are strands of smooth muscle, the **superior tarsal muscle of Müller**. Embedded in the tarsal plate and arranged in a single row with their long axes perpendicular are the **tarsal** or **meibomian glands**. These modified, elongated sebaceous glands are of a simple branched alveolar nature and have a long, straight central excretory duct. This duct is lined by stratified squamous epithelium and opens into the margin of the eyelid by a series of minute orifices. Secretions from these glands prevent the eyelids from sticking together by lubricating the edges of the lids.

The free margins of the eyelids are bordered by the **eyelashes** which are curved hairs, usually arranged in 3 irregular rows. Associated with their deeply buried follicles are the large **sebaceous glands of Zeis**, and between the follicles are the large **sweat glands of Moll.** The glands of Moll are unlike other sweat glands in that their terminal portions are relatively straight rather than coiled.

A transparent **mucous membrane** lines the posterior inner surface of the eyelids (the **palpebral conjunctiva**), folding back upon itself at the fornix to also cover the anterior surface of the eyeball to its junction with the corneal epithelium (the **bulbar conjunctiva**). It consists of stratified squamous epithelium studded with spherical goblet cells, resting on a thin layer of fibrous connective tissue that is infiltrated with lymphocytes and contains blood vessels, lymphatics and nerves. Over the tarsal plate, the epithelium becomes reduced to a double layer which consists of tall surface columnar cells and a deeper layer of flattened cuboidal cells.

The **lacrimal glands**, which are divided into superior and inferior lobes, are located in the superior temporal region of the orbit above the eyelids. They are compound tubulo-acinous serous glands which are provided with a series of ducts (10 to 14) that open into the conjunctival sac. As one of their functions, the eyelids open and close the conjunctival sac to provide the conjunctiva and the cornea with a film of moisture. Excessive secretion finds its way to the medial portion of the lid margins where there are two small papillae, each of which contains an opening of one of the lacrimal ducts. These in turn empty their secretions into the lacrimal sac and ultimately into the nose via the nasolacrimal duct.

II. EAR

A. Introduction

Via the acoustic nerve and its pathways to the central nervous system, information concerning variations in air pressure is transmitted through a unique and complex mechanism consisting of the **external**, the **middle** and the **internal ears.**

The **external ear** consists of the **auricle** or **pinna**, the **external auditory meatus** and the **tympanic membrane** or **eardrum**. Sound waves enter the external auditory meatus and strike the tympanic membrane which acts as a sensitive pressure detector.

The **middle ear** includes the **tympanic cavity** and the **auditory ossicles**, the **malleus**, the **incus** and the **stapes**, within the cavity. The **auditory (eustachian) tube** is also considered as a part of the middle ear, since it opens into that chamber. The middle ear transmits sound waves to the internal ear. Vibrations of the tympanic membrane cause the ossicles to vibrate and transmit these impulses to the enclosed fluid of the inner ear by pressing on the oval window. The air pressure in the tympanic cavity is adjusted by the Eustachian tube so that equal pressure is maintained on both sides of the tympanic membrane.

The **internal ear** consists of the **vestibule** with its contained parts, the **saccule**, the **utricle** and the **semicircular canals**, along with the **bony cochlea** which houses the sensory portion of the organ of hearing, the **organ of Corti**. The vestibular portions are concerned with balance, the cochlear division with hearing. Slight movements in the fluid of the inner ear are transmitted to the hair cells of the organ of Corti and converted into nerve impulses that travel along the fibers of the acoustic nerve to the hearing center in the brain.

B. External Ear

1. The funnel-shaped **auricle (pinna)** is an irregular plate of cellular elastic cartilage with its perichondrium containing abundant elastic fibers. It is covered by typical thin skin that has a distinct subcutaneous layer only on the posterior convex surface. Small hairs and numerous sebaceous glands are present in the skin. Sweat glands, small and few in number, occur on the posterior surface. The **ear lobe** is composed of connective tissue and fat covered externally with skin.

2. The **external auditory meatus**, a narrow canal leading from the auricle to the tympanic membrane, is lined with stratified squamous epithelium derived from the skin of the auricle. Its supporting walls consist of an outer elastic cartilaginous part that is continuous with the cartilage of the auricle and an inner bony portion that is formed by the temporal bone. Numerous stiff hairs are found in the cartilaginous portion; these guard the meatus against the entrance of foreign bodies. Associated with the hair follicles are large sebaceous glands. Deep to these glands are simple coiled tubular glands that secrete **cerumen**, a waxy substance. The ducts of the ceruminous glands open either onto the free surface of the canal or, together with the sebaceous glands, into the necks of the hair follicles. The brown, waxy secretion called cerumen is a combined secretion of the sebaceous and the ceruminous glands that lubricates the skin of the canal and also protects it from tiny invading organisms.

3. The **tympanic membrane** is a thin, oval, semitransparent structure separating the external ear from the middle ear. It consists of two epithelial sheets enclosing the substantia propria. The outer epithelial coat is composed of very thin skin (consisting of only 2 cell layers of stratum germinativum and a loose stratum corneum) which is continuous with the stratified squamous epithelium of the external auditory meatus. The inner epithelial coat is composed of the tympanic mucosa which is very thin and consists of a single layer of squamous cells. The substantia propria lies between the two epithelial coats. It constitutes a thin supporting bed of collagenous fibers arranged into an outer layer with its fibers disposed in a radial manner and an inner layer of circularly directed fibers. The upper part of the tympanic membrane, the **pars flaccida**, or **Schrapnell's membrane**, lacks collagenic fibrous layers and thus appears thin and flaccid.

C. Middle Ear

1. The **tympanic cavity** is a tiny, irregular, epithelium-lined chamber in the temporal bone. Its lateral wall is largely formed by the tympanic membrane, while the medial wall is formed by a wall of bone (osseous labyrinth) that separates the middle ear from the internal ear. Posteriorly, the tympanic cavity is connected, through the **tympanic antrum**, with the **mastoid air cells** in the mastoid process of the temporal bone.

The epithelium of the tympanic mucosa consists generally of the simple squamous type except near the edge of the tympanic membrane. In this location it is ciliated cuboidal in nature. Deep to the epithelium of the tympanic mucosa is a lamina propria of thin connective tissue.

On the medial wall of the tympanic cavity behind the **promontory**, a rounded eminence that defines the first coil of the cochlea, two **fenestrae** (windows) are present. The **fenestra vestibuli** (oval window) is closed by the base of the stapes which is attached to the cartilaginous edges of the window by an annular fibroelastic ligament. Below and behind the fenestra vestibuli is the second window, the **fenestra tympanica** or **rotunda**, which is closed by the **secondary tympanic membrane**, a thin fibrous membrane.

2. The **auditory ossicles** are 3 small, compact bones located in the tympanic cavity. These include the **malleus**, which is attached to the tympanic membrane, the **incus**, intermediate in position between the other two ossicles, and the **stapes** which fits into the oval window. The ossicles are jointed by means of articular surfaces covered with hyaline cartilage and thus form a chain across the cavity. A thin periosteal covering of the ossicles is fused with the lamina propria of the tympanic mucosa. By means of this lever system, vibrations are transmitted from the tympanic membrane to the perilymph of the vestibule.

Two tiny skeletal muscles, the **tensor tympani** and the **stapedium**, are associated with the ossicles. The tensor tympani muscle lies in a bony canal above the roof of the auditory tube. Its tendon crosses the tympanic cavity laterally to be inserted into the manubrium of the malleus. Contraction of this muscle draws the manubrium inwardly and exerts tension on the tympanic membrane. The stapedius muscle is housed in a small bony projection on the posterior wall of the tympanic cavity, the **pyramidal eminence**. Its tendon passes through the summit of the pyramidal eminence to insert into the neck of the stapes. Contraction of the stapedius muscle pulls the base of the stapes outwardly so as to reduce intralabyrinthine pressure.

3. The **auditory (Eustachian) tube** has a flattened shape. Near the tympanic cavity it has a bony wall, but the rest of the wall is supported mainly by a plate of hyaline cartilage. In the bony portion, the mucosa is thin and is lined by a low ciliated columnar type of epithelium. The mucosa of the cartilaginous part of the auditory tube is characterized by a pseudostratified ciliated epithelium which contains goblet cells near the pharyngeal opening. A submucosa is also present near the pharyngeal end and contains mixed seromucous glands. Normally, the auditory tube is opened only during the act of swallowing.

D. Internal Ear

The **internal ear** is housed within the petrous portion of the temporal bone. It is constructed of a series of bony canals and chambers, the **osseous labyrinth**, and of a series of membranous sacs and canals, the **membranous labyrinth**. The membranous structures are located within the spaces of the osseous labyrinth.

1. The **osseous labyrinth** consists of the **vestibule**, an irregular, oval, central chamber, which lies just medial to the middle ear and from which arise the 3 **semicircular canals** and the **cochlea**. The walls of the osseous labyrinth are composed of compact bone, whose periosteum is covered with mesenchymal epithelium.

The semicircular canals are oriented in space so that the plane of any one canal is at right angles to the planes of the other two. Accordingly, two of the semicircular canals, the **superior** and the **posterior canals**, are disposed vertically, while one, the **lateral canal**, is disposed horizontally. The lateral canals of both ears lie in nearly the same plane. On the other hand, the superior canal of one side is approximately parallel with the posterior canal of the opposite side.

The semicircular canals, close to their connection with the vestibule, have expanded parts or dilatations, the **ampullae**. In addition, since the medial end of the superior canal and the upper end of the posterior canal fuse to form the **crus commune**, the ampullae of these canals have a common return opening into the medial part of the vestibule. The lateral canal has an independent return opening into the upper part of the vestibule. Extending from the medial wall of the vestibule to the posterior surface of the petrous portion of the temporal bone is a narrow canal, the **vestibular aqueduct**.

2. Most of the structures constituting the **membranous labyrinth** are separated from the periosteum of the osseous labyrinth. The delicate membranes are suspended in a

fluid, the **perilymph**, by connective tissue trabeculae arising from the periosteum. Perilymph fills all the spaces between the bony and the membranous structures. The membranous labyrinth itself is lined by a simple squamous epithelium of ectodermal origin and is filled with another fluid, the **endolymph**. Subjacent to the epithelium, a tunica propria of fine connective tissue is present. In this connective tissue are also found stellate-shaped fibroblasts and occasional melanocytes.

That part of the membranous labyrinth surrounded by the osseous vestibule is divided into two sacs, a larger elliptical one, the **utricle**, and a smaller spherical sac, the **saccule**. These sacs are in communication with one another by means of the slender **utriculosaccular duct** which gives off a long side branch, the **endolymphatic duct**. The latter duct runs through the vestibular aqueduct and, in the petrous portion of the temporal bone, ends as a blind enlargement, the **endolymphatic sac**. Arising from its lower surface the saccule communicates, in addition, with the cochlear duct by means of a short narrow canal, the **ductus reuniens**.

The wall of the membranous labyrinth, especially its epithelial component, becomes modified into complex sensory regions where the fibers of the stato-acoustic nerve terminate. Six such sensory areas are found, namely, the **macula utriculi**, the **macula sacculi**, the three **cristae ampullares** of the semicircular canals and the **organ of Corti** in the cochlear duct.

a. The **maculae** in both utricle and saccule contain a modified columnar type of epithelium. This epithelium, made up of **supporting cells** and **sensory hair cells**, rests on a thickened tunica propria which is firmly attached to the endosteum. Each supporting cell is a tall columnar element and contains an oval nucleus at its basal end. Cuticular plates, interconnected by terminal bars, are characteristic of the free surfaces of these cells. **Hair cells**, found between the supporting cells, occupy the outer part of the epithelial layer. Each sensory hair cell has a characteristic flask shape with a rounded bottom and contains a large, basally located oval nucleus. The free surface of this cell is covered by a cuticular plate, connecting with those of the supporting cells, and through this plate rises a long tuft of fine nonmotile cilia.

Covering the surface of the maculae is a gelatinous material, the **otolithic membrane**, which contains many small crystalline bodies composed of calcium carbonate and protein, the **otoconia** or **otoliths**. The tufts of hair project upward through narrow endolymph-filled channels finally to become embedded in the otolithic membrane. This structural arrangement enables movements of the otolithic membrane weighted down by the otoconia to be transferred to the tufts of hair. Since the hair cells are intimately related to the vestibular fibers of the acoustic nerve, stimuli affecting them, such as those produced by changes in the position of the head, set up nervous impulses which are passed centrally.

b. Each of the three **cristae ampullares** of the semicircular canals consists of a regional thickening running across the wall of the ampullar portion of the canal. This crest or ridge consists of two elements, a vascularized connective tissue bed that receives stato-acoustic nerve fibers and a covering of specialized epithelium. The structure of this epithelium is basically similar to that described for the maculae. In fixed preparations, the epithelium appears to be topped by a longitudinally striated gelatinous mass, the **cupula.** The cupula possesses no otoconia. Thus, movement of the endolymph within the semicircular canals, brought about by postural movements, serves as stimuli for the hair cells. These stimuli give rise to nervous impulses which are conducted centrally via the vestibular division of the acoustic nerve.

E. Cochlea
(Plate 175)

The organ concerned with hearing, the **cochlea**, like the organs responsive to position and movement of the head, is contained within the osseous labyrinth. This osseous cochlea consists of a central pillar of spongy bone, the **modiolus**, around which the bony canal spirals two and a half turns. The apex of the cochlea is directed anterolaterally, while the base faces the fundus of the internal auditory meatus. Through this portion of the meatus, the nerve fibers of the cochlear division of the stato-acoustic nerve penetrate the modiolus, coursing upward and turning outward to reach the spiral ganglion.

A thin shelf of bone, the **osseous spiral lamina**, extends from the modiolus and follows the coils of the cochlea. Along the outer wall of the osseous canal of the cochlea, directly opposite the osseous spiral lamina, the fibrous periosteum is thickened to form the **spiral ligament**. The spiral ligament makes up the outer wall of the cochlear duct. A crest on the spiral ligament containing dense converging collagen fibers forms the **crista basilaris**. Above the crista basilaris is the **spiral prominence**, a slight ridge covered by simple cuboidal epithelium. It contains blood vessels, including a large vein, the **vas prominens**. Between the crista basilaris and the spiral prominence is a depression, the **external spiral sulcus**, whose surface is covered by cuboidal epithelium. The lower surface of the external spiral sulcus is lined by the **cells of Claudius**, cuboidal cells with a clear cytoplasm. In certain parts of the basal coil, scattered between the basilar membrane and the cells of Claudius, are small nests of polyhedral cells. These, the **cells of Boettcher**, have a cytoplasm that contains fine granules.

The superficial region of the spiral ligament that extends to the external spiral sulcus is extremely vascular and is known as the **stria vascularis**. This region is covered by an epithelium, variously described as pseudostratified or stratified columnar, that is considerably thicker than that elsewhere in the internal ear. The subepithelial connective tissue of the stria vascularis is abundantly supplied with capillaries which form loops that penetrate the epithelium. It is believed that secretory activity by cells of the stria vascularis may be the source of the endolymphatic fluid within the adjacent cochlear duct. **Endolymph** supplies nutritive materials and oxygen to the sensory end organ for hearing.

The **basilar membrane**, a connective tissue membrane, bridges the gap between the osseous spiral lamina and the spiral ligament. It constitutes the floor of the cochlear duct. A thin connective tissue membrane, covered on both sides by simple squamous epithelium, the nonvascular **vestibular** or **Reissner's membrane**, extends obliquely from the upper part of the spiral ligament to the **limbus spiralis**, the thickened periosteum on the outer surface of the osseous spiral lamina. The vestibular membrane forms the roof of the cochlear duct.

Thus, within the osseous canal of the cochlea, cross sections show three spaces, an upper **scala vestibuli**, a membranous **scala media** (**cochlear duct**) and a lower **scala tympani**.

The scala vestibuli and the scala tympani represent spiraling perilymphatic channels. The scala vestibuli arises in the vestibule and reaches the inner surface of the oval window. It courses to the apex of the cochlea where it communicates with the scala tympani through a small opening, the **helicotrema**. The scala tympani ends at the round window. The bony walls of the scala are lined by a thin layer of connective tissue covered with mesenchymal epithelium.

The scala media or cochlear duct, which is part of the membranous labyrinth, is a narrow membranous tube that is triangular in cross section. Its basal, vestibular end forms a small outpocketing, the **cecum vestibulare**, which lies between the oval and the round windows. The upper or apical end of the cochlear duct is closed, this portion being known as the **cecum cupulare**.

The upper surface of the osseous spiral lamina (limbus spiralis) bulges into the cochlear duct. The edges of the limbus terminate in an upper **vestibular lip** and a lower **tympanic lip** which overhang a groove, the

internal spiral sulcus, which is lined by a layer of epithelial cells. The connective tissue of the limbus is firm and contains stellate connective tissue cells in its deeper portions. On the surface of the vestibular lip, the connective tissue elements are alternately elevated into a series of radial ridges that project from the edge of this lip as the **auditory teeth of Huschke.** The upper surface of the limbus consists of cuticular plates derived from columnar cells found in the trenches between the auditory teeth.

A thin membrane, formed from the cuticle, extends from the vestibular lip of the limbus. This, the **tectorial membrane**, becomes gradually gelatinous and extends outward to come into intimate relationship with the cilia of the hair cells of the organ of Corti. By this arrangement, slight changes in position of the tectorial membrane brought about by movements in the endolymph may stimulate the cilia.

The tympanic lip continues outward into the basilar membrane. This membrane is divided into the inner **zona arcuata** and an outer **zona pectinata**. In both zones, the central portion consists of the **auditory strings** or **basilar fibers**. These are embedded in a small amount of homogeneous ground substance.

On the upper surface of the basilar membrane is found the specialized end organ of hearing, the **spiral organ of Corti** or **papilla basilaris**. This is a complex arrangement of epithelial cells specialized into supporting and sensory elements.

These specialized cells will now be described in order, from the periphery toward the modiolus.

1. *Cells of Hensen*. These are supporting cells and are continuous with the cells of Claudius. They have a tall columnar shape and are arranged in several rows. These cells rapidly decrease in height as they approach the cells of Claudius.

2. *Outer Hair Cells*. These are columnar sensory elements that occupy the outermost third of the organ of Corti. They are suspended between the outer phalangeal and the outer pillar cells, are arranged in 3 rows, contain basally located nuclei and have a granular cytoplasm. The free cuticular surfaces of the outer hair cells bear short hairs which are in contact with the tectorial membrane. Cochlear fibers of the stato-acoustic nerve form an arborization around the bases of the hair cells. Thus, endolymphatic movements which stimulate the hair cells bring about nerve impulses in these fibers.

3. *Outer Phalangeal Cells* (*Deiters' Cells*). These are rows of tall, prism-shaped columnar elements. Each of them underlies and supports a single hair cell. There are 3 rows of Deiters' cells in the basal coil of the cochlea, 4 in the second coil and 5 in the apical coil. The bases of the outer phalangeal cells rest on the basilar membrane. Flat cuticular plates are found on the free surface of each row of cells, and these plates interdigitate with those of the next row to form the **reticular membranes**. Round openings in the reticular membrane contain the free ends of the hair cells. Between the first row of outer phalangeal cells and the next cell type to be described (outer pillar cells) is the **space of Nuel**.

4. *Outer and Inner Pillar Cells*. These are supporting cells that are located at the basal angles of a spiraling canal, triangular in cross section, the **inner tunnel** or **Corti's tunnel**. The outer and the inner pillars form part of its walls. Also bounding the inner tunnel and extending along its full length is the basilar membrane.

On this membrane rest the broad bases of the pillar cells, with each base containing a single nucleus, present as elongated bodies. Unusual condensations of dark-staining tonofibrils are found in the outer pillars. The end of each body approaching the surface is thickened and is known as the head. The head bears a convexity in its inner side which fits into an excavation in the head of the corresponding inner pillar cell. The articulation of pairs of adjacent pillar cells forms a series of arches over the inner tunnel. Cuticular plates cover the free surfaces of these cells.

The inner pillar cells are basically similar to the outer pillars, except that they are somewhat shorter and have concavities on the outer surface of the head of the tonofibrillar bodies.

5. *Inner Phalangeal Cells*. These also are supporting cells, shaped like stemless goblets, and are arranged in a single row along the inner surface of the inner pillar cells. Like the outer phalangeal cells, their bases rest on the basilar membrane. The cell has a small basally located spherical nucleus and contains fewer tonofibrils than the outer phalangeal cells. Each cell contains small radially elongated cuticular plates at the surface.

6. *Inner Hair Cells*. These sensory elements, supported by the inner pillar, the phalangeal and the border cells, are arranged in a single row. Except for being broader and somewhat longer, they are similar to the outer hair cells.

7. *Border Cells*. These constitute a single row of attenuated columnar supporting cells and are molded against the inner faces of the inner hair cells and the inner phalangeal cells. The surfaces of the border cells have a thin cuticle.

Index

(References to plates are in *italics*)